CORNELL STUDIES IN CLASSICAL PHILOLOGY

EDITED BY

HARRY CAPLAN * JAMES HUTTON

G. M. KIRKWOOD * FRIEDRICH SOLMSEN

VOLUME XXXIII

Aristotle's System of the Physical World

A COMPARISON WITH HIS PREDECESSORS

BY FRIEDRICH SOLMSEN

Aristotle's System of the Physical World

A COMPARISON WITH

HIS PREDECESSORS

By Friedrich Solmsen

CORNELL UNIVERSITY

CORNELL UNIVERSITY PRESS

ITHACA, NEW YORK

Reprinted with the permission of Cornell University Press

JOHNSON REPRINT CORPORATION   JOHNSON REPRINT COMPANY LTD.
111 Fifth Avenue, New York, N.Y. 10003   Berkeley Square House, London, W1X6BA

CORNELL UNIVERSITY PRESS

First published 1960

This work has been brought to publication
with the assistance of grants from the Ford
Foundation and the Hull Memorial Publication
Fund of Cornell University.

Library of Congress Catalogue Card Number: 78-142433

First reprinting 1970, Johnson Reprint Corporation

Printed in the United States of America

To WERNER JAEGER

Preface

THE title and subtitle of this book will go far to explain its purpose. It may be described as a study in continuity and transformation. My original intention was to trace the fate of Presocratic topics, ideas, and motifs in Aristotle's scientific treatises. And as the convictions which prompted my research seem now to be borne out, a frank statement of them may not be out of place.

The scientific endeavors of the Presocratics have a sequel, even if the books on which we are wont to rely for these thinkers leave us with the contrary impression. If there is a break, it is only temporary. On a new level, with different methods and different intellectual equipment, the inquiry of the physicists is carried on. Aristotle did not discover the subjects with which he deals in his physical treatises. In the questions which he takes up he is neither as free nor as arbitrary as some students of his thought appear to believe, and in the answers which he provides he is not as invariably original as he himself in the course of his arguments may lead us to think.

Having addressed myself to the task of connecting Aristotle with the Presocratics, I soon realized the necessity of examining also the influence of Plato's later philosophy on Aristotle's scientific work. Thus the study has grown, and the book has become longer than I meant it to be; yet it still deals only with Aristotle's achievements in the realm of physics. In the biological treatises the situation is comparable, and a similar study could be undertaken; but the methods of analysis there needed would have to be somewhat different.

For a long time I have wished to dedicate a book to my teacher and friend Werner Jaeger as a small token of my gratitude for what I owe to his example and inspiration. It is not only in Aristotelian studies that I am his pupil and not only in scholarship that I know myself in his debt. To offer him a study of the author to whom he has linked his name so closely and brilliantly gives me pleasure, but the pleasure is mixed with hesitation since the only excuse for venturing on so large a subject is *in magnis et voluisse sat est.*

Next to Jaeger, the students of Greek philosophy from whom I have learned most are Harold Cherniss, Gregory Vlastos, and the late Francis Macdonald Cornford. I have often referred to their work but am conscious of owing them more than any number of references would indicate.

To my colleagues, friends, and fellow editors of the Cornell Studies in Classical Philology—Harry Caplan, James Hutton, and Gordon M. Kirkwood—I am deeply grateful for their readiness to examine the manuscript at a time when all of them were burdened with many duties. Each of them has read it with the greatest care, and each has contributed many improvements which have saved the book from stylistic obscurities as well as from material errors. The entire manuscript was also submitted to Gregory Vlastos, who has read it with the same patience, friendly understanding, and critical acumen with which he used to listen to me in former years while he was my colleague at Cornell. For the errors which after so much kind help have remained in the book I myself am solely responsible.

My wife, Lieselotte Solmsen, has made it possible for me to find the time and concentration necessary for this work and has helped me at every stage with her judgment and criticism.

To the John Simon Guggenheim Memorial Foundation I wish to express my gratitude for the award of a fellowship in the year 1947–1948 which enabled me to begin research on the subject. Cornell University twice granted me a year of sabbatical leave. The University Faculty Committee which administers the Hull Memorial Publication Fund made a generous grant toward the expenses connected with the printing of the book.

Routledge & Kegan Paul Ltd. have given me permission to incorporate quotations of F. M. Cornford's translation and commentary of the *Timaeus* from his *Plato's Cosmology.* Harvard University Press has granted me the same permission with regard to *Aristotle: On the Heavens, with an English Translation* (Loeb Classical Library) by W. K. C. Guthrie.

For technical reasons it has been necessary to present Greek terms as far as possible in transliteration. I have also found it necessary to reduce the number of cross references. Sometimes I have referred to a chapter when reference to a page might have been more helpful. I trust that in such instances time may be saved and uncertainties resolved by use of the Index.

On the whole the manuscript was completed in the fall of 1958, and only a few additions have been made since then.

F. S.

Ithaca, New York
May 1960

Contents

Abbreviations

Bailey, *Atomists*	Cyril Bailey. *The Greek Atomists and Epicurus.* Oxford, 1928.
Bonitz	*Index Aristotelicus.* Ed. by Hermannus Bonitz. (*Aristotelis Opera*, ed. by Academia Regia Borussica, vol. 5.) Berlin, 1870; 2d ed., Graz, 1955.
Burnet, *E. G. Ph.*	John Burnet. *Early Greek Philosophy.* 4th ed., London, 1930; reprinted, New York, 1957.
Cherniss, *Pl. and the Acad.*	Harold Cherniss. *Aristotle's Criticism of Plato and the Academy.* Baltimore, 1944.
Cherniss, *Presocr.*	——. *Aristotle's Criticism of Presocratic Philosophy.* Baltimore, 1935.
Cornford, *Cosmology*	Francis Macdonald Cornford. *Plato's Cosmology.* London, 1937; reprinted, New York, 1957.
Cornford, *Pl. and Parm.*	——. *Plato and Parmenides.* London, 1939; 2d impression, 1950; reprinted, New York, 1957.
Cornford, *Theory*	——. *Plato's Theory of Knowledge.* London, 1935; reprinted, New York, 1957.
Fränkel, *Dichtg. u. Philos.*	Hermann Fränkel. *Dichtung und Philosophie des Fruehen Griechentums.* (Philological Monographs, vol. 13, pub. by the American Philological Association.) New York, 1951.

Jaeger, *Aristotle*	Werner Jaeger. *Aristotle: Fundamentals of the History of His Development.* Trans. by Richard Robinson. 2d Eng. ed., Oxford, 1948.
Jaeger, *Paideia*	———. *Paideia: The Ideals of Greek Culture.* Trans. by Gilbert Highet. 3 vols. New York, 1939–1944. Vol. 1, 4th ed., Oxford, 1954.
Jaeger, *Theology*	———. *The Theology of the Early Greek Philosophers.* (The Gifford Lectures, 1936.) Trans. by Edward S. Robinson. Oxford, 1947.
Joachim	*Aristotle: On Coming-to-Be and Passing-Away (De generatione et corruptione).* A revised text with Introduction and Commentary by Harold H. Joachim. Oxford, 1922.
Kranz's Index	Included in the *Vorsokr., q.v.*
Ross, *Physics*	*Aristotle's Physics.* A revised text with Introduction and Commentary by W. D. Ross. Oxford, 1936.
Skemp	J. B. Skemp. *The Theory of Motion in Plato's Later Dialogues.* (Cambridge Classical Studies.) Cambridge, 1942.
St. V. F.	*Stoicorum Veterum Fragmenta.* Collegit Joannes ab Arnim. 4 vols. Leipzig, 1903–1924.
Vorsokr.	Hermann Diels. *Die Fragmente der Vorsokratiker.* 8th ed., with Index, by Walther Kranz. Berlin, 1952.
Wehrli	*Die Schule des Aristoteles: Texte und Kommentar.* Herausgegeben von Fritz Wehrli. 10 vols. Basel and Stuttgart, 1944–1959.

Part One

HISTORICAL INTRODUCTION

1

Presocratic Legacies

PARMENIDES' conception of unchanging and eternal being heralded a crisis for the vigorous cosmological speculation which had developed in Ionia. If there was no place for becoming in the realm of truth, how could physical thought survive as anything better than an assemblage of "opinions" and a "deceptive order of words"? [1] The rigor and merciless logic of his reasoning allowed no ignoring or evading, and those thinkers who fully accepted his conclusions ceased indeed to concern themselves with the origin, evolution, and ultimate fate of the Cosmos. Others, as is well known, accepted only a part of his conclusions and by defying the remainder found the way once more open toward constructing coherent and intrinsically unified cosmological systems. Still, what they accepted forced them into new paths of thinking; they had to grapple with questions which for their Ionian predecessors had not existed and to define their attitude toward fundamental concepts whose validity had formerly been taken for granted. By facing these tasks, they added new philosophical subjects to those previously discussed, yet also came to approach traditional problems in a new setting and under a changed perspective.

Becoming (*genesis*) and the complementary concept of perishing (*olethros*) were perhaps the most important implements of physical thought whose use Parmenides had vetoed, but they were not the only ones. If being can only be, but not come into being, it cannot grow either. It can have no past or future, i.e., no temporal beginning or

---

[1] B8.51f. Translations of short passages are usually my own. In longer passages for which no translator is indicated, I am nevertheless conscious of benefit derived from consulting the standard translations.

end (Anaximander's Infinite presumably too had neither, yet other "being things" in his system had both).[2] And if it remains forever in its perfect state of being, no change is possible. Parmenides does not present a systematic enumeration of the changes and their various forms, yet he does mention those that were later to figure prominently in comprehensive accounts. He rules out change of place and rejects alteration of color.[3] The former repudiation covers a large area of phenomena in its entirety whereas the latter seems to select something of more restricted range; yet change of color may well to Parmenides' mind have symbolized "qualitative alterations" in general (which were later to be comprehended under the term ἀλλοίωσις). There can certainly be no doubt that changes from hot to cold or from dry to moist and their opposites have as little standing in the realm of truth as those from black to white or from bright to dark.[4] Furthermore, "degrees of reality" are ruled out repeatedly and emphatically. Being cannot have greater strength, fullness, or intensity in some of its places—or phases —than in others;[5] if physicists had supposed that water, air, or fire represented the true nature of things and that other elements or formations were passing phases of them, their error is now patent. "Everything is filled with being"[6] is a thought which seems to imply the denial of any empty intervals (and was so understood by some of Parmenides' followers); yet to accept it in this sense involves an unwarranted translation of Parmenides' rigidly ontological thought into conceptions of a more physical or spatial nature. Similarly, when he speaks of being as "remaining in the same"[7] and "resting by itself," he is not so much indicating its place (which would again be too physical an interpretation) as excluding the possibility of any conceivable relationship to other entities. Of such entities there are none. No more can there be any relationship within being itself, since being has no parts. It is an absolute continuum, not a divisible.[8] Continuity, in fact, is the quality which accompanies and in a way specifies its "oneness." It is a safeguard against the "many."

Each of the concepts thus banished from the discussion of truth (and degraded to a mere "word") was destined for an illustrious career

---

[2] Parm. B8.7; 8.5 (cf. 8.9f.); Anaximander B1.   [3] B8.41.
[4] Cf. W. J. Verdenius, *Parmenides: Some Comments on His Poem* (Groningen, 1942), 54ff.
[5] B8.44–49; see also 23f.   [6] *Ibid.*, 24.
[7] *Ibid.*, 29; against "spatial" interpretations see also Verdenius, *op. cit.*, 43.
[8] B4; 8.6, 22–25.

in the later history of physical thought;—in fact, each was to form the core concept for a large body of theories, arguments, and problems. Parmenides seems to have denied Greek physics any future, and the future actually unfolds by positing now this and now that concept that he had rejected (and rejecting a corresponding antiphysical concept that he had posited) until Plato was able to posit both what Parmenides had rejected and what he had endorsed. In this introductory survey it cannot be our purpose to trace the history and significance of each of these concepts separately and individually. Only a few directions of the later developments can be indicated.

The crucial issue which divided the thinkers of the next generations was the reality of movement. *Genesis* seems to have had no defenders; rather, it appears that those who accepted the nonexistence of movement accepted that of *genesis* a fortiori. For Zeno no attack on, or *reductio ad absurdum* of, *genesis* is recorded, and it is possible that he regarded this issue as closed, seeing no reason to waste his polemical sallies on it.[9] The other orthodox Parmenidean whom we know, Melissus, refashioned some of the master's arguments against *genesis* and developed new and more specific ones against the reality of movement. By movement he seems to mean locomotion, i.e., what Parmenides had called change of place. Basing on the fullness of being one of his new arguments against movement, he mentions the void by name (as the opposite of the "full").[10] Elsewhere too we find him speaking more specifically and introducing terms of more physical connotations than Parmenides had seen fit to use. Thus one of the experiences or changes of which being must be kept free is "reordering," a change in the intrinsic organization or structure of being, and among the "qualities" that cannot materialize in being are dense and rare, warm and cold, hard and soft.[11] As the fragmentary material is not likely to give us altogether wrong impressions, we may conclude that Melissus struck out more directly against some favorite and pivotal

[9] For topics likely to have been taken up by Zeno see Cornford, *Pl. and Parm.*, 57f. Zeno could feel that by disproving *kinesis* he rendered *genesis* too impossible (this was suggested to me by Gregory Vlastos, who doubts whether the two concepts were originally distinguished). In this brief sketch I have seen no need for referring to the "Pythagorean atomism" which for Cornford and other scholars is the chief target of Zeno's polemic.

[10] Melissus B7.7, 9f. (cf. also A5.5).

[11] See esp. B7.3, 8; 8.2f. The word ἑτεροιοῦσθαι, which he uses (7.2; 8.3), does not have the same meaning which later attaches to ἀλλοιοῦσθαι.

concepts of the physicists. The void in particular seems to have figured in Pythagorean cosmology. On the other hand, "infinity," which Melissus, in opposition to Parmenides, attaches to his "being"—whether or not borrowed from Anaximander—bids fair to be the revival of an Ionian motif.[12]

Clearly on this orthodox basis no return to physical and cosmological theory was possible. For this the minimal requirements were the reality of movement and the existence of a plurality of things. The latter, as a matter of fact, was hardly reintroduced when it proliferated into an infinity; yet essential as it is for physical reasoning, it interests us less than the restoration of movement. Neither Empedocles nor Anaxagoras seems to have felt any need of justifying his use of this concept—unless there be a hint in the former that, since the rhythm of the basic physical processes remains eternally the same, his four physical elements are in a sense unchanging (i.e., "unmoved").[13] Another "change" rejected by Parmenides and brought back already by Empedocles is growth; though the sum of things cannot grow, the cosmic aggregations of each element decidedly can.[14]

Yet Parmenides' interdict of becoming and passing away remained binding. Whether or not they echo his reasons, Empedocles, Anaxagoras, the Abderites, and probably also Diogenes of Apollonia are at one in their conviction that the Cosmos and whatever other entities they chose to include in their accounts could originate and attain their forms without an act of becoming and could dissolve without a real perishing. We can see that some of them are agreed on replacing one of these stigmatized concepts, becoming, by association or mixture and the other by dissociation or the dissolving of the mixture.[15] The

---

[12] On Melissus' critical attitude to the Ionians cf. Burnet, *E. G. Ph.*, 326ff. For the Pythagorean "void" see Arist. *Phys.* IV,6.213b22ff. (= *Vorsokr.*, 59A30); cf. Cornford, *Pl. and Parm.*, 21f. Cornford goes farther—probably too far—in *Essays in Honour of Gilbert Murray* (London, 1936), 222ff.

[13] Emped. B17.12f. (Kranz's "unerschüttert" is not quite satisfactory, yet he brings out the ἢ-ταύτῃ relationship of vv. 12 and 13).

[14] See Emped. B17.32 and by way of contrast B37. The meaning and reference of B26.2 are not quite certain; yet A70 (1.296.18,30) and 77 may here be mentioned. For Anaxagoras, from whom we have no firsthand statement, reference may be made to A46 and B10, and for the Abderites, where the same situation prevails, e.g., to Leuc. A24, Democr. A40.

[15] μίξις and διάλλαξις μιγέντων are Empedocles' words, yet he also speaks of ἀποκρίνεσθαι (B8, 9). We shall later have occasion to discuss nuances between some of the terms employed (p. 372). See also Anaxag. B17. Democr. A1.44; 37; 57 suggest that he basically adhered to the Parmenidean canon of not-becoming and

processes thus denoted have the advantage of materializing from something that is already in existence.[16] Thus the sum of existing things suffers no addition or diminution. Here it is apparent that the argument of Parmenides which struck his successors with overpowering force was that not-being could not change into being. To distinguish between an absolute and a relative *genesis* and to define the latter as the formation of a new object from the components of previously existing ones would have overtaxed the mental equipment of these thinkers; in agreeing to eschew absolute *genesis* they felt that they were held to eschew *genesis* altogether.[17]

The fact that the later Presocratics, if they wished to keep up the tradition of cosmological thought, had to declare their stand on the issue of *genesis* is important in more than one respect. The reality or nonreality of *genesis* is not by itself a cosmological problem. It is prior to all more specific questions regarding the processes by which the Cosmos has formed and by which its various parts have taken their places and entered into mutual relations. In fact, it is an issue of a more general and theoretic type, and, remembering that the nature of *genesis* engages Aristotle in his *Physics*, we may feel justified in speaking here of a physical as distinct from a cosmological problem.[18] Nor is the nature of *genesis* and of its complement, destruction, the only problem of this type that called for a clear and definite stand. As the physicists operate with principles of all formation which they regard as eternal and therefore in the realm of being, they are in honor bound to explain which qualities of Parmenides' being they attach to them. Can the principles still pass into one another? Can they change at all? Not as readily as Anaximenes' air or Heraclitus' fire. Diogenes of Apollonia seems to have been the only thinker of this group bold enough to posit one principle and to declare that it had to "fall" "in manifold ways" from one form into another.[19] Another question of a physical rather than cosmological type had been raised by Zeno's discovery of infinite divisibility. Anaxagoras and the Abderites reacted to it in opposite ways,

---

operated with association and dissociation (scil., of the atoms). For Diogenes I rely on A1 but admit that it is not conclusive. Cf. on the whole Cornford, *Pl. and Parm.*, 53ff.

[16] Although disagreeing about the nature of the basic and persisting entities, Empedocles, Anaxagoras, Democritus, and presumably also Leucippus were at one in regarding them as *onta*.

[17] For the later developments of this problem see esp. Chs. 2, 4, and 16.

[18] *Phys.* I,4ff., 7ff.   [19] See esp. B2.

and we are fortunate enough to read the actual words in which the former declares his wholehearted acceptance of the new idea.[20] Finally, on the void too, its existence or nonexistence, a declaration was necessary, and on this issue, as is well known, the Abderites went their own way, positing it while the other successors of Parmenides denied it.[21] Since the void is identical with not-being, it may here be used to illustrate the nature of the earliest "physics." This physics arose through the application of Parmenides' ontological concepts to the world of multiple objects that exist in separation from one another.

The new concepts which replace coming into existence and passing away apply not only to the Cosmos as a whole but to physical objects in general. To be sure, the Cosmos itself arises by the separation or dissociation of entities that had previously been mixed and "together," at least to the point of being indistinguishable. Basically this idea may already have been present in Anaximander.[22] Yet the nature and composition of physical or biological substances had not, so far as we know, invited the ingenuity of the early physicists. After Parmenides these topics move into the scope of physical speculation. This development may owe something to an increased interest in physiological matters as such; [23] yet its more potent or in any case its more philosophical cause is that here the concepts of mixture and association must test their validity. They must prove that they really can replace *genesis*. In Empedocles no living being and none of its parts, whether tissue or organ, "comes into being" or "perishes"; he expressly declares that he uses these discredited words merely as a matter of "convention" [24] (and, we may suspect, of convenience). These beings are simply mixtures—mixtures of the eternal elements. In addition Empedocles, who, it seems, started philosophy on this new course, may have derived a

---

[20] B3. This fundamental issue too is taken up in Aristotle's *Physics* (VI,2ff.; cf. below, pp. 199–221.

[21] Emped. B13f.; Anaxag. A44 *et al.;* Leuc. A1 *et al.* (for further passages see Kranz's Index to the *Vorsokr.*, 233a4ff.). Cf. on the whole Karl Reinhardt, *Parmenides u. d. Gesch. d. griech. Philos.* (Bonn, 1916), 52.

[22] Anaximander A10; Emped. A49; Anaxag. B12, 13, 15; Leuc. A1.31ff. (cf. Democr. B5.1.1 = Diod. 1.7.1, and B164); see also Archelaus A4.2. For the condition prevailing before the διάκρισις see esp. Emped. B27–29; Anaxag. B1 (A48; Arist. *Phys.* VIII,1.250b24ff.); Leuc. *loc.cit.* Cf. Burnet, *E. G. Ph.*, 236, 269; Bailey, *Atomists*, 93ff., 138ff.

[23] For the increasing interest of the later physicists in medical subjects and methods cf. Jaeger, *Theology*, 156f.

[24] Emped. B9.5 (cf. B8, 11, 15).

special personal satisfaction from the realization of an intrinsic kinship connecting all living beings;[25] for as all are formed out of the same principles, the portions of the elements which have now composed a human being will later combine into an animal of the fields or forests, into a bird, a fish, or a plant. It stands to reason that Anaxagoras and the atomists were less fascinated by such glimpses of the basic oneness and continuity of all life; yet they share Empedocles' concern with the formation and composition of substances. Thus simultaneously with introducing new leading concepts the post-Parmenidean thinkers discovered a large area for their application and enriched philosophy through incorporating a broad new field of study and interest.[26]

The impression that tissues and organs—in a measure even living beings as a whole—were the chief gainers of this development is well grounded. It is not reported that the later Presocratics went to great length in specifying the mixtures present in, say, metals or that they offered more than a very general statement as to the mixed nature of oil and other fluids. There are chapters in Plato's *Timaeus*[27] which give us chemical definitions (based on the concept of mixture) not only of oil and other liquids but also of gold, copper, earthenware, and similar objects. Starting with the *Timaeus*, we may trace the persistence of such inquiries in the Peripatus where Book IV of the *Meteorologica*—hardly a genuine work of Aristotle—testifies to similar interests;[28] but antecedents to the *Timaeus* chapters are not so easy to find. And even in the area of biology, statements as specific as Empedocles' about the ratio of mixture in blood, flesh, bone, and sinews[29] remained an exceptionally daring venture which others, as far as we can see, did not see fit to emulate. Anaxagoras appears to have confined himself to the assertion that there are "portions" of everything in all physical entities without attempting to suggest numerical ratios between, say, cold and

[25] The continuity of life beyond the span of individual existence is in any case affirmed in B15.

[26] As is well known, Parmenides had shown the way by his own use of "mixture"; yet it is not clear how far he carried the ideas expressed in B12.4ff., 13 and whether he used them in his "Way of Opinion" for the explanation of physical substances (Simplicius *In de caelo* 559.25 reports that Parmenides explained the parts of living beings, and we know that he spoke, though for a very specific purpose, of the mixture of hot and cold in them, B18, A46; see also A46a and 52f.).

[27] *Tim.* 58d4–61c1.

[28] *Meteor.* IV, esp. 10 (388a30ff., b12ff.; 389a8ff.). Note also IV,8.384b31 (cf. my comments, *Gnomon* 28 [1957], 132ff.).

[29] Emped. A78, B96, 98.

hot, or cold and dark, in any physical mixture.[30] Needless to say, these thinkers had no devices—experimental or of whatever kind—for implementing their "chemical" interests. They had throughout to rely on general probabilities, unverifiable impressions, and intuition. Thus it was safer to say that certain powers, certain types of atoms, perhaps also certain elements or *homoeomere* "predominate" in a mixture.[31]

One could also be specific, in fact the atomists evidently were very specific and detailed, about the basic realities which retain their being and their nature through all the varying combinations in which they find themselves entangled. And as for the manner and mechanism of these combinations, the same point which for Aristotle seemed to defeat the idea of a mixture was vital for its original conception: unchanged and unamalgamated, not fused and not transformed in substance, portions of the elements lie side by side, though of course the individual particles thus grouped are far below the threshold of perception.[32] In the atomist system, some of the unbreakable units are, thanks to their shapes and general configuration, capable of entering into firmer union with one another than are certain others. Thus they form more compact substances.[33]

In Empedocles we may observe that even though Love is the agent of mixture some elements contribute more actively to this process than the others: when bone is formed, fire may not only be a part of the mixture but also the hardening factor.[34] This points ahead to the status of "active powers" which hot and cold have in the Peripatetic scheme (in contrast to the passive moist and dry) but also back to the active role which the hot apparently already played in Anaximander. For although no instance of hardening is attested for him, the hot clearly had the power of changing moist to dry.[35] As for the cold, the wording of a

---

[30] For "a portion of everything in everything" see Anaxag. B6, 11, 12.

[31] See Anaxag. B12 (39.6f.). Cf. A41, 44.

[32] That the particles when mixed cannot change is especially evident in the case of the atoms, yet similar assumptions may be postulated for the other major systems. "Being things" cannot temporarily give up their nature, though they may "run through one another" (Emped. B17.34; 21.13) and thus become "different in appearance" (21.14) but not different in being. Cf. also Emped. A86.11. For Aristotle (*De gen. et corr.* I,10.327a34ff., 328a5ff.) see below, Ch. 19.

[33] See esp. Lucr. II,444 (nothing exactly parallel is attested for Democritus, yet see Bailey, *Atomists*, 137).

[34] See Emped. B73 and 96 (which I have perhaps brought too closely together) and B56. See also A30 (on the moon) and A52 (on the heavenly vault as hardened by the fire); cf. Burnet, *E. G. Ph.*, 237.

[35] For the distinction between ποιητικαί and παθητικαί δυνάμεις see *De gen.* II,2.329b24ff. (*Meteor.* IV,1.378b12 and *passim*). For Anaximander see A27.

verbatim preserved statement of Anaxagoras leaves us in no doubt that
it too could act as a "solidifier." In the mixture of which it is a part
it does not content itself with mere presence but hardens earth into
stone.[36]

Physical, or chemical, composition of substances and cosmogony are
not of necessity closely connected subjects. However, the objects
whose composition interested the later Presocratics were all within the
Cosmos and in a sense parts of it. Composition could be understood as
"origin" and the origin of specific entities, especially of living beings
in some way or other linked to that of the world as a whole.[37] And as
these thinkers had inherited a cosmogonic framework, it need not surprise us if they fitted their new subject into this frame. How and how
far they actually did this is not quite clear. The sequence of Empedocles' fragments is far from being completely settled. Nevertheless it
seems beyond doubt that he introduced the concept of mixture (to replace *genesis*) in the beginning of his poem [38] but, contenting himself
here with a few typical illustrations, reserved all details and specific
formulas to sections which must have their place after the cosmogony
or, in any case, after some of its phases. Going a step farther, one may
find reasons to think that he fitted the evolution of living beings (in
four distinct stages) into the evolutionary history of the Cosmos as a
whole, but when we come to the fragments that indicate the composition of bone, blood, flesh, eyes, and the like, their connection with the
large evolutionary scheme is not quite so close.[39] An alternative procedure—which we might think more logical—would be to treat the
variety of combinations and mixtures immediately after describing

---

[36] Anaxag. B16, λίθοι συμπήγνυνται ὑπὸ τοῦ ψυχροῦ. Cf. also W. K. C. Guthrie,
Cl. Q., 49 (1956), 40f., on Anaximenes.

[37] For this there may have been a precedent in Anaximander if the origin of the
first living beings ἐν ὑγρῷ (A30) took place at a time while the moist condition
still prevailed on the earth (A27; cf. A11.6). Cf. Kathleen Freeman, *The Presocratic Philosophers* (London, 1946), 62; Olof Gigon, *Der Ursprung d. griech.
Philosophie* (Basel, 1945), 95f.

[38] B6ff.

[39] B57–61 (cf. A70) 85ff., 96, 98. The almost regular references to Cypris indicate, however, in what period of the *kyklos* the tissues and organs were formed.
B71 (and 73) may well have been the beginning of the section to which 85ff., 96,
and 98 and also 82f. belong; on the other hand, it is very tempting to think of
B71 as following closely upon B35. There is nothing in Simplicius or others that
would militate against this sequence. A closer study of the question must be left
to another occasion. In Anaxagoras cosmogony and the origin of composite substances seem to have been treated *pari passu*. However, as we are in the dark
about the place of, e.g., B10, we can hardly arrive at well-founded opinions.

the eternal "roots" or elements of things, since it is these which combine and by their combinations produce the temporary formations. A physicist who preferred this scheme could explain the composition of physical substances in a more general or "timeless" fashion without reference to their "first origin" in the pattern of the Cosmos, in fact before the origin of the Cosmos itself was set forth. We do not know whether any of the later group of Presocratics emancipated himself so far from the tradition. The first account in which we meet the sequence just indicated, i.e., first the principles, their nature and actions, including the formation of other substances by their mixture, and only after this a cosmogony, is the Epicurean system as reflected in Lucretius; [40] but there is no way of knowing whether Epicurus himself was the first to rearrange the sequence of the major topics or whether Democritus had anticipated him. In the *Timaeus* the "chemical" definitions of composite things are for some reasons—more precisely, for new and Platonic reasons—part of the account of the Cosmos and have their place after the "cosmogony." [41] For Aristotle, on the other hand, the cosmological theory of the elements and the study of their behavior in *genesis* and mixture are two entirely distinct subjects, which find their treatment in different works, offering scanty evidence of mutual acquaintance and making little effort at utilizing each other's results.[42] Clearly, however, neither Plato nor Aristotle allows any inference as to the standard arrangement—if there was such a thing—in earlier systems.

"Composition" could not give much help toward solving questions about the meteorological phenomena (thunder and lightning, wind, waterspouts, etc.) which must have bulked large in the early stages of philosophical curiosity. Anaximenes' basic principle has an immediate bearing on a goodly number of these phenomena; his air turns readily into clouds, water (rain), hail, and snow, while also causing thunder, lightning, and waterspouts.[43] By contrast with this, Empedocles' brilliant explanation of night as the shadow thrown by the earth [44] strikes us as remote from his four "roots" as well as from Love and Strife. Are subjects of the kind no longer in the foreground? Has meteorology

---

[40] See Lucr. II,333ff., 381–477, 581ff., 661ff.

[41] *Tim.* 58d4–61c1. The geometrical figures which are essential for this account (as well as for the sections on the tissues, *Tim.* 73bff.) are a characteristic of cosmic, not of purely physical, *genesis* (cf. 53bff.); see below, pp. 46–52.

[42] See below, Chs. 11 and 17, but also the first paragraphs of Ch. 21.

[43] Anaximenes A7.7f.; cf. A17.   [44] Emped. B48.

become a poor third beside cosmology and the doctrine of composition
—to say nothing of other new subjects such as physiology (including
reproduction) and the explanation of the sense functions? It may be
safer merely to say that meteorology has become a third, a status not
necessarily to be identified with that of a pauper. Anaxagoras and
Democritus were clearly convinced that the same basic assumptions as
they used in explaining composition also held the key for the explanation of meteorological phenomena; in the subjects of thunder,
lightning, and thunderbolt we find Anaxagoras operating with the hot
and the cold, two fundamental opposites in his world stuff, while
Democritus uses his concept of the void and sees atoms of a specific
nature and shape involved in these events.[45] If meteorology later suffers
a loss of status, being almost totally ignored in the *Timaeus,* treated in
a cavalier fashion by Epicurus, and given a place after, and presupposing, cosmology and the theory of *genesis* by Aristotle, it still is not
necessary to infer that it must have been on the decline before Plato;
for each of these developments had its specific and independent causes.

Celestial phenomena, too, continued to challenge the ingenuity of the
later thinkers. New discoveries, such as the borrowed light of the
moon, undoubtedly supplied a strong stimulus for continued research.[46]
To composition and mixture, things in heaven had no more relation
than "things on high"; their explanation has now been tied to another
and (presumably) new conception, the cosmogonic whirl, which had to
pass the test of satisfactorily accounting for many continuing phenomena of our world as well as for its first organization.[47] It is obvious,
however, that movements of the heaven and the heavenly bodies could
be more easily related to the original world formation than thunder
and lightning, rainbow, and the flooding of the Nile. By discussing
phenomena of the latter type without reference to "first origins," the
physicists created a pattern which was to survive in the cosmology
and meteorology of the Peripatus after world formation and first
origins had become outmoded notions. Curiously the distinction between the two types of phenomena persists and becomes even more
accentuated; the reason for this is that the subjects which the Presocratics had treated in close relation to cosmic origins are those in

[45] Anaxag. A84 (cf. *Doxogr.* 368); Democr. A93.

[46] Parm. B14f.; cf. Emped. B45 (47); Anaxag. B18; Democr. A89a.

[47] Against the hypothesis that the "whirl" motif goes back to the earlier systems
(Anaximander) cf. Cornford, *Cl. Q.,* 28 (1934), 15f. General considerations favor
Cornford's view, although Arist. *De caelo* II,13.295a10 remains a stumbling block.

which Plato and Aristotle find the clearest evidence for order, perfection, and a teleological causality operating in the world. Thanks to this new causality, the mechanical explanations which Presocratic physicists had given for the heavenly movements and for the formation of the firmament, the sun, and other bodies could be discarded and by and large ignored. And should not cosmogony as such, which had been the matrix of these explanations, share their fate? The new causality might point to this conclusion, and so would other new insights and discoveries. Yet Plato—if he made a "conscious" choice—did not see fit to drop this "scheme." And are we sure that the μύθου σχῆμα was for him no more than a scheme?

In Empedocles and Anaxagoras a whirl separates the lighter or quicker stuff which is to fill the peripheral regions from the heavier and inert material that remains and settles in the center where it builds up earth and sea. But the whirl does not arise by itself. Both thinkers assume at this stage the operation of a divine force. Empedocles' "Strife" primarily manifests itself in dividing or separating; Anaxagoras' mind divides too, but is also credited with an ordering activity.[48] Actually Empedocles' vivid and vivifying imagination seems to have found ample evidence for the presence of Strife in the world around him; and as this evidence included processes more immediately familiar than the origin of the Cosmos,[49] we need not at all suppose that he first discovered Strife in brooding over this great question and then realized its activity in other processes. It remains that fire, air, earth, and water, though alive, divine, and active, do not by their own impulse move toward, and settle in, their cosmic regions. Have they lost some of their former "self-moving" power and initiative? No other physicist can have been more emphatic than Empedocles in giving his basic realities divine honors[50]—in fact, they are for him more than ordinary gods. Yet in spite of their high dignity and august func-

---

[48] Emped. B30 (cf. 35, 36); Anaxag. B12 (διεκόσμησε 38.11f.). With regard to Empedocles, neither the origin of the whirl nor its relation to Strife can be reconstructed satisfactorily. We are entitled, I think, to gather from 31B30f. that the first commotion in the *Sphairos* was brought about by Strife. This implies that the δίνη materializes subsequently, during the period of Strife's ascendance (this is presupposed in B35). As for the effects of Empedocles' δίνη, Arist. *De caelo* II,13. 295a9–21 deserves more attention than it receives from Diels and Kranz, who print a13–21 as a testimony for Empedocles (31A67) and include a9–13 among those for Anaxagoras (59A88), in spite of πάντες in a10. I can see no justification for this decision.

[49] See, e.g., B20, 21.   [50] See, e.g., B6; 21 (note v. 12); 17.27–35; 35.14.

tions they are not able to regulate their mutual relations by their own decision. No more can Anaxagoras' primordial stuff move or change by itself or the opposite "powers" present in it display themselves without an impulse coming from the outside. To be sure, this stuff and the powers which compose it make no pretension to divinity—though one hesitates to believe that Anaxagoras could have conceived of powers or seeds as dead, i.e., as powerless and unproductive. Still, the language of the fragments suggests for them a passive rather than an active role, and it has been observed that the traditional predicates of divinity are reserved for the Mind which creates the movements and knows what comes to pass in the world.[51] Some of the life once pulsating in the world stuff—the life quality which used to be described by the now disparaged term "hylozoism"—seems to have by imperceptible stages gone out of it, until physical thought finally reached the condition which Plato so eloquently denounces in Book X of the *Laws:* elements entirely devoid of life are supposed to build up the Cosmos and everything in it; nature—lifeless too—and chance are the only forces active in these formations; nothing divine, mental, or spiritual guides their operations, and living entities are late and incidental products of these dead elements.[52] Among the outstanding systems that of the atomists (to which Plato never clearly alludes) would seem to answer this description most fully. Leucippus and Democritus may not, like Epicurus, have marshaled a series of arguments to prove that the atoms are lifeless;[53] for as far as we can see, nobody had become aware of this great issue before Plato formulated it. In fact, Democritus seems to have marked out one particular shape of atom as constituting the soul or the vital heat.[54] Yet his atoms when moving at large or gathering in a whirl and being thrust forth from it do not display any characteristics of living beings. And Democritus may well have considered it a distinctive superiority of his account that the whirl arises without any external agency. The atoms themselves set it up, since there is no condition of equilibrium among them, as

---

[51] "Nach Anaxagoras sind, im Gegensatz zu allen früheren Theorien, die Weltkörper rein materiell" (Walther Kranz, "Kosmos," *Archiv f. Begriffsgeschichte,* 2 [1955], 41). Anaxagoras may have more often than we can know (see B15) used the active voice in speaking of the cold, the warm, etc., yet it remains significant that he refers to them as being set in motion, separated, and, in principle at least, also "ordered" (i.e., arranged) by *Nous* (B12). For the predicates of divinity applied to the *Nous* see Jaeger, *Theology,* 161ff.

[52] *Legg.* X,888e–889c.   [53] See Lucr. 2.865–990.   [54] Democr. A101–106.

there had been for the "being things" mixed in Anaxagoras' initial condition of the world stuff or, one would suppose, for the elements in Empedocles' *Sphairos*.[55]

Diogenes of Apollonia found a way of putting the moving power back into the world stuff, the prime reality. His air, which takes so many shapes, is conscious and thinking, presumably even planning.[56] Empedocles and Anaxagoras did not think in terms of different types of causes; and for this reason it is incorrect and unhistorical to find in them a differentiation of the efficient cause from the material. Yet when this has been said and when in addition the difference between their "being things" and Aristotle's matter is kept in mind, one may do justice to the facts and to Aristotle's historical survey by crediting these men with the introduction of specific movers and originators of changes in the physical world. "If all things were at rest together" (as they actually are in Anaxagoras), "what first movement could we assume to arise in them," asks Plato, and his answer is soul,[57] as Anaxagoras' had been mind. It should be said, however, that Plato had come to his source of movement along another route; movement has a different place in his scheme; and he is not, in this context, concerned with the origin of the Cosmos. The continuity between his conception and that of Anaxagoras is not an organic development, but rather a return after a long detour ("Der Weg des Geistes ist der Umweg," as Hegel knew). Similarly, purpose was not in late Presocratic speculation introduced as a "cause" but rather as a proof for the conscious intellectual activity of the (divine) principle and as its manifestation; for at this stage the intelligent manifestations of this principle have become distinct from the purely physical or vital, and they are grasped and studied separately. Since Plato attests that Anaxagoras did not spell out the activities of his "mind," Diogenes is today regarded as the first proponent of a consistent teleological scheme.[58] This view seems fundamentally correct; still, it may be argued that already Empedocles had shown his Cypris as the creator of

---

[55] For the στηρίζειν operative at this stage see Emped. B27.3. The same word occurs in Anaxag. A50 and may well reflect Anaxagoras' own language. If this testimony does not suffice, we may argue that there should be an even distribution of all powers in the original mixture. For contrast see Leuc. A1.31 and Plato *Tim.* 52e.

[56] Diog. B3–5. For Diogenes as teleologist see esp. W. Theiler's analysis of Xenophon's *Memorabilia* I,4 and IV,3 (*Zur Geschichte d. teleol. Naturbetrachtung* [Zürich and Leipzig, 1925], 14ff.).

[57] *Legg.* X,895a6ff.   [58] Cf. Theiler (see Note 56); Jaeger, *Theology*, 165ff.

perfect formations, describing her actions in terms of human work-
men or craftsmen (*demiourgoi*, like carpenters, metalworkers, and
smelters).[59] Blood, which seems to be her "perfect" work, provides
living beings with the power of thinking—of thinking adequately about
their environment, since it is the ideal mixture of the four physical elements. The language of the fragments suggests a deliberate, not an accidental, achievement, and to this extent—admittedly not a large extent
—the "movers" have a tendency to become teleological agents.

In Empedocles, Love and Strife operate on the four physical elements, whereas Anaxagoras' Mind works directly on the "powers." If
our knowledge of the Presocratics were less meager, the relation between elements and powers might well present itself as one of the
most crucial problems, as it certainly was one of the most persistent.
The place and the relative importance of the powers may vary from
system to system; yet no system could dispense with them altogether.
In that of Anaximander two of them, hot and cold, seem to have been
of dominating importance; in fact, they are the only ones that can
with confidence be discerned, though it is possible that other pairs
like bright and dark clustered around these leading opposites, and
there is every reason to think that dry and moist also figured in his
account.[60] Later too it is not always easy to determine which powers
an individual thinker recognized, nor can one know whether those
that on a given occasion are specified exhaust the list even of the more
important. In principle there need be no limit to their number; anything that affects either man or any other part of the physical world
has or is a power. The Pythagorean "table of opposites" was probably
not meant to restrict their number (for "physical" powers hardly appear in it); nor need we assume that Alcmaeon intended to protest
against it when he mentioned other powers and did not commit himself as to their number.[61] To a Greek physician it would be repugnant
to limit them; and the discovery of many strong qualities in the food-
stuff of which we read in the Hippocratic writings [62] may have helped
to keep the number of the "powers" open or unlimited. When ele-

[59] See esp. 71, 73, 86ff., 96, 98 (note v. 3), perhaps also 34.
[60] See esp. A10, and for moist and dry A27.
[61] Arist. *Metaph.* A5.986a22ff. = Alcm. A3; cf. also B4.
[62] See, e.g., *De pr. med.* 14, also *De vent.* 7f. and *passim* (although the author of
this work does not insist on labeling the *dynameis* that he has observed or discovered). On the whole cf. J. Souilhé, *Etudes sur le terme δύναμις dans les dialogues
de Platon* (Paris, 1919).

ments or "principles" were introduced, this could have the result of making the powers relative and impermanent (as presumably already in Anaximenes); although the element itself persists in the changes, the powers may change to the point of losing their identity.[63] When Parmenides' being made it imperative for his successors to operate with unchanging entities, the powers could become attached to elements in a more enduring and substantial fashion—where Empedocles speaks of the sun-fire as bright to look at and hot and of water as darkish and cool, he does not use these words as mere ornaments.[64] Alternatively, the powers themselves could advance to the position of "being things," not capable of changing their nature but only of regrouping. This is the status which, it has been argued with force,[65] they receive in Anaxagoras; here they seem to have made their last bid for a central place in the physical system. For with the Abderites the pendulum swings to the opposite extreme. In their scheme the once independent and independently active powers have become functions of shape. The shape of the atoms is real, i.e., "by nature"; sweet and cold, bright and pungent are impressions recorded by our organism and in particular by our sense organs when in contact with specific atom shapes.[66] Being thus assigned to a place between the reality of atomic figures and the feeling of our body, the "powers" have suffered a decided loss of status, compared with the days when the destiny of the Cosmos was tied up with their struggle for domination. In his *Timaeus*

[63] Anaximenes A7.1ff.; Heracl. B126. Heraclitus' fire remains through the changes, yet does not remain "dry."

[64] On the basis of B21.3 it is hardly possible to set up an exact correspondence between the four roots and the four basic powers (hot, cold, moist, and dry); nor does Kirk's reference (*Heraclitus: The Cosmic Fragments* [Cambridge, 1954], 154) to Philistion's doctrine as reported by the Anon. Lond. 20.25 establish a presumption for Empedocles. That Empedocles should have used the epithets in a purely decorative way is a priori unlikely, and the contrary may be inferred from his view that "the white" prevails in a mixture to which fire has contributed more than any other "root" (B96). B23 teaches that the elements mix like colors, a thought which has a bearing on their own colors.

[65] Cf. Gregory Vlastos, *Philos. Rev.*, 59 (1950), 41ff. See also P. Tannery, *Pour l'hist. de la science hell.* (2d ed.; Paris, 1930), 294ff.

[66] See Democr. B125 and for details esp. A129, 133, 135. Size and shape (of the atoms), the so-called primary qualities, are not "powers" (*dynameis*). Weight and lightness which the atoms acquire in the whirl do not seem to have been treated by Democritus with reference to *aisthesis*. For Plato and Aristotle see below, Ch. 13. Bailey, *Atomists*, 105, is hesitant about tracing Democritus' views on "secondary qualities" to Leucippus. On the later fate of the "powers" (in Plato and Aristotle) see below, Ch. 17 and the Index, *s.v.*

Plato adopts Empedocles' elements, not Anaxagoras' powers, as the "principles" of his Cosmos. To construct the powers mathematically would probably have been more difficult than to compose the elements by means of geometrical figures, and the mathematical assumptions stand Plato in good stead even when he comes to deal with the mixtures of these elements and the nature of compounds. Here too he is able to dispense with the powers. He criticizes those who know only "accessory causes" and are prone to resort to "heating, cooling, compacting, rarefying," and other similar processes. Such processes must have bulked large in the scheme of the Presocratics.[67] For Plato, as for the atomists, hot and cold, black and white, sweet and bitter are sensations, and even heavy and light find their place in the class of παθήματα, though in the end they turn out to be more.[68] Was there any hope for the powers of moving back into their erstwhile position?

[67] *Tim.* 46a1ff. For Plato stones are not, as for Anaxagoras (B16), "compacted out of earth by action of the cold"; instead certain geometrically defined water units or earth units combine to form rock or metals (*Tim.* 59a8ff., 60c5ff.). See also *Vorsokr.*, 13A7 (71.17); 31B56; 64A1.

[68] *Tim.* 61d5ff., 67e2ff., 65c6–66c7, 62c3–63e8.

2

Topics of Plato's Later Philosophy

MOVEMENT AND *GENESIS:* THEIR PLACE IN PLATO'S SCHEME

BEFORE and after Parmenides the Presocratics built their systems around eternal and indestructible principles; yet the later generations also took care to make their principles unchanging and employed them in such fashion that *genesis* could nowhere make its disturbing appearance. There is no evidence that Plato ever shared their prejudice against this concept. In definite contrast to Empedocles and Anaxagoras he had never subscribed to the Parmenidean doctrine that "becoming is extinguished and passing away unknown." His own eternal and unchanging principles are as a matter of course exempt from both, as they are also strangers to movement and to many other characteristics of physical things. Yet they readily take their place in a scheme in which coming to be and passing away are likewise firmly established. The relations in which the Forms stand to things that come and go may even serve for their own closer description and for their characterization by contrast.[1] Yet contrast is only one facet of this relationship; another is the presence of the Forms in physical objects or the participation of the latter in the Forms,[2] conceptions whose precise meaning and technical intricacies are outside the scope of this study.

[1] See, e.g., *Conv.* 211b and *Phaedo* 78dff.
[2] E.g., *Phaedo* 100cff.; for a list of the terms which Plato employs to describe this relationship see W. D. Ross, *Plato's Theory of Ideas* (Oxford, 1949), 228ff.

Far from thwarting *genesis* or militating against its perennial existence, the Forms make it possible and keep it in operation. In fact, *genesis* is a much more obvious and convincing manifestation of the Forms in the physical world than association or dissociation, the Presocratic substitutes for it, could be. Relationships of the latter type materialize for the Forms in the patterns of combination which they organize among themselves.[3]

Compared with the late Presocratics, Plato is thus in an advantageous position. He does not labor under the difficulty of having to ignore two central facts in the realm of physical and human experience. Moreover, his early philosophical concerns are so different from those of the Presocratics that for a long time he saw no need of distinguishing, let alone protecting, his position from the unfriendly attitude which had lately prevailed toward *genesis*. The rehabilitation of *genesis*—an important event in the history of philosophical problems—seems to have been achieved accidentally rather than deliberately. An explicit justification of his new approach Plato, as a matter of fact, never presents. Even in the late dialogues, where he joins issue with Parmenides about the reality of not-being and supports "the many" against the monopolistic tendencies of Parmenides' "one," [4] he never sees a necessity to challenge his veto of all *genesis*. It remained for Aristotle to safeguard this concept against Parmenides' negation and thus to add the final stroke to Plato's "patricide." [5] Still, the late dialogues in which Plato goes more deeply into the physical aspects of physical processes include situations where his own concept of *genesis* comes into contact with the notions of association and dissociation that had lately usurped its place. Here it becomes clear that *genesis* is not merely another name for the process that had been treated as association or mixture but involves a decidedly different conception of its nature. However, there is no criticism of the Presocratic concepts. If we wish to find out what Plato thought of them, we must analyze his own doctrines. From these

[3] For good reasons the words συγκρίνεσθαι and διακρίνεσθαι are on the whole not used where Plato discusses the combination and separation of Forms in the dialectical *diaeresis*. *Parm.* 129e2 is an exception. μείγνυσθαι, which had also figured prominently in Presocratic accounts of physical things and their origin, is employed somewhat more readily for the combination of Forms. Cf. Cornford, *Theory*, 255f.

[4] *Soph.* 244bff.; *Parm.* 136aff. For an earlier verdict about the ontological status of the many (scil., between being and not-being and participating of both) see *Rep.* V,476e–480a; the section includes no reference to *genesis*.

[5] See below, Chs. 4 and 16.

it may be inferred that Plato considered the "aggregational" point of view not entirely wrong or useless but rather as stopping short of a complete understanding and penetration.

The contribution which the Forms make to *genesis* cannot be stated in the same terms used to describe the change of an "element" into something else or the mixing of elements in a compound. The relation of physical objects to nonphysical puts the *genesis* of the former under an entirely new aspect. Somewhat schematically Aristotle could sum up the situation in his statement that the Presocratic physicists had left the "formal cause" out of account.[6] The role of Plato's "formal cause" in his more detailed account of *genesis* in the *Timaeus* will engage us presently. Where Plato is close to the traditional problems of physical origin and physical composition, a comparison between his own answers and those proposed by his forerunners may be profitable. Yet in the early dialogues he is rarely, if ever, close to them. Even the *Phaedo*, which includes some important propositions about the nature and conditions of becoming, does not use this concept in a technical sense or with reference to subjects around which Presocratic discussions of *genesis* had revolved. The new propositions are not formulated for the benefit of the "professionals"; they do not refer to the coming into being of the elements, of the Cosmos, or of other physical entities. When Plato here explains that the process invariably takes place between opposites, he uses "becoming" in what we may call its copulative meaning, speaking of smaller things that become larger, of stronger that become weaker, and indeed of human beings now alive who will "become" dead and who, he concludes, must somehow also go through the opposite process of passing from death to life.[7] The becoming which he discusses is primarily the arising of a new quality in a subject, not the *genesis* of this subject itself, and one noteworthy conclusion is in fact that the subject as such persists while its qualities change.[8]

It is obvious that Plato regards the propositions here worked out as universally valid. If they extend beyond the subjects taken up by the physicists—and primarily hold good of different subjects—they also apply to becoming warm and becoming cold, to decrease and increase, and even to association and dissociation.[9] All of these are used as illus-

---

[6] See esp. *Metaph.* A3 (in ch. 5 some allowance is made for the achievements of Parmenides and of the Pythagoreans, 986b19, 987a13–27); cf. Cherniss, *Presocr.*, 227 n.44.

[7] *Phaedo* 70dff.; cf. 102dff.   [8] 102e; cf. 103b.   [9] *Phaedo* 71b.

trations of the rule that becoming takes place between opposites. Here we are definitely in the orbit of Presocratic thought. In Plato's later works and in Aristotle's treatises processes of this type are on the whole regarded as outside the range of *genesis*. Increase and decrease in particular form a class by themselves;[10] becoming warm and cold would be instances of qualitative alteration (*alloiosis*); and such alteration as well as increase and decrease is a "species" of the genus "change" and as such on a par with *genesis*, not subordinated to it (that association and dissociation are rivals rather than partners of it has already been said). In this more developed and differentiated scheme becoming is confined to the emergence of a substance, like fire, gold, flesh, etc.[11] Still, the Greeks used the verb "to become" as an auxiliary verb in the wider and less specialized meaning, and a philosopher wishing to comprehend all forms of becoming could accept this usage—even Aristotle, despite his tendency to restrict *genesis* to the category of substance, falls back on it.[12] We need not doubt that Parmenides' universal veto embraced the auxiliary becoming of common parlance as well as the substantial becoming of the physicists.[13] The becoming that Plato in the *Phaedo* brings back—with complete indifference to professional opinions—has as wide a range as that which Parmenides threw out. The later Presocratics, concerned as they were with physical processes, had confined themselves to a few segments of it.

From his new point of vantage Plato in the *Phaedo* not only restores and reorganizes the doctrine of becoming but also sets limits to the occurrence of this phenomenon. Where a change into the opposite cannot take place, *genesis* has no possibility of materializing. This principle keeps not only the Forms themselves out of the grasp of becoming but also prevents physical substances from accepting into their being

[10] Cf. *Legg.* X,893e. In the *Phaedo* passage (71b3) Plato uses the words "growth" and "decline" (or "increase" and "decrease") while putting these processes under the heading and under the rules of *genesis*.

[11] In the early chapters of *De gen. et corr.* Aristotle does not for the first time proclaim the difference between *genesis* on the one hand and qualitative change and growth on the other (see esp. I,4.5); their fundamental "otherness" was by that time established. His purpose is rather to define each of them as precisely as possible.

[12] See below, Ch. 4, on the theory of *genesis* in *Phys.* I.

[13] It may be argued that Melissus (B8.3ff.) understood him in this sense and developed his implications, something that Parmenides himself would consider unnecessary—and perhaps undignified. Note, in any case, the denial of all change (28B8.26; *ibid.* 4of. is as specific as Parmenides here would allow himself to be).

the opposite of the Forms with which their existence is tied up. Snow
is so essentially cold that it can never become warm, nor can soul (for
which life is an essential) ever become dead.[14] It is to establish the latter
proposition that Plato takes up cases of this kind. In his more technical
discussions of *genesis* he never returns to them; for what matters about
physical objects is that they are changeable, i.e., capable of accepting
different and even contrary qualities. Still, Plato's thesis has implications of considerable importance for physics (even if he himself does
not develop them here): if fire cannot remain fire when it "receives"
the cold, none of the traditional elements can be the principle of all
physical things. For fire to become water (which is considered as cold)
would entail an abandonment of its nature, nor could water turn into
dry earth and still be water. If physical theory requires that in the
change of things and in their mutual transformation something persists,
this something must be more basic than the elements. It must be capable
of receiving all contrary qualities.[15]

Thus the doctrine of Forms carried with it a new appreciation and
understanding of becoming. On movement it did not have so direct a
bearing. As we know, Parmenides' interdict of movement had been less
effective than his repudiation of *genesis*. Movement had long since been
brought back into the accounts of nature. Yet the dialogues of Plato's
early and middle period leave us with the impression that although he
regards *genesis*, which Parmenides' followers had so readily abandoned,
as indispensable, movement is philosophically much less important and
much less interesting. This impression may well be deceptive. For individual objects in the physical world that become, perish, and change
must also move, especially if movement comprehends as large a variety
of "changes" as it often does in Greek philosophy—and we shall presently see that Plato himself has given the word this broad meaning.[16]
If the *Phaedo* suggests anything to the contrary, it would be that Plato
thinks it more fruitful to understand changes as instances of becoming
than as aspects of movement. If they were movements, the Forms
would not shed much light on them. For even in Plato's later thought,

---

[14] *Phaedo* 102d–103e.

[15] Arist. *De gen.* II,5.332a8–18 is perhaps not too remote for a reference in this
connection.

[16] See the next section of this chapter on the range and content of *kinesis* in
Plato. Another important term is *metabole;* contrasts between the Forms and
physical objects may turn on their different relations to (i.e., their participation or
not in) *metabole* as much as on those to *genesis*.

when movement with all its varieties had become included in its scope, the Forms continue to remain aloof from it. They cannot take care of it in the same direct way in which they are responsible for *genesis*. For Plato to incorporate movement (*kinesis*) in his philosophy entailed a broadening of its conceptual basis. Movement cannot be made subject to the Forms, yet it can be set up in its own domain side by side with theirs.[17] It can complement them, provided it represents all types of change, and can serve as generic heading for everything that stands in opposition to the rest and the unchanging stability of the Forms. Actually the Greek word and concept of "movement" could have this wide range (though we shall see that Aristotle at times inclines to regard "change," *metabole*, as the better generic term [18]).

When in Plato's late dialogues movement was incorporated and when it was understood in this broad sense, it became almost inevitable that *genesis* too should be drawn into its orbit. And not only *genesis* true and simple, but the entire variety of physical phenomena that Plato in the *Phaedo* treats as *genesis* and thereby brings into connection with the Forms.[19] As it turned out, these somewhat dubious forms of *genesis*—growth and decline, association and dissociation—have little capacity of resistance; as soon as movement asserts its magnetic powers, they are found in its train. The true and essential *genesis*, on the other hand, could only gain strength when thrown back upon itself and stripped of these accessories. Thus it can hold out with ultimate success.

The first dialogue to bring the fundamental opposition between rest and movement into view is the *Cratylus*, which offers first the one and then the other concept as the "root" of all important words and asks whether the ultimate root of words reveals something about the basic nature of things.[20] Since the opposition recurs in the *Theaetetus* and *Sophist*, it is tempting to think that all three dialogues may not be far apart in their date of composition. Yet, whatever its date, the *Cratylus* embodies the first and still rather mild stirrings of the dramatic antagonism that unfolds more fully in the two other dialogues. Of

[17] That movement itself becomes a Form and one of the μέγιστα γένη (*Soph.* 254cff.) is a different development. It is the prior condition for the application of *diaeresis* to it, a subject to which we shall presently turn.

[18] See below, pp. 178–179.

[19] See above, p. 22. For what follows, cf. Skemp throughout.

[20] *Crat.* 402bff. (cf. 411bff.), 437aff. A late date for the *Cratylus* (near the *Theaetetus*) was advocated by M. A. Warburg, *Zwei Fragen zum Cratylus* (Berlin, 1928).

these, the *Theaetetus* presents the case for movement with extraordinary resourcefulness and with a kind of partisan zeal. For a time movement is allowed to reign supreme, unchecked by any alternative principle, and this approach is kept up until it finally leads to results that discredit it altogether.[21] A goodly number of earlier thinkers are assembled under the bannerhead of movement; though diverging in their more specific doctrines, they seem united in regarding movement as the ultimate principle.[22] The entire presentation is deliberately one-sided and extravagant. Moreover, the representation of movement as the only mode of reality is coupled with the equally one-sided doctrine of sensation as the only form of knowledge. This doctrine implies that every sensation is as true as every other, there being no objective criterion by appeal to which their validity could be judged. The only reality is what the interaction of a perceived object and an individual's perception brings into being, and such reality can last no longer than the perception itself. Short-lived realities of this kind are, in fact, constantly giving way to one another; they cannot be said to "be" but only to "become" or come into being.[23] To produce them there must be movement on the part of the perceived object as well as on that of the percipient; these two movements meet, if only for a moment. From this point of view becoming—*genesis*—presents itself as a function and product of movement. But even without recourse to "epistemological" considerations, it may be argued that movement must both precede and produce *genesis*. The Oceanus whom Homer described as the origin of all the gods is the principle of flux and movement, and if the origin of things is to be stated less mythically, it will suffice to remember that fire is held to generate everything else while being itself generated by friction and movement. Again there is the movement, to wit, the yearly revolution, of the sun with its generally known effect of making things sprout and grow.[24] Clearly, then, there is much to be said for regarding *genesis* as following in the wake of movement and finding a place in its all-embracing scheme. There is no indication here that Plato knows another kind of *genesis* which is simple and "absolute"

---

[21] 152dff., 156aff. Most of the counterarguments are directed against the identification of αἴσθησις and ἐπιστήμη; see, however, 181cff.

[22] 152dff.; cf. 160d.   [23] 156aff., 156e, 157a; cf. 153e, 160b.

[24] 152e, 153a, 153cf. Plato actually speaks 153d1 of the heavenly revolution and of the sun as keeping everything in existence. Both of them are to reappear as *arche* of all *genesis;* see below, Ch. 20.

(that of our *Theaetetus* section being as relative as the sensations which create it [25]) and which will not so readily submit to movement. As for movement itself, Plato sees fit, for methodical and pedagogical reasons, to study it in isolation as though it were an absolute, before he proceeds to the task of integrating it in a larger pattern.

The integration is proclaimed in the *Sophist.* This dialogue re-examines some problems of the *Theaetetus* from the perspective of being—the Platonic being which is here appreciated in its true philosophical status and seems no longer in danger of being dissolved into its opposite, becoming. The battle between being and becoming, rest and movement, sensation and thought is here joined in force, and precisely at the juncture where Plato has brought the antagonism to a head and is feeling his way from opposition to reconciliation movement makes its appearance and is, surprisingly enough, shown to be integral in being.[26] For without movement and life being itself would be static, dead, unknowable, no more than a holy statue. Even the act of knowing what *is* brings knowledge and being into a relationship in which the former is active, the latter passive; and, as the *Theaetetus* has already pointed out, acting and suffering are complementary "forms," or aspects, of movement.[27] Thus there can be no knowing without movement; yet no more would knowing be possible without rest, since it needs as its object something stable and enduring.[28] "The philosopher, then, who values these things [knowledge, intelligence, etc.] above all else . . . must declare that Being and the sum of things are both combined, all that is unmovable [or unchangeable] and all that is in motion." [29] This conciliatory formula which redefines the philosopher's task should also settle the antagonism between being and becoming, "idealism" and materialism; for all of them have presented themselves simultaneously for an adjudication of their claims, although with the concentration on movement and rest the others are gradually passing from sight. Being, movement, and rest are the three basic Forms, the highest genera; yet as soon as they are set up, they suggest the question how they can exist side by side without once again isolating being and cutting it off from all intercourse with the rest of things. The study of this problem leads to the introduction of two further genera, same-

[25] See esp. 160a–c.

[26] 245eff. (γένεσις φερομένη 246c1f.), 248dff.

[27] 248c–249a; cf. *Theaet.* 156a, 157a, and *passim.*

[28] 249b.

[29] 249cf. (Cornford's translation, slightly altered).

ness and difference.[30] With the help of these, relationships may be established not only between being, rest, and movement but for all instances in which a Form is either set apart from others or joined to them in a meaningful combination.

All this provides a new basis for logical operations, for the organization of the world of Forms [31]—and for the incorporation of the physical world in the philosopher's sphere of interest. There is nothing here, or in other late dialogues, to intimate that the new demarcation of the philosopher's subject is a mere makeshift in the course of the discussion. Quite to the contrary, we find the "philosopher" henceforth studying the things which are in motion with no less care and penetration and, if everything is taken into consideration, only slightly less seriousness than he gives to the things at rest.

While the *Sophist* enlightens us about the philosophical status of movement, the third dialogue of this sequence shows us where to look for its realization. The myth of the *Statesman*, although far from attempting a full account of cosmic movements and changes, includes an important reference to the movement which "leads" all others and continues forever without change of direction or effect. "To revolve by its own strength is possible only for the principle of all things that are in motion. This principle has no right to move [scil., the Cosmos] now in the one sense now in the other." [32] The rotation of the Cosmos cannot aspire to such exalted status and such never-varying identity of direction. It is subject to reversals which come about at stated periods, and while moving in one of the two alternating directions, it is liable to lose its order and regularity.[33] The *Timaeus* will give us an account of cosmic movements which is much fuller and more developed than what the *Statesman* has to say on this subject; it will also show that the threat of disorder does not extend to the basic movement of the Cosmos. Instead of alternating between order and disorder, the Cosmos can combine them, one part of it exhibiting sameness and the other change,

[30] 250cff., 254df. For our purpose it is not necessary to go deeper into the technical aspects of διαίρεσις and συμπλοκὴ εἰδῶν, subjects which have lately been under very lively discussion.

[31] I am aware that some Platonic scholars question this ontological significance of the *diaeresis*. A closer study of these matters is outside the scope of our inquiry.

[32] *Polit.* 269e5ff. I have taken considerable liberty with Skemp's translation and interpretation (*Plato's Statesman* [London, 1952], 146). As long as we keep the neuter of the pronouns (αὐτὸ . . . ἑαυτό e5), it seems advisable not to make the reference to the deity too explicit.

[33] 269dff.

whose "errant cause" is far from being unchecked. Although the *Timaeus* again deals with these subjects under the form of a myth, it is obvious that the myth is now considerably more "scientific." Nevertheless the myth of the *Statesman*, brief though it is on "cosmological" matters, gives us glimpses of Plato's characteristic approach to cosmic movements. Besides making the distinction between perfect and imperfect movements, it also insists on a causal link between the rotary movement of the cosmic globe as a whole and all changes and processes that come to pass within the Cosmos.[34]

Of the source and fountainhead of all movements the *Phaedrus* speaks with even greater solemnity than does the *Statesman*.[35] While not concerning itself with the Cosmos and not referring in any but the most general terms to what comes to pass in it, it stresses all the more the necessity of positing an everlasting source of movement—and of *genesis*.[36] As for the nature of this source, Plato stipulates that it must be outside the realm of *genesis*, having never come into being and being immune to destruction; yet far from being similarly exempt from movement, it must persist in eternal, never interrupted motion.[37] The concepts of a self-mover and of a *perpetuum mobile* have taken form. Moreover, Plato here identifies this never-failing source of movement as soul and avails himself of soul's eternal motion for a new proof of its immortality. Soul thus becomes a new principle, a new *arche* for the physical world. The date of the *Phaedrus* and its precise place in the gradual unfolding of Plato's thought are today once more in dispute. Strong arguments have been advanced for assigning it to the years after the completion of the *Republic* and before the composition of *Theaetetus* and the related set of dialogues. Other arguments, likewise strong, point to a date in the last decade of Plato's life (i.e., later not only than the *Theaetetus* group but also than the *Timaeus* and presumably the *Philebus*).[38] This is not the place to review the conflicting evidence

[34] *Ibid.* 270bff., 272eff.　　　　[35] *Phaedr.* 245c5–246a1.

[36] *Ibid.*, esp. 245c5–9 and 245d8–e2.

[37] 245c5, c7. (As I see it c6f. strongly supports the reading δεικίνητον in c5; yet even if αὐτοκίνητον were to be adopted, the conception of an eternal mover would clearly be present in c7. On the textual problem see, e.g., G. Pasquali, *Storia della tradizione* [2d ed.; Florence, 1952], 255 n.5; P. Maas, *Textkritik* [2d ed.; Leipzig, 1950], 23f.) Cf. *Polit.* 269e5.

[38] R. Hackforth (*Plato's Phaedrus* [Cambridge, 1952], 3) is probably right in considering the statistics about hiatus the best argument that "Sprachstatistik" has to contribute. For the *Phaedrus* they would indicate a date shortly after the *Republic*. See Hackforth, pp. 3ff., for the status of the question and the more im-

in full. The identification of soul with the first and eternal mover has close parallels in *Laws* X, and it was to be expected that the advocates of a late dating would make the most of this argument.³⁹ The *Timaeus* implements the assertions of the *Phaedrus* by indicating how soul causes the changes and movements in the Cosmos, and *Laws* X defines the place of its movement in the general scheme and system of movements more precisely than the *Phaedrus* can attempt.⁴⁰ The basic insight may have preceded the details of the implementation; alternatively Plato while engaged on the *Phaedrus* may have thought of the two other works as lending substance to its brief indications.⁴¹

It may be said that with the exception of the *Philebus* every dialogue of Plato's later period makes some contribution to the theory of movement, which seems to grow and consolidate itself apace. One aspect of this consolidation is the intrinsic organization of the subject which—naturally enough at this period of Plato's thought—tends to take the form of a "division" or, less technically speaking, distinction between its various forms. From this point of view we may once more look briefly at the dialogues already considered before proceeding to the evidence that is found in others.

THE FORMS OF MOVEMENT

"Movement" (*kinesis*), as we have seen, serves Plato as a generic concept which includes every kind of change. It stands for local move-

---

portant opinions advanced before 1950. Hackforth fails, however, to take account of Jaeger, *Paideia*, 3.147 and n.109, where the chronological question is discussed from a new point of view. He could not yet know Regenbogen's important study in *Miscellanea Academica Berolinensia* ([Berlin, 1950] 2.1.198ff.), which makes a strong case for a very late date. As Jaeger, *loc.cit.*, says, it is very difficult to believe that the *Phaedrus* should have been composed before Aristotle's *Gryllus*. I may add that it is not much easier to think of it as being written shortly before or while Aristotle delivered his first "course" on rhetoric. The vigorous denunciation of *psychagogia* in *Rhet.* I,1 (1354a14ff., 24ff., b19ff.) contrasts sharply with Plato's attitude to it (*Phaedr.* 270bff.). I confess that I see no way of squaring these observations with the results of "Sprachstatistik."

³⁹ Regenbogen, *op.cit.*, 2.1.203ff. The similarities had been noted and carefully studied for their intrinsic interest, without reference to the problem of date, by J. Stenzel, *Über zwei Begriffe der platon. Mystik* ([Breslau, 1914] reprinted in *Kleine Schriften zur griech. Philos.* [Darmstadt, 1956], 1ff.).

⁴⁰ *Tim.* 57d7–58c4 (cf. below, p. 64); *Legg.* X,893b–896b. Cf. Regenbogen, *op.cit.*, 2.1.203ff., and my *Entwicklung d. aristot. Logik* (Berlin, 1929), 284ff. and 288 n.1.

⁴¹ This would agree with Regenbogen's opinion (*op.cit.*) that the *Phaedrus* falls within the years in which Plato was at work on the *Laws*. For an early reference to "motion which moves itself" see *Charm.* 168 (cf. Cherniss, *Pl. and the Acad.*, 435); it is impossible to say what Plato at the time had in mind.

ment, yet also for other processes which entail movement but which might easily and for our feeling perhaps more obviously be defined with the help of other terms. In the *Theaetetus* and the *Parmenides* we find the first efforts at differentiation; [42] in both, Plato distinguishes between movement in place and one other "form" for which he uses a word (*alloiosis*) that may be rendered as "alteration" or "qualitative change." As illustrations of such change Plato mentions the process of ageing and the alternation between black and white, hard and soft.[43] We are on the way toward the concept of "quality" with which this type of movement will remain associated.[44] Changes of this kind, albeit with emphasis on their epistemological aspect, are discussed throughout the early sections of the *Theaetetus* where Plato points out that in the never-ceasing flux of things both the percipient and the thing perceived constantly become different. In the same passage in which Plato sets qualitative change apart from locomotion he also suggests, without trying to develop the point, that locomotion may occur either as movement from place to place or as a "turning around" in one and the same place.[45]

Thus, as soon as the concept of movement enters the range of Plato's thought, there is some intimation of its having species. Of the classes here set up, locomotion and qualitative change proved strong enough to survive, yet not, in the long run, to divide the entire territory between them. In the Aristotelian classification of movements they have admitted the pair "growth" and "decline" into partnership with themselves and have at times even to tolerate "becoming" and "passing away" as additional species of movement.[46]

We are prepared to find the relation between becoming and movement a complex problem. Becoming may be treated as a paraphenom-

---

[42] *Theaet.* 181cf. (182c); *Parm.* 138b8. The latter passage adds the comment: "these are the only movements." At *Theaet.* 181cff. Plato uses the differentiation at once to administer a telling defeat to the Heracliteans; cf. Cornford (*Theory*, 95), who refers to the occurrence of the verb ἀλλοιοῦσθαι in Heraclitus B67.

[43] *Theaet.* 181c9ff.

[44] Note the introduction of the term (with apologies) in 182a. Diogenes of Appollonia (*Vorsokr.*, 64B2.5) uses the word ἑτεροίωσις when speaking of his principle, the air, as becoming moister, dryer, etc. It is, however, unlikely that he had in any way anticipated the Platonic and Aristotelian concept of quality, and if he understood "qualitative changes" as being due to condensation and rarefaction (*ibid.*, A1), this would suffice to set him apart from the later developments. W. A. Heidel, *Arch. f. Gesch. d. Philos.*, 19 (1906), 333ff., has shown that the Aristotelian concept of qualitative change cannot be found in the Presocratics (see *ibid.*, 377f., on Diogenes).

[45] *Theaet.* 181c6f. (contrast 180e3f.).   [46] See below, pp. 178–179.

enon of movement or as a form of it, but also as a subject *sui generis* which refuses to be subsumed under movement. In Plato's scheme the antithesis between being and becoming is as fundamental as that between rest and movement. Do the propositions which hold good for movement extend to becoming—and vice versa? Does movement too always come to pass between opposites; does becoming need an originator other than the Forms? Neither when completely severed from movement, nor when completely incorporated in it, can becoming be quite at ease. The problematic aspects of this relationship are implicitly present in Plato's later dialogues, even if the problems become explicit only in Aristotle.

Growth and decline (*auxesis* and *phthisis*) could be more easily incorporated in the system of movements. For reasons that are not stated in the dialogues Plato (or the Academy) decided that they should not be classed either under locomotion or under qualitative change but were to form a separate class. In terms of the Platonic "divisions" this means that a genuine "difference" (διαφορά) had been found to set them apart from the other "forms." Still, one may wonder whether their past history did not help them to secure so noble a status. The Presocratics' interest in growth and decline is evident from the fragmentary material at our disposal. Empedocles' verse "Earth increases its own body, *aether* that of *aether*" [47] may indicate the context in which it arose. As soon as any entity, whether a part of the Cosmos or a tissue or organ of living beings, has come into existence, it will grow. It does so by assimilating homogeneous material.[48] Empedocles, Anaxagoras, and Democritus had all concerned themselves with this process while Hippocratic writers had come forward with theories relating to its physiological aspects. From the little that we know, we form the impression that the idea of aggregation dominated here as much as in the formation of physical entities. There is an obvious continuity between the two subjects: what comes into being by the aggregation of material grows by the further addition of identical material. Conversely the decline of an entity, being a dissociation of its parts, continues until everything has disintegrated.

[47] *Vorsokr.*, 31B37. I have not found a satisfactory rendering for δέμας. As Aristotle in *De gen.* I,5 raises the question whether growth takes place in the Form or in the matter, it is noteworthy that Empedocles uses a word which has connotations of Form; but neither "form" nor "shape" gives the right meaning here.

[48] For what follows, see the discussion and the references in my paper "Epicurus on the Growth and Decline of the Cosmos," *A. J. Ph.*, 74 (1953), 25ff.

How many phenomena theories of this kind were meant to embrace is not quite clear; yet one type of growth in which the Presocratics were particularly interested is growth by nutrition. This includes also embryonic growth. All physical growth, they held, comes about by the addition of homogeneous material to the substances or powers present in a living being from the time of its conception. Once more a fragment of Empedocles—"Thus sweet seized on sweet, bitter rushed towards bitter, sour moved towards sour, and hot settled upon hot" [49]— may serve as an epitome of this approach. It appears that the subjects of growth and of nutrition, being treated along the same lines, tended to become identified in the thinking of these men; [50] yet it could not be long before the obvious fact that a living being continues to take nourishment even after it has ceased to grow forced them to make a distinction. We do not know who devised the theory which henceforth kept the subjects distinct, but we can see what form it took.[51] It starts from the observation that all organic growth is accompanied by decrease (i.e., loss of particles). As long as a being grows, the addition of new material exceeds the loss; next comes a period in which the two processes balance one another; and ever after the material given off surpasses that which is added and incorporated.

In his earlier dialogues Plato here and there touches on the subject of biological growth. The passages show that he does not think of it as an organic process—to discover organic growth was left to Aristotle.[52] For Plato, as for the later Presocratics, growth and nutrition consist in the addition ($\pi\rho o\sigma\gamma i\gamma\nu\epsilon\sigma\theta a\iota$) of new material. The *Timaeus*, which provides more detail than the earlier dialogues, confirms this impression: new matter that "flows in" by way of food and drink replaces the material given off, and in the course of an individual life the balance between both processes goes through the changes already specified

---

[49] *Vorsokr.*, 31B90 (Kathleen Freeman's translation). The authors (Plutarch and Macrobius) who quote these lines make clear that they refer to nutrition. For the Presocratic and Hippocratic doctrines of nutrition see my paper in *A. J. Ph.*, 74 (1953), 34ff., esp. 43f. where the evidence is cited.

[50] See again my paper in *A. J. Ph.* To the evidence there assembled may be added Plato *Phileb.* 29c5, where $\tau\rho\epsilon\phi\epsilon\tau a\iota$, $\gamma i\gamma\nu\epsilon\tau a\iota$, $a\upsilon\xi\epsilon\tau a\iota$ (the last is Jackson's excellent emendation for $a\rho\chi\epsilon\tau a\iota$) are used as an obvious triad of concepts.

[51] For what follows, see *A. J. Ph.*, 74 (1953), 40ff., 45ff. The theory to which reference is made in the text is found in *Tim.* 81b (cf. Lucr. II,1122ff.). As for its origin, the best hypothesis would be that Plato borrowed it from medical authorities of his own (or possibly a slightly earlier) generation.

[52] *Phaedo* 96c8ff., *Conv.* 207d6: man is $\nu\epsilon os$ $a\epsilon\iota$ $\gamma i\gamma\nu o\mu\epsilon\nu os$ $\langle\tau a$ $\mu\epsilon\nu$ $\pi\rho o\sigma\kappa\tau\omega\mu\epsilon\nu os\rangle$ τa $\delta'a\pi o\lambda\lambda\upsilon s$. For Aristotle see *De gen.* I,5.

(Plato is actually our chief witness for this theory).[53] Plato has his specific explanation why an organism in its youth can retain more of the inflowing material than in old age;[54] yet this hardly affects the basic idea, and it would take us too far from our subject if we were to follow him into the details of his physiological theory.

All that we need is evidence for Plato's awareness of growth and decline as specific kinds of change, and the section of the *Timaeus* supplies this evidence. As treated there, they are different from locomotion as well as from qualitative change—as a matter of fact, we shall presently find reason to think that Plato was not altogether satisfied with the concept of qualitative change. In any case, growth and decline are included in the "catalogue" of movements in Book X of the *Laws*.[55] This catalogue is at once the most thoroughgoing classification of movements that we find in Plato and his last discussion of the subject. Here movement is the generic heading of all changes while local movement figures as the source of the others, preceding them both in the temporal and causal sequence. Growth, in particular, is explained as resulting from the coalescence—note the Presocratic motif [56]—of one moving body with another, decline as due to the splitting up of this body into its parts. To this principle of explanation we shall revert before long.

There is much else in this catalogue of movements that calls for comment. Yet before we go farther, it may be well to notice a conspicuous absence: qualitative change, the concept which was the first to establish itself on a par with local motion, has no place in this list.

Knowing how readily Plato in this period uses the method of division, it may strike us that the heavy guns of technical *diaeresis* are this time barely brought into play. The divisions are made on physical grounds. A body, it is stated, may either turn around in one place or move from one place to another [57] (this is the point already briefly made in the *Theaetetus*). The latter kind of movement is again subdivided: movement from place to place may materialize either as rolling or as gliding.[58] The three kinds of movement so far distinguished could clearly be regarded as species of locomotion; yet Plato does not here wish to bring them under a heading of their own or to cut them off from the other forms to whose description he proceeds. When bodies that are thus in motion clash with others, they may either be split by

---

[53] *Tim.* 71b2, 4.   [54] *Ibid.*, b5–d3.   [55] *Legg.* X,893b–894c, 893e6f.
[56] The terms συγκρίνεσθαι and διακρίνεσθαι are here used (893e6).
[57] 893c3ff. Cf. Skemp, 96ff.   [58] 893d6–e1.

them or coalesce with them. This gives us two more species of motion, yet no longer of locomotion (this being now merely the cause of the new processes), and we may note in passing that these species are identical with, or in any case ready to bear, the thought-provoking names of association and dissociation.[59] That the former leads to growth, the latter to decrease, and that these constitute two further classes of "movement" have already been mentioned. The next point is that decrease may end in passing away; the difference between the one process and the other is that in decrease the "existing condition," which may be Plato's equivalent for Aristotle's substance, remains unimpaired; if this is not the case, the object passes out of existence.[60] From passing away Plato, naturally enough, proceeds to coming into existence, i.e., *genesis.* As the former process is closely and causally connected with decrease, so the latter has, clearly, relations to growth. Yet Plato has important additional stipulations to make for *genesis:* it needs a principle or origin (an ἀρχή) which not only "grows" but makes a transition from the first dimension to the second and from this to the third in which it becomes perceptible.[61] Thus even if *genesis* is this time included in the list of eight movements so far enumerated—yet it is not wholly clear how the number "eight" is reached—it keeps a distinct character of its own and is not entirely amenable to subsumption under Movement.[62] The ninth and tenth forms of "movement" are defined with the help of a new criterion. Plato here introduces his distinction

[59] 893e (4.6). For a polemic in Aristotle's *Physics* against the attempt to make *synkrisis* and *diakrisis* species of movement see below, p. 177.

[60] 893e7. The precise meaning of ἡ καθεστηκυῖα ἕξις is rather elusive; perhaps Plato did not wish to use the word οὐσία (see, however, 894a6f.). Cf. Skemp, 103. On the whole I find Ross's reference (recorded by Skemp, *loc.cit.*) to Aristotle's differentiation between *genesis* and *auxesis,* presumably in *De gen.* I, 2 and 5, more helpful and pertinent than Skemp's and Cornford's attempt to bring this section into a maximum of conformity with the *Timaeus.*

[61] 894a1–8.

[62] Plato characterizes *genesis* here as a μεταβάλλειν and μετακινεῖσθαι (894a5f.). The latter compound can hardly have the same meaning as the simple verb; as for μεταβάλλειν one wonders whether it is an accident that this is the term which in Aristotle comprehends *kinesis* as well as *genesis;* see below, pp. 178–179. It is tempting to account for the number of eight movements (cf. 894c5, and for the status of this question Skemp, 99) by not counting *genesis* but making up the count from the three types of locomotion (circular, gliding, and rolling), the two pairs that come next, and passing away; yet on this point we can hardly advance beyond guesses. 894a1 makes in any case a much sharper break between growth (or increase) and *genesis* than the preceding sentence made between decrease and passing away. I should read γίγνεται δὲ (δὴ MSS, *editores,* which seems hard to defend) πάντων γένεσις.

between the self-mover or true originator of movement and entities
that cannot originate movement but merely pass it on.[63] Although this
point of view cuts across the eight classes previously set up, Plato does
not hesitate to add the two new forms as ninth and tenth. The logical
tidiness of the entire division also suffers from the discovery that the
self-mover, being the tenth form, actually has the movement that was
introduced as the first, i.e., revolution in a circle; for this is the movement of soul, and soul alone can qualify as a self-mover.[64] Moreover, the
movement of this principle may manifest itself in associations, dissociations, growth, decrease, and even in becoming and passing away.[65]
All this, it may be held, disturbs the neatness of the division still further.
In all probability Plato did not here aim at the same degree of logical
precision which characterizes his procedure in more technical dialogues
(such as the *Sophist* or the *Statesman*). Nevertheless this "catalogue" is
of the greatest importance, and we shall again and again need to refer to
it. In particular the relation between the tenth form and the others and
the place of *genesis* in the system of movements pose problems that
present themselves also in other works of Plato's latest period and reappear in Aristotle's physical system.

Here we may briefly note certain other classifications and further
"forms" of movement that are met with in Plato's late dialogues. In a
passage of the *Timaeus* allusion is made to a differentiation of local
movements on the basis of their direction: they may be to the right or
to the left, upward or downward, forward or backward. Yet the noblest is the seventh, which has no contrary and which is movement in
the same place, that is to say, again the movement of a sphere or globe
around its center.[66] This movement may be designated as the first, the
tenth, or the seventh; its leading position is above dispute, no matter
what other movements Plato in a given context decides to admit and
by what principle he classifies them—no matter, in fact, whether the
point of view is physical, cosmological, or philosophical. Regular movement in a circle has something of the eternal and unchanging sameness
which characterizes the realm of the eternal Forms. Actually it seems
in a way to belong to both the large realms into which the *Sophist*
divided the philosopher's kingdom; for in the *Laws* Plato says that this

---

[63] 894bf.
[64] 897eff. On somewhat different grounds the tenth is already (894d) said to be
in truth the first.
[65] 896eff.   [66] *Tim.* 34a.

movement "encompasses in its center the power of things at rest." [67] Plato as well as Aristotle repeatedly speaks of this movement in a tone of admiration and enthusiasm; to both it is the most beautiful of all movements—the sphere being the "perfect" figure—and the mathematical law by which it imparts in due proportion greater or lesser speed to all circles contained in it is the "source of all wonder." [68] It must have been a great satisfaction to Plato that both by logical argument and in his actual construction of the Cosmos he could show that this form of movement is the source and principle of all others.

In the *Theaetetus*, while speaking of the philosophical schools for whom everything is movement, Plato states: "There are two forms (εἴδη) of movement, each of them infinitely manifold; one has the power to act (ποιεῖν), the other to suffer (πάσχειν)." [69] What are we to think of these "forms"? On the strength of this passage they would seem inherent in an approach which Plato would accept only with very serious reservations, yet the pair reappears elsewhere in contexts of Plato's own thought.[70] There is no evidence that earlier thinkers actually used these two terms in as comprehensive a meaning as is here suggested, but there is abundant confirmation that Presocratic physicists and medical writers dealt with phenomena and situations to which they are applicable.[71] However close they may have come to "abstracting" them, the final step probably remained for Plato, who is in the habit of seeking the largest common denominators and whose power of extracting them from a welter of facts far surpassed that of his precursors. Our passage is nevertheless the only one in which acting and suffering are presented as "two forms [or species] of movement," with the obvious implication that between them they divide the entire genus. In what sense, then, are they forms? It would be absurd to put them on a par with the ten "forms" embodied in the catalogue of the *Laws,* or even only with locomotion and alteration into which movement is divided in another passage of the *Theaetetus*. Clearly "acting" and "suffering" are two aspects or poles of one and the same "movement," change, or process (Aristotle in the *Physics* says that to act and to suffer when relating to the same process are one and the same in the

---

[67] *Legg.* X,893c4. [68] *Ibid.,* d3. [69] *Theaet.* 156a.

[70] See esp. *Soph.* 247dff., *Phaedr.* 270d, *Tim.* 57a. Note also the occurrence of these terms in the catalogue of movements in *Laws* X (894c5f.).

[71] See for a fuller discussion below, Ch. 18, in connection with Aristotle's use of these concepts. There consideration will be given to the antecedents suggested by our *Theaetetus* passage.

sense in which the way from Athens to Thebes and from Thebes to Athens is one and the same—and again not one and the same [72]). In the act of sensation one thing produces, another receives, the impression. The same obtains when a physical body causes physical change in another. In none of their many exhaustive accounts of movement does Plato or Aristotle use these concepts as species; yet in their hands the pair was to prove most useful for the analysis of various processes which they regarded as movements—in fact, even for the understanding of *genesis*.[73] This is not the place to trace the history of these concepts in the physical systems of Plato and Aristotle or of the Stoics and Epicureans. Suffice it to quote a sentence from the *Timaeus* which represents Plato's authoritative pronouncement on the interaction of the elements, a question which earlier thinkers had studied with divergent results, though again, we may suppose, without stating their views in terms of comparable generality: "Things can never effect a change in what is similar or identical in kind, nor can they suffer anything from what is in an identical or similar condition." [74]

The section of the *Laws* which gives us the final classification of movements includes a statement to the effect that everything is "fully real" while it "endures," "yet when it changes into another condition it is altogether destroyed." [75] We have no choice but to refer this pronouncement to individual physical objects—the same objects whose *genesis* Plato has in the preceding sentences described. As a matter of fact, Plato here once more brings out the essential difference between being and becoming; what is remarkable is that he this time does not associate the former with the Forms and the latter with particulars but first makes clear how particulars come into "being" (this phrase is here applicable) and then actually grants them the status of being. We have already seen that the things that become had from the beginning a firm and safe place in Plato's scheme.[76] In the latest phase of his thought this place is reasserted in very significant contexts. If a particular object is ὄντως ὄν, the gulf which originally separated Forms and particulars has

---

[72] Arist. *Phys.* III,3.202b11–16.   [73] See below, Chs. 17 and 18.   [74] *Tim.* 57a.

[75] *Legg.* X,894a6f. The word which Plato used a few lines earlier to define the difference between decrease and passing away recurs here when Plato says that what changes into another ἕξις suffers complete destruction (i.e., passes altogether out of existence). Probably, then, what "remains" as long as something is ὄντως ὄν is also the ἕξις. Again one has the feeling that Aristotle would here have spoken of *ousia*.

[76] See above, the first paragraphs of this Ch. 2.

narrowed and the two hemispheres begin to meet, or even to overlap. The *Philebus*, which coins the notion of *"genesis* into being," goes far to substantiate this impression.[77] The term applies to the "third" class which originates from the mixture of the limited and the unlimited and shapeless. What comes into being is not shapeless or chaotic; the qualities of measure, limit, and shape that have formed it also guarantee it a foothold in the realm of being. All becoming is for the sake of being, we learn in a later passage of the *Philebus* [78] (where, however, being is not clearly that of individual things, so that it is not easy to "combine" the two passages). We may further refer to a passage in the *Parmenides* where becoming is defined as "acquiring [a share in] being" and passing away as "losing being." [79] This gives us one more piece of evidence that there are no unsurmountable barriers between being and becoming.

It cannot be our intention here to appreciate this development in its full significance; as our concern is with the antecedents of Aristotle's physics rather than of his metaphysics, the status of things which have gone through the process of *genesis* matters less for our study than the account which Plato gives of this physical process. To be sure, for

---

[77] *Phileb.* 26d.   [78] *Ibid.*, 54a–c.

[79] *Parm.* 155ef. (156a4ff.). It should surely not be assumed that phenomenal objects in any of the passages here mentioned are given the same kind of οὐσία as the Forms. Vlastos has rightly reminded us (*Philos. Rev.*, 63 [1954], 335) that Plato has a "degrees of reality" theory. Yet I believe that G. M. A. Grube (*Plato's Thought* [London, 1935], 303) and R. Hackforth (*Plato's Examination of Pleasure* [Cambridge, 1945], 49 n.2) go too far in their attempts to minimize the significance of οὐσία in *Phileb.* 26d where Plato speaks of the γένεσις εἰς οὐσίαν (Cornford, *Pl. and Parm.*, 195f., 218, expresses himself more cautiously). The words which Plato here uses to characterize the third class must have been chosen with care and with the intention of conferring upon the objects of this class the status of οὐσία. As we have seen, in *Legg.*X,894a6 Plato does not hesitate to employ words like ἔστι δ'ὄντως ὄν with reference to physical entities. Skemp, 106, rightly brings this expression into connection with the γεγενημένη οὐσία of the *Philebus* and with sections of the *Parmenides*. Cherniss, *A. J. Ph.*, 78 (1957), 239, denies that such statements are typical of or confined to Plato's later period. Of the passages from earlier works which he adduces, *Conv.* 205b9 impresses me most, on account of its similarity with *Phileb.* 26d8. From a comparison of these two passages it should perhaps be concluded that Plato has not changed his view about the status of γεγονότα but is now more concerned about their being or having οὐσία. However, *Legg.* X,894a6f. remains unique, even when compared with the goodly number of passages collected by Cherniss. I agree with him (240 n.44) that οὐσία is not here predicated of a γιγνόμενον (or of γένεσις), but as no change of the grammatical subject is indicated between this sentence and the preceding, Plato is likely here to speak of γεγονότα, objects that have completed their γένεσις.

Plato himself *genesis* is more than a "physical process," and he is not inclined to isolate its physical aspects.

GENESIS IN THE *TIMAEUS*

The *Timaeus* as a whole is our best evidence that Plato in his old age found *genesis* neither entirely unknowable nor unworthy of a philosopher's efforts. Its testimony is barely impaired by the overgenerous dose of remarks scattered through it which depreciate the subject, stressing its opaqueness and the inevitable uncertainty of all assertions about it.[80] Plato may have felt more doubtful about the *Timaeus* and the effort put into it than about any other work that he gave to the world; he may often have been in the mood to laugh off the entire venture which, although it cost him more time and trouble than other dialogues, came less near to the truth. The fact is that the venture was made, the account of the physical world worked out.

In the *Timaeus* Plato certainly "lays violent hands on father Parmenides." Although admitting that *genesis* cannot be an object of knowledge, he reintroduces it into philosophical discourse and into physical theory; emphatically and with unflinching determination he demands a place for it.

However, the status of objects that come to be and pass away falls somewhat short of what the *Philebus* and the passage in *Laws* X might lead us to expect. We must, in fact, distinguish between *genesis* itself, which goes on without interruption, and the particular physical objects which it creates.[81] The former is an essential and permanent characteristic of nature which Plato here raises to the level of reality. As regards the latter, Plato is perhaps even more eloquent than elsewhere in describing them as shadowy and unsubstantial, floating about and passing away. They should not even, he asserts, be referred to by the demonstrative pronoun "this," because thereby we would attribute to them a mode of substantial existence in their own right which they do not possess.[82] "Coming to be" has its counterpart in "passing away," and though Plato here is not particularly concerned with the latter process, he avails himself of the complementary relationship between the

---

[80] See esp. 28b3ff., 44c7f., 48d1ff., 55d2ff., 59c5ff., 68b6ff., d2ff.

[81] The following discussion of necessity concentrates on the section 48e2–53c3 which introduces the receptacle and brings it to bear on the explanation of *genesis* (see 49a5).

[82] 49c7ff., d5, 50a2–4 (cf. Note 91).

two to bring out the impermanent nature of all particulars. They are objects of belief, sense perception, and illusion, and there are passages in this section where Plato does not even allow himself to speak of them as becoming and passing away but qualifies these terms by saying that particulars are "imagined" to go through these processes.[83]

In summing up his disquisition, Plato recognizes that there are three entities: "Let this, then, be given as the tale summed according to my judgment: that there exist Being, Space, Becoming—three distinct things—even before the Heaven [scil., the Cosmos] came into being." This is as far as he will go. Of the particulars he says, a few lines earlier, that they "somehow hold on to Being" (since without this they would "be" nothing at all). Such a mode of existence, if it can be at all honored by this name, contrasts sharply with the true being of the Forms.[84]

As in the *Republic* and other dialogues, Plato thinks of particular objects as "imitations" or "images" of the Forms.[85] Although they are corporeal and in this respect different from the Forms, Plato does not trace their material nature to another principle. The other principle which he introduces and, in a sense, places beside the Forms is meant to account not for the materiality but for the place of particular things and for their being "somewhere" in space. When at the end of this section Plato once more formulates the difference between particular objects and the Forms, this difference is that the former are in space and the latter are not.[86]

Because space is an integral factor in every process of becoming and co-operates with the Forms in creating visible things, it is given a status beside them. Yet not full status. It remains an illegitimate denizen of the realm of being.[87] There is little to be gained by seeing, in this new concept of space, Plato's answer to criticisms leveled at his earlier theory (or theories) concerning the relation between the Forms and their counterparts in the visible world. The origin of the departure eludes us; all that we can say is that when Plato gave

---

[83] 49e7 (φαντάζεσθαι can hardly have the meaning "to be manifested" which Cherniss, *A. J. Ph.*, 75 [1954], 114, gives it), 50c4; cf. 52a6.

[84] 52d2ff. (Cornford's translation), c4ff.

[85] 50c5, d4, 51b6, 52c2. Cf. esp. *Rep.* VI,510b4; *Phaedr.* 250a6ff.

[86] 51e6–52d1, esp. 52b3ff., c2ff. (on c6ff. in particular cf. Cornford, *Cosmology*, 194).

[87] See esp. 52b2 (cf. 49a3).

fuller consideration to the physical world he decided that in addition
to the Forms another and supplementary principle was needed to provide such limited existence as the objects of becoming possess.[88]

What Aristotle calls matter and what has since been known under
this name is something that Plato cannot even "separate in thought"
by distinguishing it from the Form or by apprehending it in particulars. Not even "bastard reason" can arrive at this concept. To be sure,
the visible, particular fire has a body and every body is three-dimen-
sional,[89] whereas the Form has neither body nor dimensions. Yet if the
corporeal nature of the physical elements cannot be accounted for by
the supposition that they are reflections of the Forms, Plato does account for it by providing a mathematical analysis of body: the units
of the physical elements are regular solid bodies; these bodies in turn
must be understood as produced by plane figures. When Plato builds
these solid units out of triangles which actually only compose their
surfaces,[90] we may feel that he skips a step and that this is the point in

[88] It is hardly possible to decide whether the new ἀρχή made in 48c2 (cf. 48a7ff.)
is a "device" of literary composition or whether it reflects a further advance in
Plato's thought.

[89] 53c4.

[90] Plato refers to the regular solid bodies as *somata* (53e1, 5, 56a4 *et al.*). It has
of course long been noticed that Plato in his account of elementary formations and
transformations neglects the factor of "volume"; see, e.g., Eva Sachs (*Die fünf
platon. Körper* [Berlin 1917], 216ff.), who wonders whether Plato's elementary
bodies are "hollow."

The suggestion that "the picture of plane surfaces being broken up and the
fragments drifting about till they find others to combine with [56c–57c] cannot
be taken literally" (Cornford, *Cosmology*, 229) is problematic, since most of the
Timaeus is a myth and not to be taken literally; yet what right do we have to
take sections that cause us difficulties less literally than others? As he is inclined to
do, Cornford looks to the concept of "powers" (*dynameis*) for help (*ibid.*); but
it is hardly correct that "Plato speaks of the contents of [his figures] as qualities
or 'motions and powers'" (56c4?), and nothing warrants the assumption that the
"powers" lead deeper into the "real nature of the process of dissolution and
recombination" or that they figured in an explanation which Plato holds back. We
cannot fill out Plato's theory with the help of Presocratic or Aristotelian motifs.
Nor does the receptacle where it is discussed account for corporeality (Plato does
not say that what arises in it is σώματα ἁπτά, στερεά), and to think that it should
do so later, in sections where no reference is made to it, is hazardous. The triangles
(or surfaces) are clearly meant to be principles of the regular solid bodies. They
are πέρατα, a factor of Form, as was well brought out by J. Stenzel in his otherwise
somewhat obscure discussion (*Zahl. u. Gestalt in Pl. u. Arist.* [2d ed.; Berlin, 1933],
72ff., 76). They are not factors of material composition. It is true that Plato uses
them for the explanation of elementary intermutations in which normally the
material composition would play a role. In Aristotelian terminology it can indeed

his reasoning where he could have discovered matter. Some of his constructions may give us the impression of being made with the conscious or unconscious purpose of bypassing the recognition of this concept. But this is surely an illusion. For Plato matter is and remains in the full sense of the word something "unthinkable."

Aristotle did arrive at this concept, and not without profiting from Plato's analysis of physical things as well as from his logical distinctions. The point at which he made a new turn and where his way parted from Plato's will be indicated in a later chapter.

While speaking of the entities that temporarily arise in "space," Plato once describes them in the following words: "That which is of some quality—hot or white or any of the opposites—and all that is made up of them should not be designated by such words," scil., as "this" or "that." [91] Elsewhere in this section these entities are spoken of as "copies" of the eternal things, and though Plato again has scruples about using a good name for something transient,[92] we may

---

be said that Plato thinks exclusively of the formal cause, not at all of the material. To put it differently, only the περιέχον, not the περιεχόμενον, has been taken into consideration (on the possibility of identifying these with Form and matter see Arist. *Phys.* IV,2.209b1f., 6ff.).

[91] *Tim.* 50a2–4. I have profited from Cornford's translation and construe the sentence as he does. The same construction is adopted by others (e.g., with regard to the point at issue, by R. Hackforth, *Cl. Q.*, 38 [1944], 35f.) whom Cherniss cites (*A. J. Ph.*, 75 [1954], 113ff., 124). The meaning which Cherniss himself finds in these words, scil., that the receptacle should not be called hot or white, etc., is in itself correct (at 51a5f., to which Cherniss refers, Plato does make this point). In our passage, however, I find it difficult to accept Cherniss' construction but believe that the other translators are guided by the right feeling. τὸ δ' ὁποιονοῦν τι . . . ἐναντίων is parallel in its place to the relative clause in the former half of this sentence, and both halves begin by indicating the entity whose designation is in question. τὸ δ' ὁποιονοῦν τι is not easily taken as predicative (i.e., as equivalent to ὁποιονοῦν δέ τι). It is possible to regard the opening words of the sentences or clauses 49d4, e5, e7, 50a2 as specifying the entities whose correct designation is the point at issue. 49e4 ταῦτα ἕκαστα μὴ λέγειν probably means, "these ways of speaking should not be used," though Plato need not have grieved if a reader also understood that the καθ' ἕκαστα should not be designated by the demonstrative pronouns; either of the interpretations seems preferable to the idea (Cherniss, *A. J. Ph.*, 75: 114, 119) that Plato should here all at once be concerned with the right use of the word ἕκαστον. I do not specify other questions of interpretation on which Cherniss has convinced me. One of them is the meaning and reference of τὸ τοιοῦτον in 49d5ff.

[92] For the meaning of 49d4ff. cf. Cherniss (*A. J. Ph.*, 75 [1954], 114 and 115f.), who considers himself in agreement with Martin, Ritter, and Fraccaroli. For Plato's use of τοιοῦτον it is interesting to compare Aristotle's use of the same word in *De gen.* II,3.330b21ff.: the simple and pure elements that he has deduced are not

think of them as what is "commonly" called fire, water, etc. i.e., the empirical instances of these elements. What, then, does Plato mean by the words which he uses in the former passage? Since hot and white are mentioned as instances of the "opposites," it is plain that he has in mind the so-called powers (*dynameis*) which are generally grouped in pairs of opposites, like hot and cold, bright and dark, dry and moist. And what are the objects "made up of them"? What, indeed, but the elements as they arise in the physical world? To say that fire consists of the bright and the hot stuff or that it combines such powers is a way of explaining its nature and *genesis*. There is no denying that Plato here alludes to this way; yet he really no more than alludes, and in another passage of our section where he seems to do so again he is even more casual and his phrasing so brief and cryptic that one can hardly be sure of his meaning [93] before one has compared that passage with the first and interpreted *obscurius ex obscuro*.

To ignore these allusions or to explain them away would be as wrong as to exaggerate their bearing. Plato does not give us his account of *genesis* in these incidental remarks. If developed, they might indeed constitute a physical approach to the elements in our world. Yet it was Aristotle, not Plato, who "developed" them.[94] Plato's own

---

like the fire, etc., that we know, but are τοιαῦτα. Aristotle, however, here leaves the names "fire" to the "empirical" element; the pure and "ideal" form of it he describes as πυροειδές. The same applies to the other elements. For "copies" and "images" see 50c5, 52c2.

[93] 514ff.: one should not speak of the receptacle as earth, air, etc., or as ὅσα ἐκ τούτων or ἐξ ὧν ταῦτα γέγονεν. The interpreters (see esp. Cornford, *Cosmology*, 186 and n.3, Robin in his translation [Paris, 1942], *ad loc.*, and Cherniss, *A. J. Ph.*, 75 [1954], 124) seem to be agreed on the meaning of this passage and its closeness to 50a2–4. In 52e1ff. Plato makes more definite use of the δυνάμεις.

[94] See below, Ch. 17. I do not suggest that Aristotle owes the impulse for his own doctrine of *genesis* to these brief passages, nor, tempting though it is to establish a closer connection between Plato's and Aristotle's theories of *genesis*, can I convince myself that the "Aristotelian" features in Plato's account are the essential ones. Cornford (*Cosmology*, 183) is sure that "the things that pass into and out of the receptacle" (50c4) are the qualities that have shortly before been spoken of as opposites. To me these things seem to be σώματα (b6), and σώματα are μιμήματα of the Forms. Plato does not here as in the *Phaedo* refer to Forms of hot, cold, etc., but only of fire, water, etc. Their μιμήματα should be the physical, transient fire and water (see 51b2–6). On the whole Cornford's interpretation (*ibid.* and 181) overemphasizes the physical and Aristotelian (or Presocratic) motifs of this section at the expense of the metaphysical. The physical point of view is surely not for Plato the only alternative to the geometrical, which Cornford rightly keeps out of the interpretation of this section.

approach remains "metaphysical." The fire in this world is an imprint which the Form of fire makes on the receptacle. The nature of the receptacle itself is not affected by these imprints; all that happens is that for the time being a part of it takes on a fiery appearance. These, at any rate, are the points on which Plato dwells; this is his way of explaining or "deriving" the physical elements which in his opinion his precursors simply posited as existing, seeing no need of rendering an account.[95] We have no choice but to accept these points as forming the core of his account of *genesis*. It is true that in the next section, which describes the movements of the elements in the receptacle, Plato does seem to think of the physical elements as slightly more substantial and of the receptacle as somewhat more affected by them, and it is true also that he now openly refers to the "powers" as being present and displaying themselves in the receptacle.[96]

Having done our conscientious best to reduce the "physical" point of view to its correct proportions, we may now stop for a moment to consider what kind of approach Plato's casual references suggest. If followed up, they would lead us to the physical vulgate, to propositions on which the Presocratics were more or less agreed. For even if not all of them would say that fire was made up of hot and white (or hot and bright, hot and dry) stuff, they would hold that it had such "powers." [97] It is to doctrines of this kind that Aristotle returns in his treatise *On Coming to Be and Passing Away*, where each of the four elements is described as matter qualified by two of these powers. We shall later see how important a departure Aristotle made by introducing matter devoid of all qualities as the common substratum of the four elements.[98] Yet in spite of this departure, Aristotle is closer to the doctrines of the "physicists" than Plato. For, granted that Plato makes a move or two in their direction, his own theory could by no stretch of the imagination be regarded as a development of theirs.[99]

---

[95] 48b5ff. See also Note 106.   [96] 52d4ff., e1ff.
[97] See above, the last paragraph of Ch. 1.   [98] See below, Chs. 6 and 17.
[99] It is noteworthy that Plato uses the preposition ἐκ (50a3, 51a6) to describe the relation between the elements and powers like hot and white. ἐκ would not easily characterize the relation between the physical or empirical fire and its Form, even though the former is called an ἔκγονος of the latter (50d3f.). One may find in these passages an admission that certain aspects of the physical objects and of *genesis*—indeed the physical aspects—are not fully covered by the theory which makes them offspring and "imitations" of the Forms. Yet these few brief remarks are enough to take care of the alternative or complementary approach. They show that it can be accommodated or incorporated in Plato's own but that by itself it

On the contrary, it makes a complete break with the traditional approach, and his own construction of *genesis* proceeds along lines novel and unorthodox.

If it was Plato's aim to establish *genesis*, this section would be sufficient. It gives us the fundamental theory, the essential conditions of it. Yet inasmuch as the subject of the *Timaeus* is not nature but the Cosmos, Plato needs something more specific, namely, the *genesis* of physical entities (and in particular of the physical elements) in the form in which they are present in the Cosmos. Moreover, Plato is particularly sensitive to the connotations of the word "Cosmos" which suggest that ours is an orderly, well-constructed world. Others had in his opinion slighted these connotations; he himself re-emphasizes them.[100] His Cosmos is the result of a divine plan, and the god who plans and builds it cannot be satisfied with the elements as they exist in nature at large. There they have come into being as reflections of the Forms in the receptacle; but to be parts of the most beautiful and perfect Cosmos they need to be endowed with some form and shape. Shape and number are qualities of order, and when building up the Cosmos, the god resorts to them to give the elements structure. This is described at length and gives us another version of their becoming.[101] Is it supplementary or alternative to the first?

To fulfill their function in the architecture of the Cosmos, the elements must partake of the perfection and regularity of mathematical entities. Plato identifies the unit of each element with a regular solid body, earth with the cube, water with the icosahedron, air with the octahedron, and fire with the pyramid. Yet he actually begins this account by constructing these mathematical solids—and constructing them in a very peculiar way. There are higher entities which as Plato

---

would be far from adequate. The details of this approach Plato does not wish to work out—here as little as anywhere else in his later dialogues. With Aristotle the qualities and contraries to which Plato so casually refers advance to a very important position.

[100] Cf. (besides *Tim.* 29eff., 53eff.) *Phileb.* 28d–29a and *Legg.* X,886a, 889bf., 897cff.

[101] For what follows cf. 53c4–55c6 and 55c7–56c7. On the relations (and differences) between the approach in 53c4ff. and in the preceding sections see the clarifying and incisive comments of Léon Robin in his recent posthumous book *Les rapports de l'être et de la connaissance d'après Platon* (Paris, 1957), 61ff. I agree with him on essential points, but my agreement ends when he begins to postulate some kind of "mathematical" substructure also for the doctrines relating to the receptacle.

puts it "beget" them. Each solid is in the first place "begotten" by the planes which form its surfaces, e.g., the cube by six squares. These squares of the cube are in turn begotten by four isosceles right-angled triangles; for such triangles, properly arranged, compose these squares. Pyramid, octahedron, and icosahedron are in similar fashion traced back to another triangle, a right-angled scalene which is half equilateral. In this context Plato refrains from going back to still higher principles, yet his language leaves no doubt that such exist. He may be thinking of the lines which compose the triangles or indeed of entities even more basic that "beget" the lines.[102] Yet whatever his hidden thought, he builds up the units of the elements by means of forms and numbers. His mathematical derivation of the elements is even capable of accounting for their characteristic qualities and for their specific behavior. As an example, fire is more mobile than earth because, of the four solids which Plato employs, the pyramid moves most easily and quickly. In addition, the hotness of the fire is due not to a hot substance or power—in the cosmological sections of the *Timaeus* Plato recognizes nothing of the kind—but to the sharp angles of the pyramid.[103]

The essence of the construction is that physical entities are produced by others that have a higher ontological status; mathematical objects are closer to the Forms than physical, and plane geometrical figures presumably closer than solid ones.[104] Instead of finding for the elements a suitable father and mother—as in the section introducing the receptacle—Plato here provides each of them with a pedigree, linking it with ancestors who, if not divine, are at least members of the nobility. Incidentally, he defines the family relationship between the elements themselves: earth, having a lineage of its own, remains apart from the others which are only distantly related to it. The three other elements have a common ancestor, the equilateral scalene. This will

[102] See 53d6. For recent suggestions regarding these ἄνωθεν ἀρχαί see A. T. Nicol, *Cl. Q.*, 30 (1936), 125; Cornford, *Cosmology*, 212ff.; Robin, *op.cit.*, 69ff. There is no need here to go into matters of detail such as the fifth *systasis* (55c4) or the indications—followed up by Cornford, 230ff.—that Plato reckons with cubes, etc., of more than one size.

[103] Cf. 55ef., 61d–62a.

[104] The place of mathematics and the nature of the mathematical ἀρχαί in Plato's philosophy are questions bristling with difficulties that are under constant discussion and scrutiny. Since I am not equipped to contribute to the discussion, I do not wish to go beyond what the text of the *Timaeus* says or indicates.

prove important when Plato proceeds to the next point, the mutual transformation of the primary bodies.[105]

If it is true that Plato restores the concept of *genesis* which the later Presocratics had shunned like something unclean, it is also true that he attaches it in particular to those first and basic physical realities which the Presocratics had, in his opinion, taken for granted yet used to account for the origin of all other entities in the physical realm.[106] A truly philosophical study of physics cannot accept the phenomenal elements as something ultimate. Their own nature must be explained or deduced, and the deduction begins, in both sections that we have considered, by positing objects that are not themselves part of the physical world—in the one instance the Forms (and the receptacle), in the other mathematical figures. This kind of *genesis* had never occurred to the minds of the Presocratic physicists. Their principles were themselves eternal and, except for the Pythagoreans, physical.[107] Parmenides' unchanging being had been naturalized and brought into the phenomenal world, not treated as something that remains above and distinct from this world. However, Plato's mathematic genealogy, although remote from Presocratic conceptions, has its bearing on subjects that had been of great and increasing concern to them. From his new derivation of elementary units Plato proceeds at once to the formation of larger aggregates of each element, to their interactions and intermutations, and finally to the formation of compound bodies.[108] And though his procedure is not that of a physicist, we cannot dismiss it as having no relation to traditional problems or as being irrelevant to physics. For Aristotle, Plato's mathematical derivation of the elements is as good—or rather as bad—a doctrine of their *genesis* as those put forward by the atomists and other Pre-

---

[105] See 54a1ff., b5ff., c3; cf. 56d1ff.

[106] See 48b. Plato's statement that the elements are generally treated as known and that nobody has explained their *genesis* is not entirely fair to the Presocratics. Neither for Anaxagoras nor for the atomists are the elements something ultimate; still others, like Anaximenes, posited one "element" and explained the others as modifications of it. Yet this is not the kind of explanation that Plato has in mind. Moreover, as referring to Empedocles, Plato's criticism would be entirely correct, and inasmuch as Plato is here on the point of accepting the Empedoclean elements as the basis of his own physics, he would wish to make clear that for him they have an entirely different status.

[107] Anaximander's *apeiron* is barely comparable. Still, whatever view be taken of it, there seems to be no need to qualify our statement.

[108] 56b7ff., c8ff., 58c5ff.

socratics; and while he is unjust to the deeper meaning of Plato's approach, he is not wrong in treating it as an alternative to Presocratic doctrines of *genesis*.[109]

If we follow Plato's own indications, we must regard the mathematical derivation of the elements as supplementary to their "metaphysical" origin; for he tells us that the god took over the elements as he found them in nature and rendered them more beautiful and perfect.[110] Cosmic *genesis* presupposes physical *genesis* and is a refinement on it. Inasmuch as Plato gives us his account of the world in the form of a cosmogony, i.e., of order arising out of disorder and haphazardness, it is quite consistent that *genesis* as such is prior to the *genesis* of the cosmic elements. Still, it is prior not only in the temporal sense of the world but also as being a more fundamental and comprehensive subject, and we may regard Plato's first account of *genesis* as holding good of it everywhere, whether it comes to pass in the Cosmos or outside of it. To be sure, there may be no coming into being, no elements, no physical material and no physical processes outside the Cosmos.[111] Yet there may still be a "general theory of nature" which is universal in its range and application and deals with problems of *genesis* more essential and all-embracing than the formation of our cosmic elements. Aristotle's physics stands beside his cosmology, its teachings holding good of all nature—though when he becomes more specific, he has perforce to refer to cosmic nature and cosmic conditions.[112] Nor is it by accident that Aristotle criticizes Plato's mathematical *genesis* or the "cosmic" elements in his own cosmological treatise, yet not in his *Physics*. His own theory of *genesis* as presented in the *Physics* is, in part, a development of doctrines like those incorporated in our section on the receptacle; it has no connection—not even of a polemical kind—with Plato's cosmology.[113] If the separation between physics and cosmology is less marked in Plato than in his pupil, the reason is in part that the section of the *Timaeus* which corresponds to Aristotle's physical approach is not pure physics but bristles with highly important metaphysical references.

Now Plato's general doctrine of Becoming actually purports to de-

[109] Esp. in *De caelo* III and *De gen.* I,2.　　　[110] 53a–c; 30a, 69b.

[111] *Tim.* 32c5ff.

[112] E.g., in *Phys.* III,5, where the concept of an infinitely large body is scrutinized, reference to the cosmic pattern shows that no such body is conceivable. See also IV,14.223b18, where the basic measuring unit of time is found in the Cosmos.

[113] See below, Chs. 4 and 16.

scribe nature in its precosmic condition. Although his Cosmos bids
fair to last for all time and although most conceptions and devices of
Presocratic cosmogony have lost all meaning,[114] Plato has not dropped
the Presocratic scheme altogether. The section on the receptacle professes to show us things as they were before the Cosmos; Plato refers
to the elements as existing and moving "even before the heaven [i.e.,
the Cosmos] was fashioned out of them." [115] As in Presocratic accounts,
the elements drift asunder and separate—though there is the difference
that for Plato this separation does not of itself form the Cosmos. The
Cosmos cannot take shape before order, form, and number have come
into operation; by their own *dynameis* the elements with their *vis
consilii expers* cannot create order.[116] Clearly one reason why Plato
has retained the Presocratic motif of "a state of things before the
Cosmos" is that it enables him once more to emphasize the factors of
order and plan which set cosmic conditions apart from noncosmic
(precosmic conditions may illustrate noncosmic).[117] Yet as we have
seen, Plato avails himself of this precosmic phase to discuss the basic
phenomenon, *genesis,* which if hardly occurring outside the Cosmos
is yet "prior" to cosmology. Actually it had already been prior to it
in the later Presocratics. The physicists who came after Parmenides
had, before proceeding to cosmological details, explained their stand
on *genesis* and declared what they regarded as being (being things)
and how other things relate to the permanently being. This corresponds to what Plato does in the section about the receptacle (even
if his attitude to becoming is the opposite of that lately in fashion).
We need not make overmuch of the fact that at least one of his precursors, Empedocles, definitely settled these matters before he went
on to show how his elements build up the Cosmos and compose the

---

[114] The Demiurge in his κοσμοποιία employs none of the mechanical devices which
had figured in the Presocratic systems. If he proceeds by "stages" (34c3), they are
utterly different from the stages of an evolutionary scheme. I accept the γέγονε of
28b7 as essential for the account of the Cosmos which Plato presents. The myth
is the only form into which Plato sees fit to cast his cosmology. We have no right
to regard this form as "accidental," and I see little point in reconstructing Plato's
"true opinion" on a subject for which he himself declares truth to be unattainable
(29b ff.): τὸν εἰκότα μῦθον ἀποδεχομένους πρέπει τούτου μηδὲν ἔτι πέρα ζητεῖν. (Cf. my
comments in *H.S.C.P.,* 63 [1958], 266, 268.)

[115] *Tim.* 52d, 53a; cf. 48b.

[116] For Aristotle's different judgment see below, Ch. 11 and esp. Ch. 12.

[117] 53a ff.

living beings in it.[118] We have seen in the preceding chapter, "Presocratic Legacies," that a set of physical questions had become detached from the body of cosmological subjects. There may have been more of such "physical" questions. Infinite divisibility, for instance, which had been worked out by Zeno without reference to cosmology, could not, once it had been put forward, be ignored by the authors of cosmological systems. Aristotle has a goodly number of subjects that find a more suitable place in physics than in cosmology (some of them, to be sure, had only originated with Plato), yet for him too *genesis* is still the first of them. His *Physics*, however, knows nothing of a state of things "before the Cosmos came to be fashioned." As he has broken completely with the Presocratic idea of an evolutionary cosmology, so he avoids referring to precosmic conditions. On the one occasion where he resorts to the traditional method [119] he makes clear that he does so for expository and pedagogical reasons and that his intellectual experiment should not be regarded as a true account of the matter. If from his position we look back at Plato, we realize that in the *Timaeus* the development which led from cosmic evolution to an eternal and static Cosmos is not yet completed. There are definite reasons why Plato's Cosmos should have no temporal beginning, but we have no right to give them more weight than did Plato himself and to set aside his unequivocal and emphatic statement that the Cosmos "has come into being." Nor need we deny that Plato's general physical theory is still tied up with the Presocratic conception of a precosmic state of things.[120] The arguments for the eternity of the Cosmos become decisive only with his pupils.

Of the world in which things come into being and pass away there can be only likely tales, no true and cogent philosophical account.

---

[118] Cf. on the whole p. 7. I know of no reason to doubt that Emped. B6–15 are correctly placed in *Vorsokr.*

[119] See *De caelo* II,14.297a12ff.

[120] *Tim.* 28b5ff., 7. To put the matter in schematic form, Plato in 48e–52c states his views about being and becoming, about their mutual relation, and about the entities which do (or do not) deserve the designation of being. From there he moves on to the description of the precosmic state in 52d–53b (there are anticipations of this in the former section, e.g., 50c2ff.—yet note c6—and the subjects are inevitably interlocked). The former section corresponds to the declarations regarding being, being things, and the questionable reality of becoming in the accounts of the later Presocratics (see above, Ch. 1); the latter has its analogues in Empedocles' *Sphairos*, Anaxagoras' condition of "all things together," etc.

From the Forms and the entities close to them more ways than one lead to *genesis*. None of them should be accepted as a dogma. The mathematical pedigree of cosmic elements contains aspects of, and approximations to, the truth that another essay on the relation between eternal and transitory things might not bring out so well.

GENESIS, ASSOCIATION, AND MIXTURE

The geometrical pedigree leaves us with "units" of fire, water, air, and earth. These units are naturally far below the threshold of perception. The fire that we see is an "assembly," a gathering of many units.[121] Plato must be thinking of the units, cubes, etc., as placing themselves side by side in every direction. Empedocles may not have had a comparable concept of "units," and Anaxagoras' principle of infinite divisibility virtually rules out this notion; yet it is not too bold a guess that for a visible body to arise its constitutive factors—powers, atoms, or whatever—had to assemble. Thus Plato is now entering upon Presocratic ways of thinking. Once his primary bodies have come into being, larger and secondary bodies form out of them by aggregation, combination, and mixture, the same processes to which his precursors had resorted. Whether their formation still is a *genesis* in the strict sense of the word is hardly relevant.[122]

Plato next turns to the question how the four elements act upon each other and how it comes about that one element may turn into another.[123] The latter possibility had not existed for Empedocles, and Plato, who accepts his four elements but does not think of them as permanent realities, finds it necessary to correct him on this point. As the units of fire, water, and air are composed of the same triangles, Plato makes them break up into these triangles and shows how the triangles thus set free regroup themselves into the solid figure which forms the unit of another element. The triangles of earth cannot recombine into another element; yet its units may break too.[124] Throughout this section Plato appears to be close to the concepts of

---

[121] *Tim.* 56b7–c3.

[122] Plato uses the word γέγονε (e.g., 59c3), yet in a very casual and unemphatic fashion. Words like συσταθῆναι, συμπαγῆναι, σύμμειξις (59c2, e4, 60b7ff., etc.) are now more characteristic.

[123] *Tim.* 56c8–57c6.

[124] 56d1–6. Plato probably knew of no "physical" reason why earth should be kept from the cycle of transformations. As he himself admits, the empirical evidence points to the opposite conclusion (49b8, c6); yet the mathematical derivation

aggregation and separation. True, he does not use the actual words which, we may suppose, had become a shibboleth of the Presocratic approach. He may well have felt that the building up of, say, a unit of fire out of its triangles was a subtler and nobler process of organization than the mechanical aggregation and separation of which the Presocratics had made so much use. Plato "composes" where the physicists had thought of material accumulating and mixing. His concern is with forms and boundaries. When he speaks of the breaking up into triangles and of their new combinations, he uses words like "solving," "cutting," "dividing," "resolving," and again "filling," "forming," "compacting." [125] Respecting his feelings, we may refrain from comparing his procedure too closely with the Presocratic devices. After all, what breaks up and combines in Plato's account is not physical parts or portions of a substance.

Now the breaking of a unit is not the same as the breaking of an aggregate. In the Cosmos large groups of elementary units are cut into smaller ones through the action of a different and, as it proves, hostile element, and as the spherical boundary of this Cosmos exerts a constant pressure upon all that is within it (forcing the elements to move and exchange their places), this breaking up and the complementary process of pressing together must continue without interruption.[126] The result is a constant regrouping of the elements. The smaller figures penetrate into the interstices between the larger, disrupting—so it seems—not only their aggregates but even their units. The larger figures, on the other hand, as far as we can understand Plato's description, merely press the smaller into tighter groupings, doing away with the intervals.[127] While describing these new groupings and formations, Plato does not hesitate to use the terms "aggregation" and "segrega-

---

overrides this evidence (54b5ff.). As one may expect, Aristotle does not fail to turn this into an argument against Plato's mathematical construction of the elements (*De caelo* III,7.206a17ff.).

[125] (δια)λύειν (56d2, 3, 57b5), μερίζειν, τέμνειν (56d6, 57a2), δια(or κατα)θραύειν (56e4, 57b1); συναρμόζειν, συμπηγνύναι, συνίστασθαι (56d4, 7, e7, b1).

[126] 57d7ff., esp. 58a4–c4. The relation of this section to the preceding ones will be presently discussed.

[127] The interstices would appear to be between units of the same kind (icosahedra, etc.). Yet there can be little doubt that the breaking-up process extends even to the units; for the final result is a change of place (b8ff.), which presupposes transformation from one element into another (each having its specific region in the Cosmos; see 57c2ff., which is taken up in 58a2ff. and b8ff., c2ff.). Cf. Cornford, *Cosmology*, 242 n.2, 3, 5, and 244f.

tion" ("association" and "dissociation").¹²⁸ They are, after all, a
suitable designation for every process that brings together or separates.

Plato must have known of the extensive use which the Presocratics
made of these two concepts and of the significance which they attached to them; as a matter of fact, he employs these terms in a passage of the *Sophist* which purports to be a summary of earlier physical systems.¹²⁹ We may suppose that where he admits them into his own
account he does so with a kind of historical consciousness and with
the intention of indicating their correct places. Our pair of concepts
is employed quite openly and, one may say, with a certain emphasis,
in the explanation of the sense perceptions. In particular the sensations
of taste and color are attributed to "contractions" or "dilations"—i.e.,
"associations" and "dissociations"—within the respective sense organs,
these processes being caused by the particles which strike the organs.¹³⁰
One may wonder whether certain "compressions" or "contractions"
by the help of which Plato accounts for a good number of physical
formations are not fundamentally of the same type. Take the formation of rocks, for example. Plato suggests that some particles of water
that have been mingled with a large body of earth become separated
from it and change into air. When this has happened, the air which
is next to this body of earth and "poured around it" "squeezes it hard"
and thrusts it together (so that no interstices are left). Thus closely
packed, the earth particles form a rock.¹³¹ The explanation of other
phenomena follows the same lines. Ice, for instance, is due to the "pressing together" of water particles, again by action of the surrounding
air.¹³²

Still other formations that Plato here "defines" are mixtures—either
of one and the same element in its different grades and sizes or of
different elements. Thus although the metals are basically water

¹²⁸ διακρίνεσθαι, συγκρίνεσθαι 58b7.

¹²⁹ *Soph.* 243b5 (Cornford and Diès rightly accept Radermacher's elegant emendation . . . ἄλλος εἴπῃ—ἄλλοθι πῃ MSS.—διακρίσεις καὶ συγκρίσεις ὑποτιθείς). Here
Plato also refers to the use which his precursors had made of the closely related
concept of *krasis;* cf. *Theaet.* 152d7.

¹³⁰ See esp. *Tim.* 65c3 (cf. 66c3–5), 67d5ff. (e4ff.); see also the explanation given
for hot and cold sensations (61d6ff., 62a6ff.; cf. Arist. *De gen.* II,2.329b26ff. with
our comments below, Ch. 17).

¹³¹ 60b7–c6.

¹³² 58d8–59a4. I have disregarded some other phases and conditions of these
processes (in the formation of ice, in particular, it is essential that the water particles be of identical size—the point which Cornford has done so much to clarify;
see *Cosmology,* 231ff.).

(scil., water in a specific state and condition), some of them, like copper, have an admixture of earth in their composition; and wine, olive oil, honey, and various "juices" present a combination of water and fire.[133] In all these instances it would be possible to speak of the *genesis* of a new physical substance, but this point of view is obviously immaterial. *Genesis* is needed to explain the origin of the four elements. This is its proper place; secondary, derivative, or compound substances hardly call for the application of this illustrious concept. These compounds are the entities that Empedocles explained as mixtures of his eternal realities—making it a special point that *genesis* does not enter into their origin; and Plato, we may say, follows his lead, even though in various ways mixture has with him become something more complex than Empedocles fancied it to be.[134] As regards the categories of association and dissociation, we may again feel that Plato could have used them in describing such derivative substances, especially since the evidence of the *Timaeus* as a whole does not suggest that he considers them with misgivings, still less that he knew of objections so fatal as those which Aristotle raises in *De generatione et corruptione*. Plato's physical substances are not organic units but rather of the nature of aggregates. Still, is it quite by accident that Plato here does not use the crucial terms? [135] They may have had connotations which he did not wish to bring into the formation of substances.

We have noted the tendency to avoid these terms also in Plato's account about the mutual transformation of the elements. Basically the way in which air here turns into water recalls the *genesis* of water as previously set forth in the "mathematical derivation": again the triangles compose themselves into surfaces, and these produce solid figures.[136] In a sense this changing of air to water is again a *genesis* of

---

[133] 58c5–61c2; see esp. 59b6ff., 60a3ff.

[134] Apart from such "organic" formations as flesh, blood, etc., which were clearly of particular importance to Empedocles, our evidence is defective as to the extent to which he actually specified the mixtures of compound substances. For Plato, too, the mixtures that are represented by the tissues (marrow, bone, flesh, etc.; see *Tim.* 73bff.) should here be taken into account. We shall do so when we return to the subject in connection with Aristotle's new departures (below, Ch. 19).

[135] He does use the words for mixture (μειγνύναι, συμμειγνύναι), e.g., 59a4, c3, d4, 73c1, 74c7, employing the concept also for the combination of different grades of one and the same element (59e6).

[136] *Tim.* 56c8–57b7.

water, but Plato does not seem to dignify the process by this name. Whatever the metaphysical parenthood or the mathematical ancestry of elements, physically elements come into being out of one another. The Presocratics had known this, and we shall see that Aristotle in a careful disquisition rules out all other possibilities.[137] As described in the section devoted to the receptacle, *genesis* has no limits (for Plato never suggests that space is bounded, and to think that there are limits to the productive capacity of the Forms would be absurd, not to say sacrilegious). Yet in actuality the material in the Cosmos is far from unlimited;[138] if a new entity is to arise, another must go out of existence. This is good physics, and if such "arising" is not what Plato means by *genesis,* this is another indication that he does not actually think of this concept in "purely physical" ways and terms. As a matter of fact, the sections where Plato seems close to the favorite motifs of the later Presocratics —association and dissociation—have other features in common with them and are altogether nearer to their pattern than is either the metaphysical or the mathematical account of *genesis.* Here we have action of the elements upon one another, constant struggle between them, the overpowering of one by the other, the "way up and down,"[139] and as has already been said, the coming into being of one at the expense of another. A contemporary reader imbued with the spirit of the later Presocratics might have granted that Plato was right (as against Empedocles) in treating the elements as capable of changing into one another. Yet the same person, while baffled by Plato's mathematical motifs, might have been pleased to see that Plato too needed separation of parts, regrouping, mixture, and aggregation to account for physical formation. In view of all this, Plato's "derivation of the elements" would strike him as an unnecessary complication and

---

[137] See Chs. 16 and 17 but cf. also *De caelo* III, 3–6. When the triangles that form several units of air recompose in the unit of water (56e6), the water that thus comes into being should also be an imprint of the Form (scil., the Form of water) upon the receptacle. At least, we have no reason to suppose that the physical (or mathematical) explanation of the process renders the basic metaphysical account of *genesis* invalid. On different levels of thought each account is true or "likely"— even if our own habits of thinking make it difficult for us to appreciate this plurality of approaches. It would be crude to suppose that they exclude one another, the one holding good (only) before the Cosmos, the other within it. To find the right starting point for Aristotle, it is essential to realize that he had become familiar with more than one approach to the phenomenon of *genesis.*

[138] The material of the Cosmos is the entire existing amount of the four elements (*Tim.* 32c5ff.), and no new material enters the Cosmos (33c6ff.).

[139] See 58b8; cf. Cornford, *Cosmology,* 245.

subtlety. On his own ground this critic would be hard to refute; for he would hardly understand that no physical substance can be something ultimate or have the character of a principle.

If the elements arise out of one another, *genesis* is horizontal rather than vertical, for the elements are all of equal standing. Yet Plato's preference is clearly for the vertical approach. In this section he steers a middle course between *genesis* and the Presocratic conceptions that had usurped its place. Can we find more light on his views concerning association and dissociation and the relation of both to his own idea of becoming?

One passage which provides considerable light is already known to us. The catalogue of movements in Book X of the *Laws* not only includes association and dissociation among their "forms" or species but treats them as necessary conditions for the materialization of other forms. Growth comes about by association, decrease by dissociation.[140] Moreover, passing away materializes through either of these processes (conceivably even through both combined); for evidently association as well as dissociation can alter and destroy the original "constitution" of something.[141] Yet to *genesis* we do not get by this route. Making himself a new beginning, Plato declares that it needs a "beginning" or principle which "grows" in one dimension, then makes a transition into the second and finally into the third. The beginning as well as the "transitions" are processes of too fundamental a nature to be

---

[140] *Legg.* X,893e6. That *diakrisis* can lead to destruction is easy to understand, yet how can *synkrisis* do the same? Because if one drop of water is mixed with ten thousand gallons of wine, the water is destroyed (λύεται τὸ εἶδος as Aristotle says in a similar connection, *De gen.* I,10.328a26ff., where εἶδος may throw light on the καθεστηκυῖα ἕξις in our passage)? Or would, in such a case, association and dissociation operate simultaneously, and is this what Plato has in mind when he says δι' ἀμφότερα? For an alternative explanation see Skemp, 103f. Skemp's references to Cornford's (*Pl. and Parm.*, 198) and Ross's divergent explanations of ἕξις bring the problem of the passage into focus: are we to interpret it in terms of the "likely tales" of the *Timaeus* or of Aristotle's doctrine of substance? Obvious reasons tell in favor of the former alternative, yet I hesitate to apply the construction of the *Timaeus* "literally." Plato's formulation is too brief to allow a clear decision.

[141] In the *Philebus* (42cf.) we read that the *physis* of things is destroyed (διαφθείρεται) as a result of σύγκρισις, διάκρισις, αὔξησις, and φθίσις. I mention this passage with some hesitation; for the διαφθείρεσθαι of which Plato here speaks may not be the same as in *Legg.* X,894a7 where διαφθείρεσθαι παντελῶς seems to be used as an equivalent of ἀπόλλυσθαι (a1). The context and wording of the *Philebus* passage suggest processes like the destruction or corruption of a constitution through disease. Cf. R. Hackforth, *Plato's Examination of Pleasure* (Cambridge, 1945), 83 n.2.

explained along aggregational lines. They break through the physical mechanism; here something new bursts into the world. As Skemp has well put it, this is "simple genesis in which Plato believes in defiance of the Parmenidean canon." [142] Aristotle will have a difficult task when he undertakes to naturalize absolute *genesis* in the physical world.[143] As Plato here conceives of *genesis*, it does not seem to need an equally "simple" and absolute counterpart; passing away may be left to the ordinary mechanical processes which can adequately account for it.[144] Whatever details Plato here has in mind but does not see fit to disclose, we are probably not wrong if we let ourselves be guided by the mathematical derivations in the *Timaeus*, except that Plato here takes us even farther back, beginning with a one-dimensional principle.[145] That, in terms of "pure" physics, one body originates out of another is here irrelevant; still, we may remember that in such mutual transformation bodies return to their principles (triangles, as far as the *Timaeus* goes, yet this passage points to even "higher" ones) and that the new body arises out of such principles.[146]

Careful interpretation of the *Parmenides* has found in this dialogue too a discrimination between simple *genesis* and *genesis* by association and dissociation. "The one," we read here in one of the alternative "hypotheses," participates in being. To become is to acquire a share in being, to pass away is to lose being.[147] If, however, the emphasis is not so much on its being but on its being one and many, then to become one (out of many) is a process of association, to become many is one of dissociation. This section of the *Parmenides* understands even growth and decrease as "becoming" larger and smaller and appears to treat

---

[142] 105; cf. p. 104: "γένεσις calls for a deeper explanation" (scil., than *phthora*). Cf. also Cornford, *Pl. and Parm.*, 199: "What is here called generation is rather a logical than a physical process." I prefer to call it an ontological *genesis* or genealogy.

[143] See below, Ch. 16.

[144] In the section on the receptacle ἀπόλλυσθαι sometimes has a place by the side of γίγνεσθαι (e.g., 52a5f.), yet does Plato really here give a metaphysical account of *phthora* in the sense in which he gives one of *genesis*? Do the Forms cause *phthora* as they cause *genesis*? Hardly. Or does one miss "passing away" when Plato sums up (52d2ff.): "Being, space and becoming are [real]"? It may be argued that *genesis* here includes *phthora*.

[145] Cf. Skemp, 105; A. T. Nicol in her paper "Indivisible Lines," *Cl. Q.*, 30 (1936), 125; Cornford, *Cosmology*, 198f.

[146] μεταβάλλον in Plato's next sentence (894a5) can hardly refer to this mutual transformation, since οὕτω links it closely to the description of *genesis* in the preceding sentence.

[147] *Parm.* 156a4ff. For what follows cf. Cornford, *Pl. and Parm.*, 196ff.

qualitative change as "becoming" similar or dissimilar. It seems correct to think that Plato here successively brings the various kinds or "forms" of *change* into the discussion.[148] The differentiation corresponds to that made in the catalogue of *Laws* X, and it is interesting that the same changes which in that catalogue are forms of movement are here varieties of becoming. We remember that the *Phaedo* took (or implied) a similar view of them [149] and are in any case prepared for a certain rivalry between becoming and movement, both tending to claim as far as they can a monopoly in the physical world. In the scheme which can be distilled from the *Parmenides*, basic and absolute *genesis* appears to stand apart from its more specific varieties. Before we leave this section, we may note that as soon as Plato has dealt with these varieties he turns to locomotion and its opposite, rest.[150] He makes, however, no attempt to bring them under the heading of *genesis* but rather suggests that coming to be and passing away have themselves the character of movements, yet that the decisive moment when something passes from not-being to becoming is outside the sphere of movement as well as of rest.[151]

[148] 156b.

[149] Esp. *Phaedo* 71af. (see above, p. 22). Cornford, *Pl. and Parm.*, 197ff., rightly compares the changes mentioned in this section of the *Parmenides* with the catalogue of movements in the *Laws*. It is, however, difficult to find "qualitative change" in that catalogue. In our passage "assimilation" ("becoming similar") may be taken as representing this "form" of change or movement. Remotely it corresponds to "becoming hot" and "cold" in the *Phaedo* (71b6). Cornford even considers in the *Parmenides* as well as in the *Laws* qualitative change as the concept that would comprehend association, dissociation, and assimilation. The term is not used by Plato in either passage. Cornford's reason for introducing it is perhaps that elsewhere in the *Parmenides* locomotion and qualitative change are said to be the "only" forms of movement (see above, p. 31). Yet in our *Parmenides* passage the various processes are not dealt with as forms of movement but of *genesis*. Altogether Plato's scheme here is not quite as close to Aristotle's classification of movements as Cornford suggests (p. 199; Aristotle, after all, never recognized association and dissociation). *Legg.* X,897a, to which Cornford refers (p. 198), does not prove that qualitative change remained for Plato to the end a basic form of movement but rather, as Cornford himself says, that it "supervenes on" association and dissociation. This is in harmony with the scheme of the *Timaeus*.

[150] 156cff.

[151] 157a2, 156e8–157a3. Plato here (156c4ff.) repeatedly uses the term *metabole* yet not in its Aristotelian meaning as comprehending all types of change, movements as well as becoming. We shall later deal with the "instant of transition from rest to movement" (pp. 204–216); here it may be noted that Plato first establishes the existence of this instant as occurring between local movement and rest and then argues that the same phenomenon must occur also in connection with the other processes, including *genesis*. It is here that *genesis* is treated as a movement (157a1f.).

This short section of the *Parmenides* may well leave us with the impression that growth and decrease, association and dissociation have not yet received the place which we find them occupying in the *Laws*. Not yet regarded as "forms" of movement, they still cling to and cluster around *genesis*. Movement itself is, in the *Parmenides* and *Theaetetus*, satisfied with two basic classes, locomotion and qualitative change, the former being again subdivided into movement in the same place and from one place to another.[152] No difficulties are created by the fact that assimilation ("becoming similar") is here treated as a variety of *genesis;* for though it has a certain affinity to qualitative change, we need not look at it as a representative of this class. At the most we may find evidence that the qualitative changes have not yet completely and irrevocably passed under the domination of movement. In the end, when working out the catalogue of the *Laws*, Plato decided to discard "qualitative change" [153] and to incorporate growth and decrease, association and dissociation, passing away, and perhaps even coming to be,[154] in his system and classification of movements. This at least is the "development" which a close and merciless comparison between our *Parmenides* section and *Laws* X would suggest. Let us not, however, be too dogmatic on the subject; in these matters there may easily have been more change and flux, more reorientation and regrouping than the dialogues reveal. Aristotle, it may here be remarked, never wavers in considering qualitative change as one of the three or four basic species of movement. If he knew the reasons why Plato discarded it, he evidently regarded them as inadequate. In all probability the better standing which qualities and the concept of quality enjoy in his system did much to strengthen his confidence in qualitative change and made him adhere to Plato's original recognition of this species.

It should be possible to say why Plato in the final analysis refuses to identify becoming with aggregation. If aggregation were accepted as an adequate explanation, it would do away with production of physical objects by the Forms as well as with their derivation from mathe-

---

[152] *Theaet.* 181c; *Parm.* 138bf., 162df.

[153] Reference has been made (above, Note 149) to *Legg.* X,897a5ff. where some qualitative changes are said to "result from" such basic forms of movement as growth, association, etc. In the *Timaeus* assimilation and dissimilation occur as aspects of the process by which the elements change into one another (57c3ff.; note also 57a3ff.); if the point must be pressed, they still are associated with *genesis* rather than with movement.

[154] See on this question above, Note 62.

matical begetters. Moreover, as far as the Forms—in whatever way or fashion—bring a physical substance into existence, it does not arise as an aggregate. The Forms give it their own character and produce it as a whole, not as a sum of parts. "Simple and absolute *genesis* is not defined by association and dissociation" says Aristotle; it comes about "when something as a whole changes from this into that." Plato too knows that "what comes into being always does so as a whole." [155] Elsewhere Aristotle speaks of "wholes" that have parts yet are not like a mere heap of them; rather "the whole is something besides [scil., over and above] the parts." In his distinction of the various types of causes Aristotle puts the whole on the side of the formal cause.[156] To what extent, then, does the discovery of "organic unity" remain Aristotle's achievement, and how much did Plato contribute to it? In the *Parmenides* and dialogues close to it Plato repeatedly discusses the relation of whole and parts. During the arguments of the *Theaetetus* a point is reached where it seems doubtful whether the syllable can be simply identical with its letters. Perhaps it is "different from them," being "one form" that has arisen from their plurality yet with a distinct "character of its own." [157] This corresponds to Aristotle's statement that the whole is something beyond its parts. That the Form organizes the parts would seem to be implicit in Plato's theory.[158] When a physical object has its "*genesis* into being," should it not, since it is stamped with "limit" and Form, acquire intrinsic unity and cease to be a mere aggregate? Thus, even if the exact measure of Aristotle's debt to Plato is beyond our grasp, the debt as such should not be questioned. The sections of the *Timaeus* in which we found Plato

[155] Arist. *De gen.* I,2.317a17f., 20ff. The last point (change from one substance into another) would, however, not figure in Plato's concept of absolute *genesis*. Cf. Plato *Soph.* 245d1ff.

[156] *Metaph.* H6.1045a8ff., Δ2.1013b22 (where ὅλον, σύνθεσις, and εἶδος appear together), 26.1023b32ff., 1024a1ff. The significant passage *Metaph.* Z17.1041b4–33 is evidently indebted to the *Theaetetus* (see the following Note).

[157] *Theaet.* 203ef. The agreement here reached seems to evaporate in the further course of the discussion. What matters is not whether Plato commits himself to this point of view but that the point of view arises in the context of his philosophy. See, further, for the relation of whole and parts *Soph.* 244eff. and *Parm.* 137c, 142cff.

[158] For the thought that in the *holon* each part must have its proper place (where it contributes to the preservation and well-being of the *holon*) see *Legg.* X,903b–d (904b). Other Platonic conceptions might be mentioned as implying this idea; what is essential for the *polis* is surely not that it has its classes but that each has its right "place" and that by their *harmonia* they form an organic whole. Cf. also *Phaedr.* 268d.

treating mixed substances as aggregates do not prove that Plato lacks the concept of organic unity but only that there were limits for its application. The intrinsic unity and homogeneity of mixtures form a special problem which Aristotle masters in *De generatione et corruptione*. Plato may not have known the answer—or may have thought it a mistake to raise the problem. But it was Plato who conceived of a whole as having beginning, middle, and end, and this is one of the ways in which Aristotle too defines the unity of a whole that has parts yet has each of them in its proper place and position.[159] For our more specific purpose it will suffice to say that, if an object is not properly defined by the enumeration of its parts, the association, i.e., the mechanical coming together, of its parts cannot be a satisfactory explanation of its *genesis*.

THE MUTUAL RELATION BETWEEN *GENESIS* AND MOVEMENT

The *Timaeus* does not include a systematic classification of all movements that could be compared with the catalogue of *Laws* X; nor does it offer a "theory" about the relationship between movement and becoming. Nevertheless by analyzing some sequences of thought we may learn a good deal about this subject. In the account of the receptacle *genesis* is not a form, a phase, or an upshot of movement. On the other hand, when the Forms have done their work and the receptacle is replete with fiery, watery, earthlike, and airlike entities, a motion arises both in these formations and in the receptacle itself.[160] This motion Plato traces to a lack of balance between the "powers" inherent in the new formations. The contents of the receptacle impart a swaying motion to it, and the receptacle, thus affected, in turn moves the contents and produces a separation of their four main varieties,

---

[159] *Parm.* 145a (cf. *Soph.* 244e); cf. Arist. *Metaph.* Δ21.1024a1ff.; *Poet.* 7.1450b27ff. The *Poetics* goes farther than other treatises in defining the mutual relationship between the "parts" of an organic whole; yet that the parts must be in their right place and be correctly "integrated" is a Platonic thought which, as a matter of fact, Plato himself applies to tragedy (*Phaedr.* 268a). In the systems of Empedocles and Anaxagoras ratio (which Aristotle calls λόγος τῆς μίξεως) figures as a principle of organization. This was possible because they were primarily interested in tissues and other "homogeneous" entities (ὁμοιομερῆ) in which each part has the same "organization" as a whole. Democritus' notion of *thesis* falls far short of organic oneness. To appreciate Aristotle's achievement it is not enough to remember that Form is for him a principle of organization. He also is the discoverer of functional unity, soul being for him the *entelecheia* of the body.

[160] *Tim.* 52d–53a.

with the result that each of them tends to take a place of its own.[161]
This physical movement, which points to, but does not fully establish,
a cosmic arrangement of the elements, is subsequent to *genesis*. Physical entities must have come into existence before they can begin to
move or display any kind of activity—or passivity.

From the mathematical *genesis* of the elements Plato must likewise
find his way to movement. When the basic triangles produce or "beget" pyramids and other solid figures,[162] we are not yet in the physical world or dealing with physical processes (which would require
movement). However, the mathematical lineage of the elements is also
meant to account for their behavior; for Plato immediately proceeds
to discuss their interaction, their effect upon one another, their mutual
destruction when they come into collision with one another, and finally
their re-formation in new shapes.[163] This is the way in which one
element turns into another. All these experiences of the elements are
determined by their geometrical nature. It does not take much imagination to realize that such interactions can take place only if there is
movement. Yet Plato throughout this section continues to ignore movement. He treats these actions of the elementary particles upon one
another as though they were due solely to their specific natures and
shapes.[164] Obviously he is anxious to settle the crucial problem regarding the change of elements into one another; and the geometrical differentiation of the elements, which they have brought along from
their *genesis*, stands him in good stead throughout this section. Nothing else seems to be needed. Finally—after clarifying one more point
which again relates to the "form" of the elements—Plato does bring
movement into the picture: "Concerning motion and rest, if we do
not agree in what manner and in what conditions they arise, many
difficulties will stand in the way of our subsequent reasoning." [165]
One may feel that even the preceding reasoning required some understanding of these matters. Actually the processes which Plato now—
after briefly indicating the origin of cosmic motion—explains with the

---

[161] 53a4–7. [162] 53c–55c.

[163] 56c8–57c6. This section at the end (57c1–6) refers to the points previously
made about the swaying motion in the receptacle and suggests that as soon as one
element has changed into another the new entity must also take up a new place
to which it is taken by that motion. Change of place and movement are here still
treated as subsequent to *genesis*.

[164] 57c1–6 (see Note 163) is not meant to describe a prior condition for their
mutual interactions and changes.

[165] 57d7ff. (Cornford's rendering); 57d7–58c4.

help of movement are essentially those that he has already explained without it, namely, the action of the elements upon each other and the transformations that result from such interaction. Again, we see aggregates of one element come into collision with those of another, and the result is the same kind of fight, mutual overpowering, and transformation that we have already witnessed. The difference is that we now know what makes the elements collide, i.e., what causes them to move against one another (some other changes of emphasis are likewise traceable to the new motif).[166] Through the introduction of movement the picture becomes more concrete and at the same time more convincing. To put it schematically, Plato has, for convenience of presentation, kept apart two causes that are simultaneously in operation. Changes from one element into another are possible owing to their specific form and nature; but this cause by itself would not suffice to bring these changes about. We also need the "source of movement" (Plato's procedure is similar in other parts of the dialogue where he for a while treats the teleological cause in isolation and then supplements this account by giving "necessity" its proper share).[167]

The specific movement which Plato here invokes as the cause of all cosmic changes is that which he always regards as the first and self-caused movement and the fountainhead of all others. What he actually says is that the cosmic movements are produced by the revolution of the outermost heaven; yet the reader of the *Timaeus* knows that this rotation is an activity and manifestation of the world soul.[168] Plato speaks of "the circuit [or revolution] of the whole" as having spherical form, "naturally wishing to come together upon itself" (scil., so as to preserve the spherical form), and thereby producing pressure on all

---

[166] 58a4ff. In the earlier section one element is pictured as surrounded by another (56e2, etc.); here the former is pressed or pushed against the latter. A new feature in our passage is the empty interstices between the particles. It is into them that the other element is pushed when a collision materializes, and it is easy to understand that Plato would reserve this feature for the section in which the cosmic elements are visualized as in movement.

[167] Cf. 46c7ff. with reference to what precedes and follows (46e6). In addition, Plato's general comment on his method (34b10ff.) may be recalled.

[168] 58a4ff. For the heavenly revolutions as movements of the world soul see 34b10-36d7. Although Plato does not now (58aff.) mention the world soul, the reference to the "circuit of the whole" suffices to link the derivative movements in the Cosmos with the first motion. Cornford's comment (*Cosmology*, 239), "The mover here is of that lower order which is itself moved and transmits motion to other things," seems to me to miss the point, nor does the "errant cause" extend to the heavenly movements. Cherniss is surely right (*Pl. and the Acad.*, 448ff.) in insisting that the world soul is here in operation.

that is inside it. As a result, the particles and aggregates of one element are forced to move against, past, and across those of another. The tendency of each element to gather in a cosmic region of its own is still active; in fact, we must look on the movement which the elements now perform as a continuation of that produced in the receptacle.[169] The world soul sees to it that the conditions for such movements never cease to exist, that the elements constantly meet, fight, and destroy one another. The victor transforms the vanquished enemy into his own form; and as soon as this has happened, the new formation must move to its proper cosmic place.[170]

If this section could be considered in isolation, we might infer that *genesis* is "posterior" to movement and presupposes it; for clearly if movement were not kept up in the Cosmos through action of the self-moving soul, the elements would have separated, each remaining forever in its own place, and nothing new would come into being. The *Phaedrus* teaches us to expect the same and if possible even worse results if the principle of movement should perish: all *genesis* would come to a standstill, and the entire Cosmos would fall in ruins. As long as we confine ourselves to the phenomenal world, the doctrines put for-

---

[169] That the triangles when recombined in another element must go to the region of this element has already been said in 57b7ff. and is here repeated in 58c1 (with the additional point that cosmic regions correspond to differences in size, scil., of the elementary particles). 57c3 still ties up with the swaying of the receptacle; yet that "cause" only separates the elements and does not thrust them together in constant interaction, which produces transformation and is in turn followed by movement of the newly formed element to its cosmic home (cf. 58a2–4).

[170] 58b4ff.; cf. Note 169. The operation of the soul as *arche* of movement is clearly limited to the *genesis* which materializes on the cosmic level and in the cosmic phase. Very specific and entirely satisfactory causes have been given for both *genesis* and movement in the noncosmic or precosmic condition of things, and no reader could be expected to draw the conclusion that an irrational element of the world soul is the real cause of what happens in the receptacle. Cornford's theory (*Cosmology*, 176, 203) is a harmonization or systematization of heterogeneous Platonic ideas for which Plato himself provides not the slightest encouragement. Cf. on the whole Gregory Vlastos, *Cl. Q.*, 33 (1939), 71ff., and also Hans Herter, *Rh. Mus.*, 104 (1957), 327ff. It is true that some passages in the *Laws* (X,891e5, 895b3ff., 896a6ff.) and perhaps also *Phaedr.* 245d8–c2 are hard to square with the idea of first motions not caused by soul, and in spite of some very sound arguments by which Vlastos (*Cl. Q.*, 33: 78ff., 81) makes the discrepancy less formidable or more intelligible, it still is there and can perhaps not be removed. On the whole it probably is true that the *genesis* which Plato in *Laws* X has in mind is not meant to include precosmic events. But I should rather accept inconsistencies of the kind between two (or three) different works than resort to a hypothesis as dubious in itself, and in its appropriateness to the question, as the irrational motion of the world soul.

ward in the section of the *Theaetetus* where everything is handed over
to movement and sensation remain valid: movement is basic, and becoming, which presupposes it, secondary (that section, in fact, includes
a reference to the movement of the heavenly circumference as the
great "preserver" of all life). Thinking along physical lines, Aristotle
may well say that in the temporal sequence *genesis* is later than local
movement.[171] But this is obviously only one way of looking at the situation, and Aristotle himself does not subscribe to it wholeheartedly.
As an antidote to it, the account of the receptacle brings home to us
that if no physical objects had come into existence there would be nothing to move (or be moved) toward creating new formations.[172] The
genesis that requires movement is not primeval but a secondary type.
Moreover, this movement can have its effects only because physical
entities have come into being from principles of a higher order into
which they can again resolve. Thus from a logical or metaphysical point
of view *genesis* is, after all, prior to movement. Another inference is
even more important. Of the two cardinal phenomena in the physical
world neither can be completely resolved into the other. One has its
arche in the Forms, the other in the self-moving soul. *Genesis* may in
the *Laws* be included in the catalogue of movements, in the *Theaetetus*
be treated as a product of movement, in the *Parmenides* be analyzed
after the pattern of movement,[173] and finally here in the *Timaeus* once
more causally linked to movement; it yet preserves its essential "otherness." If Plato's predecessors needed movement to bring things into
existence, yet also eternal physical principles for their formation and
composition, the *Timaeus* shows us the same dualism, with the important difference that the physical principles themselves now have a
genesis. The fact that Plato "separates" the two aspects in his account,
doing justice first to the one, then to the other, merely serves to bring
the dualism into focus.[174]

[171] Plato *Phaedr.* 245d7 and *Theaet.* 153cf.; Arist. *Phys.* VIII,7, esp. 260b26ff., 29ff.
[172] Thus far, as a matter of fact, Aristotle too is prepared to go (*Phys.* VIII,7.
260b30ff.), though on the whole the reasons which in Plato could secure *genesis*
its priority no longer exist for him. As we shall see later, Aristotle is confronted
with the problem of preserving for *genesis*—even for absolute *genesis*—the reality
and some of the status that Plato had given it, although the assumptions on which
Plato had proceeded are no longer valid.
[173] *Legg.* X,893a1; *Parm.* 157a2.
[174] The formation of the world soul (*Tim.* 34cff.) is so utterly different in character that it would be pointless to mention it in this connection. The most that
might be said is that here, too, the *genesis* of an entity reveals its nature and the
principles to which it owes its being.

Part Two

ARISTOTLE'S *PHYSICS*

3

Introductory Remarks

IT was decisive for Aristotle's philosophical future that he participated in the life of the Academy during a period in which the problems of movement and becoming acquired greater philosophical interest.[1] This was a development to which he felt able to make contributions; here he saw a possibility of laying firm foundations for his own philosophical outlook. As far as we know, none of Aristotle's fellow workers in the Academy responded to this phase of Plato's philosophy with the same productive energy and the same enthusiasm.

Genesis and movement were by now in all probability subjects of good standing; yet Aristotle went farther and soon also attacked questions of more specific character, such as the stratification of the Cosmos. The system of nature and the Cosmos which Plato had presented in the *Timaeus* had its philosophical *points d'appui* and embraced subjects unquestionably relevant for the more "serious" pursuits of the Academy. Still, to carry the explanation of natural processes and formations to such length as Plato here did was an enterprise about which even its author could not conceal misgivings. Compared with truly philosophical studies, this field promised only a limited harvest; more than "likelihood" could not be claimed for the results; and in spite of the immense labor that must have gone into them, Plato speaks repeatedly of these investigations in a slightly disparaging vein, offering what amounts to apologies for engaging in this kind of pastime.

Some of Plato's outstanding pupils may have agreed that apologies

---

[1] Cf. Jaeger, *Aristotle*, 15: "In order to understand Aristotle . . . it is important not to set out from the vague notion of 'Plato' as a whole but to substitute the precise conception of his last period . . . that began about 369."

were in order; willing as they were to follow the master into the intricacies of the doctrine of Forms (or into his theory of soul and other genuinely philosophical concerns), they may well have thought of the larger part of the *Timaeus* as labor expended on a *corpus vile*. For Aristotle, on the contrary, physical research seems never to have carried a stigma of inferior standing. Investigations of the kind are entirely legitimate and respectable; there was no need to preface them with a word of justification. That persistent thinking and correct reasoning, if applied to these matters, should fall short of conclusive results is a worry which he leaves to others. He moves ahead with confidence, untroubled by epistemological doubts or hesitations.

It may be argued that the *Physics* itself remains on a rather high level of generality and seldom descends to specific statements about the phenomena of the Cosmos. Clearly the *Meteorologica*, to say nothing of the biological and psychophysical treatises, shows a much more persistent concern with the explanation of such items. Yet even the *Physics* stays within the area of perishable phenomena; it clarifies concepts applicable only to these, and it deals with conditions and characteristics of physical objects without contrasting them with the properties of things eternal. The world of Forms, whether still acknowledged or not, is no longer as in the *Timaeus* the background from which the happenings in the physical realm are set off. The discussion of place does not need realities that are not in place as a foil for those that are. Time can be understood without reference to eternity. This may be departmentalization, but it is actually more, and more also than a method or even a habit of mind. It carries with it a certain autonomy for the subject thus treated.

We have made an attempt to distinguish between "physical" and "cosmological" topics. Physics crystallized through the discussion and the questioning of some vital concepts that had been implied or taken for granted in the beginnings of cosmology. A clear understanding of these concepts and of their legitimate and illegitimate use had become a prior condition for new ventures. The number of such concepts had lately increased. *Genesis*, which had been discarded much longer than movement, had finally been reclaimed and recognized as something essential. The relation of place and time to physical objects or events had been defined with profound care. Different kinds of causes had come to be distinguished, and their difference and mutual relations were now a subject which demanded precedence over the investigation of specific causes, whether in cosmology or anywhere else. Plato had put his finger on an ambiguity of grave consequences in the concept of *physis*. Other schools which Aristotle would not allow himself to ignore regarded the void as an indispensable assumption if movement and other changes that presuppose movement were to materialize in the Universe. It is easy to see that none of these topics would have its proper place in a cosmological treatise, and even the Infinite, though for long closely connected with cosmology (and though actually taken up in the *De caelo*), had aspects that required its discussion in more generalized terms and in a more general and basic treatise. Yet contentions like those here put forward perhaps beg a question as long as we do not know the root problem of Aristotle's own cosmology.

One might wonder why Aristotle did not, like Empedocles and others, include the simple bodies or elements among the subjects to be settled before more specialized inquiries might begin. The *Physics* never identifies these prime realities of the "visible" world, nor does it make significant statements regarding their nature or number. By and large it assumes their existence and identity. When dealing with *genesis* in the *Physics*, Aristotle considers it in terms so general that another study is needed to explain the kind of *genesis* which should be of primary concern to an explorer of the physical world. This study, embodied in the *De generatione et corruptione*, covers the formation and transformation of the sublunary elements; it also derives and identifies them. This may go some way toward solving our problem, yet it is certainly not the complete answer.

Although Aristotle's *Physics* has reached us as a unit, it does not possess a high degree of intrinsic unity, and among the various meanings of "the one" that Aristotle himself knows and distinguishes none would readily fit its present condition. Surely it would not be wise to carry speculations of this kind very far; even his stipulation that, for things to form a continuum, the end of one part must coincide with the beginning of the next [2] would furnish us only with a very extrinsic unity. In some instances there is no transition at all from one part of the work to the next, and at the beginning of the "second half," i.e., in the opening sentences of Book V, we find neither a link with the preceding inquiries nor anything in the nature of the usual statements about the subject to be treated or about the reasons which recommend it for study. Books V–VIII are a "relatively" coherent treatment of one sub-

[2] *Phys.* V,3.227a11; VI,1.231a23 *et al.*

ject—the subject of movement or physical change. There are good reasons for thinking that this study of movement originally formed an independent treatise.[3] Evidently when this treatise was combined with the other four books, no attempt was made to supply a connection; one may even suspect that the original "introduction" of the treatise "On Movement" was sacrificed. Books I–IV, whose subject we may, as a matter of convenience, describe as fundamental physical concepts, include a brief inquiry into movement which arrives at a definition of this phenomenon; yet this inquiry never refers to a much fuller study to come.[4] Clearly movement was one of the fundamental concepts in the realm of physics—nature itself is in Book II defined as a principle of movement [5]—and thus claimed consideration also in this set of books. But the fundamental importance of movement also required that it be singled out for the most thoroughgoing analysis and a scrutiny of all its ramifications and philosophically relevant aspects.

In the earlier set of books the first, being an investigation of the basic physical principles, stands somewhat apart.[6] The other three appear to be unified by the idea that since nature is a principle of movement the Infinite, place, the void, and time must be defined because each of them may throw light on the nature of movement.[7] In fact, Aristotle, while dealing with these concepts in III and IV, keeps movement within sight. This will not surprise us after we have seen that in the late Platonic Academy movement had become the key phenomenon of nature. Its transcendent importance now makes itself felt in every phase of physical inquiry. The justification which Aristotle offers for linking up the study of these problematic concepts (Books III and IV) with that of nature itself (Book II) may have been given *ex post*.[8] But while

---

[3] Book IV has an "end" (224a15–17), yet V goes very brusquely *in medias res*, and nothing has prepared us for the very comprehensive investigation of *metabole*. I speak of "relative" coherence because the relation of Book VII as well as of VIII to the preceding books presents some problems. These will be considered below, in Ch. 10.

[4] III,1–3. Although this section never refers to the discussion of movement in V–VII, the latter set of books utilizes the definition of movement as *energeia* which is here provided (III,1.201a9ff.). This will be seen in detail later; at present it suffices to refer to V,1.224b10.

[5] II,1.192b8ff.   [6] Cf. Ross, *Physics*, "Introduction," 5ff.

[7] See III,1.200b15. Here also the first account of movement itself which Aristotle gives in III,1–3 is justified with reference to the definition of nature (*ibid.*, 1.200b12).

[8] A. Mansion, in *Introduction à la physique arist.* (2d ed.; Louvain and Paris, 1945), 51, infers from the connection which the subjects of Books III and IV have

nature, movement, place, time, and the Infinite may originally have been investigated each by itself, the connection which we find in Book IV between place and the void is an organic one.[9] In fact, Aristotle was probably the first to treat these two subjects with reference to each other, and it would be arbitrary to suppose that this connection came to him as an afterthought. On the whole, however, it seems legitimate to study by itself each of the major subjects now incorporated in the *Physics*, giving little attention to the tenuous link between one topic and another.[10]

---

with the phenomenon of *kinesis* that these books belong to the second part of the *Physics*, i.e., form a unit with V–VIII. For the reasons indicated in the text I am unable to accept this suggestion.

[9] IV,6; see below, the "Digression" to Ch. 6.

[10] As regards the date of composition, I am fully satisfied that Jaeger, *Aristotle*, 295ff., and Ross, *Physics*, "Introduction," 6ff., rightly assign the origin of Books I–VII to the early, i.e., presumably the Academic, period of Aristotle's philosophy. The possibility of a later revision cannot be excluded, but I have found no reason for believing that it was substantial.

4

Genesis

AS we know that *genesis* after a long period of disgrace had finally been rehabilitated by Plato, we may wonder whether Aristotle's discussion still reflects the problematic status of this concept. We shall see that it does so in a certain degree, yet perhaps it is characteristic that Aristotle in the *Physics* sees no need for a frontal attack on this delicate question. What must be settled in the *Physics,* and in fact at the very beginning of it, is the nature of the basic physical principles. But soon enough it becomes clear that this subject and the controversial reality of *genesis* have become so thoroughly interlocked that it is impossible to discuss the one without giving attention to the other.

As Aristotle knows, the thinker responsible for this situation is Parmenides. If all things are one and thus "the one" is the only principle, not only would it be futile to look for a plurality of principles but there would also be no physical world of which they could be principles. For the conception of a physical world must include a plurality of things and must allow for changes, movements, and mutual transformations between them. "For the principle is the principle of something or some things. . . . Let it be our basic assumption that of things that are by nature either all or some are in motion." [1] On the whole the refutation of Parmenides operates with logical and "metaphysical" rather than with physical arguments. It concentrates on developing the different meanings of "the one," which once grasped can be used as a solvent for this massive and undifferentiated concept. [2]

[1] *Phys.* I,2.185a4, 12.
[2] For differentiations of the kind as applied to the concept of being see 185a20ff., of "the one" 185b5ff. There is no need here to go into the details of Aristotle's refutation of Parmenides or Melissus.

That the Parmenidean "one" excludes *genesis* and vetoes "not-being" becomes more acute when Aristotle moves on from the examination of Parmenides' doctrine to those of his successors. With some exaggeration Aristotle refers to the canon "nothing can come to be out of not-being" as the "common opinion of the physicists" and remarks that they turned *genesis* either into qualitative change or into association and dissociation.[3]

A glance at the later treatise *On Coming to Be* strengthens our impression that here are three problems so closely intertwined that it is very difficult to discuss one of them without at the same time taking account of the others. These problems are the reality of *genesis*, the question of not-being, and the nature and number of the physical principles.[4] In *Physics* I, as has already been said, Aristotle's primary interest is to lay secure foundations for his theory of principles. To this subject we shall return; at present we are anxious to see how Aristotle himself can come to terms with the long-disqualified concepts of not-being and *genesis*. If, as he seems to imply, the Presocratics capitulated before Parmenides' condemnation[5] of these concepts, from what *locus standi* can he himself defy this condemnation?

As one may expect, he can defy it with the help of a new distinction. In every process of coming into being there are two senses in which the product may be said to come "out of" something different. There is the substratum (or "matter") which persists in the process yet takes on a new form, and there is the previous condition of this substratum from which a change takes place into the new. The typical situation is change from "privation" to "form" (e.g., from not-white to white). Substratum, privation, and form are the three principles.[6] As form and privation are opposites, privation is in fact a "not-being," and in this sense it is, Aristotle admits, quite correct to say that in passing from privation to form something comes to be out of "not-being." Actually,

---

[3] I,4.187a12ff.; see esp. 26ff., 34f.

[4] See *De gen. et corr.* I,3; II,1–3. It is true, however, that the problem of not-being in this treatise recedes into the background and is no longer acute when Aristotle explains the *genesis* of (and out of) the elements in Book II.

[5] See Note 2. Aristotle does not here mention Parmenides by name. For the later Presocratics (i.e., for those after Parmenides) his description of the philosophical situation is correct; he refers in particular to Empedocles and Anaxagoras (187a22ff.), though he also mentions Anaximander, and his generalized statements would seem to suggest that all physicists made it their concern to steer clear of "not-being."

[6] I,5–7.

however, that which passes from privation to form is the substratum. This is present and remains so; it has not the quality of "not-being"— not in this context at least—and if we focus on this aspect of the process, we should not speak of the new product as coming into being from "not-being." Aristotle goes to the length of describing this aspect of becoming as essential and the other as accidental.[7] As long, however, as the passing from "not-being" to being is merely an accidental feature and does not touch the essence of becoming, we need not be afraid of it, and the reason why the later Presocratics worried so much about it is simply that they did not perceive the difference between what is essential and what is accidental.[8]

Aristotle has no intention of reintroducing absolute *genesis*. For him, too, the substratum persists; in this respect nothing entirely new comes into existence. To be sure, his concept of a substratum which persists and only receives form would enable him to reject the Presocratic theory that the formation of a physical entity is a process of association, its disappearance one of dissociation; yet at present he is not interested in this.[9] What he wishes to do is to clear *genesis* of the stigma which attached to it (and which kept the later Presocratics from using this concept) and to show where and how not-being enters into this process.

It is true that the relation of the substratum to being is not without problems. Aristotle himself discusses it in terms reminiscent of what

[7] 8.191a33–b16.

[8] 191b10ff. Aristotle realizes that by disposing of the possibility that coming to be presupposes not-being he opens the door to the alternative possibility of being coming from being. Yet the second horn of Parmenides' dilemma frightens him as little as the first. He is determined to destroy the Parmenidean position root and branch and therefore goes on to show the fallacy also of this notion. The argument which he uses is, however, somewhat obscure (191b17–27). His point is again that what comes into existence may well have the quality of being yet again only accidentally. What, then, is it primarily and essentially? Presumably an individual object. Being is as little essential to it as animal would be to a dog produced by another dog. This dog does not come into being qua animal. The coming into being of animal would be quite a different process (e.g., I suppose, the formation of animal from mud or moistened earth, perhaps also from seed or egg). My interpretation diverges slightly from Ross's (*Physics*, "Introduction," 23, and commentary on 191b29) and A. Mansion's (*Introduction à la physique arist.* [2d ed.; Louvain-Paris, 1945], 76). Text and interpretation have both suffered from a disturbance of the former which Ross has eliminated; even Simplicius' explanation is affected by it.

[9] On an argument of the kind in *De gen. et corr.* see below, Ch. 16.

Plato said about the receptacle.[10] This will presently help us to trace connections between Plato's and Aristotle's doctrine of *genesis*. It is important that even though the substratum may not have full being [11] no connotations of not-being are allowed to come near its nature. Not-being is definitely associated with privation. In the Platonic "triad" of the *Timaeus* the entity that co-operates with the receptacle is the eternal Forms. It is a measure of Aristotle's distance from Plato that instead of the Forms he uses a concept which can bear the quality—and the burden—of not-being. That the Forms themselves are eliminated from Aristotle's discussion is highly significant, yet for the moment we may acquiesce in the notion that their possible reality and supposed function are a subject not for *Physics* but for the "First Philosophy."

Quite patently *genesis* is tied to not-being. With an iron bond Parmenides had fastened these concepts to one another and banished both from philosophical discourse.[12] Among his successors Empedocles offers the most outspoken testimony for this insoluble connection; he clearly eschews *genesis* because it carries not-being with it.[13] When Anaxagoras says that all that comes to pass in the physical world is "mixing" (and unmixing) of "being things," [14] the point of his statement is that neither *genesis* nor "not-being" has any place in these processes. Thus whoever brings back *genesis* must either show how he can account for it without not-being—which Plato does by introducing the receptacle [15] —or choose the place of not-being so carefully that there is no room left for the dreaded indictment: you make something arise from nothing. Precisely this is what Aristotle attempted. Thanks to his substratum he can confidently maintain that in the essential sense *genesis* does not come to pass out of not-being. This suffices here where the fundamental issue has to be settled. More specific points will be made in the treatise *On Coming to Be* where Aristotle shows that all elements have the same substratum and that the change from one element into another does not involve the arising of something new that previously "was not." For whenever, say, a certain amount of water comes into being, it does so because at the same time a corresponding amount of air passes away,

[10] 7.191a7ff.; see below, pp. 118–123.   [11] See 191a8ff., 192a5ff.
[12] See *Vorsokr.*, 28B12ff., 20.   [13] *Ibid.*, 31B12, 13, 15.
[14] *Ibid.*, 59B17.
[15] The receptacle is an ἀμυδρὸν εἶδος (*Tim.* 49a3), and its kind of being is very peculiar, yet Plato definitely affirms that it "is" (esp. 52d3, also a8). With the "great and small," matters are different (cf. *Phys.* I,9.192a6ff.).

and what really happens is that the one underlying substratum passes from the condition of air into that of water.[16] This would prove again that *genesis* need not be *genesis* out of not-being. However, as has been said, the fundamental investigation of the *Physics* does not stoop to such details; instead it treats the concept of becoming in the most generalized fashion, setting up principles of a much more comprehensive nature than the cosmic elements.

We must cast one more glance at the Presocratic systems from which Aristotle has inherited the connection of *genesis* with not-being. Determined as they were to exclude not-being completely from their accounts, thinkers such as Empedocles and Anaxagoras composed all substances from principles that they regarded as "being." In all historical probability they never made as clear-cut and explicit a distinction as Aristotle between a substratum (or underlying matter) and the previous condition from which "being things" pass into new formations. Still, in their less sophisticated way they took care of both aspects. For they definitely tell us out of what entities any given substance is composed: it is made up of "being" entities, whether elements, powers, or atoms, that in each instance are present in a specific mixture. And they also make clear that these entities pass from one state of mixture into another. The same elements that some time ago made up a plant are now combined in an animal; the same powers that were found in the food now constitute a tissue. Thus they pass from one temporary arrangement to another, and the only difference of status that matters is between the eternity of the principles which enter into these combinations and the temporary nature of the combinations themselves. Yet temporary arrangements are certainly not the same as a state of "not-being"; it would clearly be absurd to suggest that by comparison to the animal which the elements are going to form the plant in which they found themselves antecedently combined had no being.

Processes of this kind would not point toward the concept of "privation" either. How, then, does Aristotle manage to find a place for privation and for not-being? Is the kind of *genesis* that he has in mind so utterly different as to make any comparison with the Presocratic schemes nugatory? His favorite instances are the passing of something from black (i.e., not-white) to white or the passing of a person from

---

[16] See *De gen.* I.3,318a23ff., also 319a5. For the *hyle* concept of this treatise and its relation to the cosmic elements see II.1,329a24ff. and the further development in chs. 2ff. Cf. Mansion, *op.cit.*, 75.

an uncultured to a cultured condition.[17] This is a "becoming," if for no other reason than that the Greek language uses the verb "to become" in such connections. Yet it is indeed clear that Aristotle has given the subject of *genesis* a completely new turn and here discusses it from a point of view which would never have suggested itself to the Presocratics.[18] How, then, can he make contact with their problem of *genesis?* The answer is that in Book I of the *Physics* he makes no contact and that it is again left to the treatise *On Coming to Be* to decide how "not-being" can be found in physical elements.[19] In Book I of the *Physics* Aristotle, it can hardly be denied, has departed from the beaten track and treats *genesis* in a radically different sense of the word which allows not-being to appear in it, albeit "accidentally" and without affecting its reality or validity.

Moreover, the not-being which thus establishes itself in the process is a new variety of this concept. It is a logical not-being. White is the contrary of nonwhite, uncultured that of cultured. There are as many possibilities for "not-being" as there are contraries. Parmenides' not-being has been split and broken down from one absolute into countless relative "not-beings." We may recall how the massive unity of Parmenides' concept is similarly broken in Plato's *Sophist;* and in spite of Plato's entirely different purpose we may imagine that Plato's precedent encouraged similar encroachments upon the once forbidden ground. However, the logical instruments employed by Aristotle bear no resemblance to those which Plato brought to his attack. In fact, one may say that Aristotle's claims are comparatively modest. He does not contemplate anything so ambitious as setting up a genus of being which should comprehend all instances of not-being but merely points out that on his view of the matter not-being has a smallish share in the process of

---

[17] E.g., I,5.188a35ff., 7.189b34ff., 190a16ff., and *passim.* It is curious that in I,6.189a13 Aristotle justifies his assumption of two, and no more, contraries by saying that substance is one category and that in each category there is only one contrariety. This may give the impression that he would allow another pair of contraries for, say, quality and quantity. Yet nothing comes of this possibility. Soon he remembers again that substance has no contrary (a32). In fact, it is difficult to explain the *genesis* of substance in terms of contraries.

[18] Or to Plato, when he is concerned with physical theory.

[19] See below, Ch. 16. Mansion (*op.cit.*, 75), although recognizing that *On Coming to Be* offers important supplements to the *Physics*, seems to me to simplify Aristotle's relation to his predecessors and to underrate the difficulty of bringing Aristotle's doctrine to bear on the subjects of Presocratic thought (see esp. p. 78 where he speaks of Aristotle's doctrine as "apte à remplacer," "les naïves spéculations des Ioniens," "vu qu'elle porte sur le même objet").

genesis. Resting his case primarily on the substratum, he can declare that not-being figures only "accidentally" in the process (on the other hand, where he worries about the logical difficulties of producing being from being he argues similarly that being is accidentally involved but that other aspects or characters of the producing entity are the essential ones).[20] Earlier in this book while criticizing Parmenides, Aristotle brings out the difference between being and being something.[21] Correspondingly his own doctrine of *genesis* is here concerned with "becoming something" rather than with becoming pure and simple, with the copulative meaning of the verb rather than with the existential.

The extent to which Aristotle with this theory has set himself apart from the tradition will be apparent when he finds himself face to face with inherited problems. To explain the *genesis* of the elements out of one another as changes from contrary to contrary is far from easy. For not only do the elements not stand to one another in the relation of contraries but also it is Aristotle's very firm conviction that substance can never be the contrary of substance.[22] Yet what kind of *genesis* could be more important and more in need of clarification than the *genesis* of substances? As Aristotle himself says, "While other things become this or that, it is only substances that come to be simply" (ἁπλῶς γίγνεσθαι). Doubtless the theory of physical transformation will eventually master these difficulties by declaring that when water turns into air or fire into water the actual change takes place between their "qualities," hot giving way to cold or dry to moist.[23] These qualities are contraries, and thus contraries are indeed the poles between which *genesis* materializes. And in the realm of biology *genesis* out of "not-being" may apply inasmuch as the seed is the animal only potentially, but actually *not* the animal (a point of view to which Aristotle resorts more readily in the *Metaphysics* than in his actual biological treatises). In Book I of the *Physics* potentiality is briefly mentioned as a possible alternative solution for the problem of "*genesis* out of not-being." [24]

[20] I,8.191a34ff.; esp. b13–17, b17–27 (I accept Ross's text and explanation, although difficulties remain, particularly in b15f.).

[21] See *Soph.* 256cff.; Arist. *Phys.* I,3.186b2ff., b14f.

[22] On the strength of this doctrine Aristotle decides in *Phys.* V,2 that *genesis* cannot be a "movement," arguing that movement must be from opposite to opposite, whereas substance—the product of *genesis*—has no opposite. The *locus classicus* for the doctrine is *Categ.* 5.3b24. For a very early application of it in the dialogue *Eudemus* see Jaeger, *Aristotle*, 41. For other evidence cf. Bonitz, 544a60ff. Note *Phys.* I,6.189a32.

[23] I,7.190a32ff. See below, Ch. 17.

[24] In *Phys.* I,8.191b27ff. it is said that the concept of potentiality could remove

Perhaps the solutions of these difficulties were clearly present to
Aristotle's mind when in *Physics* I he worked out his theory that *genesis* comes to pass between contraries. Perhaps he was all the more
pleased with his theory because he knew that by one device or another
it could be made applicable to the concrete problems of *genesis*. Nevertheless it is hard to believe that the theory was actually devised for
these problems. Why, then, and for what purpose did Aristotle devise
it? Because *genesis* of contraries from contraries provided a handy
weapon in the fight against Parmenides' not-being? A reader of Book
I will hardly get the impression that this is Aristotle's main objective.
The solution inherent in the doctrine of contraries is welcomed, but to
think that Aristotle constructed the entire theory with a view of using
it against Parmenides would mean to discount all specific arguments
by which Aristotle endeavors to establish it. His principal argument
is a "historical" one. Whatever specific doctrines the earlier thinkers
advanced, all of them "meant" to have *genesis* take place between contraries. All that he himself does is to bring a philosophical development
to its logical conclusion, to render explicit a doctrine and a purpose that
had been implicit in all earlier systems.[25] Fortunately it is not necessary
for us here to follow him into his interpretation of the Presocratic systems. The manipulations by which he makes the Presocratics yield the
most welcome results have already been pointed out by others.[26] Contemporary students of early Greek philosophy may even feel that they
could select better illustrations of the "contraries" or (to call them by
their usual name) "opposites" from the cosmological systems of the
Presocratics. Still, Parmenides' "hot" and "cold" are pertinent, and so
are (Anaximenes'?) "dense" and "rare." [27] The opposites were not only
present but fundamental in Presocratic cosmology.[28] The former is all
that Aristotle says; the latter he may be held to imply by calling them
principles (*archai*). He does not contend that in the earlier systems the
contraries come to be out of one another directly; rather when he has

---

the difficulties inherent in "*genesis* out of not-being." Yet other arguments—reported above, pp. 75–76—are developed at greater length, and Aristotle appears to
set more store by them here, since they keep closer to his new doctrine of *genesis*.

[25] See I,5.188a19ff. in connection with ch. 4. Note also 188b27–30.

[26] See esp. Cherniss, *Presocr.*, 50ff.

[27] 188a20, 22. The opposites have an important place in Parmenides' "Way of
Opinion" (see 28B8.56ff.). To this extent Aristotle is right and Cherniss' comment
"when he [Aristotle] is hunting for contrarieties he finds them even in the Eleatic
doctrine" (*Presocr.*, 53) is not quite to the point.

[28] For a study of the Presocratics which stresses this motif in particular see
Fränkel, *Dichtg. u. Philos.*, 341ff., 349, 440, 465, and *passim*.

shown that in addition to them a substratum is needed he tries to find this concept as well anticipated in Presocratic thought.[29] Undoubtedly he is guilty of simplification, undue generalization, and indeed also of indifference toward much that ought to figure in a complete survey of Presocratic "principles," yet not of an outrageous misconstruction of his own historical position. What mainly separates him from his precursors is that his contraries have no materiality, no independent existence, and no independent power; in fact, they are no longer "powers." They now are tied to a substratum and enable this substratum to become "something." Their active role, their life and death struggle, even what Aristotle himself calls their capacity for acting and suffering,[30] are gone. At best they are a shadow of their former selves—although in the treatise *On Coming to Be* they will show themselves able to regain something of their former status. These differences do not necessarily invalidate Aristotle's historical deduction of his own position, yet it seems easier to suppose that Aristotle read his own doctrine into earlier systems (which implies that he already had it) than that he actually constructed it from a careful study of the Presocratic cosmologies. However, his "historical" studies may have confirmed him in his inclination.

Thus far Aristotle's motives have eluded us, yet we need not lose heart. It may be a mistake to consider the doctrine of *genesis* out of contraries, as we have done, in isolation from other tenets. Is it relevant that according to Aristotle all changes take place between opposites? Book V applies this point of view to local movement, qualitative change, and growth and decrease.[31] The relation between *genesis* and these other changes poses a problem which will engage our attention in a later chapter.[32] Anticipating some of our conclusions, we may say that although the other changes are species of "movement" *genesis* is in principle not in this class. Yet this principle is repeatedly broken, and *genesis* is often treated from the same points of view and subjected to the same laws as the three species of movement. If *genesis* is not a movement, it is certainly a "change" (*metabole*), and all changes have certain common characteristics. Thus it would be possible that Aristotle

---

[29] *Phys.* I,6.189b2–16.

[30] See in this connection 189a22: ἀπορήσειε ἄν τις πῶς ἢ ἡ πυκνότης τὴν μανότητα ποιεῖν τι πέφυκε ἢ αὕτη τὴν πυκνότητα (note the abstract nouns and also the choice of "powers" for which this relationship is much harder to visualize than, e.g., for hot and cold).

[31] V,1.2; see, e.g., 224b35ff., 226a25.   [32] See below, the first section of Ch. 9.

applies to *genesis* a principle that he has found valid in the case of all
other changes and that he does so regardless of the awkward consequences.[33] The fact that the principle causes less difficulty elsewhere
may be in favor of regarding its application to *genesis* as secondary.

This can hardly be the whole story, however. So far we have left
Plato out of account, a serious omission and the more so because a
passage in the *Phaedo* has been indicated by Professor Cherniss as the
source of Aristotle's doctrine. We have already seen that this dialogue
establishes several very important propositions about *genesis*. In one
section Plato speaks of *genesis* of the large from the small, or the smaller
from the larger, the worse from the better, etc., and on the strength of
such instances comes forward with the proposition that "all things that
have an opposite come to be from their opposite." [34] In a later passage
where the point must be expressed more precisely Plato makes clear
that not opposites (in the sense of opposite Forms) change into one
another, but things "having the opposites" change from the one opposite
to the other.[35] Here we can indeed find Form, an opposite Form, and,
with some stretching of the term, also substratum. If the "substratum"
in Plato is far from amorphous, it may be countered that in Aristotle's
scheme, too, completely formless matter represents an extreme case
(what changes, e.g., from nonwhite to white or from uncultured to
cultured is, after all, man, something that should not be altogether
amorphous). As for the opposites, we may note that when they became
Forms they lost their power of direct communication—change, interaction, etc.—with one another.

There can be no serious doubt that these passages in the *Phaedo* embody the germ of Aristotle's doctrine. Whether they are its actual
source is another question. On the whole it is reasonable to think that
the day-to-day discussions within the Academy inspired Aristotle more
directly than the study of dialogues which reflected an earlier stage of
Plato's thought. This view, however sound, leaves room for exceptions,
and where agreement between a relatively early dialogue and Aristotle's
thought is as close as in this instance, the exception may well have materialized. The real problem, it seems, is that the passages in the *Phaedo*

[33] It is on account of a different orientation that Aristotle in Book V. (4.229b10)
denies the presence of two contraries in *genesis*. He also emphasizes that substance
has no contrary (225b10, etc.); yet, as we have observed, this does not worry him
in Book I.

[34] *Phaedo* 70eff. (esp. e4ff.). See above, pp. 22–23.

[35] *Phaedo* 102b5ff., 103b. Cf. Cherniss, *Pl. and the Acad.*, 90ff., 95.

are not Plato's final word on the phenomenon of *genesis*. When in later dialogues he comes back to the subject, his primary concern is to establish a connection between becoming and being. *Genesis* may be understood as a function of the Forms, or the *genesis* of a physical body may be traced to mathematical entities of higher ontological status than the body itself. In the *Timaeus* alone we have found three approaches to *genesis*, each differing from the others in details as well as in general orientation and none of them operating with the opposites.[36] We may add that in his lectures "On the Good" Plato appears to have constructed the numbers from a meeting of "the one" and the great and small. If the former represents being, the latter two not-being, this would mean that Plato was here concerned with the problem of not-being, and though in the *Physics* Aristotle is investigating the principles not of numbers but of physical objects, it is not astonishing that he mentions this Platonic doctrine among the historical antecedents of his own.[37] All told, the problem of *genesis* had in the years while Aristotle was a member of the Academy taken on many new forms and developed new implications, and if Aristotle really, as it might seem, reverts to an earlier state of Plato's doctrine, he must have done so for specific reasons which we should try to find out.

Although the *Timaeus* does not actually in any of its discussions of *genesis* make use of the opposites, it does embody some rather interesting references to them. Clearly what works upon the receptacle when it becomes pregnant is the Forms. Yet there must be some point—even if the point is not immediately evident—to Plato's statement that although the receptacle deserves the designation "this" or "that" "we must not apply these words to something qualitative [τὸ ὁποιονοῦν], like hot or white or any of the opposites, and whatever consists of them." [38] These opposites are of the same kind as those with which Aristotle likes to operate—also, to be sure, as those instanced in the *Phaedo*—and it is hard to resist the impression that in some way and from some point of view they contribute to the formation of elements in the receptacle. As we have seen in an earlier chapter,[39] Cornford went very far in developing these "hints" of a physical theory of *genesis* which to him seemed

---

[36] See above, pp. 40–56.

[37] I,9.191b35ff.; cf. 3.187a1. Ross in his commentary on the former passage refers to *Metaph.* N2.1088b35ff.

[38] *Tim.* 50a2ff.; see above, p. 43 n.91, for my discussion of Cherniss' understanding of the pasasge.

[39] Above, pp. 43–45 and n.94.

even to take precedence over the metaphysical. If we cannot follow him in this attempt, we may yet agree that underneath Plato's metaphysical account there are suggestions of a "physical" approach. Nowhere in this section does Plato allow this "physical" motif to become dominant, though he alludes to it once again when he says: "We must not call the mother and receptacle of all that has become visible or in any way sense-perceived earth or air or fire or water nor any of the things that come into being out of them or out of which they have come into being."[40] The things "out of which" phenomenal elements come into being must once more be the opposites. The receptacle, which endures, changes from one opposite which enters to the other.[41] For Plato the true begetter of whatever comes to be and partakes of *genesis* is the Forms. Aristotle need not have thrown them overboard when in the first book of the *Physics* he develops a doctrine of *genesis* which, generally speaking, ignores the Platonic status of the Forms as much as the function which Plato had given them in his scheme of becoming. Their reality is simply not up for discussion now. A good and truly physical theory of *genesis*, Aristotle here shows, can be worked out without settling, nay, without even touching on questions regarding their status.[42] It can be done by developing those aspects of *genesis* which Plato, though aware of them, minimized—deeming a few brief allusions to be sufficient—when he described becoming as brought about by the Forms.[43] Yet even if Aristotle's intention was not so much to cast doubt on the reality of the Platonic Forms as to operate in this particular instance without them, a concept which is not used tends to become useless and a hypothesis which can be dispensed with loses some of its prestige and attraction.[44]

[40] *Tim.* 51a4ff.; see Note 39. [41] See 50e1–4.

[42] In the section of the *Phaedo* which may be compared the Forms are transcendent—but also immanent. Plato has a way of referring to the "greatness in us," "the opposite in us," and ἐν τῇ φύσει, etc. (102d, 103b); cf. Cornford, *Pl. and Parm.*, 78, and R. Hackforth, *Plato's Phaedo* (Cambridge, 1955), 150 n.1, 153f.

[43] It might be argued that given the importance of the elements in the *Timaeus* it was natural for Plato in our section to refer to the Forms of fire, etc., rather than of warm, cold, and the like, yet that in a different context he would not have hesitated to introduce Forms of these "powers." However plausible this may sound, I do not think that much is gained by speculating about such possibilities. The later dialogues do not suggest that Plato was interested in Forms of the powers.

[44] Aristotle does not in *Phys.* I gather ammunition for his attacks against Plato's Forms. To us it may seem significant that the Form which he introduces is much closer to the substratum and that this Form is paired with another condition of the substratum; but the new explanation of *genesis* does not figure in the arguments

Aristotle replaces Plato's vertical approach to *genesis* by a horizontal. But he too operates occasionally with a concept of Form. If a man hitherto uncultured becomes cultured, he passes from privation to Form, or, to put it differently, the substratum formerly characterized by the privation has now come under the influence of the Form.[45] By and large what matters about Form, as Aristotle here uses the concept, is that it is the opposite of privation. What reality and what ontological status it may have, whether it exists apart from the individual or not, are questions never even mooted. Still, there is one rather noteworthy passage in which Aristotle, for the moment less insistent upon the opposition between Form and privation, admits that Form alone might suffice. It would be sufficient, he says, that Form by its "presence" or "absence" causes the change, i.e., accounts for the passing of something from the state of privation to that of Form.[46] One is apt to be startled by what appears like a sudden relapse into Platonic ways of speaking and thinking. Nor can it be accidental that this statement occurs in the section which also describes the nature of the substratum in terms strongly reminiscent of Plato's receptacle. The substratum, we here learn, is knowable (only) in an "analogical" sense. Moreover, it is in relation to being and the individual "what the bronze is in relation to a statue or the wood to a bed or what the formless before it received Form is in relation to something that has Form." [47] These remarks indicate the genetic connection between Aristotle's concept of the substratum and Plato's "formless" receptacle.[48] Finally Aristotle, still in the same section, states: "Whether the Form or the substratum is substance (*ousia*) is not yet clear." [49] These statements are the more noteworthy as the section in which they occur marks the end of Aristotle's deduction of his own three principles, substratum, Form, and privation. (What follows is an appraisal of the Presocratic "not-being" from the newly won basis.[50]) Needless to say, Aristotle has no serious intention

---

of the *Metaphysics*. *Metaph.* Λ2 and 4 have important points in common with *Phys.* I but are not pointed against Plato, and N5.1092a33ff., though directed against Plato, does not refer to the Forms. See, however, Willy Theiler, *Mus. Helv.*, 15 (1958), 97ff., for a different estimate of these passages.

[45] μορφή is introduced (rather late) in I,7.190b20, εἶδος in 28. On the whole Aristotle is content to speak of τὰ ἐναντία.

[46] Ch. 7.191a5ff.　　　　　　　　　　[47] *Ibid.*, 8ff.

[48] Cf. George S. Claghorn, *Aristotle's Criticism of Plato's Timaeus* (The Hague, 1954), 5ff., 18f. We shall come back to the subject in the chapter "Matter and Place."

[49] 191a19f.　　　　　　　　　　　　[50] Ch. 8.

of abandoning privation. The section which offhand may strike us as a return or concession to Platonic ways of thinking is probably best understood as an attempt to go for once beyond the relatively narrow limits within which Aristotle so far kept the discussion of *genesis*. He has used concepts like substratum, the contraries, and finally also Form as he needed them to account for *genesis*, ignoring all questions relating to their nature, status, and reality. When finally he looks beyond these self-imposed barriers to indicate their place in a larger scheme, this scheme turns out to be more Platonic than the discussion of *genesis* in deliberate isolation from other and larger matters has led us to expect.

Although one should not be dogmatic about the three different accounts of *genesis* in the *Timaeus*, it may yet be said that a member of the Academy had a "choice" between several approaches. Obviously Aristotle's decision reflects fundamental traits of his intellect and outlook. He seems determined to stay strictly within the boundaries of physics, keeping his subject free from mathematical as well as ontological-metaphysical entanglements.[51] This inevitably restricted the scope of his "choice."

In any case, by deciding on his particular line of approach Aristotle lost contact with the traditional, i.e., Presocratic interests in *genesis*. Ironically, this happens at the very point where he is pleased to regard himself as continuing and completing the work of the Presocratics. The opposites understood as privation and Form have their uses in connection with the kind of problems that Aristotle cites as illustrations (passing from not-white to white, from uncultured to cultured); they also provide an answer to the issue of *genesis* out of not-being. Yet they do not lead by a straight route to the origin of the elements or other substances. As matters now stand, this once central problem has no longer a place in the *Physics*. Premises of a more specific type and concepts less general than Form and privation are needed to take care of it, and even the substratum must move nearer to the elements if it is to account for their *genesis*. In the *Physics* the account of *genesis* is so general—not to say, so abstract—that no thought can be given to the

---

[51] Aristotle's conviction that physical inquiry must be kept clear of mathematics finds its strongest expression in the *De caelo* (see below, p. 259); yet this un-Platonic or anti-Platonic tendency is also discernible in his *Physics*. The account of *genesis* needs no help from mathematics. As Aristotle does not here deal with the *genesis* of the elements, he has no reason for polemizing against mathematical derivations of the *Timaeus*. The proper place for such polemic is in the *De caelo* and the *De generatione*, both of which deal with the nature of the elements.

questions that had been the matrix of *genesis*.[52] They must be left to another treatise. Form and privation may be the principles of every-thing—or principles of every *genesis*—yet they are not very obvious or effective principles of the *genesis* of fire, water, earth, and air. It is true that the qualities hot and cold, moist and dry, which are effective in this process, may be distributed between Form and privation, yet what really makes them useful for Aristotle is their character as qualities or as "sense-perceived [qualitative] differences." [53] Occasionally, in-deed, Form and privation claim consideration also in the treatise *On Coming to Be*. For as this treatise takes up the *genesis* of the elements, it must also once more face the possibility of *genesis* out of not-being—and must do so with the help of more specific arguments. In handling this specter, Aristotle remains faithful to the general propositions about *genesis* that he has laid down in the *Physics*. He is even prepared to identify some elements with being, others with not-being, so that, for instance, a change from earth to fire would be *genesis* out of not-being.[54] This means that some of the suggestions embodied in Par-menides' "Way of Opinion" would be quite acceptable and might even be played off against "The Way of Truth" with its radical denial of *genesis* from not-being. The reason why Aristotle here (tentatively) treats fire as being, earth as not-being, is that the one has the quality warm, the other the quality cold—qualities that to each other stand in the relation of affirmation (i.e., Form) and privation.[55] In this regard his position here is close to that of the *Physics*. However, as he points out, the distinction between being and not-being might also be made to rest on other criteria. Air might be regarded as not-being because it is invisible and its very existence is sometimes questioned, whereas earth, which is definitely there and whose existence common sense would al-ways admit, might be entered on the side of being.[56] Again one might describe elements as being or not-being on the basis of their greater or lesser approximation to Form and perfection.[57] This would be a more philosophical point of view; if it were to be adopted, fire would be be-

---

[52] If it is asked what phases of a Presocratic system "correspond" to *Phys*. I, we cannot refer to doctrines concerning elements, etc., and their transformations or combinations, but only to such fundamental statements as 31B8–12, 15, and 59B17 in which thinkers such as Empedocles and Anaxagoras define their stand on the issue of being and becoming. The relation of Aristotle's theory to Parmenides himself has already been discussed.

[53] *De gen*. II,2.329b7ff.

[54] *Ibid*., I,3.318a35ff.; note the reference to Parmenides in b6ff.   [55] *Ibid*., b14ff

[56] *Ibid*., b18ff.; here the criterion is *aisthesis*.   [57] *Ibid*., b27ff.

ing since it is nearer to perfection, earth not-being (what this in truth comes to is not so much a distinction between being and not-being as between a higher and lower degree of being). In the course of this disquisition Aristotle comes dangerously near to making substance the opposite of substance and allowing substance to arise from non-substance—doctrines which he normally abhors. This may be the reason why at the end of this section he shows some qualms about what he has said and somehow, retracing his steps, declares it not yet settled whether not-being in the process of *genesis* should be identified with one of the contraries or rather with the substratum—the substratum which in the *Physics* guaranteed that *genesis* materialized from being.[58] Altogether we may say that Parmenides' veto has even less horror for him here than it does in the *Physics*.[59] If becoming is to be out of not-being, well and good; on no possible interpretation or construction can this do physical theory any real harm. At the same time he meets the Presocratic worries about *genesis* on a physical level by the affirmation that the coming to be of one entity is always balanced by the passing out of existence of another.[60] This, we may comment, the Presocratics knew too; from a historical point of view what this affirmation means is that the later Presocratics had taken sufficient precaution against *genesis* out of not-being.

Thus the Parmenidean legacy is still there to plague Aristotle when he discusses *genesis* in fundamental terms. But where he deals with concrete instances of *genesis*—including the actual mechanical process by which elements arise out of one another[61]—the old problem is hardly within sight. If the Stoics and Epicureans could dispense with such preliminary worries and, coming at once to grips with the physical aspects of becoming, understand the process in terms of "acting" and "suffering," they owe Aristotle as great a debt for clearing the field of debris as for putting effective new tools into their hands.[62]

[58] *Ibid.*, 319a29 (the words which Joachim perhaps wrongly deletes in a30 describe this question as an *aporia*, i.e., in need of fuller investigation). For the different doctrines of the *Physics* cf. above, pp. 77–80.

[59] See also 319a22ff.   [60] *Ibid.*, 19; cf. 318a23ff.   [61] *De gen.* II,1.2f., 4ff.

[62] To be sure, Epicurus emphatically reaffirms the axiom that nothing can arise from not-being (*Ep. ad Herod.* 38f.; for a new slant see my comments in *A. J. Ph.*, 72 [1951], 21), but there is no evidence that either he or the Stoics were wary of the concept of *genesis* as such. For ποιεῖν and πάσχειν in Stoic physics and ontology see esp. *St. V. F.*, 1.85; 2.299ff. Epicurus' use of this pair as reflected in Lucretius' *facere et fungi* (1.440ff.) which help to define *corpus* (σῶμα) recalls Plato's definition of τὸ ὄν in *Soph.* 247d8ff. These matters require further study and elucidation.

It is patent that by severing *genesis* from the Platonic Forms and making the Form-privation contrast all-important, Aristotle gives the entire subject a new orientation. He loosens the hold which *genesis* used to have on substance with the result that his primary topic is no longer Becoming pure and simple but "becoming something" (such as becoming white or warm).[63] On the other hand, what is loss for substance is gain for the other categories, and the principal gainer would appear to be quality (it can hardly be accident that Aristotle's illustrations are usually taken from the realm of this category). Still, Aristotle casts his net wide, and if it is impossible for him to let substance come into being out of a contrary substance, he can at least insist that everything composite arises from its contrary, namely, from a state in which things are not composite, i.e., not put together. And there seems to be no limit to what his class of "composite things" may embrace: "Anything that is in harmony must arise out of what is not in harmony and pass away into it. . . . And it makes no difference whether we speak of harmony or of order or of combination; for the rule is clearly the same. Indeed, a house or a statue or anything else comes to be in a similar way. For a house comes into being out of things that are not put together but separated in such and such fashion and a statue out of things that have not received shape but are shapeless. . . . And all these things represent either an ordering or a combining." [64] This would mean that although a house cannot come into being from nonhouse—since there is definitely no contrary for a substance—it can at least insofar as it has a structure come into being from nonstructure. The wide net seems to have large meshes. Moreover, what Aristotle here regards as a state of shapelessness and lack of organization or Form he would as a rule identify with the substratum, so that the substratum is this time made to serve in the dual role of substratum and privation. Here it is obvious that Aristotle paid a price for severing becoming from being (in Plato's sense of the word [65]) and that the generalized theory of becoming has its difficulties. It is easy to put one's finger on them, but before one proceeds to criti-

---

[63] In a revealing passage of Book II (2.193b20) Aristotle admits that it is not yet decided whether there are privation and a contrary also in the case of "simple *genesis*" (= *genesis* of a substance).

[64] I,5.188b10–22; cf. 7.190b28ff.

[65] The point is not that Plato would recognize Ideas of artifacts—which is highly doubtful—but that the doctrine of Forms can explain the existence as well as the coming into being of physical substances.

cize his attempt, it is fair to stop and consider how these difficulties could be avoided if *genesis* was to be universalized. An item that should be entered on the credit side of the ledger is that Aristotle can treat the qualities—including the basic ones, hot and cold, dry and moist—as belonging to the nature of physical entities; he need not, like Plato, degrade them to the status of sensations.[66] Moreover, Aristotle has a way of turning the difficulties to advantage. When he comes to explaining the *genesis* of the elements—historically speaking, the test for any theory of *genesis*—he propounds a doctrine which holds good of the elements themselves as well as of their constitutive qualities, puts both in a fairly well-defined relation to the substratum, and yet keeps intact the principle that change comes to pass between contraries.[67]

[66] On the qualities in the *Timaeus* see esp. below, Ch. 17.   [67] *De gen.* II,2–5, 7.

5

Physis

IF in the case of *genesis* Aristotle seeks to reduce its metaphysical mortgage, he is a priori likely to approach the central concept of *physis* with similar intentions. To make physics, in Aristotle's sense of the word, possible, nature itself must be brought down to the physical level. In some respects the conditions for this attempt were more auspicious than in the parallel instance of *genesis*. Plato had built up a doctrine of *physis* which did not emphasize the relations between this concept and the Forms. For though the true and ultimate *physis* of things is the Forms, *physis* also denotes the realm of movement which contrasts with and complements the realm of rest. In this realm of movement there is a phase of sameness, self-identity, and perfection which somehow reflects these qualities of the Forms but is not directly related to the Forms. What accounts for them is entities like soul and mind.[1] The Forms themselves are never thought of as causing movement or as affecting it in an important way. Book X of the *Laws* shows that as long as Plato dwells on the connection between *physis* and the world of movement the Forms need not be considered, and the *Timaeus*, far from contradicting this impression, rather confirms it; for here, too, the Forms are not needed to explain movement and changes whereas they are necessary for the *genesis* and existence of physical entities which are still regarded as their "copies." [2] Thus Aristotle's doctrine of movement and nature, and in particular of nature as principle of movement, starts with a great initial advantage. The Forms need neither to be eliminated nor to be naturalized; they simply do not figure in the legacy, as long, at least, as it is ignored

[1] See esp. *Legg.* X,898aff.   [2] *Tim.* 48eff.

that the realm of movement was not meant to be the only realm but one of two. What Aristotle does eliminate this time is the Platonic soul concept, and this departure has implications and consequences no less important than those entailed by the abandonment of the Platonic Forms in the context of *genesis*.

As Plato's soul concept had been the unifying principle of his theory of nature, Aristotle, who is determined to do without this concept, inherits fragments, yet fragments that can be reshaped into new wholes. When he defines nature as the principle (or originator) of movement, he in effect advances it to the place of Plato's soul and must show how nature, even when deprived of soul, can still give such an impulse. When he has to explain the regular and perfect movement of the rotating heavens—in Plato likewise a manifestation of soul—he credits the element of these regions with a natural tendency toward such movement.[3] To preserve the priority of nature over craft and chance he must, instead of proving the primacy of soul among the movements of nature, again rely on nature as such and contrast nature's mode of operation with the working of chance, accident, and craft. Finally nature itself must become teleological. To be sure, Aristotle, when securing to it this character, refers to the presence of mind in the physical world. In Plato mind operates as "ally" of soul;[4] once again the concept which had functioned as link has been discarded. What for Plato had been one great topic, the cosmic operation of soul, has thus become split into two or three, if not four different ones, and although they are not completely drifting apart, a centrifugal tendency is gaining. They have lost their common point of reference. Eventually, it is true, a new connection will be established through the concept of the prime mover whose nature is mind and

[3] For details see below, pp. 95–100 and p. 291. On Aristotle's new conception of *physis* and its relation to the world soul of the *Laws* see W. Theiler, *Zur Geschichte der teleolog. Naturbetrachtung bis auf Aristoteles* (Zürich, 1925), 84f., and E. Grumach, *Physis und Agathon in der Alten Stoa* (Berlin, 1932), 47f.

[4] See esp. *Legg.* X,897b1 (νοῦν προσλαβοῦσα). In the *Timaeus* the relationship between mind and soul is conceived somewhat differently: the world soul contributes—and contributes more than anything else—to the perfection and teleological quality of the Cosmos as the divine mind designs it. In Plato, too, it is possible to distinguish between the teleological point of view and the theory of movement, and it is precisely in his theology that this duality of approaches makes itself to a certain extent felt. (See Solmsen, *Plato's Theology*, 75ff., and on the integration in *Laws* X see *ibid.*, 131ff.) At the very least these approaches are "separable in thought" and may be distinguished in an analytical study. In Aristotle the gulf has widened.

who, in the last analysis, activates all movement and change in the world. In this way nature and mind once more join in controlling the physical world—a physical world in which soul is properly limited to living beings. Even so, there remains a certain break between a doctrine of movement which finds its principle in the first mover and the teleological conception of nature at large in which everything has its own "end"; nor is the role of the first mover fully in harmony with the conception which makes nature itself the principle of movement.[5]

In the second book of the *Physics* the separation of these topics has gone far; their eventual reintegration is either not yet in view or irrelevant to the general lines of the argument here pursued. Nature itself can take on the sponsorship of all physical movements, while mind guarantees that nature operates toward good and valuable ends.[6] If we are sanguine, we may surmise that these two ideas complement each other and that the movements which nature initiates are somehow all "reasonable." Yet even this relatively modest hypothesis would run the risk of integrating what Aristotle himself has left unintegrated. As we find them in Book II, the doctrines of nature as mind-directed and of nature as source of movement are fragments of the Platonic structure. There is little tendency or possibility to preserve their original connection. In *Physics* II, Aristotle's teleology does not care for close contact with his theory of naturally prompted motions but looks for realization in the realm of biology.[7] Even in the chapters which uphold the rights of mind against chance and haphazardness Aristotle, as his illustrations show, has biological causality in mind.[8] That natural movements too have their teleology will become apparent only in the treatise *On the Heaven*.

Nor should we doubt that a teleological scheme could more easily be associated with mind than with soul. Plato too had traced the purposefulness of things to the operation of God as mind rather than

---

[5] See below, pp. 101–102. On the last point cf. H. von Arnim, *S.B.W.A.*, 212 (1931), 5.11ff. and *passim*.

[6] *Phys.* II,1.192b13ff.; II,8.

[7] On the teleological motif in Aristotle's biology cf. W. D. Ross, *Aristotle* (5th ed.; London, 1949), 123ff. The diffusion of the ἀγαθόν throughout the ὄντα is asserted in *Metaph.* Λ10.1075a11ff.; for the celestial world and the heavenly bodies see also *De caelo* II,12.292a14–293a14.

[8] See II,8, esp. 199a20ff. On the place of mind in the teleological scheme of *Phys.* II see below, p. 112.

as soul.[9] In Book X of the *Laws* mind insures that the movements of soul are rational and have a happy issue.[10] Soul's own portion corresponds to that which it has in other dialogues of Plato's later philosophy.[11] It is the principle and source of all movements and the only entity capable of moving itself.

NATURE AND SOUL

When Aristotle defines nature and natural objects as having the principle of movement in themselves, we realize that nature is taking over the function which Plato assigned to soul. By contrast to the works of craft, physical entities have "in their nature" (ἔμφυτον) the tendency to move or change.[12] They do not need soul, and nothing here gives us the impression that they need any outside mover or outside help at all. Nature itself is now entrusted with the highly important role of initiating movement. We shall have more to say about the far-reaching implications of this idea.

However, Aristotle's concept of nature as developed in *Physics* II has still another aspect, so different from those hitherto discussed that instead of another aspect one might as well speak of another concept. The "nature" of a physical object, we learn in the second part of chapter 1, consists of its material substratum and its form, and it may be asked which of these two factors deserves the name of *physis* in a higher and fuller sense of the word. Aristotle's decision is in favor of the Form. The question as well as the decision remind us of the *Metaphysics* where the same claimants present themselves for the contested name of substance (*ousia*).[13] In any case it is patent that this *physis* does not have its place in the theory of movement and that we cannot relate it to the problems clustering around the Platonic world soul. Instead here we find ourselves in the shadow of the doctrine of Forms. Nevertheless Aristotle provides for connections between this concept of *physis* and its definition as source of movement. He simply says, "All these things [scil., that have a principle of movement in themselves] are substances. For there is a substratum, and nature is always in a substratum." [14] Furthermore, where Aristotle

[9] Besides the conception of the Demiurge and his activities in the *Timaeus* cf. especially the discussion of divine care and planning in *Legg.* X,903b4ff.; cf. *Plato's Theology*, 152ff.

[10] ὀρθὰ καὶ εὐδαίμονα, *Legg.* X,897b2.   [11] See above, pp. 28–30.

[12] II,1.192b12ff.; for ὁρμὴ μεταβολῆς ἔμφυτος see b18.

[13] II,1.193a9ff., 28ff., b6f. Cf. *Metaph.* Z3.   [14] *Ibid.* 192b32–4.

derives from substratum and Form additional definitions of *physis*, he is careful to say that in one of the new senses *physis* is "the first matter of each thing that has in itself the principle of movement and change" and that in another sense it is the Form (μορφή, εἶδος) of the things that have such a principle.[15] Thus the "source" or "principle of movement" is incorporated also in these definitions of "nature," and it helps again substantially to set physical things apart from, e.g., the products of craft. The reasoning proceeds smoothly enough, showing neither break nor fissure. One concept of nature is, so to speak, superimposed upon another, and only historical analysis reveals that the two concepts are quite different in origin and that Aristotle's procedure is eminently synthetic.[16]

At the end of the section dealing with substratum and Form, Aristotle briefly gives thought to still another meaning of *physis*, in which it is a synonym of *genesis*. This is the meaning in which the Presocratics like to employ it.[17] In taking care of it, Aristotle emphasizes that *physis* thus understood does (or should) denote the *genesis* not of the substratum but of Form or rather the formed object.[18]

It was a bold departure to define nature (*physis*) simply and without any qualification as a principle and cause of movement.[19] For although "nature" is here clearly succeeding to the legacy of soul, the problems inherent in this succession are obvious. "What do we say," asks the Athenian in the *Laws*, "if we see that this [the power of moving itself] is present in something that is made of either earth or water or even fire," and the answer is, as one might expect, "We say it is alive." From the concept of life it is not hard to take the next step which leads to soul.[20] Thus soul and the power of causing motion (both in others and in itself) are to be considered identical. In the course of

---

[15] 193a28ff., b3f.

[16] The same meanings of φύσις as in *Phys.* II,1 are also distinguished in *Metaph.* Δ4, where Aristotle, however, knows additional varieties.

[17] II,1.193b12ff.; cf., e.g., Empedocles in *Vorsokr.*, 31B8.1 (see also B63, as well as Plutarch in B11) and Plato *Legg.* X,892c. It may be noted, however, that Aristotle himself fails to recognize this meaning in Emped. B8 (*Metaph.* Δ4.1014b37; *De gen.* II,6.333b13ff. is not clear) and that the extent and even the occurrence of this usage in the Presocratics are disputed. Cf. Ross on *Metaph.* 1014b37 and *Phys.* II,1.193b12; he refers to Burnet, *E. G. Ph.*, 10ff., 363f., and A. O. Lovejoy, *Philos. Rev.* 18 (1909), 371ff. See per contra the convincing discussion by Felix Heinimann, *Nomos und Physis* (Basel, 1945), 90, who finds this meaning also in Parm. B10. Cf. further Cherniss, *Presocr.*, 243 n.114.

[18] 193b17f.   [19] ἀρχή τις καὶ αἰτία, *Phys.* II,1.192b20f.   [20] *Legg.* X,895cff.

the same argument soul also emerges as the first and supreme ruler in the entire realm of nature.[21]

What Plato achieves by these new doctrines is to reduce the role of nature itself. At any rate, nature in the sense in which we associate it with the material elements and with body must now content itself with a second place while soul takes over the first. Yet Plato also hints that his discovery of soul's primary role may as well lead to a revision of the traditional concept of nature.[22] This is the way which Aristotle preferred to go. With him the idea of nature itself has acquired a completely new meaning. It has absorbed as many of the qualities and powers of soul as it could. Yet how many of them can nature absorb and how completely? This seems to be the question which Aristotle's new concept of nature inevitably suggests.

In a sense, to be sure, movement belonged to nature and should have its place in a theory of nature. But since the elements as Plato found them were dead and he would not wish to endow them with life, something else was needed to produce movement in them. But they had not always been dead. We can hardly decide what makes the powers break away from Anaximander's Infinite and concentrate in different parts of the Cosmos; yet there can be no doubt that Anaximenes' air and Heraclitus' fire had abundant mobility and moving power in themselves. In fact, they had life. Heraclitus speaks of his fire as "ever-living." Although the term "hylozoism" is today in disrepute, we need not lose sight of the characteristic which it was once used to describe. It would be tempting to say that the need for an "external" source of motion becomes felt in the measure in which the physical principles lose the quality of life—the divine life and ever-active mobility with which they were once instinct. But Empedocles' four elements are certainly divine and alive, and yet they need Love and Strife to build up a Cosmos and mix in the form of living beings. Anaxagoras may be the first for whom the world stuff as such is devoid

[21] *Ibid.*, 896aff.

[22] Of special importance is *Legg.* X,892b7 where Plato points out that the word φύσις is misused when applied to material forces and elements. Cf. Jaeger, *Aristotle,* 75 n.1, and for the connection between Plato's soul and Aristotle's *physis* A. Rivaud's brief statement (*Le problème du devenir* [Paris, 1906], 452). George S. Claghorn, *Aristotle's Criticism of Plato's "Timaeus"* (The Hague, 1954), 124ff., seems to me to underrate the differences between Plato and Aristotle and to make somewhat hazardous use of *Tim.* 46e. I agree with Claghorn on the continuity of the teleological motif.

of life, hard though it is to believe that the naturalized powers should have no "power" left; still, they do not stir as long as they are by themselves and mind does not yet operate. In contrast to him and Empedocles, the atomists had movement without a deity or another agent to cause it; as far as we can see, they simply posited movement as one of their basic data and as requiring no cause or explanation (by taking this line they find themselves in even sharper antithesis to Parmenides). This movement is no longer inherent in the nature of the basic world stuff but is postulated beside and in addition to it.

Aristotle too has a mover, but his function has little resemblance to Empedocles' two agents or to Anaxagoras' "mind." His mover and his concept of nature as principle of movement call rather for a comparison with the Platonic world soul. For one thing, it is no longer their role to create the Cosmos (which in the meantime has become eternal). For another, both Plato and Aristotle approach the task of finding a "principle of movement" with full awareness of its complexity and its importance. Aristotle's self-moving nature has its analogue in the systems not of Empedocles, Anaxagoras, and the Abderites but of the early Presocratics; with them nature had possessed such immanent dynamic force as Aristotle seeks to restore to it. If nature could take over the entire legacy of the world soul, it would move itself and change itself thanks to its own inherent capacities. It would have as much life as one of the early Presocratic principles. As "the hot" in Parmenides and presumably in Anaximander by its own impulse (μένος) rushed to the circumference of the Cosmos, so in Aristotle fire (being by nature light) moves to the place above the other elements. But the position of the archaic thinkers could not be regained.

Aristotle's new doctrine of nature as the principle of movement has analogies to his doctrine of the principles. Not some specific contraries or opposites are principles, as with Anaximander, but simply the contraries as such—defined as Form and privation. Similarly not any specific physical substance is a principle of motion and has an "inborn tendency to move," but nature as such. As soon, however, as the theory is carried into the stage of concrete application, it is again the elements which have by nature motion and a tendency to move—in fact, all four of them, and in the end a new and fifth. Still, Aristotle's first and basic decision was to endow nature as such with this time-honored yet of late somewhat problematic capacity; and by thus generalizing the idea he loses some of its historical essence. In addition the new principle of movement labors under other disabilities which will soon become apparent.

We may now return to the Platonic world soul as the more obvious antecedent of Aristotle's "nature." To it the term "principle of movement" points back, and in the same years in which Aristotle worked out the bulk of his *Physics* Plato was engaged on the *Laws*, where in Book X the position of soul is not only reaffirmed but, if possible, strengthened.

Aristotle may have felt that by once again eliminating soul from the physical world picture he was discarding a particularly unscientific feature of Plato's thought. As a "departmentalist" who wishes to build up every subject from its own specific principles and premises he is opposed to what he calls *metabasis eis allo genos*. The *genos* (subject) to which soul, for his feeling, belonged was the study of living beings (ἔμψυχα). However, by transferring the source of motion from the world soul to nature, while yet not thinking of nature as alive in all its parts or as one great living organism, he is certainly straining the concept of nature. The boldness which inspired Plato's conception of the world soul is less provocative by comparison because it is of a piece with other insights of the Platonic genius and thus somehow falls into place. The yardstick of exact science is not the adequate criterion for appreciating Plato's great and synthetic visions. Aristotle set himself a difficult task when he decided to make nature the source of motion yet at the same time cut it off from soul, the principle of life. By its own strength and with the help of its own resources nature must now cope with this arduous role.

The root of the difficulty lies in the fact that nature is not synonymous with living beings. As the theory of nature had taken shape in Presocratic systems and as it had been further developed by Plato, it inevitably included the elements. And besides the elements the physicist had also to deal with composite inorganic substances. Thus we are driven to assume that when Aristotle put forward his new definition of nature he saw his way to endowing the four elements with an immanent tendency to motion. This, in fact, is the doctrine that the latter books (III and IV) of the treatise *On the Heaven* develop. Here it is said to be the "nature" of air and fire to move upward, and of earth and water to follow their natural inclination downward, to the center of the Cosmos (the extension of the same approach to still another element, the "fifth body," may here be disregarded).[23] We cannot decide whether this epoch-making doctrine sprang from the new conception of nature or whether it preceded this conception and encouraged Aristotle while he was feeling his way toward it. With the more highly organized products of nature, living beings, the new definition could anyhow work; after all, life had been the middle term through which Plato could bring the principle of motion and soul together. As for "unorganic" entities other than the elements—stones, metal, etc.—Aristotle could take the view that since each of them was composed of two or more elements it must combine the motions or tendencies that characterize these elements.[24]

Plato's world soul does not animate the elements. As we know, in the *Timaeus* the elements begin to move in their own characteristic way even before the world soul is present.[25] In the *Laws* the affirmation of soul's all-pervading power is if possible even more emphatic, yet what does Plato actually say about its relation to the elements? Although soul has its own characteristic movements—psychic movements, like planning, watching, loving, hating—it avails itself of the physical motions possessed by bodies to direct everything toward its own wise ends.[26] Aristotle, it is hardly necessary to say, allows only motions of the latter kind. As he points out in the treatise *On the Heaven*, the first hypotheses of a subject must be "homogeneous" to the subject.[27] Finding it possible to credit even the elements or "simple bodies" with physical motions of their own, he could feel assured that his new venture of making nature itself the principle of motion worked out in the entire physical realm.[28]

To have the principle of motion in oneself is not entirely the same

---

[23] See, e.g., III,2.301b16ff.; IV,1 (307b31ff., 308a15ff., etc.). Cf. also I,2.268b14ff., 7.274a33ff. For the relation of the first two books of *De caelo* to Books III and IV see below, Ch. 14. The basic impression which the *De caelo* conveys is that the physical bodies, i.e., the elements, move themselves and do not depend on an outside agency to actualize their motion (cf. W. K. C. Guthrie's "Introduction" to the Loeb edition [London and Cambridge, Mass., 1943], xix–xxix and *passim*).

[24] See, e.g., *De caelo* I,2.268b26ff. *Phys.* II,1.192b19ff. appears to make the same point.

[25] *Tim.* 52d–53a.   [26] *Legg.* X,896e8ff.

[27] *De caelo* III,7.306a9ff.; see below, Ch. 11.

[28] If the heavenly bodies are living beings and their movements voluntary (as seems to be implied in *De caelo* II,12.292a20ff.), they ought to have the principle of movement in themselves.

as to be moved by oneself. This nice difference may not be relevant in the first chapter of Book II where the new definition of nature is put forward, and Aristotle himself seems at times to regard the two notions as synonymous;[29] yet the distinction becomes important when in Book VIII Aristotle works up to his doctrine of the prime mover by making a distinction between entities moved by themselves and those moved by something outside themselves. Here it is clearly stated that to be moved by itself is "a characteristic of life and a peculiarity of living beings."[30] This characteristic then does not apply to the four elements; although Aristotle tries not to surrender the position of Book II, he admits that to actualize their motion they depend on the help of something else. An element that is out of its place will only begin its "natural" motion toward that place when someone removes the obstacles (if there were no such obstacles, it would long since have joined its kin in its "natural" place).[31] To have the source of motion in oneself and yet not to be able to actualize it by one's own power would seem to be a border-line case—and a compromise. Yet in Book VIII even living beings need an impulse from the outside to actualize their capacity of movement;[32] a being that is asleep may wake up and start moving because the food which has entered it (and which, while it was being digested, induced sleep) is now distributed in the body and thus causes motion.

Throughout Book VIII Aristotle's endeavor is to show that an outside mover—in the last analysis, the first mover—is needed. Although he does not recant his definition of nature, he does restrict the capacity of physical objects to initiate movement by themselves. The upshot of the book is that they cannot do it. Nature is, after all, not able to succeed to the position of the Platonic world soul. The prime mover —he, too, a legatee of the world soul[33]—is the real originator of movement in the physical world. In a way the legacy is divided between him and "nature," and both must co-operate to keep movement

---

[29] See, e.g., VIII,4.254b14ff. Here, however, the two notions are said to apply (only) to living beings, and the further development of the argument in Book VIII goes far to minimize even this conclusion. Cf. below, pp. 244–245.

[30] VIII,4.255a5ff.

[31] *Ibid.*, 255b13–256a3. Here the ἀρχὴ κινήσεως becomes an ἀρχὴ not of ποιεῖν but of πάσχειν (255b30)—a far cry from the ἔμφυτος ἀρχὴ μεταβολῆς of II,1.192b18. Clearly Aristotle himself is here removing obstacles, scil., those which his theory of nature as the principle of movement creates for his doctrine of the first mover.

[32] See esp. VIII,6.259b1–20. Cf. H. von Arnim, *S.B.W.A.*, 212 (1931), 5.42.

[33] Cf. below, Ch. 10.

going. Book II tells us nothing about nature's limitation. With full confidence nature here assumes the task of functioning as the principle of movement. The partner is not in sight. Nor is he in the substantial sections and central argument of *De caelo*. In his absence Aristotle is willing to let nature have the field to itself. Wherever it is possible, each of the two heirs of the world soul receives his full share—in fact, more than his share. They are allowed to encroach on one another's domain, and the final settlement of their rival claims is postponed.[34] It remained for another philosophical school to find a solution by making the first mover a principle that is immanent in nature.[35]

NATURE AND MIND; CHANCE AND NECESSITY

As Aristotle's *physis* has essential traits in common with Plato's soul, the antagonism between soul and nature on which the argument of *Laws* X turns can no longer take the same form. For him nature is not, as for Plato, the sum total of all that is material and obeys mechanical necessities.[36] Where a comparable antagonism arises in Aristotle, the forces arrayed on both sides must go by different names, and the issue itself must take on a new character. In Plato we find on the one side soul itself as the protagonist; allied to it are, as is fitting, all intellectual, moral, and spiritual forces, in particular mind and craft. On the other side are the material *physis* and chance.[37] In Aristotle soul no longer has any concern with the battle at all. Nature has undergone so thorough a reform that it can take over its place. Mind makes its appearance at a highly strategic juncture, on the side of nature,[38] yet mind too has already passed on so much of its capacity and specific powers to nature that it hardly needs to appear in person. As regards craft Plato had given it a position in the train of soul, rescuing it

---

[34] This conflict is not removed by insisting that Book VIII of the *Physics* which gives us the theory of the first mover is later than the other books and perhaps also than *De caelo*. After all, the cosmology of this work with its emphasis on natural movement retained its validity for Aristotle (as far as we can make out). On the other hand, we seem in *Phys.* VII to have an earlier attempt to arrive at the concept of the first mover. Guthrie touches on the situation described in the text when he calls the different sources of motion "uneasy bedfellows" ("Introduction," Loeb ed., xix). Cf. also H. von Arnim, *S.B.W.A.*, 212 (1931), 11ff., 30ff.

[35] Cf. the Stoic identification of the self-mover (and by implication, the first mover) with the fire or vital heat (Cic. *De nat. deor.* 2.23; *St. V. F.*, 1.513; see my comment in *J. H. St.*, 77 [1957], 122).

[36] See *Legg.* X,888eff., esp. 889b. For *ananke* and mechanical laws see below, p. 110. On *Legg.* 892b cf. Grumach, *op.cit.*, 46ff.

[37] *Legg.* X,888e, 891e.   [38] *Phys.* II,6.198a5ff.

from its somewhat undignified association with mechanical nature.[39] Now it is again on the friendliest terms with nature because nature itself has reformed and operates along teleological lines.[40] Both nature and craft aim at the realization of valuable ends. The originality is on the side of *physis*, which craft "imitates," a relationship which superficially corresponds to that set up by Plato's adversaries, but its meaning has radically changed inasmuch as nature has become oriented toward a purpose.[41] In the other camp we again find chance (*tyche*), strengthened by an ally, spontaneity or accident (*automaton*), and what is left of the former mechanical nature. Among these remnants necessity is now particularly conspicuous, and with it the battle is joined in the first place.[42] After a time something else is found to hide behind necessity, to wit, the material factors or, as Aristotle here puts it, the substratum and its movements.[43] For these the *Physics* has already made a place; as we have learned in chapter 1, they are one aspect and definition of *physis*, though not the noblest. As Plato had no concept comparable to Aristotle's "matter," he could not say with the same precision where necessity resides. Aristotle has given this "errant" principle its definite place both within his system of nature and in his quadripartite scheme of causes.

Thus the contest ends not with the annihilation of the adversaries but with their incorporation. This on the whole is also the upshot in Book X of the *Laws;* the forces on the other side who originally claimed almost the whole territory for themselves must content themselves with the second place. For the rest, the contest has in Aristotle not quite the same dramatic quality as in Plato because Aristotle sees fit to take on the enemies one by one. This corresponds in some degree to the separation of different aspects within his own concept of nature. Yet apart from this, chance (spontaneity) and necessity clearly represent quite distinct, if not mutually exclusive, approaches

[39] For *techne* as understood by Plato's opponents see *Legg.* X,889a, cff. (cf. *Phys.* II,1.193a12ff.); for Plato's own estimate of it see 890d, 892b, and (after the issue has been decided) 896c5ff. Cf. George K. Plochmann, *J. Hist. Ideas,* 14 (1953), 173.

[40] See esp. II,8.199a8ff., 33ff., b26ff. Cf. also 2.194a21ff.

[41] For craft as *mimesis* of nature see Democr. in *Vorsokr.*, 68B154, with Kranz's references. In the passages mentioned in Note 39 in which Plato describes the views held by his opponents the word *mimesis* does not occur, yet the concept would easily find a place in their theory as there set forth. For Aristotle cf., besides II,2.194a21ff., *Protrept.* frg. 11 (48.5ff. Walzer); on this see Jaeger's comments, *Aristotle,* 75.

[42] II,9.199b34ff.   [43] *Ibid.,* 200a30ff.

to physical events and other happenings. Examining them with reference to his four causes, Aristotle classes chance (and spontaneity) among the efficient causes.[44] Necessity, on the other hand, offers the principal obstacle to his conviction that nature is teleological, so that its claims must be matched against the evidence for purpose in the physical world.[45] In the end, as we already know, these claims turn out to coincide with what can be said on behalf of the substratum and its movements, which means that the opposition between necessity and purpose resolves into a side-by-side existence of the material and the teleological cause. They are mutually complementary, although not of equal worth.

However, it lies in the nature of things that chance too makes claims which interfere with the dominion of purpose. Thus even in the chapters in which Aristotle is primarily concerned with studying the compatibility or incompatibility of necessity and purpose, he finds it necessary once more to consider also the arguments that may be advanced on behalf of chance.[46] For a short time chance here seems to figure as a third claimant, though in truth its place is on the side of necessity. If only necessity, but no purpose, were at work, the valuable and viable products of nature would have to be ascribed to chance.[47] As matters work out, the claims of chance can be rather easily warded off. The specific reason why Aristotle here for a moment gives attention to chance is that Empedocles (as he understands him) had allowed it to operate in the origin of living beings. In Aristotle's opinion biology provides particularly strong evidence for the teleological conception of nature. He makes an effort—or the semblance of an effort—to go along with Empedocles' evolutionary approach yet immediately decides that chance should have found no place in it.[48]

[44] II,6.198a2ff. Actually, however, what must be cleared up in chs. 4 and 5 is the relation between chance and purpose.

[45] II,8f.   [46] II,8.198b23ff., 199b1ff.

[47] Speaking of the Presocratic cosmologies which have no place for mind, God, or craft, Plato (*Legg.* X,889c1) says that in them the world and everything in it have come into existence κατὰ τύχην ἐξ ἀνάγκης (cf. c6). There can indeed be no οὗ ἕνεκα. *Tim.* 46e5 where ἀνάγκη can only produce τὸ τυχὸν ἄτακτον is different. That Democritus too saw ἀνάγκη and τὸ αὐτόματον jointly operate, e.g., in the formation of the whirl (Bailey, *Atomists*, 138ff.), seems to me far from certain; Simplicius *In Phys.* 327.25 Diels did not actually find τὸ αὐτόματον in Democritus' text.

[48] See esp. 199b5ff. In Aristotle's static and eternal Cosmos there is no room for

Aristotle says that in the systems of the early thinkers he has looked in vain for a definition, or any kind of statement about the nature, of chance.[49] On the other hand, he seems to agree with Plato in holding that they made ample use of this "cause."[50] This opinion is not completely borne out by the independent evidence at our disposal. In particular it is difficult to find confirmation for Plato's rather sweeping indictment that nature and chance have jointly brought the elements into existence and created the Cosmos with everything in it (including, of course, the living beings).[51] Undoubtedly both Plato and Aristotle missed in the earlier systems something corresponding to their own concept of design or purpose; finding nothing of the kind —and apart from Anaxagoras' *nous* no agency that could represent them —they were prone to feel that things came to pass at random and by accident. In actual fact, Plato and Aristotle found the belief in chance and its powerful sway not so much in the Presocratic systems as in the thinking habits of their own contemporaries. As Aristotle himself plainly enough says, "everybody" ascribes to chance a good deal of what happens.[52] Nor was this just a thoughtless habit of the man in the street, but in the measure in which the belief in the traditional gods lost ground blind, irrational chance established itself in their place. Soon enough chance became deified and was regarded as the supreme power to whose will or caprice everything is subject. New Comedy

---

evolution. In our passage he tries to think in terms of this concept; yet his references to the *sperma* (b7ff.) show that this is far from easy for him. Cf. for a more detailed analysis Cherniss, *Presocr.*, 253ff.

[49] II,4.196a8.   [50] *Ibid.*, a19 and esp. 25ff.

[51] *Legg.* X,889bff. (for the role in the Cosmos of chance and τὸ ἄλογον see also *Phileb.* 28d). Aristotle in II,4 indicates that the Presocratics do not explicitly make use of *tyche;* in fact, he admits that they deny her existence (see 196a1 with Ross's note). And yet he finds them in effect giving *tyche* a good deal of power in their cosmogony. 196a24ff. may well refer in particular to the more recent schools, including the atomists—the same atomists who, according to 196a1, provided the accepted interpretation of this passage is correct, deny the influence of *tyche*. Incidentally, Simplicius says (330.1b) that Democritus in his cosmology "gave the appearance" of employing (or "was held" to employ, ἐδόκει) *tyche*. The same Simplicius seems to have diligently scanned Empedocles' physical poem for references to *tyche*. The results are not too impressive. I am not sure that even B103 could survive as evidence under close scrutiny; for ultimately Cypris is responsible for the mixture of the elements in our blood—as well as in our eyes. Wilamowitz (*D. Glaube d. Hellenen*, 2 [1932], 300) is probably correct in explaining such references to *tyche* as a feature of Empedocles' poetic "style." Cherniss seems to make unnecessarily large concessions to Aristotle (*Presocr.*, 190).

[52] πάντες, 196a15, which Ross in his "Analysis" rightly paraphrases "all men."

is generally regarded as our first witness to these beliefs, yet we have in fact considerably earlier evidence. In particular, the tragedies of Euripides' last period anticipate in this point as in so many others the pattern and outlook of New Comedy.[53]

Quite logically, then, Aristotle in defining chance and delimiting its scope of operation has his eye on the realm of human actions and experiences. As regards the Cosmos he is so firmly convinced of its inherent order and regularity that no word of refutation needs to be wasted on those who find chance operating in it.[54]

We speak of chance and chance happenings, Aristotle explains, when something that is normally done on purpose or by deliberate choice comes about without such antecedents. This, however, does not mean that there is no causal nexus. On the contrary, causes are definitely present, though what they would normally cause—or are intended to cause—is different from what "happens" to come about. This is illustrated by the case of the man who came to the market place in order to buy something and happened to meet his debtor in the act of acquiring the needed money.[55] The causes or reasons which brought the creditor to the market caused "by themselves" his coming and "accidentally" his meeting the debtor. Now the distinction between the essential which belongs to a thing (or event) by itself and the accidental is one which Aristotle employs readily and frequently. The origin of this distinction has not yet been cleared up, but the "essential" which is close to substance (*ousia*) and the definition [56] must somehow go back to the doctrine of Forms; and, as in all such cases, we should make allowance for the possibility that it figured in Academic discussions. Thanks to this differentiation Aristotle can absorb "chance" into his system, yet the "accidental" can surely never become a mainstay of it nor can it form a valid principle of physical explanation. The causes

---

[53] Especially important are *Ion* 1512ff. and *Hel.* 711; see also *El.* 610, *Iph. T.* 907, and *Hel.* 698f. Cf. W. Schadewaldt, *Monolog. u. Selbstgespräch* (Neue philol. Untersuchgg. 2; Berlin, 1926), 255ff.; my *Entwicklung d. arist. Logik* (N. phil. Unt. 4; Berlin, 1929), 138ff.; Gerda Busch, *Untersuchgg. z. Wesen der Tyche in d. Trag. d. Eurip.* (diss., Heidelberg, 1937); M. P. Nilsson, *Gesch. d. griech. Rel.* (Munich, 1941–1950), I, 732; II, 190ff.

[54] II,4.196a24–b5; cf. Plato *Phileb.* 28d.

[55] II,5.196b15ff. (b29ff., 197a12ff.). In the *Protrepticus* (frg. 11; 47 Walzer) Aristotle says simply that chance events have no purpose. A closer investigation of the relation between chance and purpose was not necessary in the context. For a critical appraisal of Aristotle's theory see H. Carteron, *La notion de force dans le système d'Ar.* (Paris, 1923), 178f.

[56] Cf., e.g., *Anal. Post.* I,4.73a34ff.; II,13.97a13; *Metaph.* Δ18.1022a24ff.; Z4.1029b13ff. See *Entwicklung d. arist. Logik*, 83f.

which Aristotle's physics seeks to determine must be in the nature
(physis) of things. For the Academy, the belief that chance reigns
supreme must have been anathema; it was a notion at once presumptuous and shapeless [57] which Plato did not so much refute as counteract by showing rational and purposeful forces in control of the world.
Now the pernicious notion has been caught in the network of Aristotle's logical distinctions. In the place where it has come to rest it can
do no harm.

Spontaneity (τὸ αὐτόματον), as Aristotle defines it, applies more widely
than chance.[58] We speak of it even with reference to events that could
never have been planned; yet to understand its nature we must again
compare it with what would have been done on purpose. Because
chance events and spontaneous happenings give the impression of being done on purpose but are not actually so done, they must be assigned to a different type of cause, namely, the effective or moving
cause. Aristotle's final statement is that chance and spontaneity operate
whenever mind or nature causes accidentally something that they
might also cause "by themselves," i.e., by working in their own
characteristic ways. At first glance it might seem that mind is here
mentioned because in the realm of human actions chance has been
found to produce the same results as deliberate planning. Actually
Aristotle is here headed for something larger: "Inasmuch as spontaneity and chance are causes of the same things as mind and nature,
materializing when one of the latter becomes accidentally a cause, and
as nothing accidental is prior to the essential, it is clear that the accidental cause cannot be prior to the essential. Therefore spontaneity
and chance are posterior to mind and nature. Consequently even if
spontaneity is ever so much a cause of the heavens, mind and nature
must of necessity be a prior cause of this all and of many other things
as well." [59]

---

[57] Cf. ἀόριστον in Aristotle (197a8f.). Quite different (as is well known) is Plato's
concept of θεία τύχη; cf. W. C. Greene, Moira: Fate, Good, and Evil in Greek
Thought (Cambridge, Mass., 1944), 298f., and Edmund G. Berry, The History and
Development of the Concept of Theia Moira (diss., Chicago, 1940). Note also Plato
Legg. IV,709af. (cf. Berry, 73). For tyche in Aristotle cf. also Helene Weiss,
Kausalität u. Zufall in d. Philos. d. Arist. (Basel, 1942), and for tyche as approxi-
mating the meaning "good luck" in the Physics D. M. Balme, "Greek Science and
Mechanism," Cl. Q., 33 (1939), 129ff.

[58] II,6.197a36ff.

[59] Ibid., 198a5ff. The first sentence of this passage seems to be misunderstood by
R. P. Hardie in the Oxford translation. Ross is surely right in preferring the first
of the alternative interpretations which he offers in his commentary (ad a6; only

Nowhere else does the *Physics* come forward so directly and emphatically with an assertion that mind and nature hold priority—in effect it amounts to primacy—among the causes of the Cosmos. The wording of this challenging proclamation, with the stress it puts on earlier and later causes, cannot but remind us of Plato's proof in *Laws* X that soul and all that belongs to it are "older" and "earlier" than material nature and chance.[60] This is the more noteworthy since the *Laws* and the *Physics* were probably worked out in the same years (roughly speaking, in the last decade of Plato's life).[61] If allowance is made for Aristotle's new concept of *physis*, the positions are not far apart.

In *Laws* X necessity too figures among the "causes" on which Plato's adversaries rely.[62] However, as the issue there lies primarily between materialism and spiritualism, necessity does not receive closer consideration. The dialogue which brings out the antagonism between mind and necessity is the *Timaeus*, and here the alternative is presented in a way quite comparable to Aristotle's discussion of necessity versus purpose in the last chapters of Book II. "The great mass of mankind," Plato here says, "regard [secondary causes] not as accessories but as the sole causes of all things, producing effects by cooling or heating, compacting or rarefying, and all such processes. But such things are incapable of any plan or intelligence for any purpose."[63] We may suppose that "the great mass of mankind" includes also and specifically the physical philosophers. They are in this respect no better than the common crowd. Aristotle's comparable statement is pointed directly at them: "All explain with the help of this cause [scil., necessity], saying that since the hot and the cold and each of these things are of such and such nature things are and come to be of necessity."[64] This need not imply that the physicists operated with elaborate definitions regarding the nature of hot, cold, and other

---

thus, it seems to me, can we do justice to the genitive τούτων αὐτῶν in a7; I refer τούτων to νοῦς and φύσις, αὐτῶν to ὧν in 6).

[60] *Legg.* X,892aff., 896cf. Plato speaks not only of πρεσβύτερον and (like Aristotle) of πρότερον but also of πρῶτον.

[61] For the presumable date of *Phys.* I–VII see Ross, *Physics*, "Introduction," 9f.

[62] Note κατὰ τύχην ἐξ ἀνάγκης *Legg.* X,889c1. Aristotle keeps the inquiry close to his study of causes; nevertheless he conveys the impression that the choice lies between two fundamentally opposed world views.

[63] 46d. For the incorporation of *ananke* in Plato's physics see 48a.

[64] II,8.198b1 1ff. On Presocratic "necessity" and Aristotle's material cause cf. Cherniss, *Presocr.*, 250ff.

"powers"; rather what Aristotle appears to have in mind is that they made use of these powers and relied—with or without explicit statements to this effect—on their operations. These operations would be the same as those instanced by Plato (cooling, heating, compacting, rarefying).

Again we may comment that, as Plato and Aristotle did not in the earlier systems find agencies representing purpose and design, to them purposeless, mechanical necessity seemed to hold a larger sway than is actually the case. Granted that Anaximander's cosmic powers may act by heating and cooling and that they, for example, turn water into dry land, we also happen to know something entirely different about them. They pay a penalty and make amends to one another. The necessity (*chreon*) which governs them is close to justice and equality; it is far from being purely mechanical. Yet when the ethical motifs of archaic cosmology were no longer appreciated, mechanical necessity seemed to dominate these systems. That the operations of Love and Strife cannot be described in terms of his necessity Aristotle admits, and all that he can do is to minimize their contributions in Empedocles' scheme. The complaint about Anaxagoras' inadequate use of his mind principle is familiar in this context,[65] and we shall here forebear to scrutinize it. As for the atomists, Leucippus is indeed on record for his conviction that "everything happens from *logos* and under necessity." [66] Here the association of *logos* and necessity would put us on guard against identifying "necessity" too readily and completely with the concept as it is used—or criticized—by Plato and Aristotle. *Logos* and *ananke* are still allied, not yet as in the *Timaeus* and the *Physics* in opposition to one another. It is certainly possible that the Presocratics allowed *ananke* much more power than we are able to discern and that they used the word often; yet we should beware of thinking that it implied for them the absence of regularity or order.[67]

[65] See *ibid.*, 14ff., for the reference to Empedocles and Anaxagoras (for the latter cf. Plato *Phaed.* 98b and the passages in the *Metaphysics* indicated by Ross, *ad loc.*).

[66] The fragment (which Bailey, *Atomists*, 68, would prefer to give to Democritus) opposes λόγος and ἀνάγκη to the μάτην (*Vorsokr.*, 67B2). Aristotle (II,6.197b22) connects the αὐτόματον with the μάτην and contrasts both with the realization of a purpose.

[67] See, e.g., Parm. B8.30; 10.6. It is tempting to surmise that Parmenides' use of Ἀνάγκη and Δίκη is not altogether out of line with Presocratic habits. Yet ἀνάγκη appears seldom in the authentic material, and it is difficult to know whether we

As we know, the *Timaeus* accepts "what comes about by necessity" as secondary causes, and Aristotle, having identified physical necessity with matter and the movements of matter, is similarly prepared to recognize these factors, provided they keep within proper bounds.[68] In the *Laws* Plato, having established the primacy of soul, suggests that it operates "taking along the movements of body"—which must, of course, again be regarded as "secondary"—and proceeds to specify a goodly number of these movements. Among them are growth and decrease, association and dissociation, yet also hot conditions and "coolings," heaviness and lightness, hard and soft, bitter and sweet.[69] One wonders whether Aristotle had similar processes in mind when in the corresponding context he refers to the "movements of matter." The first kind of movement that comes to mind is the natural movements of the elements upward or downward which in Aristotle's thought are closely associated with the qualities heavy and light.[70] However, they are not necessarily the best illustrations of what he has in mind.

We hope to get more light on the working of necessity by looking at the details of Plato's and Aristotle's physical doctrine. In the *Timaeus*, however, this attempt is beset with difficulties because the elements when shown in action are no longer in the condition in which they issued forth from their mother, the receptacle, but have received a higher degree of Form—mathematical shape. Some movements, it is true, do arise in the receptacle, and it may not be fanciful to relate them to the inherent and peculiar qualities of the four elements.[71] Elsewhere the actions, interactions, and changes in the physical world are traced to the elements—either to the specific mathematical shape of their units or simply to the presence or absence of an element in a given situation. Fire burns, cuts, and separates because it has the form of a pyramid. (Having nothing like Aristotle's concept of matter, Plato here and often makes a "form" responsible for what is "of necessity" and what Aristotle might well regard as an action or

---

should attach any importance to its rather frequent appearance in secondhand accounts (see Kranz's Index, 42a). Eur. *Tro.* 886 should be significant.

[68] II,9.200a30; see above, p. 108.

[69] *Legg.* X,896eff. (If most of these items are not, properly speaking, "movements" or changes, we should probably think of them as conditions brought about by movements.)

[70] *De caelo* IV,1.308a29 and *passim*.

[71] *Tim.* 52e1ff.; note the reference to the *dynameis*, e2.

"movement" of matter.) Cooling comes about through the withdrawal
of fire.[72] Here we should note that "the cold" as such does not operate. We know that in the *Timaeus* the powers are not given an independent status and not allowed independent activities.[73] In this point
Aristotle's attitude stands in sharp contrast to Plato's. Finding it possible
to establish a very close connection between his "matter" and the
powers, he uses the latter extensively. It is they which change—appear
and depart, and thus certainly "move"—when elements turn into one
another.[74] Moreover, the hot and the cold play an essential role in the
formation of living beings. A glance at the treatise *On the Generation
of Animals* would convince us of the extent to which Aristotle uses
the very processes which Plato somewhat contemptuously describes
as the explanations resorted to by "most men." Without heating and
cooling, compacting and rarefying, Aristotle could not have made
much headway in his biological research. Processes of this kind could
probably be called "movements of matter." [75] Yet his biology is emphatically teleological, and when Aristotle explains in detail how
the hot and the cold work in fashioning the parts and organs of an
animal, it is axiomatic that they operate for a purpose, and the purpose
can often be specified. "The hot" and "the cold" are the instruments
of *physis* which it uses in achieving its ends.[76] In the treatise *On Coming to Be* the teleological cause is less in evidence, and it is difficult to
say in what form it could be present. The powers here work rather
freely in their own way. The treatise which we read as the fourth book
of Aristotle's *Meteorologica* allows them even greater freedom and
seems to fall in with the method of "most men" which Plato criticized
and wished to restrict.[77] Thus the wheel has come full circle; but this

[72] See, e.g., *Tim.* 56d1, 67e5ff., 78e5ff. (cf. 80d3), 59a6f.
[73] See below, Ch. 17.
[74] *De gen.* II,4. To say that "there are no properties [scil., in Aristotle's system]
which are not purposeful" (D. M. Balme, *Cl. Q.*, 33 [1939], 136) is not entirely
correct. Aristotle finds it quite possible to discuss the activity of the "powers"
without relating it to purpose. Balme, while rightly stressing the teleological connotations of *physis*, seems at times to forget that teleology is only one of its facets.
It goes too far to call Aristotle's distinction between purpose and necessity "a
relative, inessential and fugitive distinction."
[75] II,9.200ab1f.   [76] See, e.g., *De gen. anim.* II,4.740b26ff., 6.743a36ff.
[77] Concentration on *hyle* and absence of the teleological point of view characterize the method employed in the fourth book of the *Meteorologica*. Cf. the author's admission (12.390b28ff., 391a4f.). His justification applies *mutatis mutandis*
also to *De gen. et corr.* Cf. H. D. P. Lee in the Loeb edition of the *Meteorologica*
(London and Cambridge, Mass., 1952), xv.

treatise is hardly Aristotle's own work, and we conclude this brief survey by repeating that Aristotle's biology keeps the "powers" in their subordinate position and that for him the "movements of matter" are and remain secondary.

In Plato's scheme the agent and representative of purpose is mind—a planning and designing mind which the *Timaeus* even "personalizes" as a creating God. Without mind Plato's entire teleological pattern would be meaningless; by showing in detail how mind organizes nature, Plato has done what in his opinion Anaxagoras attempted but failed to carry through. Now the sentence of the *Physics*, which has already been quoted—"Chance and spontaneity are posterior to mind and nature, and if spontaneity is ever so much a cause of the heavens, mind and nature must be prior causes of this all and of many other things" [78] —may suggest that Aristotle is determined to preserve this Platonic connection between mind and the presence of purpose in the world. In some way Aristotle will indeed implement this statement; yet it is a new way. The existence of this "all" depends on the prime mover who causes the circular movement of the first heaven and is in principle responsible for order and regularity in the world. This prime mover is entirely devoid of matter, his being is mind, and his only activity is thinking.[79]

But the juxtaposition of nature and mind in our sentence points in a new direction. If nature itself becomes teleological, it may supplant mind in a good part of its cosmological functions. Nature itself is now capable of working toward ends and achieving them by making the best use of its material. In Aristotle's biological studies it is always nature—and never mind—which is credited with such procedure. Aristotle has full confidence in its capacity.[80]

Just as the new concept of nature incorporates the principle of motion, having shaken off the "outside" control by soul, so nature absorbs into its own structure the orientation toward ends for which it formerly had to rely on mind. And just as nature is not ideally qualified for the one new task, because some of its phases lack life, so it is prima facie not too well prepared for the other, since it does not either think or plan. Yet it will no longer permit anyone else to do the thinking and planning for it: "If it is by nature and for a purpose that the swallow

---

[78] II,6.198a5ff.; see above, p. 107.   [79] *Metaph.* Λ7.1072b14ff.; 9.

[80] See above, Note 22, and the passages collected by Bonitz, 836a51ff., b40ff., 47ff. (note the phrase ἡ φύσις αὐτή).

makes her nest and the spider his web and that plants make leaves for
the sake of fruits and send their roots downward for the sake of nourishment, it is evident that this kind of cause exists in things that come
about and are by nature." [81]

Aristotle's thesis in the chapter from which we quote is that "nature
is a purpose cause." [82] In fact, it is nature itself—not nature and mind—
which he upholds in the contest with necessity. Still it would be unfair
to regard the joint reference to mind and nature in the earlier passage
as a mere courtesy bow in the direction of the former; for the tone of
this sentence is genuinely enthusiastic. Mind is still honored and appreciated (in this regard it fares better than the world soul, which does not
even receive a compliment on the occasion of its demise). The reason
is hardly that nature owes its new strength to the corresponding position of mind in Plato—for this kind of "historical gratitude" is quite
foreign to Aristotle—nor should we suspect that Aristotle is not yet
entirely convinced of nature's capacity to fill the new role and therefore keeps mind in reserve. What accounts for his comparatively generous treatment of mind is that he indeed means to employ it, if in a
new function. His doctrine of the first mover may not yet have taken
definite shape; yet Aristotle is confident that mind is to have an important place in this cosmic scheme.[83]

[81] II,8.198a26ff. In 198b16 Aristotle refers to one of his most significant meteorological doctrines, the cycle of exhalation and precipitation, apparently with a view
to denying it a teleological function. Rain has no purpose. Popular teleological
views of it are mistaken. Actually all that Aristotle probably has in mind is to
repudiate the naïve and popular teleology. Zeus does not send rain to make good
corn grow. In his own cosmic scheme precipitation has an essential function. It is a
part of the cosmic *taxis* and *kyklos* which imitate the perfect heavenly *kyklos*,
contributing not a little to the eternal order of the world.

[82] II,8.198b10.

[83] Cherniss (*Pl. and the Acad.*, 595) points to II,7.198a35–b4 as proving Aristotle's
familiarity with the concept of the unmoved mover; combining the passage with
II,2.194a35, he infers that this idea appeared already in the dialogue *On Philosophy*.
That the idea appeared there in some form I should not wish to deny, yet I doubt
whether the two passages of the *Physics* are good evidence. 194a35 gives no indication about the context in which a distinction between two meanings or aspects of
the teleological cause was made in the dialogues, and of 198a32–b9 I am far from
sure that it belonged to the original conception of this section. The argument
beginning at a24 to the effect that three causes—formal cause, purpose cause, and
efficient cause—often coincide ends logically in 32 before the addition of καὶ εἰς τὸ
κινῆσαν πρῶτον. These words and what follows change the direction of the thought
and may well have been added at a later time, Aristotle feeling that the moving
cause did not get its due if it was said here to coincide with the formal. From a
more practical and methodical point of view he must insist that the efficient cause

On the other hand, when Aristotle in his argument for a teleological world view refers to people as wondering "whether the works of spiders and ants and other beings of the kind should be attributed to intelligence (*nous*) or some other faculty," [84] he is far from endorsing the notion that animals have a mind or that their actions are prompted by conscious thinking. It is nature itself which operates here and offers proof of its intrinsic direction toward "ends." Deliberately Aristotle selects his illustrations from the lower biological species (plants and insects [85]) where the operation of a planning mind is out of the question. In this respect his procedure differs markedly from the *Timaeus* where the Demiurge begins his purposeful creation with the noblest regions of the Cosmos and when he comes to deal with man bids his helpers to carry on the work in his spirit.[86] The perfect order of the Cosmos—in particular of its celestial area—and the "usefulness" of man's organs were for Plato the principal evidence for a planning mind. As for the lower animals and the plants, the *Timaeus* says just enough of them to indicate that they may be included in the teleological scheme, provided man, who is endowed with a mind, is considered as the end (*telos*) which they serve.[87] Aristotle briefly rejects this conception of "end,"

---

be not slighted. I do not pretend to be sure of what happened here. After all, the "afterthought" may have occurred to Aristotle soon after putting down a21–32; and there is another reference to unmoved movers in the "parenthesis" (Ross) a28–31. All I say is that the ground is not very firm; the section must be used with great caution for chronological and similar inferences, and if there are good reasons for regarding the doctrine of the unmoved mover as later than the bulk of the *Physics*, the hypothesis that our section consists of or includes later additions should not be considered a violation of good philological principles.

[84] II,8.199a21ff.

[85] *Ibid.*, 23. It is, however, clear that the presence of purpose is much more readily accepted in the case of insects than of plants. Aristotle here justifies the application of the teleological principle to the latter by saying that if one goes ahead step by step one can convince oneself of its operation. This may be a reference to slow transitions obtaining between the lowest species of animals and the plants. Physiological similarities between plants and animals had been pointed out by Empedocles (and probably also by some of his followers), but the teleological point of view had not yet been applied to plants. Our sentence proclaims Aristotle's intention of including them and points to the task which he assigned to Theophrastus. In the teleological study of the organs of man Plato and Aristotle had precursors (cf. Theiler, *op.cit.*, esp. 13ff. on Diogenes of Apollonia), and in referring to people wondering about spiders, etc., Aristotle may easily think of Democritus in particular (B154; cf. Ross on 199a22).

[86] *Tim.* 41a, 42e.

[87] *Tim.* 77a–c, 91d–92c. Note Plato's remark in 90e4 that without "necessity" one would not go at length into these matters. One can imagine that the "length" to

asserting that the end must always be stated "with reference to the being of each." [88] His own biological treatises supply ample proof that
his teleology is anything but anthropocentric. Just as by defining nature
itself as principle of movement he extends this principle to entities devoid of life, so by transferring teleology from mind to nature he ensures
its operation in every biological entity, including those devoid of mind
and incapable of conscious planning. This extension was justified because teleological studies tended to concentrate on tissues and organs.
If tissues and organs have functions and "ends," man could not for long
remain the only subject of these studies. True, Plato had channeled
this inquiry in a specific direction, wishing it to show how the structure
of organs and tissues helps to secure the ends of a rational soul.[89] It is
hardly necessary to say that here again Aristotle does not follow him.

To establish the teleological concept of nature Aristotle relies on the
analogy between nature and craft. He gives this analogy additional
force by insisting that action, which belongs to the sphere of craft, and
physical growth proceed along the same lines: "Surely as in [intelli-
gent] action, so in nature, and as it is in nature, so it is in each action
if nothing interferes. Now [intelligent] action is for the sake of an
end. Therefore natural things too have come to be for the sake of an
end." [90] So strong is his antecedent confidence in this parallelism that
he does not hesitate to affirm: "If a house were among the things that
come into being by nature, it would come into being in the same form
as it now does by craftsmanship. And if natural things came into being
not only by nature but also by craft they would so come into being
as it is in their nature." [91] Furthermore, to account for the fact that
nature does not always attain its end and that there are monstrous and
abnormal developments, the parallel situation in the crafts comes in
handily. The craftsman sometimes misses his end, but this is no proof

---

which Aristotle did go in his zoological treatises would seem to him quite "unnecessary."

[88] II,7.198b9 is a brief "methodological" direction.

[89] See, e.g., *Tim.* 70eff., 74e, etc.

[90] II,8.199a9ff. (I have followed the Oxford translation in putting in "intelligent";
the main difficulty, however, is to bring out the connotations of *physis* in πέφυκε.
I am not sure why Aristotle uses the perfect instead of the present which one
might expect, and I wonder whether besides other meanings of *physis* its equation
with *genesis* should also be borne in mind; 193b12).

[91] *Ibid.*, 12ff. Early Stoic definitions of nature as πῦρ τεχνικόν, etc. (*St. V. F.*,
I.120, 171f.; note *natura artificiose ambulans* in Cic. *De nat. deor.* 3.27, *natura
artificiosa* and *artifex* in *ibid.*, 2.58), betray the influence of Aristotle's physics.

that he did not aim at it. So nature too, while aiming at its ends, sometimes miscarries.[92]

To realize the Platonic nature of this confidence it suffices to recall the Demiurge of the *Timaeus*. Plato actually needs a craftsman to make sure of the teleological structure of the Cosmos. We may also remember that in *Laws* X craft is, like soul, one of the "older" causes and that its prerogatives are defended along with those of soul.[93] Now soul's association with all intellectual activities and endeavors is obvious enough; with craft it shares in particular the factor of mind. But Aristotle, when driving home his parallel between nature and craft, does not refer to the presence of mind and thought in the craftsman's activities.[94]

In Book II nature is understood and discussed as a cause in all four meanings of the term. We have given special attention to nature as principle of movement and as operating in a teleological fashion. After what has been said, it would be pointless to add further arguments for the genetic connection of these conceptions with Plato's philosophy. Actually, Ross and others have already shown that all four Aristotelian types of causes can be found in Plato.[95] It is true that there is no passage in the dialogues where all of them are enumerated and set apart from one another—the section of the *Philebus* in which the formal cause, the efficient cause, and something closely resembling the material cause are all simultaneously brought to bear on the *genesis* of a particular thing is the nearest that Plato comes to this.[96] The fact that in the *Metaphysics* Aristotle criticizes Plato for operating only with the formal and material cause [97] should not keep us from drawing the obvious conclusion: Aristotle's theory of the four causes systematizes distinctions

---

[92] *Ibid.,* 33ff.   [93] Cf. *Legg.* X,890d6, 892b2.

[94] See *ibid.,* 897bff.; cf. 896c9ff., 903b4ff., and 890d7, 892b3. One cannot help recalling that Aristotle in his biological works occasionally compares the operation of *physis* to those of a good and carefully planning house manager; see *De gen. anim.* II,6.744b12ff. For comparisons of *physis* and *techne* in Diogenes of Apollonia see again Theiler, *op.cit.,* 29ff., who deals very illuminatingly with Diogenes' teleological arguments and also comments on the position of the *nous* in his physical system. I cannot here trace in detail the history of the teleological motif before Aristotle. Cf. also Jaeger, *Theology,* 165ff., with nn.72 and 91.

[95] Ross, *Physics,* "Introduction," 37f. See also Claghorn, *op.cit.,* 118ff., and for the purpose cause 127ff. (Note the observation on p. 130: "Aristotle saw rationality issuing out of the world. . . . Plato on the other hand spoke of it as being planted in the world and its arrangements.")

[96] *Phileb.* 26d–27c (cf. Ross, *Physics,* "Introduction," 38).

[97] *Metaph.* A6.988a7ff.; 7.988a34ff.

that were known and applied in the Academy. As regards details it is noteworthy that in the *Philebus* the efficient cause appears as "the cause of mixture and *genesis*," not as cause of movement, whereas in the *Timaeus* and the *Laws* Plato is profoundly interested in the cause of movement and states in general terms as well as in detail how soul is the originator of all movements and changes in the Cosmos.[98] We cannot say exactly in what form the efficient cause was first conceived in the Academy—whether as cause of movement, of change, of *genesis*, or of happenings in general (Aristotle's favorite illustration is that man begets man;[99] yet if anything is a shibboleth of his own specific interests, it is the biological point of view). No more can we decide whether the efficient cause is a concession to the Presocratics. Aristotle was scarcely the only member of the Academy who would scrutinize the earlier systems; others too may have seen that Empedocles' Love and Strife and Anaxagoras' mind represented a type of cause that was essential for specific accounts of physical origins or changes. Shall we say that when Plato's own thought was moving in this direction he came to appreciate these Presocratic hypotheses as taking care of a real need? It may be better not to go so far. Plato's self-moving soul is, after all, different from the "moving causes" introduced by thinkers like Empedocles and Anaxagoras when the basic world stuff could no longer initiate motion.[100] The differences may have obscured for Plato the features or functions that the world soul has in common with earlier agents of movement. The turn in a parallel direction is now taken on a new level of thought and may not owe much to the predecessors.[101]

[98] *Legg.* X,984eff.; *Tim.* 58aff.

[99] See, e.g., II,3.194b30f.; 7.198a26f.; III,2.202a10ff., and other passages in Bonitz, 59b41ff.

[100] About this development see above, pp. 14–16.

[101] As Aristotle persistently ignores Plato's world soul (and not only when speaking of causes), one hesitates to think that his "efficient cause" owes much to this Platonic conception. There may have been some measure of agreement within the Academy regarding the need for a cause (or principle) of motion. In the *Metaphysics* Aristotle gives the Presocratics credit for operating with such a "cause"— in fact, he goes back as far as Hesiod's Eros (I,3f., see esp. 984a18ff., b18ff., b23ff.). Still, it is hardly possible to use these "acknowledgments" for specific conclusions regarding the origin of the "moving cause" principle as held by the late Platonic Academy.

6

Matter and Place

OF all the problems that arise in connection with Aristotle's scheme of four causes the most tantalizing is certainly whether Plato approximated the conception of a material cause. Neither the receptacle of the *Timaeus* nor the Infinite of the *Philebus* is an exact equivalent of Aristotle's matter or substratum. Of the latter it is at least correct to say that it receives Form,[1] whereas of the receptacle not even this could be asserted, at least not in a sense that would help us in our inquiry. Still, there is a good deal of common ground, and a passage toward the end of Aristotle's discussion of *genesis* may guide us in delimiting the area of agreement.[2] If *genesis* of any kind is to take place, there must be something that co-operates toward this end with the Forms, and this something must itself be utterly "formless"—so formless indeed that it is not knowable, in the strict sense of the word. It must stand in the same relation to the Forms in which gold or bronze stand to the completed statue. Now what is this something? A question of this kind could only be raised after the Forms had been set up as one of the two factors that determine a concrete object. This made it necessary also to identify the other factor.

Yet although Form is a novel concept and presents a novel contrast for the indefinite and indeterminate entity which is sought, something inarticulate and devoid of all specific shape and specific characteristic had for a long time figured in the speculations of the physicists. Anaximander's Infinite is eternal and prior to the emergence of the concrete

---

[1] Speaking more precisely, it receives *peras* and *metra*, *Phileb.* 25aff.), and thus the γένεσις εἰς οὐσίαν comes about.

[2] *Phys.* I,7.191a5ff.; see above, p. 86.

and individual powers (such as the hot and the cold and perhaps also the bright and dark, the moist and dry), and we may think of it as having no determination of quality or form.[3] Its individual character is transcendent but not specific. Empedocles' *Sphairos*, in which the elements have disappeared, and Anaxagoras' initial condition of things, when "all was together" and "nothing distinguishable because of its smallness," are linear descendants of Anaximander's conception.[4] Anaximander and Empedocles speak of their undifferentiated entities in exalted terms befitting a divinity. This suffices to show that the "inarticulate" need not by any means be the lowliest item of the system.[5] If Anaxagoras cannot on this point be cited as witness, he yet joins Empedocles and perhaps also Anaximander in putting the emphasis on the absence of distinguishable and effective "powers," a motif which survives in Plato and Aristotle.[6] This emphasis befits the followers of Parmenides. Things cannot lose their entity, because nothing new must come to be; they merely are invisible.[7] As Anaximander did not have the benefit of Parmenides' warning, he was probably less anxious to preserve the entities in his *Apeiron*. Finally all three, Anaximander, Empedocles, and Anaxagoras, agree in placing this condition of things before the origin of the Cosmos; in fact, it is from this that the Cosmos evolves. Of this idea too Plato's receptacle, being the mother of things "even before the whole [Cosmos] by a process of ordering distribution

[3] See Anaximander A9, 10, 16. Of recent interpreters cf. esp. Fränkel, *Dichtg. u. Philos.*, 341f. If we wish to be very cautious, we may say that the *Apeiron* as a whole has no determination. We do not exactly know what has become of the "powers" in it, except that they must be somehow merged, if not submerged.

[4] Emped. B27; Anaxag. B1. Cherniss has conclusively shown (*Presocr.*, 52ff.) that Aristotle, when reviewing the doctrines of the early physicists, foists upon their systems his own concept of a material substratum underlying the "contraries." In view of the misinterpretations and distortions thereby committed, every account of Presocratic physics must carefully guard itself against succumbing to the influence of his statements. This makes any search for antecedents of his indefinite and unqualified substratum precarious, but we need not, I believe, resign ourselves to the extreme position of dismissing all possibility of historical continuity.

[5] See Anaximander A15; Emped. B29; cf. Jaeger, *Theology*, 30ff., 141f.

[6] See *Tim.* 50e, 51a6 (compare the ἔνδηλον of 50e9 with Anaxag. B1). Aristotle does not in so many words say that ὕλη is ἄποιος, yet it is implied in *Metaph.* Z3.1029a20, where none of the categories is said to be applicable to matter, and in passages where ὕλη is called the substratum of the opposites (e.g., *De gen.* II,1.329a30, 32).

[7] When Anaxagoras says that in the original condition all things were "together" (ὁμοῦ B1, 4), he is careful, for the reason here stated, not to say that they are one. Empedocles (B35.5) is less precise.

came into being," [8] preserves memories, whereas Aristotle's static cosmology has no room for such a conception. Quite logically the formless substratum with him finds its place in physics, to wit, in the universalized theory of *genesis*, and in the doctrines concerning the formation of the elements. His question is no longer, "How does the fiery part (or stratum) of the Cosmos come into being from an inarticulate matrix?" but rather, "How does fire come into being from inarticulate matter?" It may be argued that the phenomenal fire which forms in the receptacle of the *Timaeus* is not the cosmic fire either but its precosmic or noncosmic counterpart.

When Heraclitus speaks of his God as changing and manifesting himself in various contrary forms but not in essence identical with any of them, he seems to have developed the concept of the inarticulate or indeterminate in a new direction.[9] Yet since the manifestations include war and peace, hunger and abundance, the connection between the indeterminate and cosmology is here less close. Again, however, its status is infinitely higher and nobler than Aristotle's "matter." In any case it is patent that the indefinite or the inarticulate, once introduced, did not lose its hold over the minds of Anaximander's successors. Even the comparison of this elusive entity with the qualitatively neutral base employed by the makers of unguents or perfumes appears to be traditional, if, besides Plato and Epicurus, Heraclitus too resorted to it.[10] One may wonder whether Epicurus' use of this simile did not have a precedent in Democritus.

However this may be, the atom clearly is the last important antecedent of Plato's and Aristotle's version of the indeterminate; for although the atoms are determined with regard to shape, they are devoid of all qualities or powers (as has been said, the "powers" had never yet lost out as grievously as in the atomist system). Later writers use the term "qualityless" ($\overset{\text{'}}{\alpha}\pi o\iota o\nu$) when describing Democritus' atoms.[11] The term as such is an anachronism, but we need not hesitate to assume that, like Epicurus, he denied the presence of colors, smells, tastes, or

---

[8] *Tim.* 53a7 (cf. 52d4).

[9] B67. For what follows cf. W. A. Heidel, *Proceed. Amer. Acad. of Arts and Sciences*, 48 (1913), 704ff., and H. Fränkel, *T.A.P.A.*, 69 (1938), 233ff.

[10] Heidel and Fränkel argue for a word like $\mu\acute{\nu}\rho o\nu$ or $\overset{\text{'}}{\epsilon}\lambda\alpha\iota o\nu$ (rather than Diels's $\pi\hat{\nu}\rho$) in the comparison where the manuscript has lost the crucial word. They compare Plato *Tim.* 50e and Lucr. 2.846ff., whose mutual similarity had previously been noticed by Paul Shorey, *H.S.C.P.*, 12 (1901), 204. G. S. Kirk, *Heraclitus: The Cosmic Fragments* (Cambridge, 1954), 191ff., is skeptical toward Fränkel's proposal.

[11] See esp. A57, 59.

any other powers, including hot and cold, in the "nature" of the atoms.[12] However, the atoms still represent "being"; that which must be kept free of all "secondary" characteristics still is the basic reality.

In Plato and Aristotle the indeterminate cannot aspire to so high a status. For, granted that the Forms too are "being that has no color and has no shape,"[13] it is not they but Plato's receptacle and Aristotle's matter which invite a comparison with the earlier concepts. We may therefore here deny ourselves a digression into the complex questions of the relations between Forms and qualities and, passing by also the Platonic doctrine of numbers, may concentrate on what seems to be comparable and relevant for our purposes. The receptacle and matter are passive principles, unable to create anything by themselves (Empedocles' *Sphairos* and Anaxagoras' "formless" state have the same inability). More important still, they are not completely excluded from the realm of being, yet not fully admitted to it either. The way in which the receptacle partakes of the intelligible is "very puzzling"; and in the *Timaeus* where Plato makes this statement he treats it not as being but as another "kind" which must co-operate with being to keep *genesis* functioning.[14] Aristotle's matter might be described in similar terms. As an exhaustive study of its relation to being is outside our scope, we may content ourselves with mentioning the extreme position which Aristotle takes in the treatise *On Coming to Be;* for if not typical it is bound to be in some way revealing. Having, as in the *Physics*, identified not-being with privation and having applied his doctrine of *genesis* out of contraries to the elements, Aristotle in a surprising turn of thought lets us see that his mind is not quite at rest on the subject of not-being. Rather suddenly he wonders whether it would not be better to identify not-being with matter rather than, as laid down in the *Physics*, with privation or one of the contraries.[15] This is a

---

[12] Cf. Lucr. 2.730–864 (for "hot" and "cold" see 843f.). The section which follows (865–900) denies the atoms also *sensus* and life. There clearly is a difference between the denial of qualities and that of life, and the thought of this section should probably not be traced back to Democritus. For although his atoms are in fact devoid of life, the question whether or not the principles should be "alive" does not appear to have been an issue in his day. It was probably raised for the first time by Plato (*Legg.* X,889aff.). See above, pp. 14–15.

[13] *Phaedr.* 247c6.   [14] *Tim.* 51b1, 52d3.

[15] *De gen.* I,2.219a29ff. (31ff.). This is an extreme statement (Clemens Bäumker in *D. Problem d. Materie in d. griech. Philos.* [Münster, 1890], 231, makes too much of it). For ὕλη as οὐσία (in some sense of the word) and other relations between these two concepts see the passages in Bonitz, 786a.

radical solution indeed—and a sad fate for the formless, indeterminate principle which had started its career as the divine and creative origin of all things, "encompassing everything and steering everything."[16] And if it escapes this fate, it must be content with the status of "potential being," another concept which would have been meaningless in the earlier systems and would run counter to the intentions of their authors.

For Aristotle matter or the substratum is that "out of which" things come into being (or are made). Plato's receptacle, on the other hand, is that "in which" they arise. Yet when Plato tries to make his idea "clearer" by comparing the receptacle to the gold which may be shaped into different forms and figures, he too speaks of molding these figures "out of" gold. It has been said that "in this point his illustration is inadequate";[17] curiously enough it would be quite adequate for Aristotle's concept of matter. We are so familiar with this concept that Aristotle's solution strikes us as the more natural. We may even be tempted to think that Plato, groping about in the opaque region where his "knowledge" has left him, "missed" the concept of matter. In truth it probably was inconceivable to him. For Plato and anyone sharing his convictions, to determine the nature of the "formless" must be a hard and unfair task. To identify the unknowable seems a self-contradictory proposition. Yet it remains a fact that Aristotle's identification of this formless entity has proved immensely fruitful both for his own system and for posterity. The only way of describing the formless was through a metaphor, and here again it was the cherished analogy between nature and craft which suggested to him the excellent metaphor: what the wood of which the craftsman makes the house is in relation to the finished house, this the substratum is to the formed particular entity.[18]

[16] Anaximander A15 (see above, Note 5).

[17] This is Cornford's comment on *Tim.* 50a (*Cosmology*, 182 n.1). For the "in which" motif see, e.g., 49e7, 52a6. Cf. also George S. Claghorn, *Aristotle's Criticism of Plato's "Timaeus"* (The Hague, 1954), 7f.

[18] Note the comparison with wood and bronze in the important passage *Phys.* I,7.191a8–12. ξύλον as used here would seem to be close to the pretechnical meaning of ὕλη. More technically speaking, the ὕλη of a house includes besides ξύλον also λίθοι and πλίνθοι (*Metaph.* H2.1043a15). Plato too uses the word ὕλη—without any intention to make it a technical term—of the material lying ready for τέκτονες (*Tim.* 69a6. Cf. the ὕλη for shipbuilding in *Legg.* IV,705c; see also Hes. *Op.* 807ff. On the whole, however, Hesiod's ὑλοτόμος seems to do more cutting and "fixing" than fashioning; *ibid.*, 420–436). On the analogy of nature and craft as presented by Aristotle see above, pp. 102–103. When Theophrastus says (*Metaph.* 6.8a19) that ὕλη must be understood κατ᾽ ἀναλογίαν ἐπὶ τὰς τέχνας καὶ εἴ τις ὁμοιότης ἄλλη, he appears unwittingly to indicate the origin of this concept. We may also note the τέχνη and τέλος elements in Plato *Phileb.* 54c2, where R. Hackforth (*Plato's Ex-*

It is very unlikely that the term *hyle* had ever before been employed for a similar purpose—if it had, one might expect to find it in such medical writers as the author of *On the Origin of the Child*.

What caused Aristotle to identify the substratum with the "out of which" rather than with the "in which" of the final product is another question. In analyzing the Presocratic systems, he likes to make the point that their primary concern was with the material cause.[19] It is possible that his study of these systems strengthened or developed his conviction that what should be set up in opposition to the Forms and co-operate with them in *genesis* was the "out of which" rather than the "in which." By all odds the identification of one cause as the "material" represents Aristotle's original contribution to the doctrine of four causes.[20]

The formless principle which is needed to explain the *genesis* of physical objects must have suffered a remarkable change of character if for Plato it was space whereas in Aristotle's scheme it has become the material substratum. Elusive though this principle is by its very nature—and hardly knowable—one would suppose that so important a change would make, if not a stir, at least a ripple in the philosopher's consciousness. Is Aristotle aware of the momentous departure which he has made? At the end of *Physics* I he contrasts his own doctrine which posits two contraries and a substratum for them with the Platonic doctrine of the great and small, yet not with the account of *genesis* that is given in the *Timaeus*. He here wishes to bring out that Plato did not arrive at the correct conception of not-being.[21] In this connection the

---

amination of Pleasure [Cambridge, 1945], 110 n.1) has found a "generalizing use" of the word ὕλη. The degree of "formlessness" varies with the context. Complete formlessness and indeterminateness need not be Aristotle's first conception of "matter"; it is reached where Aristotle uses the concept to explain the *genesis* of the element. This may well have been the point where the tradition as we have traced it became important for Aristotle (cf. *Phys.* I,6.189b2–10, esp. 5ff.). Cherniss' contention (*Presocr.*, 56, 88 n.372, etc.) that Aristotle thinks of the substratum in terms of the grammatical or propositional subject proves more applicable to ὑποκείμενον than to ὕλη.

[19] Esp. *Metaph.* A3.983b6ff. Cf. Cherniss, *Presocr.*, 220ff.

[20] If it is correct that it remained for Aristotle to develop the concept of the material cause (whereas the efficient cause was already familiar in the Academy), there is more point in surmising that he here owed something to the Presocratic antecedents; nevertheless any reconstruction of the mental processes by which Aristotle arrived at this new concept is inevitably hypothetical.

[21] I,9.191b35ff. If IV,2.209b13–16 means that Plato (in his lecture "On the Good") designated the great and the small as τόπος or χώρα, a reference to a spatial conception of this principle would have been possible even in I,9; however, as has

difference between a spatial and a material conception of the formless principle need not be mentioned. The contrast between *genesis* "in" something and "out of" something is never referred to in Books I and II. Now if the section dealing with *genesis* is silent on *genesis* "in," we may turn to the chapters on place, on the assumption that "in" may be more relevant to place than to the substratum, which seems to have emancipated itself from this preposition. Does the theory of place as set forth in Book IV throw light on the separation or distinction of the substratum from the spatial matrix?

Aristotle fully agrees with Plato on the proposition that "every sense-perceived body is in place," [22] yet for him this agreement carries no implication that the opposition between sense-perceived and intelligible entities is essential for the correct understanding of place. Nevertheless Aristotle, while concentrating on sense-perceived, physical bodies,[23] had to consider doctrines that made place (or space) a constitutive factor of these bodies. In the *Timaeus* space co-operates with the eternal Forms in bringing physical objects into existence. Whether or not Aristotle believed in eternal Forms, the role given to space in the formation of individual things could not be ignored. In fact, Aristotle does not ignore it; yet so completely does the concept of matter now replace the receptacle that Aristotle cannot help rephrasing Plato's doctrine in terms of this new concept. From his point of view what Plato did was to make matter identical with space.[24]

---

been said, Aristotle is here interested in another point of disagreement. At 209b13ff. Aristotle says that although Plato in his "Unwritten Doctrines" gave an account of the "participant" (μεταληπτικόν) which differs from the *Timaeus*, ὅμως τὸν τόπον καὶ τὴν χώραν τὸ αὐτὸ ἀπεφήνατο. I take the last words to mean that Plato again asserted the identity of space and place with the participant (cf. b13), i.e., this time with the great and small. Wicksteed and Cornford (in their translation) and Hardie think that τὸ αὐτό merely links space and place (Ross's position is not quite clear). Philoponus and Themistius understand an identification of ὕλη and τόπος, A. E. Taylor (*A Commentary on Plato's Timaeus* [Oxford, 1928], 668) of ὕλη and χώρα.

[22] IV,1.208b28. It may be noted, however, that Aristotle reaches this Platonic dogma (cf. *Tim.* 52a4–7, c2–5) along more empirical lines (208b1–25).

[23] For Aristotle what is not in τόπος is not, as for Plato, the Forms (see again *Tim.* 52aff.) but the Cosmos as a whole (see esp. 5.212b8222) and, as he elsewhere (*De caelo* I,9.279a18) states, the deity.

[24] IV,2.209b11. See also Note 21. For this identification of Plato's χώρα with his own ὕλη Aristotle has often been criticized. See, e.g., Taylor, *op.cit.*, 346f.; Ross, *ad loc.*; Cherniss, *The Riddle of the Early Acad.* (Berkeley and Los Angeles, 1945), 16. On Cherniss' interpretation of this passage cf. my comments in *Cl. Weekly*, 40 (1947), 166.

Aristotle readily grants that there were reasons for this identification. Even in terms of his own system (which he cannot keep out of the discussion) there are some prima-facie plausible arguments for identifying place with matter. However, they are balanced by others suggesting that place should be identified with Form. Inasmuch as the place of an object delimits it and marks out its shape, it would seem to be the Form of this object—the Form, needless to say, being here not something subsisting apart. On the other hand, if one thinks of this place as actually occupied by the object which stretches out from limit to limit, matter and place tend to coincide.[25] Thus the identification of place with one of the two constitutive factors of a physical body would make sense even in Aristotle's terms; in fact, these possibilities emerge quite naturally during his inquiry into the nature and properties of place, though the concepts with which he operates (limit, delimiting, surrounding, surrounded, size, distance between the limits) are not those that figure in Plato's description of the receptacle. Still, it stands to reason that the need of clarifying the relationship between place and the constitutive factors of a physical body had been made acute by Plato's doctrine of the receptacle. What is at stake, even though Aristotle does not *expressis verbis* say so, is his own conception of the substratum as something material, not spatial or local. The substratum is saved from being merged in place, and its distinct character is vindicated as soon as Aristotle points out that place and the object in it are separable from each other.[26] If an object can be removed from its present place to another, its place cannot belong to it in the same sense in which its material nature and its form are indispensable ingredients of its being. Physical objects which occupy a place are "movable." At the very beginning of his inquiry Aristotle mentions change (or alternation) of place as evidence that space must be something and that it must be distinct from the objects in it.[27]

---

[25] IV,2.209b1–11. Aristotle returns to this alternative in 4.211b5. The tentative identification of place and εἶδος (209b1–5) is worked out in terms which might appeal to a Platonist. Yet we do not know whether any member of the Academy really advocated this equation, and, considering Plato's own conception of χώρα, one would hesitate to believe it. Robin (*Les rapports de l'être et de la connaissance d'après Platon* [Paris, 1957], 73f.) seems to stretch a point when arguing that not only the identification of place and matter but also of place and Form is inherent in Plato's own derivation of the element.

[26] 2.209b21–32; for some further arguments against the identification of τόπος with either ὕλη or εἶδος see 4.211b5–212a2.

[27] IV,1.208b1–8.

Here, then, we find the clear distinction between place and matter which Books I and II never bring out. To be sure, in Book IV Aristotle is no longer concerned with *genesis* and sees no need of pointing out how different his *genesis* out of matter is from Plato's *genesis* in space. Nevertheless there are a number of arguments and statements that bear directly on our question. Speaking of the behavior of things in movement, Aristotle explains that what is a part of a physical object moves "with" this object which surrounds it, not "in" it; by contrast what exists by itself—and is not a part—moves "in" the surrounding place. Actually an "in" relation—note how important this motif is here—exists also in the former case; yet this "in" denotes the relation between part and whole and is not a local "in." A thing that can move away relates to its surroundings not like a part to a whole; it is "in" them and, as long as it does not move away, contained by them; yet what contains it is the inner surfaces of the surrounding bodies which are not a whole of which it could be a part.[28] Slightly later, Aristotle says that Form as well as place are "limits" and surround what they contain but that only Form is the limit of the "thing," whereas place is the boundary of the "body" which contains it.[29]

Again, he admits, matter might seem to be identical with place because if an object changes, the same thing that was black is now white, and the same thing that was hard is now soft; this actually is the reason why we speak of (a persisting) matter. It is quite true that, also in the case of place, the same place is now occupied by air and then again by water. The difference is that we have to say, "Water is now where air was," not "What was air is now water." The "what" would indeed refer to matter.[30] If these differences of meaning and relationship seem obvious to us, we yet understand why Aristotle takes such pains to clarify them. Matter is his own discovery, and it was necessary for him to insist that the relation between an object and its matter as he conceived it was quite different from the relation between space and physical objects which in Plato's scheme occupied an analogous position. Place (or space) contributes nothing to the being of a thing; as Aristotle here once more points out, matter is not separable from the object and does not surround it, whereas place is separable and surrounds the object.[31]

To the fact that physical bodies change their place, that they now enter a place and later leave it again, Aristotle refers already in the

[28] IV,3.211a12ff., esp. 29–36.   [29] *Ibid.*, 211b12–14.   [30] 211b29–36.
[31] 211b36–212a2.

first sentences of this section, where he uses this phenomenon as argument that place must have some kind of reality. It must be an entity distinct from the objects. "Where water is now, there in turn, when the water has gone out as from a vessel, air is present and then again another body occupies this same place. Thus place is thought of as different from all things that keep entering it and changing. . . . Clearly both the place and the space into which and from which water and air change must be something other than either of them." [32] We may note that Aristotle here still speaks of space as well as place; later in his discussion the former concept recurs only in definite and direct references to Plato's views.[33] On the whole the phrasing of these sentences cannot fail to remind us of what Plato says about the receptacle and the objects that enter into it. However, Plato speaks of physical things as "coming to be and passing away" in a place.[34] The change which Aristotle mentions at the end of the passage just quoted introduces a different point of view. As we know, he is thinking of local movement. More generally Plato's emphasis is on the changeability and unstable nature of the objects that come to occupy space or a place in it; along with space he wishes to explain the nature of *genesis*. Since for Aristotle *genesis* is no longer connected with space or place, he can have no such intention.

To put it roughly, Plato proceeds from a discussion of space to one of place. At the beginning of his account it is space as such which matters, not parts, fractions, or units of space. When later he speaks of space in a more specific sense, he refers to places occupied by the various elements.[35] Each of the elements is, or a least has a tendency to be, in its proper cosmic place. Where Plato makes this point he approximates Aristotle's concept of natural places.[36] Now the concept of natural places appears in Aristotle immediately after the sentences quoted in the foregoing paragraph; that there are natural places is his second argument for the reality of place.[37] Yet although natural places are mentioned later in Aristotle's inquiry, it is place, not natural place, that he seeks to define in our chapter. The definition that "place is . . . the

---

[32] IV,1.208b2ff.

[33] 2.209b12f., 15. H. R. King (*Cl. Q.*, 44 [1950], 75ff.) contrasts Aristotle's concept of place with a notion of space which is not, however, the Platonic. His interesting paper deals largely with conceptual possibilities that were unknown to Aristotle and thus hardly anywhere overlaps my chapter which tries to relate Aristotle's doctrine to conceptions with which he was, or could be, familiar.

[34] *Tim.* 52a6, 49e7.   [35] *Ibid.*, 52eff.   [36] See Ch. 12.

[37] IV,1.208b8ff.; cf. 2.210a2ff.

[inner] boundary of the containing body" [38] applies to place, not to natural place; it rests on the fact that bodies can be moved from a place, not that they tend to move toward "their" place. True, Aristotle in the end makes some effort to show that the definition found covers natural places too; [39] yet the arguments which he here uses do not reflect the essentials of the doctrine of natural places as expounded in the books *On the Heaven*. This doctrine relates specific places in the Cosmos to the "nature" of the bodies. It is natural for fire to be at or near the circumference of the Cosmos, for earth to be in the center. This means that in contrast to the *Physics* the treatise *On the Heaven* recognizes an organic connection between place and body. The natural place of a body must be more than the "inner surface of the surrounding bodies." Aristotle does not seem to be very mindful of natural places when in the *Physics* he allows bodies to move about at will. Surely even "natural places" are neither the substratum nor the form of a body occupying them—for we should not make too much of a passage [40] where Aristotle goes so far as to call the natural place of an element its "form." Yet the place of an element belongs to its *physis* and cannot be as extrinsic to it as the "place" which Aristotle investigates in the *Physics*. Once more departmentalization appears as a significant characteristic of Aristotle's scientific work.

We do not maintain that the doctrine of place and that of natural places stand in flagrant contradiction to one another. Undoubtedly when an element, say air, is in its natural place, it still makes good sense to say that fire and water, in Aristotle's cosmic scheme, form its bound-

[38] IV,4.212a6.

[39] IV,5.212b29–213a10. Aristotle operates here with the "like to like" motif and also compares adjacent elements to the relation between matter and form (as he similarly does in *De caelo* IV,4.312a12ff.); nowhere in *Phys.* IV does he say that it is in the *physis* of an element to move to or occupy a particular cosmic region. He himself indicates that he has not made quite clear what he means by specific places and refers to a fuller and clearer account to be given later (213a4–6; the promise is not fully implemented, but we may reconstruct Aristotle's thought by consulting the passage of *De caelo* cited above and *De gen.* I.3 to which Ross refers; cf. Ross's explanations *ad* 213a1ff. and a3f.).

[40] *De caelo* IV,3.310a33 (see also b9, where, however, the surrounding element is only "in some way" the Form of the surrounded). Cf. V. Goldschmidt, "La théorie Arist. du lieu," in *Mélanges de philos. gr. offerts à Mgr. Diès* (Paris, 1956), 108. Goldschmidt lays great stress on the connection of place with movement and moving bodies (cf. IV,3.211a12f.). He appears to me at times to go too far; yet I may well have sinned in the opposite direction, as a result of my particular interest in traditional motifs.

aries and that they do so specifically where they touch the air and are in immediate contact with it. In fact, the *De caelo* occasionally resorts to the motif of "surrounding" or "containing" and operates with this relationship.[41] Moreover, the doctrine of place as set forth in the *Physics* is in its way and for some purposes (including those here studied) as satisfactory as the theory of natural places is in its cosmological context. But it remains true that *De caelo* establishes a more organic connection between the elements and their places. By doing so it is fairer to a particular tradition of Greek thought. What we read in the *Physics* about place would leave us with the impression that a thing may be anywhere.[42] Place seems here to be thought of as something very extrinsic and accidental; hammering as he does on the separability of thing and place, Aristotle may well have been led to carry this point of view to extreme lengths. As we shall see, he is following certain strands of Greek thought and losing contact with others.

In the first chapter of our section Aristotle refers briefly to Hesiod's *chaos* and says the idea behind this conception was that things to come into being must first of all have a place where they can do so.[43] The chances are that he may for once be at least approximately right with his guess about the motives from which a "philosophical" concept had

---

[41] See esp. *De caelo* IV,3.310b7ff.; 4.312a11 (see below, however, Ch. 13, Note 32). In the former of these passages Aristotle actually "quotes" the definition of place given in the *Physics;* in the latter passage he defines "containing" in terms which employ the relationship of Form and matter—the same relationship which in the *Physics* he is anxious to keep distinct from that between place and the object in it.

[42] Here again the section dealing with "natural place" (IV,5.212b29ff.; see above, Note 39) would form an exception. As has been said, Aristotle at the beginning of his discussion of place refers to the movements of elements into their natural places and treats them as evidence for the reality of "place"! In fact, this phenomenon here indicates to him that place "even has some power" (*dynamis*). Yet it is precisely this power of which the discussion in the *Physics* takes no account.

[43] IV,1.208b29ff.; Hes. *Theog.* 116f. The Stoic school, beginning with its founder, Zeno (*St. V. F.* 1.103f.; cf. 2.564f.), identified Hesiod's *chaos* with water or the moist condition of things that obtained before the world and its parts were articulated. However, Aristotle's local or "spatial" interpretation of χάος maintained itself side by side with the Stoic (see., e.g., Sext. Emp. *Adv. math.* 10.11). In our scholia of the *Theogony* the Stoic point of view prevails. The history of the various meanings and interpretations attached to Hesiod's *chaos* by later philosophers and theologians still remains to be written. Apart from the Hesiod scholia, it would find much interesting material not only in writers such as Philo of Alexandria and Sextus but also in the Christian Fathers, especially in the commentaries and other discussions of Genesis. For incidental references to the subject see R. M. Grant, *Miracle and Natural Law* (Amsterdam, 1952), 135ff., 143, and *passim*.

been created.[44] For, although the local or spatial point of view is not expressed in Hesiod's description of the *chaos,* the earliest section of his *Theogony* is a cosmogony; and here come into being the large parts (scil., the *maxima membra*) of the world in which all other and later gods are to find their places. In the case of Earth, who emerges immediately after *chaos,* Hesiod is quite explicit about the idea that she is the "firm seat" of all other beings. Some others of his first deities, like the Mountains and the Sea (Pontos), perhaps also Heaven, have a similar function: they are the place or "room" for the later gods.[45] This is not the only motif which operates here; primarily Earth is conceived as the mother or ancestress of all other gods. Yet precisely this same dual function of being "seat" ($\tilde{\epsilon}\delta\rho a$) and mother characterizes Plato's receptacle, the $\chi\dot{\omega}\rho a$ as he himself calls it.[46] That Plato, when expressing himself in mythical or semimythical form, finds it possible to revive this "archaic" dual conception is indeed remarkable. For Aristotle it can no longer come to life. Whether it had been kept alive between Hesiod and Plato is uncertain; our limited evidence includes nothing that could be regarded as an intermediate stage.

Our case is better with another conception of place which likewise makes its first appearance in Hesiod: entities have their place with their kin or their like, the Muses with the Graces and Himeros, Hades with Night and Death; even figures who for our view would represent essential attributes of a god, as Strength and Force in relation to Zeus, are said to be "forever seated" with Zeus and to share his "home," "ways," and "seats." [47] In the Presocratic systems the idea that like joins like is basic for the distribution of the elements in the Cosmos, but it also

---

[44] *Theog.* 116, the basic passage on the *chaos,* offers nothing that could directly support Aristotle's interpretation. A spatial factor may be discerned in *Theog.* 700 —*chaos* between heaven and earth; but primarily Hesiod even here visualizes entities, not areas. *Theog.* 736ff. (and its "revised version," 807ff.) says that the "sources" and "ends" of the four large parts of the world are located in *chaos.* "Sources" suggests *genesis* and beginnings, and the $\tilde{\epsilon}\nu\theta a$ (736) indicates that the poet tries to localize them (scil., in regions below the earth) rather than to arrive at a generalized concept of space. Paul Tannery in *Mémoires scientifiques,* 7 (Paris, 1925), 261, accepts too readily Aristotle's interpretation of Hesiod's *chaos.*

[45] *Theog.* 117; see also 129, 131f. (v. 130 is hardly genuine, nor do I believe that Hesiod is the author of either v. 118 or 128; however, the latter verse seems to have originated with an early poet who was in sympathy with the idea expressed in 117).

[46] For $\tilde{\epsilon}\delta\rho a$ (comparable to Hesiod's $\tilde{\epsilon}\delta os$) see *Tim.* 52b1 (also 53a2), for $\chi\dot{\omega}\rho a$ as $\mu\dot{\eta}\tau\eta\rho$ esp. 50d3.

[47] *Theog.* 64f., 767ff., 386–388.

enters into the discussion of biological processes, such as nutrition, in the form that the various "powers" (sweet, sour, astringent, etc.) join their counterparts in the body.[48] In Plato's account of the receptacle the entities that have found their seat in it show, as soon as they begin to move, the same tendency of associating "like with like." [49] In all these instances place is not something accidental or arbitrary but belongs to a thing in virtue of its nature, quality, or substantial and organic connection with other things. This is the tradition with which we said that Aristotle has lost contact in Book IV of the *Physics*. By contrast the doctrine of natural places in *De caelo* does establish a connection between the place of a physical entity and its nature; but by and large it is a new connection. In the few instances in which Aristotle there takes up the traditional idea that like joins like in the Cosmos he reinterprets it, usually to the effect that elements adjacent to each other in the cosmic scheme are in some respect alike.[50]

For the *Timaeus* it is, on the whole, space (*chora*) rather than place (*topos*) which helps to set individual physical things—floating appearances as they are—apart from the eternal Forms. To be in space is the metaphysical condition of all concrete, individual entities. The concept of "place" too can be used for this purpose.[51] As it refers to cosmological conditions and collocations as well as to metaphysical, it can serve as link between the metaphysical status of things and their cosmic place.[52] It is obvious how much of metaphysical background and perspective Aristotle lost by almost completely ignoring space and concentrating on physical aspects of place. However, we know that it is not by accident but from purpose that his account of place has lost all connection with the subject of *genesis*. It is matter, not space or place, which makes a substantial contribution to this process. And as the *Physics* is also indifferent to the relations between a thing's place and its nature, its conception of place must belong to another tradition.

[48] See *Vorsokr.*, 31B90. For the operation of the well-known "like to like" motif in Presocratic cosmology see the evidence in Kranz's Index, 309b30ff.

[49] *Tim.* 52e5ff.

[50] *De caelo* IV,3.310b10; cf. the same reinterpretation of the related συγγενές motif in *Phys.* IV,5.212b31 (see Ross, *ad loc.*). The συγγενές is here again the adjacent element; in Plato *Tim.* 79d6 the word is used of an element (fire) moving toward its kin, i.e., to the larger aggregation of fire in the Cosmos (note εἰς τὴν αὐτοῦ χώραν, *ibid.*).

[51] See *Tim.* 52a6.

[52] See, e.g., 57c3. With τόπος as used here we may compare ἕδρα, 53a2 (in the section dealing with the receptacle).

In arguments of a more "abstract" type when no reference is made either to the cosmic pattern or to the nature of a thing, place had come to be thought of as "containing" the object in it. There are reasons for supposing that Zeno of Elea had discussed it in this sense, and an interesting passage in Gorgias which embodies this approach is held to reflect that discussion.[53] This passage describes in remarkably technical language place as the "in which" of a thing and in the same breath speaks of the thing as contained (i.e., enclosed or surrounded) by something else, presumably another thing. Aristotle could hardly fail to be interested by the fact that, besides Zeno and Gorgias, Plato too had found it useful. In the hypotheses of the *Parmenides*, Plato finds or denies, as the argument or his manipulation of it suggests, a relationship of containing and being contained between "the one" and the others, between the one and its parts, and finally even between the one and itself.[54] These alternatives are tied up with the question whether or not the one is "somewhere," i.e., in place. The one which is not contained by anything and is nowhere is the one that has neither extension nor parts;[55] it cannot be a physical object. Obviously this one does not lend itself to a comparison with Aristotle's theory, which deals with place as occupied by bodies and proceeds throughout on the Platonic assumption that (only) sense-perceived objects are in place.[56] Yet another one may have something in common with Aristotle's doctrine, to wit, the one that is "in itself" and—from a different point of view—"in another" and whose parts are "in it."[57] However, not all "in" relationships are for Aristotle local relationships. The parts, he recognizes, are "in the whole" (and also the whole in the parts); yet here we do not use "in" quite in its strict and basic meaning, which is the local.[58] And to speak of anything as "being in itself" is for Aristotle something like a misuse of language—although he surely knew that this misuse had a distinguished history and on another occasion makes himself guilty of it.[59] Yet from the one that is "in something else" there is a way to

---

[53] Gorgias in *Vorsokr.*, 82B3, 69–70. For a tentative reconstruction of Zeno's arguments see Cornford, *Pl. and Parm.*, 148ff.

[54] See esp. *Parm.* 138af., 145b–e, 150e–151b.

[55] 138a; cf. 137cff. for the one without parts or extension. Cf. Cornford, *Pl. and Parm.*, 118f.

[56] IV,1.208b27f.   [57] *Parm.* 145b–e.

[58] *Phys.* IV,3.210a15f., 24; see also, e.g., 4.211c29ff. A somewhat different view is taken in 5.212b33ff., where the relation of place and the object in it is compared with that between whole and part.

[59] *Ibid.*, 210a25–b21; yet see VIII,6.259b26. On the whole cf. Note 69.

Aristotle's conception of place; but again it would seem that he insists on focusing more exclusively upon the local aspect of this "in" relationship. Likewise when Plato still later in the *Parmenides* speaks of the one as "contained" [60] by the others, the "containing" could be welcomed by Aristotle as contributing something essential to the definition of "place"; however, as Plato in the same context speaks of the one as "containing itself" (and being contained by itself), it is once more evident that the local point of view does not dominate his thinking, nor is it kept clear of other shades of meaning.

Aristotle complains that with the exception of Plato none of his precursors has attempted actually to define the nature of place. He himself wonders not only whether there is place and what it may be but also in what sense it may be held to exist.[61] He would not allow it any reality of existence by itself, i.e., independent of bodies. In his Cosmos—and there is no "place" outside it [62]—body touches on body and element on element, with no vacant space between them.[63] Thus there are always surrounding bodies whose inner surfaces can form the limit and, by the same token, the place of the object between them. From this point of view, to think of something as being in place would indeed come to the same as to think of it as contained by others or being "in others"; so far there is continuity between this noncosmological tradition and Aristotle's own noncosmological doctrine of place. However, just as the concept of "limit" has, besides its local connotations, certain others which Aristotle is anxious to discard from the definition of place,[64] so the notion of "containing" too has meanings that fall outside a purely local relationship. In the arguments of the *Parmenides* to which we have referred, the local point of view is clearly present when Plato speaks of an entity as containing another or being contained by it; what is not so certain is that other connotations are completely absent, for instance, when Plato speaks of the relation between the one as a whole and the parts that are "contained" by it.[65] In earlier thought the word "contain" (or "encompass") had been used in a very exalted meaning; principles like Anaximander's Infinite had been described as "containing" everything. In the *Parmenides* Plato likes to avail himself

---

[60] *Parm.* 150e–151a.   [61] IV,2.209b16f., 1.208a27f.

[62] 5.212b13–22; cf. *De caelo* I,9.279a11ff.

[63] Aristotle is probably the first thinker to connect the problem of the void with that of place and actually to treat it in the context of the latter concept (IV,7–9). See the discussion of the void in the "Digression" which follows.

[64] See above, pp. 124–126.   [65] 145bff.

of the different meanings of a term and to play with ambiguities. Aristotle's aim, on the contrary, is to distinguish between the various meanings that are latent in one and the same word and to be on his guard against the pitfalls of ambiguity. He knows that not only place but also Form encompasses and that both are "limits"; [66] all the more important is it to isolate the sense in which place encompasses and limits.

Ambiguity arises also when in philosophical discourse an object is said to "be in" others; again, Plato's arguments in the *Parmenides* have played with this ambiguity rather than exposed it. Thus it is easy to understand that Aristotle, before proceeding to a precise definition of place, finds it necessary to distinguish the different senses in which something can be spoken of as "being in" something else.[67] A special paragraph takes care of this task of sorting out the different meanings of "in," and it is interesting that besides mentioning the presence of a genus "in" its species, of the species "in" the genus, and of the Form "in" matter—Aristotle's own *enhylon eidos*—reference is also made to the whole as being "in" the parts and the parts as being "in" the whole. This is one of the relationships which in the *Parmenides* still appears under the heading of "containing"—and also, of course, as an "in" relationship; [68] it certainly was not kept completely distinct from local relations.

After Aristotle has set forth the other meanings of "in," he winds up very appropriately with the statement: "Yet of all meanings the principal one is to be in a container as it were, and generally in a place." [69]

[66] See Anaximander A15; Anaximenes B2 (of dubious authenticity). Cf. Jaeger, *Theology*, 30ff. and n.39. For Aristotle see *Phys.* IV,2.209b1ff.; cf. also 4.211b10ff. For the περιέχον as standing to the περιεχόμενον in the relation of whole to part see 211a29ff.

[67] IV,3.210a14-24. To be "in another" (*Parm.* 145e5) would for Aristotle be an inadequate definition of place. Moreover, Plato (immediately afterward) deduces the movement of "the one" from its being "in another," playing, I suspect, on the ambiguity of the words ἐν ἑτέρῳ ἀεὶ ὄν (146a4). Aristotle too is interested in "place" as the place of a movable body (IV,3.211a12ff.-b1, b14ff., 212a6). I have not found any significant agreements between him and Plato on this specific subject. Aristotle may be said to disagree in that he knows a local movement which does not require the moving object "always to be in something different." For if something moves as part of a whole, it moves in the whole or rather with it, not changing its immediate surroundings. This, however, is to move *per accidens*. See 4.211a17ff., esp. 34f.

[68] 210a15ff.; cf. *Parm.* 145b. It is perhaps not quite certain whether Aristotle's comment that "the whole cannot be outside [or, apart from] its parts" is a direct reference to the difficulties which Plato in the *Parmenides* passage finds militating against a complete identification of the whole and its parts.

[69] 210a24 (the word κυριώτατον may be understood in more than one way; Ross

In the subsequent argument the distinction between this meaning and the part-whole relation stands Aristotle in good stead. If an object moves as part of a whole—being "in" the whole—it moves not by itself but only accidentally; if, on the other hand, it is separate, it touches its surroundings, and its primary place is in fact what it touches, namely, the inner surface of the surrounding thing.[70] This precisely is Aristotle's definition of place. Here he has reached it for the first time in his inquiry. He adds that the inner surface of the containing objects cannot possibly be a "part" of the thing contained, nor can it be larger than the "interval" (or the area occupied by the contained object). The last point has again a certain historical significance; for in the arguments of Gorgias and of Plato's *Parmenides* it had been maintained that the container must be larger than the contained.[71] The "others" "in" which an object finds itself, and which contain it, would indeed be larger than it, yet in the precise and purely local sense which Aristotle has now given to the container it is only the inner surface of the "others," and this is exactly as large as what it contains.

THE VOID: A DIGRESSION

Aristotle found it not only convenient but also logically correct to go from the investigation of place to a study of the void.[72] For it is

---

in his "Analysis" paraphrases "the strictest"; we should perhaps remember the distinction which the *Poetics* 21.1457b1ff. and 22 *passim* makes between *kyria* as words used in their common, everyday meaning and other kinds of words, including metaphors). A special question which engages Aristotle here is whether anything can be said to be "in itself" (210a25-b22). On the whole Aristotle's attitude is negative—he would admit the phrase only in one particular sense which has no relation to its original significance. As to this, of the two alternative suggestions made by Ross (*ad loc.*) I should not hesitate to prefer that which connects Aristotle's discussion of this question with Plato *Parm.* 138a7ff. and 145b6ff., especially as we have now found additional evidence that Aristotle is close to the problems there taken up. Again this idea—that something rests in itself and has no other τόπος—can be traced farther back to Gorgias and perhaps Zeno (*Vorsokr.*, 82B3,70; read καὶ μὴν οὐδ' ἐν αὐτῷ ⟨ὂν αὐτῷ⟩ περιέχεται). The fountainhead may be *Parm.* B8,29, and Aristotle himself seems to be under the influence of this tradition in *Phys.* VIII,6.259b26 where—oblivious, it would seem, of what he said in IV,3—he speaks of the existing world, τὸ ὄν, as remaining, thanks to the unmoved mover, "in the same and in itself" (cf. also Anaxag. in *Vorsokr.*, 59A50—Ross's alternative suggestion—and Plato *Tim.* 34a3; of the Anaxagoras testimonium at least two words ἑαυτὸ στηρίζει(ν) are a verbatim quotation, as is shown by the occurrence of the verb in the corresponding context, Emped. B27,3).

[70] 3.211a17-34, esp. 31-34.
[71] *Vorsokr.*, 82B3, 69; Plato *Parm.* 150e5, 151b1ff. Cf. Goldschmidt, *op.cit.*, 111.
[72] IV,6.213a12ff.

possible to think of the void as a place which happens to be deprived of its content, i.e., which is temporarily not occupied by a body. Moreover, for place and void alike the question is not only what either of them is but also "whether" they "are," and at the beginning of the discussion it looks as though the reality of the one were tied up with that of the other. Aristotle's comments on their interconnection lead one to expect that the definition of place at which he has just arrived will be the basis for his inquiry about the void.[73] Yet this is not the case; as he sees it, the belief in void spaces rests not on the correct conception of place but on one of the misconceptions which he has combated. From a historical point of view the right conception and the wrong conception are equally irrelevant; what is true is that the void had figured in two large questions which Aristotle has inherited from earlier physical thought: "Is the void needed to make movement possible?" and "Do the processes of condensation and rarefaction presuppose its existence?" The latter question, it may be added at once, again involves a decision on whether or not these two processes as such have a status in physics, more precisely on whether the *genesis* of one element out of another cannot be understood without them.

That movement could not materialize without the void was an essential position in the atomists' scheme.[74] In a plenum, in a world entirely made of Parmenidean being and having no intervals of not-being, nothing would ever be able to change its place. True, a way out of this difficulty had been found by the doctrine of simultaneous mutual replacement, the so-called "circular thrust" or *antiperistasis*. Fish can move in water because while they push aside the water in front of them other water simultaneously fills the place vacated behind them. If sufficiently generalized, this pattern will allow movement in a plenum. Plato had adopted this method of explanation in the *Timaeus* to bring out the mutual connection of exhalation and inhalation: the air breathed out imparts movement to the air around our body with the result that some of the latter enters our body and fills the space left vacant by the air exhaled.[75] It has been noticed that he resorts to the same principle elsewhere in the work, and in the section which follows his account of the breathing process he seems to wonder how many other phenomena, especially of a "meteorological" nature, *antiperistasis* might explain.[76]

---

[73] *Ibid.*, a12–19; 7.213b31ff.; 214a16ff.   [74] See esp. Leuc. A7; Democr. A58, 165.
[75] *Tim.* 79a5–e9.
[76] 79a10–80d8 (a very compressed and rather obscure section where I am in doubt how far one may follow Cornford's ingenious explanations, *Cosmology*, 319ff.).

Still, its significance is definitely secondary, and its place peripheral. The question as to the cause of movement has for him an entirely different meaning. The cause and principle of movement are the soul, not the void or *antiperistasis*. Aristotle's thinking operates along essentially similar lines. He does deny the necessity of a void for movement on the ground that *antiperistasis* would suffice to make movement possible; [77] yet his main argument against the atomist position takes the form that the causes of movement are of a perfectly different kind. These causes lie for him in the nature of the elements. Some elements move by nature upward, some downward.[78] The void could not explain the movement in either direction; in fact, it could only create difficulties in Aristotle's scheme of directional movements, and the gist of Aristotle's arguments against its existence is simply that it does not fit into his own cosmic system. That Democritus, if he spoke at all of the void as cause of movement, used the concept of cause in a different sense Aristotle is unwilling to perceive.[79]

To show even more conclusively how disturbing the assumption of a void would be in a theory of movement Aristotle here develops doctrines to the effect that the speed of a moving body stands in an inverse ratio to the density (and consequent resistance) of the medium through which it moves.[80] This principle, he argues, would break down if a body were to move through the void, since there is a ratio only between strong and weak resistance yet not between resistance and no resistance. The same would be true of the complementary principle that speed is proportional to the size of the moving body; for if a larger body moves faster because it cuts through the medium with more strength, the void offers nothing to be cut.[81] It should be noted that Aristotle puts forward these famous or notorious doctrines only here while engaged in rejecting the assumption of the void. There is no reference or allusion

----

Thomas F. Gould in his master's thesis submitted in 1951 (Cornell Univ.), "Motion and the Void in Aristotle's Philosophy," 33ff., points out that Plato uses *antiperistasis* also in 59a, df., 60bf. to account for the freezing of water, the formation of rocks, etc.

[77] 7.214a28–32. Ross, *ad loc.*, refers to three other passages where in his opinion Aristotle employs the concept of *antiperistasis;* note that 215a15 and 267a16 refer to one and the same phenomenon; 208b2 should probably be discarded. Read in 214a28f.: ἀλλὰ δὴ οὐδὲ ⟨διὰ⟩ τὴν κατὰ τόπον κίνησιν (scil., ἀνάγκη κενὸν εἶναι).

[78] See esp. 8.214b12ff.; cf. 215a1ff.

[79] At least not in 214b12ff.; for a somewhat different attitude see a24f.

[80] For what follows cf. 8.215a24–216a11.   [81] See 216a11–21.

to them in the full and systematic exposé of movement that he presents in the latter books of the *Physics;* and the treatise *On the Heaven* merely states his conviction that larger bodies move faster than smaller ones of the same substance.[82] One wonders whether the more "precise" doctrines of our section have not been devised *ad hoc.* The fame or notoriety which these doctrines of inverse ratio have acquired stands itself in inverse ratio to their importance in his own system.[83] The history of science may know other instances in which theories that are of peripheral significance for their proponent later acquire a central place and become a touchstone for the validity of his system.

The other argument for the existence of the void that Aristotle considers at some length is its role in the doctrine of rarefaction and condensation.[84] Is rarefaction due to the development of void in a body, condensation to the elimination of void spaces in it? It is conceivable, but not certain, that Aristotle found this view too in the atomist systems.[85] Processes of this type have some links with the theory of movement; yet they belong specifically to *genesis* and normally take the form that one element (or one body) changes into another of either denser or less dense texture, the transformation of water into air and vice versa being a stock example. In Aristotle's system the gulf between movement and *genesis* is widening; while the theory of the former is dominated by the qualities of heavy and light, the latter rests on four

[82] IV,2.308b18ff. (only fire is mentioned, and we should perhaps not generalize). For weight and time see I,6.273b30ff. H. Carterton, *La notion de force dans le syst. d'Arist.* (Paris, 1923), 11ff., cites the passage of *Phys.* VI,8 along with others in which a moving *dynamis* is assumed. He admits, however, that it is difficult to take the passages out of context and to construct a "doctrine générale" (p. 16).

[83] Objections were raised and alternatives explored by the Greek commentators of Aristotle; medieval Arabic philosophers, especially Avempace (12th cent.), emphasized the problematic nature of the Aristotelian doctrines; late Schoolmen developed instead the so-called impetus theory. The development culminates in Galileo, who was familiar with some of these criticisms and alternative ideas. Cf. the illuminating study by Ernest A. Moody, *J. Hist. Ideas,* 12 (1951), 163ff., 375, where further references will be found.

[84] IV,9.

[85] Aristotle does not refer to a view that bodies are denser or rarer in texture in the measure in which they have more or less void between their parts. Such a view might be traced to the atomists, though it is not attested for either Leucippus or Democritus. The one thinker whom Aristotle here (216b25f.) mentions is the Pythagorean Xuthos, who seems to have regarded the void as essential for movement (cf. the following Note 86). Apart from the atomist theory of movement it is difficult to identify the proponents of the arguments put forward for the void (cf. Ross on 213b4ff.).

others, hot and cold, moist and dry. This dichotomy will engage our attention more fully later; [86] for the present we are content to note how it makes itself felt in his discussion of the void. Just as the infinitely large can be accommodated neither in Aristotle's scheme of movement nor in that of *genesis*, so the void is unwelcome in both.[87] *Genesis* and the transformation of one element into another can dispense with this concept because matter, as Aristotle understands it, takes on opposite qualities. As one and the same basic matter can become hot and cold or heavy and light,[88] so it can also be either rare or dense, in fact either large or small. His concept of matter as capable of contrary qualifications makes it unnecessary to worry about the actual physical process of a change from rare to dense or, indeed, about the nature of dense and rare. It will be seen that in order really to explain the physical change from hot to cold or moist to dry Aristotle must treat all these qualities as "powers" in the traditional sense of the word. [89] The identity of the matter underlying heavy and light is for Aristotle in *De caelo*

---

[86] See below, esp. Chs. 17 and 21. Aristotle actually begins this part of his argument against the void by discussing the role which dense and rare are supposed to have in the context of movements (216b23; see also 34ff.); and certainly not in 216b22–217a10, perhaps nowhere in this section, does he use κίνησις in the wider meaning of change. Yet as he himself believes in the reality of movement and change and cannot allow any "bulging" of the Cosmos (216b25, 217a15), two questions soon emerge as particularly pressing (217a10ff.): "How is it possible for bodies of rare texture to change into dense (and the reverse) without the existence of a void?" and "How can these processes be so balanced all the time that there is no increase in the volume of rare bodies, in which event our bounded Cosmos could not contain them?" The second question neither requires nor receives an answer in this chapter—nor anywhere else, as far as I see; for even the meteorological cycles would not answer it quite satisfactorily, since exhalation and precipitation prevail in different seasons. (But Aristotle, if he seriously worried about it, might console himself with the thought that sublunary expansions are trifling in comparison to the spaces filled by the first body.) With the first question we find ourselves in the realm of *genesis*.

[87] See *Phys.* III,5 with our comments below, pp. 165–166.

[88] 217a20ff. Aristotle does not actually refer here to heavy and light, yet the situation would be the same. Cf. *De caelo* 312a18ff., 30ff. and also *De gen. et corr.* 319a33–b4. These passages, incidentally, confirm one's suspicion that in our section the clause τὸ δ' εἶναι ἕτερον (scil., for the informed hyle; 217a24) should have its place after the words μία τῷ ἀριθμῷ (scil., ἡ ὕλη; a25) to which they introduce a restriction. The clause may be a later insertion by Aristotle himself, and it would in any case best be put at the end of the sentence. I should also depart from Ross's text by not opening a new paragraph in a26 (the δή of some MSS seems better than δέ as the second word of the sentence) and should consider deleting ἐγένετο in a28.

[89] See below, Ch. 17.

a conviction rather than a problem.[90] Dense and rare, which had been
of cardinal importance in some Presocratic systems and had changed
their status several times, but perhaps never disappeared, seldom engage Aristotle's attention in the physical treatises; what little he has to
say about them springs from the confident belief that the same matter
is capable of accepting either of these qualifications.[91]

There are some further facets and problems of the void that would
repay study either in a historical or in a systematic context; but the
most noteworthy departure of Aristotle is probably that, in principle
at least, he treats the void as place—place not filled by body. There
is no evidence that it had ever before him been brought into relation
with place—in fact, Aristotle himself (as we have seen) finds it necessary to resort to other lines of approach. The void, whether accepted
or rejected, had been "not-being," a conception which Aristotle remembers only once in the course of his discussion.[92] There are no
obvious links between not-being and place, and physicists who knew
it as not-being had the less reason for considering it in their discussion
of place.[93] When Aristotle represents it as a common belief that

[90] On *De caelo* 312a17ff. and 30ff. see below, Ch. 13 (with Note 32).

[91] *Phys.* IV,9.217a26-b20 (omitting with Ross b12-16). The changing fates of
dense and rare in earlier thought (Anaximenes, Anaxagoras, the atomists) demand
a special study. The main difficulty with which this would have to contend lies
in our ignorance of the precise manner in which thinkers like Anaximenes and the
atomists spoke of these opposites. For Anaxagoras they seem to have been a peculiar kind of power or power stuff (quality stuff in Cornford's phrase); see
59B12 (2.38.16D.-K), B15. For others they appear not to have been "being things"
(ἐόντα) but rather a mode of organization of these being things; see Emped.
31B104 and perhaps also B75. In B104 I should regard ἀραιότατα as an adverb, not,
like Kranz, as an adjective. This fragment, however, especially if considered in
conjunction with A86.11 (1.302.28ff.), where it probably belongs, suggests the
question how Empedocles could reckon with loose or "rare" arrangements of elementary particles and yet deny the existence of the void. That the atomists used
the void to account for these opposite conditions is hardly open to doubt.

[92] IV,8.215a11. For the void as not-being in Melissus see 213b14 (cf. above, pp.
4-5, on Parmenides and Melissus); for the atomists see Leuc. A6 and Democr.
A38 *et al.* (note, however, Bailey, *Atomists*, 118). If the *apeiron* was ever identified with the external κενόν (supposed to surround the Cosmos), Aristotle, except
perhaps for 6.213b22ff., shows no awareness of this. Cornford (*Essays in Honour
of Gilbert Murray* [London, 1936], 215ff.) has argued for this original identification, especially on the part of the Pythagoreans, and has presented an attractive,
if largely hypothetical, reconstruction of such early beliefs.

[93] There is, for instance, no connection between the two concepts in the *Timaeus*,
even though Plato has occasions to mention both and to deal with "place" at some
length (52aff.)—and even though Plato does not conceive of the void as not-being.

"every body is in a place" and that "void is a place in which no body happens to be," it is he who puts this "belief" or at any rate the second half of it into words.[94] Having foisted upon his—presumably imaginary —adversaries the notion that the void is a place, he goes even farther by pinning them down to one of the definitions of "place" that he has refuted. Those who believe in the void, he says, identify it with the distance between bodies.[95] But to think of place as a distance is a grave error. For Aristotle, place is not a distance, but something surrounding, or containing, a limit.

The only evidence that Democritus regarded his void as "place" comes significantly from Aristotle himself; in the extracts which Simplicius [96] offers from Aristotle's treatise on Democritus the latter is described as providing "a place" for his atoms and calling this place variously "nothing," "the void," or "the infinite." Here it is not pretended that Democritus himself spoke of his void as place; on the contrary, the indications are that, although Democritus used other words, Aristotle likes to think of the void as place. The *Physics* shows us why. Thus Aristotle's testimony about Democritus certainly does not militate against his own priority in establishing a close connection between place and void. For Democritus the atoms were being, the void not-being.[97] If for Epicurus the void is a place (*locus* in Lucretius),[98] he has "modernized" the system by adopting the Aristotelian definition. Whether he took the parallel step of regarding the atoms as "matter" cannot be decided.[99] In any case they are no longer "being";

[94] See esp. IV,7.213b31ff. (where these statements are parts of a "syllogism" which includes some further premises); see also 6.213a15ff.

[95] E.g., 6.213a27ff., 214a19; 30. A different view amounting to the identification of the void with matter is reported at 214a13; Ross, *ad loc.*, rightly calls this statement "unhistorical"; its historical value would be discredited by the fact that Aristotle has imputed to Plato similar views about place in a previous passage to which he here refers (209b11ff.).

[96] *In de caelo* 294.33 Heib. (= *Vorsokr.*, 68A37).

[97] For this well-known fact it will suffice to refer to Leuc. A6 and Democr. A37.

[98] I,334, 426. For Epicurus' own use of τόπος in this sense see frg. B14, Bailey (76 Usener). For attempts to introduce this word into Epic. *Epist.* 1.39 see the editions of Von der Mühll (*Epicuri Epistulae* [Leipzig, 1923]) or Bailey (*Epicurus* [Oxford, 1926]).

[99] There is some evidence for Epicurus' familiarity with the concept and word ὕλη (*Epist.* 2.93, 112 and see also the passage adduced in L. & S., *s.v.* γεννητικός), and I should regard it possible that *materies* in Lucretius either regularly or at least sometimes renders this word. Although not having all its Aristotelian connotations, the word (which the Stoics too adopted) could well serve to describe the atoms, especially in relation to the objects composed of them (συγκρίματα).

the once fundamental opposition between being and not-being has evidently lost its significance and interest. That Aristotle's definition of the void as a particular kind of place was preparatory to a rejection of the concept would not trouble Epicurus. Holding as firmly as the earlier atomists that the void was essential for movement as well as for differences of density and weight, he would not easily be shaken in his conviction of its existence. We do not know whether he considered Aristotle's arguments against these assumptions worth refuting (there is no evidence for his having firsthand acquaintance with the *Physics*). He does refute *antiperistasis* [100] but not necessarily because Aristotle had for a moment seen fit to endorse it.

We know that physicists such as Empedocles and Anaxagoras refused to operate with the void but not whether they actually explained how movement was possible without it. Was the *antiperistasis* which is employed in the *Timaeus* Plato's own discovery? Or had some version of it figured in the Presocratic systems? No definite answer can be given, though it may be argued that some doctrines attested for the late Presocratics create a presumption for their familiarity with this principle. Further study of these matters must be left to others. [101] We may notice, however, that although both Plato and Aristotle have the *horror vacui* they do not have it in exactly the same form. For Aristotle the void is simply not there; though he nowhere says in so many words that all cosmic space is filled with body, he evidently cannot envisage the possibility that the void could arise anywhere in the world, be it only for a moment. Plato, on the other hand, seems to contemplate such occurrences with equanimity. There are void spaces in our body because the elements which surround it constantly draw off some of its substance. And there are empty interstices between the geometrical figures which compose the elements and their aggregates. [102] To be sure, they may be filled, and there appears to be material ready to move up and fill them. Plato's doctrine may not be entirely consistent, but he seems less opposed than Aristotle to the idea of temporary voids

---

In the brief summary of *Epist.* 1 Epicurus may have seen no reason for using this technical or semitechnical word. Unfortunately it is not possible to settle this question with anything approaching certainty.

[100] See Lucr. I, 370–397 (with the comments of Bailey, *ad loc.*).

[101] Gould (*op.cit.*, 21) refers, among other matters, to Anaxagoras' and Diogenes' explanation of the breathing process performed by fish (Anaxag. A114): when the water is discharged from the gills, air enters the mouth; "for there is no void."

[102] *Tim.* 81a1; 58b3; 61a5.

forming between the material components of a body. Neither of them makes a special effort to prove that the entire Cosmos—everything within the "heaven"—must be filled with the four or five elements, to the exclusion of any vacant spaces (though both argue that the entire existing amount of the elements is in this Cosmos). Still, in principle Parmenides' pronouncement, "Everything is filled with being," [103] would be acceptable to both; the doctrine has in fact acquired a new reality in the Platonic Cosmos. The void and not-being, for some time identified, have now become so thoroughly separated that Aristotle, while he has no hesitation in consigning sublunary elements to not-being,[104] refuses to have traffic with the void. His objections are not of a metaphysical or ontological nature; they keep strictly to the sphere of physics. If deeper reasons account for his antipathy to the void, one may surmise that it offended either his aesthetic sense or his religious belief that some degree of perfection must obtain even in the subcelestial regions.

[103] Parm. B8, 24.   [104] *De gen. et corr.* I,3.318b9ff.

7

Time

WE have seen that Aristotle studies place without allowing the contrast between things that are and those that are not in place a decisive role in his inquiry.[1] The same elimination of metaphysics and the Platonic realm of being characterizes his investigation of time. To be understood and defined time need not be related to eternity.

Plato's famous definition of time in the *Timaeus* bears the imprint of the dichotomy which is basic for his system. Time is at once related to and contrasted with eternity, and the factor of movement which enters into the definition gets its point from the opposition to the "rest" of the eternal Forms. "Of eternity abiding in one [the Demiurge made] an everlasting image moving according to number." This image is time. Against this we may set Aristotle's definition: "Time is that in virtue of which movement is numerable" (scil., the aspect of movement which is numerable).[2] Evidently this definition has some connection with Plato's even if the contrast between the sphere of being and that of becoming has been discarded. Both definitions, besides relating time to movement, also incorporate the element of num-

[1] That "everything" must be in place Aristotle too, as one may see from IV,1.208b33, regards as a prejudice of οἱ πολλοί. Cf. 5.212b13ff. and *De caelo* I,9.279a11ff. It is possible that in the Academy (under the influence of the *Timaeus*) place and time were felt to present similar problems. Yet the successive treatment of these topics in *Phys.* IV proves little. In part it is due to the fact that for both of them there is doubt as to their reality (the εἰ ἔστιν, as distinct from the τί ἐστιν; see 1.208a28; 10.217b30ff.). But in the case of time this doubt is much more serious, and the arguments against its reality receive much more attention.

[2] Plato *Tim.* 37d6f.; Arist. *Phys.* IV,11.219b2f. For the relations between movement and time in Aristotle cf. Walter Bröcker, *Aristoteles* (2d ed., Frankfurt, 1957), 88ff., 92ff.

ber or counting. Plato seems to make number something like a structural principle of time whereas Aristotle goes perhaps a step farther when, immediately after giving his definition, he says: "Time is some kind of number." [3] Common to both is the conviction that the principle of number determines the relation between time and movement. What is again absent in Aristotle is the pointed contrast between number as belonging to movement and time and "the one" as associated with eternity and rest. This contrast as Plato formulates it suggests at the same time a reflection of the higher entity in the lower. Thanks to its connection with "the one"—which is obvious, although not specified—number gives to time form and structure; to the extent in which it has number, time is no longer an amorphous *apeiron*. Of this larger vision and metaphysical background the *Physics* preserves but little.

This loss may well be the deeper reason why in Aristotle, despite his efforts for a precise definition, the relationship between time and number still seems to be rather fluid and not entirely settled. When he feels the need of stating clearly and definitely in what sense "time is some kind of number," he decides that time itself is "that which is counted" and not "that by which we count." [4] Yet this decision seems to have little binding force; at least it does not prevent Aristotle in later passages of this section from referring to time as the yardstick by which we measure movement and whatever else may be "in time." "Inasmuch as time measures movement and the moving and does so by marking off some movement which will measure the whole movement . . . and as for movement to 'be in time' consists in being measured by time—both movement itself and its being . . . it is clear that also in the case of other things to 'be in time' means that their being is measured in time." [5] Between the two basic entities, time and movement, the measuring is reciprocal: "Through time we measure movement and through movement time." [6] Precisely in what way movement measures time would be obvious even if Plato were not much more explicit on this subject than Aristotle throughout the largest part of his discussion permits himself to be. The movements that not only measure but, as Plato sees it, actually constitute and even create time are of course those of the sun and the other planets as well as that of the entire heavenly vault.[7] This was the Platonic doctrine which had

[3] 219b5. [4] *Ibid.*, 7. [5] IV,12.220b32ff.
[6] *Ibid.*, b14ff., 22ff. [7] Plato *Tim.* 37e1ff., 38b6ff., c3ff., 39b2ff.

provided firm foundations for the intimate connection between time, movement, and number. As far as possible Aristotle tries to do without these specific movements. As he eliminates Plato's metaphysical point of view—the opposition between time and eternity—from his own account of time, so he at least limits the cosmological motif to a minimum significance. What he seeks to do is to establish the connection of time with movement in general, not, as far as he can help it, with any particular movement or movements.

At the beginning of his inquiry he rejects what he describes as the identification of time with the revolution of the whole (Cosmos), arguing that also a part of this revolution would be time but that this part would no longer be a revolution. This argument seems to be directly aimed against Plato.[8] It disposes to Aristotle's satisfaction of the "cosmological" approach and enables him to ignore it throughout the larger part of his inquiry. It is only at the very end of it, and after the relation of movement and time has been discussed from many points of view, that Aristotle rather suddenly makes a step toward Plato's position. Here he admits that, since in every counting there must be a unit, time too must have one and that the regular circular movement has something to recommend itself as this unit; for this movement is after all the first and its number is best known.[9] By this reasoning Aristotle may seem to have regained the Platonic position. We may recall that also in Aristotle's investigation of the principles

[8] 10.218a33ff. Simplicius (adduced by Ross, *ad loc.*) 700.18 reports that Theophrastus and Eudemus (as well as, later, Alexander of Aphrodisias) attributed this definition of time to Plato. The diurnal revolution of the heaven to which Aristotle appears to refer is indeed in Plato's time scheme the basic *metron* and unit of counting (*Tim.* 39b2ff., esp. b7). Next Aristotle alludes to a presumably Pythagorean theory which identifies time with the cosmic sphere; this he considers too naïve for discussion (218b1, 7ff.). There is, *pace* Cherniss (*Presocr.*, 217 and n.279), no evidence that time had been described or defined with reference to movement (or change). The doxographical statements (Diog. Laert. 8.48 *et al.*) do not come near to asserting it. *Phys.* VIII,1.251b12 (like IV,10.218b9f.) is slanted toward Aristotle's own definition. Cherniss' reconstruction of the Pythagorean notion of time (*Presocr.*, 215f.) is ingenious but makes several assumptions which need not be granted.

[9] IV,14.223b12-20. Cf. Pierre Duhem, *Le système du monde*, 1 (Paris, 1913), 184. This basic movement is the unit for measuring and counting time and, by way of time, movement. As Aristotle puts it, by the movement of the sphere "the other movements and time" are measured (IV,14.223b21ff.). He simplifies matters here; for in strictness time is not a movement but an aspect of movement (cf. ch. 10 and also 11; see, further, the similar thoughts in the different context of VIII,9.-265b8-11).

and of the Infinite there is toward the end a—somewhat surprising—turn which reduces the distance between his own position and that of Plato.[10]

Yet how much of the Platonic conception has Aristotle this time really recovered? The reasons which Aristotle adduces for giving circular movement a place of honor preserve very little of the high dignity to which Plato had raised the movements of the heavenly bodies. Rather these reasons have a decidedly practical ring: the circular movement is uniform, and its number is best known.[11] This means nothing more exalted than that we have no difficulty in counting the days, each day being marked by a revolution of the heavenly vault. By counting the days we arrive at the month and the year—though we can, of course, count years also by another circular movement. It is indeed true that no other movement or change could furnish us with so reliable and practical a unit for measuring time, but must one be a Platonist to make this discovery? Would not the man in the street also know that time is measured by the revolutions of the heaven? As a matter of fact, our passage also speaks of (or alludes to) the "first" place which movement or circular movement holds among the various kinds of change.[12] This recalls a Platonic doctrine which Aristotle elsewhere is at pains to re-establish.[13] Yet we must not make too much of these details. Once Aristotle had set up a connection between time and counting, he could hardly help returning sooner or later to the obvious Platonic units. The profundity of Plato's conception lies not in his choice of these units, nor even in his insistence on periodicity, but in his emphasis on the decisive importance of number for the nature of time (as well as in his contrapuntal connection of time and eternity).[14] Aristotle's fundamental Platonic commitment is the inclusion of "number" in his own definition of time; after this commitment had been made, mention of the heavenly revolutions could be postponed while other implications and associations of time were examined;

[10] See the new reference to Plato's doctrine, 223b21f.; cf. Note 8. For another approximation to Plato cf. J. F. Callahan, *Four Views of Time in Ancient Philosophy* (Cambridge, Mass., 1948), 87. For the comparable situations see *Phys.* I,7.191a5ff.; III,6.207a24ff. (cf. above, p. 86, and below, p. 162).

[11] IV,14.223b18–20.

[12] *Ibid.*, 18; note also Prantl's and Torstrik's conjectural addition of "first" in 12 (as recorded in Ross's *apparatus*). As Ross observes (*ad loc.*), an addition of the kind seems desirable, if not absolutely necessary.

[13] *Phys.* VIII,7.261a27ff.; 8 *passim*, esp. 264b9ff.; 9.265a13ff.

[14] *Tim.* 37d6; see also 38b7, 39c6ff.

but it could hardly be altogether omitted if the theory was to have its concrete meaning. If time is defined by number, it would be rather cruel never to say where the numbers are to be found. That it takes Aristotle so long to come to this point is indeed characteristic. For him the reality of time and our experience or awareness of it are in principle independent of the heavenly movements, and time is and does many other things besides being periodic. This sets him apart from Plato, for whom it is of the essence of time to be periodic and the *periodoi* from which it cannot be severed are the heavenly revolutions.[15]

Having finally accepted circular movement as the unit, Aristotle declares that a good deal may be said for the cyclical conception not only of time but of human affairs in general.[16] By this turn of thought Plato's specific contribution loses much of its distinctness and becomes merged, as it were, in widely held popular notions. For when Plato conceived of time as cyclical, he did more than give expression to a feeling which had been in the minds of his countrymen from early and perhaps earliest days. He transformed this feeling into philosophic insight, creating parallel relations between time and eternity, movement and rest, number and "one." Thus understood, the cyclical nature of time has little in common with the "cycle" of human life or of human affairs. If we wish to know what meaning Aristotle connects with the cyclical conception of life, we should consult the two treatises which deal with physical generation, growth, and decline.[17] They tell us that life is measured by days and nights, months and years, all of which are *periodoi* (in the heavenly region); in sum, "everything has its order [*taxis*] and every life and time-span is measured by a period, though it is not the same for all but some have a smaller, others a larger period as their measure."[18] Life is thus brought under the rule of the same measurements as time. By doing so, we may comment, Aristotle reads more of the cyclical nature of time into the "cycle of human affairs" than had been originally in it. Yet may it

---

[15] *Ibid.*, 37c5–39e2.

[16] *Phys.* IV,14.223b23–224a2. Note, however, the use of δοκεῖ, which does not mean (any more or much more than at 21, where it is found in the reference to Plato's definition) that Aristotle identifies himself unreservedly with the opinions here recorded.

[17] *De gen.* II,10.336b12ff., 27ff., 34ff. (note also 337a22ff.); *De gen. anim.* IV,10.-777b17–778a9. See also *Meteor.* I,9.346b21–347a8. For a discussion of the relevant meteorological doctrines see below, pp. 420–437.

[18] *De gen.* II,10.336b12ff.

not be said that Plato on his part has done less than justice to the compelling force of an age-old idea when he tried to absorb its meaning into his new doctrine of time, giving cyclical *genesis* only a rather perfunctory endorsement [19] which the details of his account hardly implement? Aristotle treats this idea more generously and with fuller sympathy; he seeks not only to find a pattern of cyclical *genesis* but also to link it to the "periods" of the heaven.[20] Of such more specific doctrines, however, our section in the *Physics* vouchsafes no glimpse. All that the sentences under discussion reveal is that, while abandoning Plato's metaphysical basis of time and of its periodicity, Aristotle has his eye on a larger realm of physical phenomena to which the cyclical pattern may be applied. Incidentally, Aristotle mentions neither here nor on similar occasions an important conviction through which he paid his tribute to the cyclical conception of time; this is the idea that "the same opinions recur in rotation among men, not once or twice or occasionally but infinitely often." [21] Nor does the "Great Year" figure among the instances of periodicity.

When Aristotle accepts the circular movement (of the heaven) as a time unit, he does not seem to think in terms of fractions or to consider that the daily movement of the sun allowed his countrymen also to measure and, if necessary, count parts of the day.[22] Besides the gnomon whose shadow indicated the hours Aristotle's contemporaries used devices, such as the water clock, that are independent of the heavenly rotations and make use of other kinds of movement. It seems probable that in the Academy (where Aristotle worked out this study) there were two indicators of time, a sundial with a gnomon which may have been used for astronomical observations, and a clepsydra which limited Plato's and his fellow workers' sleep to what he considered the necessary minimum.[23] The idea underlying our

---

[19] *Tim.* 37c5–39e2; 49c6f. (qualified by ὡς φαίνεται; the actual transformation of the elements into one another falls short of being cyclical, if only because earth does not participate in it).

[20] See esp. *Meteor.* I,9.346b36ff.; *De gen.* II,10.336b32ff.

[21] *Meteor.* I,3.339b28ff. (H. D. P. Lee's translation). See, further, *De caelo* I,3.270b16; *Metaph.* Λ8.1074b10ff.; *Pol.* VII,9.1329b25. Cf. Jaeger, *Aristotle*, 131.

[22] See H. Diels, *Antike Technik* (2d ed.; Leipzig, 1920), 155ff., on "Die antike Uhr," and for a short review of the early evidence regarding the use of the *gnomon* or *polos*, D. S. Robertson, *Cl. R.*, 54 (1940), 180ff. Note Herod. 2.109.3, τὰ δυώδεκα μέρεα τῆς ἡμέρης (a passage whose authenticity Robertson upholds against J. E. Powell).

[23] For Plato's κλέψυδρα (a νυκτερινὸν ὡρολόγιον) see Athen. 4.174cff. I rely on Diels, *op.cit.*, 16ff., 198ff. The "philosophers' mosaic" of Torre Annunziata (re-

watches—a uniform circular movement divided into equal parts—seems to be Aristotelian enough; yet in the fourth century B.C. men did not know a movement, and had devised none, by which they could measure or count short periods of time. If the "earlier" and "later" which, according to Aristotle, cut off a time stretch were near at hand, there was no movement by whose numbers one could measure this stretch.[24] To speak more concretely, the "earlier" would make time numberable, if it marked off a time two days ago or even two hours ago, yet not if its place was half an hour or two minutes ago. Apart from the heavenly revolutions Aristotle had few movements on which he could fall back as concrete illustration of his basic ideas, and much that he says about measuring movement must be considered as mere "theory"—theory with which practice was to catch up only later. Our admiration for the intellectual determination with which he develops this theory may be all the greater for this reason; yet it is also clear that Aristotle, when he finally becomes specific about the basic movement, had motives quite other than the Platonic precedent for identifying it with the heavenly revolution.

How far he is elsewhere from Plato's position comes out most strikingly in the short section in which Aristotle gives very serious thought to the possibility that the reality of time depends on the existence of a human soul. For if it is essential for time to be counted, there must be somebody to do the counting. Actually nothing is able to count but soul, and in soul, mind.[25] On the whole Aristotle takes an affirmative view of this notion—that time cannot exist without soul. This veering in the direction of philosophical idealism need not surprise us; for this idealistic—if the term is permissible—speculation has a

---

produced by Diels as a frontispiece) which presents Plato and his school shows a sundial on a column. For Aristotle's own clepsydra (if the word may be used) see Diog. Laert. 5.16, with the comments by P. Moraux, *Et. class.*, 19 (1951), 305ff., and I. Düring, *Aristotle in the Biographical Tradition* (Göteborg, 1957), 65f.

[24] Cf. ch. 11. 13.222b7ff. defines a number of other temporal concepts, like ἤδη, ἄρτι, πάλαι. The first is said to be "close to the present indivisible part of time." One wonders how this closeness could be measured. An interpretation of our section which puts more emphasis on Aristotle's "theoretic" arguments for selecting circular motion as the unit is given in Callahan, *op.cit.*, 8of., 85.

[25] IV,14.223a16ff., esp. 21–29. In Plato's cosmic scheme the presence of time enables man to count; this is a part of the divine purpose (*Tim.* 39b5); the seeing of the time movements and the resulting χρόνου ἔννοια have an important function in causing man to develop his mind (*ibid.*, 47a)—clearly a very different connection between time and soul.

psychological basis and is quite in accord with earlier arguments by which Aristotle had tried to secure a first hold on his elusive subject.[26]

Instead of relating time to eternity or starting with the cosmic system, Aristotle begins by wondering how something so transient and so vaguely apprehended as time can at all be real.[27] And as his argument proceeds, the same experience which furnishes him with the basic evidence for its reality gives him also a clue to its nature. When we are cognizant of movement and distinguish in it an "earlier" and a "later" stage we are also aware of time. "Earlier" and "later" function here as limits, cutting off a stretch of time. Both are a "now." As long as our mind is only concerned with one "now"—which like the point is an indivisible "one"—we have no awareness of change and cannot experience time.[28] Thus it is our psychological experience which establishes a presumption that time must have some kind of reality— what kind of reality Aristotle does not specify. Plato had answered this question by making time the "image" or "imitation" of eternity, which is the mode of being for the eternal Forms.[29]

[26] For some interesting observations on the relation of time and the soul in Aristotle and St. Augustine see Callahan, *op.cit.*, 75f., 162ff.

[27] Time, he says at the beginning, hardly exists at all or only ἀμυδρῶς (10.217b33) —the same word which Plato uses when introducing the receptacle ("space") into the discussion of the *Timaeus* (49a3). An argument against its reality—against its μετέχειν οὐσίας—(217b33–218a3) is found in the fact that the time which belongs to future and past "is" not. From a somewhat different point of view Plato emphasizes that words referring to past or future cannot be used of the true *ousia* (*Tim.* 37e4ff.); his conclusion, however, is that they must therefore belong to time —and not to eternal being. In contrast to this Aristotle here wonders about the "being" of time. What kind of being is in his mind? A Platonic? For a (tentative?) connection of the present with being in Plato see *Parm.* 152b2ff.

[28] See IV,11.218b21–219a10 and 219a10–b2. Speaking of the "earlier" and "later," Aristotle first states that it is to be found in place, i.e., in position. Here, he seems to feel, their existence is least open to doubt. Now this means that it can be found in magnitude (presumably in the sense of an extended body or a distance). Next Aristotle transfers it from magnitude to movement, and then again from movement to time (219a14–19). As Book VI shows in detail, magnitudes, movements, and time have the same structure, and the same physical principles apply to all three of them; in particular they are continua and infinitely divisible. In view of Aristotle's approach to time from our experience of it I should hesitate to say with Ross (p. 65) that time is for him the *ratio essendi* of change (cf. again Callahan, *op.cit.*, 202 n.2).

[29] Aristotle does not say what kind of reality a *metron* has. He does not return to the question formulated in the first sentence (10.217b31) whether time is or is not—a question which, as he there indicates, was discussed also in his dialogues. Yet he does go into the nature of "the now," deciding that in some regard it always is the same, in another constantly changing (218a8ff.; see also 11.219b12ff.),

Yet the same "now" which is so essential for our realization of time is also a constitutive factor of its nature. The now which in some respect constantly changes but in another remains always the same serves Aristotle to establish the continuity of time. Time present and time future are not identical for Aristotle; yet the now, though it is something different at any given time, has always the same basic character.[30] And inasmuch as throughout his discussion Aristotle keeps the relation of time and movement in view, he makes sure that there is something in movement that corresponds to what the now is in time. This is the moving body which, while changing its place, shows the same "identity in difference" as the now and also is more "knowable" than the movement (just as the now is more knowable than time).[31]

For Plato's interest in the relation between the now and time our evidence is limited to a short section of the *Parmenides* which would suggest that Plato thought of the now as interrupting the process of becoming and bringing it to a temporary halt.[32] Aristotle too can think of the now as separating the before and the after. Yet it also holds them together.[33] The now which is the end of the past and the now which is the beginning of the future are not two different nows but one and the same. Although the now can cut off time stretches everywhere, it does not interrupt the flow of time.[34]

---

and in view of the close connection between the now and time he may well have felt that his comments about the former throw light also on the reality of the latter. For Plato see *Tim.* 37d6f., 38a7.

[30] 11.219b9–15 (the function of the sentence b10–12, which Ross puts in parentheses, is still rather obscure). For the now as securing continuity see 220a4f. Cf. Bröcker's (*op.cit.*, 102ff.) chapter on "Zeit und Jetzt."

[31] See 219b15–33. For the difficulties inherent in the comparison of the now with the moving body see Ross, *Physics*, "Introduction," 67. I take it that Aristotle would not be satisfied with calling the now at different times and occasions the "same type of thing" (so Ross); for him it really is the same thing; its basic nature and character persist throughout all changes. Plato says (*Parm.* 152d8f.) that the now is present to "the one" throughout its being. It appears that both he and Aristotle have found in the now something enduring and persisting in the changes, including the change of time, the one stable and steady entity in the whole realm of time. Another concept which for both gives time form and structure is number; this may be the reason why Aristotle here, in b25, defines the now as the numerical aspect of the "earlier" and the "later."

[32] *Parm.* 152b2ff.

[33] IV,11.220a4f. The parallel with movement which follows this passage seems to suggest that time is one by virtue of the now.

[34] This thought is developed more clearly in the treatise "On Movement," VI,3.233b33ff., esp. 234a3ff. In our section Aristotle draws a somewhat different conclusion: the now cannot be like the point which separates parts of a magnitude,

The relation between time and the now engages Aristotle's attention also in the treatise "On Movement" where the now remains the only indivisible entity in the midst of a theory of infinitely divisible continua.[35] There as here he operates with the parallel structure of time, movement, and magnitude, and there as well as here he makes the point that the now, although present everywhere in time, is not a part of it in the sense of a fraction.[36] Time cannot be built up out of now's. Actually this point receives more emphasis in the treatise "On Movement," while our section brings out more clearly that the now is the factor which throughout the flow of constantly changing time keeps up its identity—the only identity that can be found in the realm of this very deceptive phenomenon.

Being indivisible, the now has some characteristics of "the one." Aristotle repeatedly compares it to the point in magnitudes.[37] The parallel may easily have been drawn in Academic speculations about "the one" and the point. As the point by its flowing builds up the line, so the movement and flow of the now creates time. We must, however, resist speculative temptations of this kind since even for the notion that the point by its movements creates the line our evidence is rather poor.[38] The impression remains that the now which preserves its basic identity and gives time continuity represents for Aristotle's feeling something more stable than time as such. For not only does time constantly change—in his own language it is always "other and other"—but it must also be remembered that the past time which is no longer, and the future time which is not yet, belong, in his view, to not-being.[39]

---

being simultaneously beginning and end; rather time should be regarded as analogous to the two ends of a line. If it were like a point in the middle of a line, there would be some stopping.

[35] See below, pp. 204–221.

[36] 10.218a6; 11.220a18, 219b33ff. Cf. VI,3 where not only is it said that the now must ἐν ἅπαντι χρόνῳ ὑπάρχειν (233b34), but at the same time it is made impossible for the now to be a fraction or component part of time, which is divisible into divisibles, whereas the now is here shown to be indivisible; cf. also VI,1.231b6f., 1off.

[37] See, e.g., 11.220a4ff., 9f., and 19ff., also 219b12–21, which suggest that the body in movement corresponds to the point in magnitude and to the now in time; see, further, VI,1.231b6.

[38] See *De an.* I,4.209a3–5 (a reference to an Academic doctrine). Ross (*ad* 219b25) appears to allude to this doctrine. Eudemus (frg. 87, Wehrli) develops the comparison between the point and the now but not in the sense that the point builds up the line.

[39] IV,11.219b9f.; 10.217b32–218a3.

Is it pertinent to recall what Plato in the *Parmenides* says about the
now: while something meets the now, it *is*, and again, the now is
present to "the one" throughout its being? [40] It would seem that a
particular kind of reality attaches to the now—the "time now present and living" as Sophocles once calls it [41]—and that Aristotle, who
had qualms about the reality of time which on both sides of the present
he saw slip away into not-being, felt reassured when in the now he
had found something more enduring.[42] The massive and overpowering reality which time had once possessed for the Greeks no longer
exists; time flows, and what has gone by (παρελήλυθε) can "be" as little
as what has not yet come into being but is still in the lap of the future.[43]
On the other hand, the now has connotations of presence (πάρεστι)
and something of the reality which goes with being, but not with
"have been" and "will be." Such a feeling (although it is more apparent in the *Parmenides* [44]) may be behind Aristotle's effort to secure
for the now's an intrinsic, substantial identity, even though he does
not stress the "presence" of the now but relates it to the numerical aspect of time.[45]

[40] *Parm.* 159b2ff., esp. b6ff., d8ff. In strictness the opposition is here between
becoming something and being something, but the emphasis is on the copula. Note
also the definition of "to be" on the basis of which the discussion here proceeds,
151e7ff.: τὸ. εἶναι . . . μέθεξις οὐσίας μετὰ χρόνου τοῦ παρόντος (as ἦν is the same
participation with the past, ἔσται with the future time).

[41] *Trach.* 1169.

[42] The section IV,10.218a8–30 states that it is not easy to decide whether the now
can remain the same and indicates difficulties connected with this notion.
IV,11.219b10–33 explains that although there are always different now's the
substratum of the now does yet remain the same. For the connection which
Aristotle establishes between this substratum of the now and the numerical aspect
of time, see above, p. 151.

[43] For χρόνος as flowing, see, e.g., Critias, frg. 18, Nauck; cf. Cornford, *Pl. and
Parm.*, 186 n.3. For the "power" of time as understood in the fifth century, cf.
H. Fränkel, *Zeitschr. f. Aesthetik*, 25 (1931), Beiheft 106ff., from whose numerous
references I select Pind. *Nem.* 7,68, *Ol.* 6.97, 10.7, and Simon. 5.5. Fränkel observes
that in Pindar χρόνος never refers to the now. See also the passages cited below,
Note 50.

[44] See Note 40, also the reference to Sophocles in Note 41. At *Tim.* 37e5ff. (cf.
3ff.) where Plato speaks of eternal being he points out that "only" ἔστιν is applicable to it. Since it is obvious that this ἔστιν has no connection with νῦν or
παρὼν χρόνος (!), Cherniss (*J. H. St.* [1957], 22 n.46) had every right to point out
the difference between this Platonic conception of eternity and Parmenides'
(28B8.5) νῦν ἔστιν ὁμοῦ πᾶν.

[45] Cf. Eudemus, frg. 88 (41.28 Wehrli): by contrast to the past and future τὸ
παρὸν ἔστιν (ἔστιν Wehrli), even though it is constantly changing. This fragment
of Eudemus relates Aristotle's problem whether "identical" time may recur

We have already questioned whether Aristotle's definition of time as the numerical aspect of movement exhausts the relation between these two concepts even for himself. When in his treatise "On Movement" Aristotle dwells on the analogous structure of time and movement, treating both as continuous and infinitely divisible, the definition is not repeated. For the new topics it could hardly be useful. If we look in Aristotle for an alternative and more comprehensive description of the relationship, his statement that every change is "in time" may recommend itself.[46] This is broader than the definition also in that it includes every kind of change, not only local movement; and Aristotle actually makes this statement for the express purpose of bringing the other changes into a relation to time. Previously he had discussed time exclusively in reference to locomotion. The other changes are not so obviously measurable (or numerable) as locomotion. In the end Aristotle does bring them under the control of measurement by setting up the circular movement as the basic measure of time.[47] While being primarily a measuring unit of locomotion, it yet can also measure the other changes. One can certainly say how many days a plant or an embryo "grows," and some qualitative changes may be measured by years, days, or conceivably fractions of a day. To make this connection between time and change convincing, Aristotle first establishes the easier proposition that all changes are "in time." They are because they exhibit the "before" and "after." These concepts have previously helped Aristotle to make movement numerable; here it suffices that they are "in time" (for they have their meaning through reference to the now which is certainly in time).[48]

Given his definition of time, Aristotle would make efforts to maintain that to be in time and to be measured by time are the same thing.[49]

(12.220b12ff.; 13.222a30ff.) to the Pythagorean doctrine of "identical" return. There is no clear indication that Aristotle himself has this doctrine in mind, but the possibility need not be ruled out. Ross's distinction (in his commentary on the two passages cited) between "specific" and "numerical" identity is perhaps unnecessary inasmuch as Aristotle himself does not qualify his statement of identity. Reading 220b12–14 after b5–12, one has the impression that this sentence is a correction of what goes before and an afterthought.

[46] IV,14.222b30–223a15; cf. VI,2.232b20; 6.236b19 and *passim*.

[47] 14.223a29–b23. While on his way toward this conclusion Aristotle states that time is the number of every change insofar as it is movement (a29f., 32f.) and explains that if two changes of different type come about simultaneously the time in which they take place is one and the same (b2–4).

[48] 222b33–223a15; cf. 11.219a18ff.

[49] See 12.221a4ff. On "being in time" cf. again Bröcker, *op.cit.*, 107ff.

Yet to "be in time" is a conception which had deep and firm roots in Greek thinking; it is difficult to keep it within the strict technical limits of an inquiry concerning the relations between time and movement. And Aristotle is too broad-minded to press his technical points. When making contact with the traditional wisdom, he broadens his own conception of time. Time, he says, is something that encompasses everything and has power over everything—except over what is eternal and what "is not" and can never be. He is also prepared to learn from common thought and usage that time shows its power even more in destroying and obliterating than in creating and making grow.[50] All this, he says, is perfectly true; it should find a place also in a purely physical study of time. Yet while incorporating these insights, he is at pains to show that his new definition of time provides the explanation for the remarkable power of time over all human affairs. As it appears to him, time has such power because "movement makes things depart from their condition" and "time is the number of movement."[51] Granted that movement in Aristotle may whenever it pleases him include every kind of change, this piece of reasoning still seems to lay rather rough hands on the old wisdom. It was the vivid experience of change in time which had led early thought to set up time itself as the great changer and destroyer. Aristotle clearly stultifies this idea when he makes movement, rather than time, the agent of the process and then works in time as the "number of movement." In doing so he falls back on his definition of time as the aspect of movement which is numerable; but the time of which Sophocles

[50] 221a26–b7; see also b27–222a9 and 13.222b16–27. Cf. Soph. *Ai.* 646ff. and *O.C.* 607ff. (also *Ai.* 713, *Ant.* 681, frg. 280). At 222b16 Aristotle refers briefly and without sympathy to the idea that time is "the wisest." Thinking of it in connection with movement, becoming, and passing away, he would not be prepared to appreciate the belief that it reveals everything (Soph. *O.R.* 614, 1213) or that it judges everything. The δίκη χρόνου occurs often in Greek literature, beginning with Solon 24.3 Diehl.

[51] 221b2. In a later part of our section Aristotle takes a somewhat different view: time is not the actual agent of the change; rather "it happens that the change comes about in time" (222b19ff., esp. 25ff.; note also a slight discrepancy between 221b1–3 and 222b24.). For Anaximander (however we may interpret 12B1) *chronos* is very far from being something accidental in the processes of becoming and passing away; nor, one may add, is it accidental for Empedocles, though we may note that in 31B30 time is not spoken of as "agent" of the alternation between Love and Strife. Moreover, Empedocles seems to have felt that time itself was not strong enough to assure the eternal rhythm of this alternation (cf. B13.29); he thinks of it as under the control of a stronger ἀνάγκη, a πλατὺς ὅρκος.

says that "it makes grow all that is hidden and takes away all that has come to light" is the innumerable or uncountable time (ἀναρίθμητος χρόνος).[52] Still, Aristotle has found a contact—perhaps a not too forced contact—between his own concept of "being in time" (i.e., taking place in time) and the idea of being subject to time, or in the power of time, valid and established notions with which Plato had not attempted to make connection. In the *Timaeus* and more generally in his dialogues Plato did not see fit to avail himself of the traditional wisdom and subject the world of *genesis* with its floating phenomena to time. This "poetic" conception of time to which he responds in one of his epigrams ("Long time knows to change name and appearance, natural condition and fortune") remained for him devoid of philosophic significance.[53]

If there is gain in Aristotle's incorporation of such thoughts, it is balanced by the fact that Aristotle has given up Plato's fundamental opposition between time and eternity. To "be in time" has its traditional meaning and pathos; it does not acquire additional significance by being viewed against the background of Platonic eternity.[54] True, eternal things are not "in time," i.e., not encompassed, not measured, not destroyed or in any way affected by time. Obviously we are not supposed to ask in what other medium they have their existence. For even while speaking of entities that are not subject to time, Aristotle does refrain from operating with the Platonic opposition between time and eternity. All he says is that they are not in time, and this must suffice.[55] When in the treatise *On the Heaven* he again speaks of beings not subject to time and the changes of time—making slightly clearer that what he has in mind is divine beings—he does use the word "eternity" (αἰών) to describe their never-ending and never-changing existence. In fact, he waxes enthusiastic about the singular appropriateness of this word for the mode of existence that should be ascribed to divine

[52] Soph. *Ai.* 646f.
[53] Plato *Epigr.* 21 Diehl (the authenticity of the poem is not generally admitted and can hardly here be discussed, inasmuch as also the other epigrams attributed to Plato in the *Anthol. Pal.* are in doubt; cf. however, Wilamowitz, *Eurip. Herakles* [2d ed.; Berlin, 1909], 364). For *chronos* in earlier philosophic thought see the last paragraphs of this chapter.
[54] *Tim.* 37d5ff.
[55] IV,12.221b3–7. The eternal beings which are here said not to be in time "insofar as they are eternal" are likely to include the heavenly bodies. Their change of position would put them in time, and their movements are measurements of time; yet with regard to their eternal existence they are not in time. The Cosmos as a whole would not for Aristotle be in time either.

beings.[56] Yet it is "the ancients," not Plato, who are given credit for introducing this admirable word, and when Aristotle goes on to establish the validity of the underlying concept, he refers to the general connotations of the word, but not to Plato's use of it in the *Timaeus*. The common and original meaning of the word being "life," Aristotle argues that just as an individual's life "comprehends" (or "encompasses") the entire time of his existence, so the life of the eternal Cosmos encompasses all time and infinity.[57] With reference to the eternal duration of the Cosmos he finds the etymological connection of *aion* and *aiei* very meaningful. This surely is Aristotle's own and new affirmation that eternity is a valid concept, not a reaffirmation of the validity given by Plato. New, too, is the idea that eternity "comprehends" all time [58]—for Plato time had been the image and reflection of eternity, while eternity itself belonged to an entirely different order. If the *Physics* teaches that everything that is in time is "encompassed" by time and the treatise *On the Heaven* that all time is "encompassed" by eternity, a combination of these two doctrines suggests a continuity hardly compatible with the sharp break which Plato had made between being and becoming, and between time and eternity. True, if Plato's Cosmos bids fair to be eternal and if this Cosmos includes time which has been built into its structure, we are not too far from a philosophical position for which eternity encompasses all time. Yet while strong arguments suggest the eternity of Plato's Cosmos, Plato himself endorses those that tell against it: the Cosmos has come into being, and time with it. There was no time before the Cosmos.[59]

[56] *De caelo* I,9.279a17ff., 22ff. That "time does not make" the gods "age" (18f.) may have been a commonplace in Greek poetry (see again Soph. *O.C.* 607). In the dialogue *On Philosophy* to which Jaeger has traced the section of *De caelo* (*Aristotle*, 330) such incorporation of old wisdom would be appropriate. The parallel thought that God is not in place seems to be new and would be Aristotle's own contribution to the description of the deity in nonphysical and nonanthropological concepts.

[57] 279a23–28. For αἰών in the sense of life, cf. again Wilamowitz, *op.cit.*, 364, and also A. J. Festugière, *La parola del passato*, 9 (1948), 172, for whose study about the meaning of αἰών this passage in *De caelo* forms the point of departure. In its fundamental form the opposition between αἰών (eternity) and χρόνος may not be older than Plato (*Tim.* 37d; even in [Isocr.] 1.1 it is probable that the "whole life," not "all eternity," is contrasted with "a short time"); Festugière shows how and by what stages αἰών came to mean "eternity." For later developments of this concept see again Festugière, *La révélation d'Hermès Trismég.* IV (1954), 146ff., where reference is also made to previous studies.

[58] 279a25–28.

[59] *Tim.* 37d, 38b.

To attach time firmly to the Cosmos was a great philosophical achievement, and when Plato came forward with his revolutionary declaration he probably realized that it spelt the end for all cosmological hypotheses and speculations that implied a different notion of time. For if time is produced by movements that take place within the Cosmos, it cannot have existed before the Cosmos, and all earlier systems which made a Cosmos arise in time or come into being and pass away in fixed periods must be radically in error. Strife, for instance, could not come to power when "the time was completed" which regulates its alternation with Love; for at that juncture there is no Cosmos. Nor can time be the arbiter that enforces justice, making the things of the Cosmos "pay penalty to each other" [60]—at least not if the arbiter's power is to extend beyond the existence of our Cosmos. A succession of worlds or of world phases governed by time is from Plato's point of view something like a contradiction in terms.

But if for Plato it was essential to absorb time into the Cosmos and if his approach to time thus becomes that of a cosmologist, Aristotle, though writing only ten or at the most fifteen years after the *Timaeus*, could afford to ignore the cosmological aspects all but completely. There was no need to defend Plato's position against the alternative Presocratic conception; the question whether time could exist outside or before and after our world had been raised and answered— and had lost all philosophical interest. The definition of time which could be established from Plato's pronouncements was unsatisfactory, and the reality and nature of time could be more successfully explored if instead of going off into the Cosmos the inquiry started with man's awareness of time. Moreover, as the Cosmos was eternal (and unique), worries about a possible materialization of time outside it were gratuitous. Not time but eternity had now to be secured for the Cosmos. This was the prize which beckoned. The *De caelo* reports triumphantly that it has been won. Time is not among the subjects of that treatise.

[60] For Empedocles see esp. *Vorsokr.*, 31A30. There are good reasons for not referring Anaximander (*Vorsokr.*, 12) B1 to the succession of cosmoi; nevertheless it is difficult to imagine that this succession should have been unrelated to time. For a contrast between Plato's conception of time and earlier views see Charles Mugler, *Deux thèmes de la cosmologie grecque* (Paris, 1953), *passim* but esp. 92ff., where the epoch-making nature and cosmological significance of the new approach are well brought out.

8

The Infinite

LIKE place and time, the Infinite is one of the fundamental concepts that must be clarified and defined before the details of a cosmological and physical system can be worked out. And again, as in the case of the two other concepts, the question is not only what the Infinite is but "whether it is." [1] Is there any reality at all that corresponds to this notion, or is the favor which it has found with earlier physicists the result of false reasoning and rash assumptions?

Aristotle's own decision about the reality of the Infinite is negative as far as the infinitely large is concerned. Of the infinitely small and the closely related idea of infinite divisibility he takes a more affirmative view. They are real—at least potentially real; for nothing can be actually divided into an infinite number of fractions.[2] As we shall see, the possibility of infinite division holds good for every continuum, including time and movement; in his treatise "On Movement" (*Physics* V–VIII) Aristotle develops the implications of this proposition. On the other hand, the infinitely large would, if it were real, seriously interfere with Aristotle's cosmological doctrines, and this is the reason why not only our section of the *Physics* but also the first book of the work *On the Heaven* argues against the existence of an infinitely large body. Thus we shall meet both aspects of the Infinite again, and we

[1] See *Phys.* III,4.202b35f.; cf. IV,1.208a28; 10.217b31ff. It has seemed advisable to treat matter and place jointly and make the discussion of time follow upon that of place, although by doing so we have departed from the sequence in the *Physics*. We now return to Book III.

[2] III,6, esp. 206a14ff. For the arguments against the infinitely large see III,5. For the infinitely large in the realm of numbers see below, p. 173 and n.57.

may reserve a fuller appreciation of Aristotle's historical position for our analysis of the treatises "On Movement" and *On the Heaven*.[3] For the present we may confine ourselves to a few facets of Aristotle's attitude.

To begin with, we may observe that, as in the case of time and place, here too Aristotle keeps his study within strictly physical limits. Still there is a difference; at the beginning of the section on the Infinite we see that Aristotle looks beyond the physical realm, taking account of attempts to treat the Infinite as a substance or as a principle. In dealing with such attempts, he distinguishes between systems for which the Infinite as such is a principle and others in which infinity is the attribute or characteristic of something else posited as principle.[4] In addition there is the Infinite associated with the existence of infinite elements, and there are mathematical varieties of it in the realm of numbers and magnitudes.[5] Yet he soon abandons this comprehensive approach as being too "general" and decides that his proper subject is the Infinite so far as it arises, or may arise, within the realm of perceptible objects ("with which our investigation is concerned"). In fact, he narrows his scope even more: "In particular it is the task of the physicist to investigate whether there is an infinite magnitude in the physical world." [6] This statement may be considered as an appropriate description of his intention; for it is the quantitative Infinite on which Aristotle concentrates. The Infinite as the qualitatively undefined, the indefinite, the formless and shapeless, the inarticulate and unknowable—aspects so important in Plato—is by and large ignored. Yet again, and in spite of all efforts to steer clear of the broader perspective, there is a passage where this self-denying attitude breaks down and larger issues come into view. Logically enough, this situation arises while Aristotle is driving home the difference between the

---

[3] See below, pp. 199–221 and Chs. 12 and 14.   [4] III,4; see esp. 203a1ff., b32ff.
[5] III,4.203a19ff., b23ff.

[6] III,4.204a1; cf. 5.204a34ff. (I have rendered the word αἰσθητόν freely.) Aristotle in these chapters ignores even varieties of infinity which he recognizes and discusses in other contexts. For infinite movement and infinite force see esp. VIII,8ff., 10. An illuminating study, in a broad historical perspective, of all these varieties and their mutual relations is to be found in Rodolfo Mondolfo, *L'infinito nel pensiero dell'antichità classica* (Florence, 1956), 119ff., 225ff., 455ff., 465ff. It is possible that the difficult passage III,6.206a21–29 envisages still another variety of the Infinite. I incline to call it "infinite repetition" but am not sure that I understand Aristotle's point correctly (Ross's explanation *ad loc.* does justice to the parenthesis but not to a22. Read in a23 ἐπὶ τούτων ⟨τὸ⟩ ἔστι καὶ δυνάμει καὶ ἐνεργείᾳ).

Infinite and the whole.[7] He has previously discredited the idea of the infinitely large or cosmic Infinite, which cannot be reconciled with his own conception of one bounded and finite cosmos. Thus it is no longer possible to identify the Infinite with the whole or the "all," and Aristotle adds a few comments by which he means to restrict the Infinite even more decisively to the modest role now left for it. Once more he speaks as Platonist: "perfection" or "completeness" and Form are on the side of the whole; the Infinite cannot aspire to such dignity: "For in relation to a complete magnitude [scil., one which has its proper form] the Infinite is matter; it is a whole only potentially, yet not in actuality."[8] The Infinite of which he here speaks is the only variety that he is prepared to recognize, something extended (or continuous) and as such divisible *ad infinitum*. For the rest it is without form or shape, liable to be broken up and certainly not a whole. The Infinite cannot as the physicists assert contain (everything else) but is itself contained, as matter is by Form. "Therefore it is qua infinite unknowable; for the matter has no form. Thus it is of the nature of a part rather than of a whole, for matter is a part of the whole."[9] Once more, then, patient physical analysis of a concept has provided a new substructure for a Platonic dogma. What Plato said of the physical objects when he contrasted them with the Forms is still true of "the nature other than the Form":[10] what is not form or has no form is infinite and therefore unknowable. The difference is that Form has moved closer to the individual object and that Aristotle thinks of it as the immanent Form. The individual physical object, being an extended body, is in some of its aspects infinite and unknowable; in others, thanks to its Form, knowable, finite, and a whole. The former aspects are taken care of by Aristotle's new concept of matter.

Aristotle's identification in the passages just quoted of the Infinite with matter and his insistence that it has no form prompt the comment

---

[7] III,6.206b33ff.

[8] *Ibid.*, 207a21. For the relation of ὅλον and τέλειον see a13f. The discussion of these concepts begins at a8. The definitions recall the use made of these concepts in Plato's cosmology (*Tim.* 32d1f., where in addition to them reference is made to the ἕν); cf. also the motif of περιέχειν in a25 (*Tim.* 33b2).

[9] 207a24ff.; cf. also 7.207b34ff.

[10] See Plato *Parm.* 158a5ff. ("whatever we at any time may see [of the nature other than the Form] will always be infinite in multitude"); see also d5f. In the passage of the *Physics* the quantitative approach is temporarily abandoned, owing to the introduction of *hyle*. This also accounts for a somewhat different use of the *morion* motif (a26ff.; *Parm.* 158c7ff.).

that he has shifted his ground from the quantitative infinite on which he meant to concentrate to the qualitative. For he thinks of something formless and his references to matter suggest the qualitative infinite, or indefinite. Some other concepts which he here employs allow him an almost imperceptible transition from the quantitative point of view to the qualitative. He thinks of the whole as bounded and as having a completeness and compactness which the infinite, in every sense of the word (also the infinitely large, in the erroneous ideas which one might entertain of it), inevitably lacks; [11] and when he speaks of matter and the infinite as being "contained" by form, he uses a term which, as we know, has spatial and thereby quantitative connotations but also describes the relation of Form to matter.[12] He is, in fact, making clear that the Infinite needs a limit (the *apeiron* a *peras*) to become knowable and fully real—and limit again would have a spatial as well as an ontological meaning.[13] There are indications, however, that Aristotle is not very much aware of going beyond the quantitative aspects; as he repeats the purely quantitative definition of the Infinite,[14] he may well be convinced that he remains faithful to his original intention. The qualitative infinite (or indefinite) and the quantitative had become separated before his day, but they still have some identical characteristics which if brought to light may allow a temporary *rapprochement*. A complete identification of the two concepts is, however, out of the question.[15]

Aristotle can visualize things in a formless indefinite condition and

[11] III,6.207a8ff. Parmenides is here given credit for having made the whole bounded. This is historically correct even if the Pythagoreans ought to share the credit. If Parmenides did not speak as a physicist in the sense in which Aristotle tries to study the Infinite, it must again be borne in mind that in our passage Aristotle takes a broader view than elsewhere in this study.

[12] See above, pp. 125, 133f.

[13] The word πέρας occurs in 207a15 where it is equated with τέλος; the latter concept serves as link between the ὅλον (which is τέλειον in more than one sense) and πέρας; see a8ff. For a different use of the "limit" motif see 5.204b4ff. (a preliminary dialectical argument whose significance may be slightly overestimated by Mondolfo).

[14] 207a22f. (cf. 206b3ff.); note in connection with the quantitative motif also the word μέγεθος, a2.

[15] See Plato *Phileb.* 24aff., where the hotter and colder are said to have the "more and less" and although they would belong to the realm of qualities are treated as a quantitative *apeiron* as long as they lack the ποσόν, a definite quantity which would give them *peras* and *telos*. For the extension of the argument to other comparatives see 25c. For an isolation of the quantitative *apeiron* (in number as well as magnitude) see Zeno in *Vorsokr.*, 29B1,3.

can use his concept of matter to describe this lack of form. Yet such a condition is not real in the sense in which Anaximander's *apeiron* (which probably combined the qualitative and quantitative aspects of the Infinite [16]) is real. Matter exists only potentially. In our section Aristotle points out that also the infinitely small has a purely potential existence. The Infinite goes back, by a different pedigree, to the same *apeiron* to which we have traced Aristotle's matter.[17] Although estranged from one another in the course of their respective histories, indefinite matter and the Infinite here find themselves assigned to one and the same status and for a brief spell enjoy the prospect of becoming again identified.

In feeling his way toward reuniting them, Aristotle has to shift from the quantitative to the ontological point of view. For a moment a richer philosophical legacy, the Pythagorean and Platonic dichotomy of the limited and the unlimited,[18] presents itself and offers its unexhausted wealth of suggestive metaphysical propositions. Aristotle seems willing to accept a large part of it, but, having declared his willingness, he contents himself with indicating in very general terms what kind of use he could make of it.

Since both matter and the infinitely small must be contained by Form and cannot themselves contain anything, Aristotle is in a position to challenge the original concept of the Infinite. Anaximander was thoroughly mistaken when he described it as "containing everything." [19] The Infinite, once the all-encompassing principle, has become the formless and the purely material; what originally was its strength—that it is

---

[16] In this disputed question I follow with some confidence Fränkel, *Dichtg. u. Philos.*, 341f., though I should not assume that Anaximander actually used the word ἄπειρον with reference to the indefiniteness, indeterminateness, or shapelessness of the ingredients of his *apeiron*.

[17] The concept of the infinitely small, to be sure, does not go so far back; however, as soon as it was discovered, it was brought into very close relation with the infinitely large (see Zeno B1 and Anaxag. B1,3). For the antecedents of Aristotle's "matter" see above, Ch. 6.

[18] For reasons which will become immediately apparent, there is not much scope for a comparison with the *Philebus*. Pythagoras seems to lurk behind the name of Prometheus in the declaration of method, 16bff. (esp. c6; cf. R. Hackforth, *Plato's Examination of Pleasure* [Cambridge, 1945], 21). Selecting points somewhat at random, I note that in 15b5 τὰ γιγνόμενα are called ἄπειρα, that in 17e3ff. there is a reference to the unintelligibility of the ἄπειρα, and that in 31a8ff. infinity is described as having no beginning or middle or end, which means that it cannot qualify as a ὅλον.

[19] IV,6.207a18–21; cf. 4.203b10–15. On the περιέχειν of Anaximander see Jaeger, *Theology*, 29f.

nothing determinate or particular—has become its weakness. It exists, insofar as it exists at all, below the level of full reality, in the Platonic as well as the Aristotelian meaning of the word. The Pythagorean and Platonic legacy, although not explicitly drawn upon, clearly strengthens Aristotle's hand when he attacks Anaximander and Melissus and dethrones the former's *apeiron*.[20]

Nevertheless the infinitely small comes off better than the infinitely large. For although Aristotle recognizes the infinite "in the direction of the smaller," scil., in the form of infinite divisibility, his cosmology inexorably requires an upper limit for magnitude; as it is quite impossible that anything could be larger than the diameter of the Cosmos, he must reject the traditional concept of the infinitely large. The arguments which Aristotle employs against this concept are of the same type as those used to dispose of the void. In both instances Aristotle shows that the concept under scrutiny conflicts hopelessly with his doctrines regarding natural movements and with those relating to change and mutual transformations between the elements.[21] We shall see later that there is little continuity between these two parts of Aristotle's physical theory. The former subject is a part of his cosmology; the latter belongs to his theory of *genesis*. These two phases of Aristotle's physical science have broken apart, one of them finding a new basis in the qualities heavy and light, the other in more material characteristics of the elements (such as warm and cold, dry and moist).[22] This dichotomy is at the root of the double-barreled attack against the notion of an infinitely large physical body, as well as of his polemic against the concept of the void. We may note, however, that none of the more specific propositions embodied in *On Coming to Be and Passing Away* figures in Aristotle's arguments against either the Infinite or the void. When he shows that the mutual transformation of elements does not need empty space or cannot brook an infinite body, he operates with rather general considerations which would make sense in terms of his own theory but do not presuppose it specifically.[23] An analysis of these general arguments

---

[20] 207a15–21. To judge by Aristotle's words, Anaximander may have said that his *apeiron* πᾶν ἐν ἑαυτῷ ἔχει (20). Anaxagoras' doctrine that the Infinite rests in itself (5.205b1ff.) is too remote to be compared (*pace* Cherniss, *Presocr.*, 23 n.85).

[21] III,5.204b10–206a8; IV,8, 9.   [22] See below, Chs. 13 and 17.

[23] III,5.204b10–205a7 (if there is no corruption in 204b26–28, Aristotle's view regarding the characteristic qualities of the elements would seem to be simpler and less developed than in *De gen. et corr.*; cf. Ross, *ad loc.*); IV,9.217a10–b20. In 217a26 it is argued that the same matter has the potentiality of becoming either large or small (and that no void is needed for a change from large to small, i.e.,

would teach us nothing about the form which Aristotle's theory of elementary *genesis* and transformation had reached by this time. By contrast, the essentials of his doctrine of natural movement have clearly taken shape; the major propositions embodied in Books III and IV of the treatise *On the Heaven* were settled in Aristotle's mind when he worked out his general physical theory.[24]

The reason why something of infinite extent would interfere with the peaceful existence of the elements and with their *genesis* is, in brief, that if one element were infinite it would overpower the others. For an element is characterized by its power or powers; if the infinite element were, say, fire, it would, even if the degree of its heat were relatively small, have this power in such quantity that the powers of the other elements would be completely squelched and these elements themselves, as a result, destroyed.[25] That there is a struggle between the qualities attached to the various elements is indeed good Aristotelian doctrine which will reappear in the mature theory of *On Coming to Be*. Aristotelian too—though not confined to Aristotle—is the belief in a certain balance and mutual toleration among the elements; each has, after all, to fill the cosmic space that is allotted to it.[26]

Of the arguments based on Aristotle's own concepts of natural movements and natural places some take the line that the infinite body could have no natural movement and no natural place. This would be true regardless of whether the Infinite is one and homogeneous throughout or whether it consists of various qualitatively different parts. Other arguments experiment with the basic distinctions of Aristotle's own cos-

---

from a rarer element into a denser). In a general way this corresponds to the doctrines of the other treatise, but it does not presuppose specific theories embodied in it. That the same matter is the substratum of the contraries is, after all, settled in *Phys.* I.

[24] See, e.g., the points made about the rest of the earth in the center, 205b10–16; see also *ibid.*, 24ff., 214b13ff.

[25] III,5.204b11–19. Slightly later (b24ff.) Aristotle supposes that considerations of this kind led Anaximander to make his *apeiron* something distinct from the elements. Cf. also 205a23–25.

[26] For the struggle see *De gen.* II,4; for the balance between the elements it will suffice to refer to the conception of cosmic *taxis* as developed in the *Meteorologica* (see below, pp. 420–439). See also *ibid.*, I,3.340a1ff. (Cherniss, *Presocr.*, 27). On corresponding Presocratic ideas see Gregory Vlastos, *Cl. Ph.*, 42 (1947), 156ff. Another argument in Aristotle's text envisages the Infinite as an element existing in the physical world side by side with the recognized four elements— regardless of the fact that in this case it could hardly be infinite in the strict sense of the word. Here Aristotle makes the relatively simple point that we have no evidence for the presence of such an entity into which things would have to pass away; see III,5.204b24–205a1.

mology and arrive at the conclusion that they are inapplicable: since there is no up and down, no center or circumference in the Infinite, how could one part (say half) of it be heavy, the other light so that they might have natural movements in opposite directions? Finally and "simply: if there can be no infinite place, yet every body is in place, there can be no infinite body." [27]

The arguments here summarized show that Aristotle tends to visualize the infinitely large as if it were a Platonic-Aristotelian Cosmos expanded into infinity. Since it is essential for his Cosmos to have limits and clearly defined spatial contraries (like up and down), any attempt to imagine an infinite body with the same characteristics is bound to get entangled in illogicalities and contradictions. To think of the Infinite as qualitatively indefinite (as Anaximander may have done) or to conceive of it as lacking the "form" and the differentiations of the Cosmos would seem to strain Aristotle's imagination.[28] For him it is natural that *physis* has the form of the Cosmos; the distinction between precosmic and cosmic conditions which had been inherent in most of the Presocratic systems and had continued into Plato's has lost all meaning for him.[29]

It goes without saying that none of the earlier thinkers pictured the Infinite as a Cosmos stretching without limits in every direction. Anaximander's and Anaxagoras' Infinite was filled with physical entities and powers capable of composing our world but far from used up in this effort.[30] A Pythagorean doctrine, for which Aristotle himself is our authority, regarded the Cosmos as surrounded by the Infinite in the shape of air and held that this air, to the extent in which it becomes absorbed into the Cosmos, creates empty intervals in it.[31] Melissus maintained that being was unlimited—yet he did not think of it in cosmic terms. Finally the atomists believed in an infinite number of Cosmoi existing simultaneously in the infinite space (not to mention the infinite

---

[27] III,5.205a35; for the other arguments see 205a8–28 (accepting the transposition made by Pacius and others), b24–35. Mondolfo, *op.cit.*, 483ff., has come to similar conclusions regarding Aristotle's arguments and their cosmological presuppositions.

[28] See, e.g., 205b31–34, also 204b14ff. (the Infinite would have the *dynamis* of an element). For Anaximander see above, Note 16.

[29] See below, Ch. 12. Plato had made the Cosmos a ἕν, ὅλον, and τέλειον. (See above, Note 8.) Cf. III,6.207a1 and *ibid.*, 8f. (For a discussion of the grammatical puzzle in a1 see Abraham Edel, *Aristotle's Theory of the Infinite* [diss., Columbia Univ., 1924], 57 n.10. I accept Ross's explanation *ad loc.*)

[30] See *Vorsokr.*, 12A10; 59B4. Anaximenes' air is infinite too, *ibid.*, 13A6, 7(1), 10.

[31] *Phys.* IV,6.213b22ff.

number of their atoms).[32] Nor does Aristotle assert in so many words that the earlier physicists pictured the infinitely large as an infinite Cosmos. What he actually says is that in our thought we can conceive of always greater and greater numbers and magnitudes and can also imagine what is "outside the heaven" as infinite; therefore we incline to think of it as actually infinite. "And if what is outside is infinite, people think that there is also an infinite body and infinite Cosmoi. For why should there be body in one part of the void rather than in another? Thus if there is body anywhere it would be everywhere." [33] Arguments of the kind "why rather in one part than in another" may indeed have been used.[34] They are not wrong in themselves, and Aristotle seems willing to accept them; yet nothing is farther from his mind than to endorse the belief in innumerable Cosmoi scattered through the infinity of space. What he himself is driving at is the conclusion that everywhere in infinite space there would have to be "bulk," i.e., body. Even the supposition that outside our Cosmos there is empty space would, if followed to its logical implications, lead to this result; for void is a place where body may be, and this "may be," under Aristotle's hand, turns at once into an "is." "In the case of eternal things there is no difference between possible and actual being." [35] Aristotle seems satisfied that he has disposed of the possibility of unfilled empty places outside our Cosmos; as a result, when in Book IV the void as such is examined at length, he only considers the possibilities of its materialization within the Cosmos. For the investigation at hand Aristotle has made sure that the only version of the infinitely large that needs further scrutiny is a compact body stretching out through infinite space, and, as we have already said, he performs this scrutiny by applying to this body the categories and concepts that are associated with his own Cosmos.

[32] See esp. *Vorsokr.*, 30B2, 5; 67A1, 68A1 (44). Note also Archytas' argument (*ibid.*, 47A24) for infinite space to which Aristotle probably alludes in 4.203b20 (or b25, as Wehrli prefers to think; see his commentary in *Die Schule des Aristoteles*, VIII [Basel, 1955], 101).

[33] III,4.203b23–28.

[34] Cf. Metrodorus of Chius in *Vorsokr.*, 70A6; Epic. *Ad Herod.* 74 (Lucr. 2.1070ff.). Even Anaxag. B4 would seem to be comparable, although it is open to other interpretations; see H. Fränkel, *Wege und Formen Frühgriechischen Denkens* (Munich, 1955), 288ff.

[35] 203b30 (the definitions of the void which Aristotle assumes in his discussion of Book IV are slightly, yet not fundamentally, different; see, e.g., 7.213b33, 214a19f.).

Elsewhere, i.e., in the treatise *On the Heaven*, Aristotle uses the argument that place as well as empty place are by definition something where body may exist but that there is no body that could have its place outside the heaven or outside our Cosmos and therefore that there is neither place nor empty place outside the Cosmos.[36] It is one of the fundamental theses of this work that all actually existing bodies, specifically the five elements, have their "natural" and only places within this Cosmos; thus there can be no infinite body, and there can be nothing at all besides our Cosmos for the simple reason that there are no bodies that might fill places outside.[37] This is Aristotle's new version of the Platonic tenet that the total existing amount of all elements has been incorporated in the Cosmos.[38] Outside the Cosmos, Plato and Aristotle agree, there is nothing,[39] simply nothing, and this nothing need not and should not be further defined. That it would be quite wrong to call this nothing "void" we have already seen. On the other hand, there is no reason why we should identify it with Parmenidean not-being. Cosmology is no longer so close to ontology, and, moreover (as we know), various ways have been found to neutralize or relativize not-being.[40]

There is something paradoxical about the tendency to think of the infinitely large in cosmic form or in analogy to our Cosmos. For does it not belong to the nature and to the very concept of the Cosmos to set limits and impose Form? Plato, at any rate, is keenly aware of these connotations of the Cosmos; it is with the help of "forms and numbers" that his Demiurge fashions the disorderly conditions that he found and transforms them into a Cosmos.[41] If in the *Timaeus* limit is not mentioned side by side with forms and numbers, it yet stands to reason that the change from formlessness to form is also a victory of limit. The Cosmos itself, we may say, inasmuch as it "contains everything"

[36] *De caelo* I,9.279a11–18. For what follows cf. Edel, *op.cit.*, 23ff.
[37] Cf. *De caelo* I,8.276b7–277a12; also 276a18–b7.   [38] Cf. Plato *Tim.* 32c5ff.
[39] See again *De caelo* I,9.279a11–18; Plato *Tim.* 32c5ff., 33c2. Since the *Physics* defines place as the inner boundary of the surrounding body, the Cosmos as such cannot have a place for Aristotle. This rather startling and provocative doctrine has been much commented upon by ancient and modern scholars (see, e.g., O. Hamelin, *Le système d'Arist.* [Paris, 1920], 291, and especially Mondolfo, *op.cit.*, 469ff., who also traces the later history of this doctrine). Technically the question belongs to the inquiry about place (IV,4.212a31–b22); in the chapters on the Infinite no reference is made to it, although Aristotle's negative answer has obvious connections with the denial of an infinitely large.
[40] See above, Ch. 4.   [41] *Tim.* 53b4.

and at the same time has its definite spherical form, provides a spatial boundary and limit for the sum total of physical entities.[42] Such being the nature of his Cosmos, we need not wonder that Plato never even considers whether the Cosmos may be infinite or whether there could be an infinite "body" of cosmic or other shape. There seems to be but one alternative to his single and bounded Cosmos, namely, the existence (simultaneously) of many, or even infinitely many, Cosmoi. This alternative Plato mentions and does his best to discredit.[43] We have seen that Aristotle's discussion of the Infinite in Book III of the *Physics* includes a passing reference to this possibility, yet it immediately gives way to the notion of one infinite body stretching out through space.[44]

Still, if the belief in several simultaneously existing Cosmoi receives less than its due in the *Physics*, the first book of *On the Heaven* makes up for this. The uniqueness of our Cosmos was a crucial part of the new (Academic) world picture—second in importance only to its eternity; it needed careful proof if it was to carry the day against the belief in many or innumerable worlds.[45] Aristotle provides this proof by once more making sure that all available material has been absorbed by our Cosmos; for him this means that all elements have their place within this Cosmos and could not be anywhere else. Side by side, however, with this argument against a plurality of Cosmoi we have here too a sustained polemic against the idea of an infinite body; and again Aristotle, in some of his arguments, thinks of this body as having the properties of our Cosmos and functioning in its manner and when these suppositions lead to impossible results regards this as fatal for the existence of an infinite body. The infinite body, he makes clear, could not be spherical, nor could it perform a revolution (as our Cosmos does); its parts could not, like the elements in our Cosmos, have weight and lightness or carry out the basic cosmic movements toward the center and away from it.[46] After all, the finite Cosmos, which is entirely by itself and has nothing to surround it, nothing to supply it with new material

---

[42] *Tim..* 33b. Plato's and Aristotle's Cosmos is a ὅλον and τέλειον; see *Tim.* 33a1ff. (also 34b2) and compare Aristotle's definition of these two concepts (III,6.207a8–15; see Notes 8 and 29). The concepts are clearly applicable to his Cosmos, since nothing can be outside it and the entire existing quantity of the elements is incorporated in it. For the *teleion* motif in Aristotle's cosmology see also below, Ch. 15.

[43] *Tim.* 31a2, 55c7–d6.   [44] III,4.203b25ff.; see above, p. 168.

[45] *De caelo* I,5–8.

[46] *Ibid.*, I,5.271b23–6.273a21 (note 272b13–16); 6.273a21–274a18; 7.274a33–b9, b22–32; 275b12–15; 276a6–12.

and nothing to dissolve into, was one of the great new conceptions that had taken shape in the last period of Plato's thought. There is no possibility of coming to terms between this idea and the belief in an infinite Universe. Yet so strong is the impact made by the new conception that when the opposition between these two world views becomes acute the infinite Universe presents itself to the defender of the Platonic position in the guise of a magnified Cosmos.

The infinitely small had in the philosophical tradition entered into a close association with the infinitely large, and Aristotle too sees his way to provide it with a counterpart.[47] Yet he is careful not to alight once more on the infinitely large which he has rejected on cosmological grounds. What answers to infinite division is not infinite multiplication but a particular kind of infinite addition: if of a given magnitude you take a fraction (like ½, ⅓, etc.), you may add "in the same ratio" without ever exhausting the original whole magnitude.[48] After adding ½ you add ¼, ⅛, and so on. In so doing it is impossible to exceed the original magnitude. If one were always again to add the original fraction, i.e., to proceed in arithmetical instead of in geometrical progression, one would not only soon go beyond the original magnitude but would in the course of continued addition "exceed every magnitude." Thus one would again arrive at a body "actually infinite," "something like that which the physicists place outside the Cosmos." [49] Since this must under all circumstances be avoided, Aristotle restricts the mathematical operation in the manner indicated. This restriction makes it necessary for him to explain precisely what he means by the "infinite in addition"—for the "infinite by division" there was less need of guarding against misunderstandings.[50] One important difference remains, however, between the two operations. In division the magnitudes become smaller and smaller, and thus indeed smaller than any given magnitude, whereas the addition, far from proceeding beyond any given magnitude, stays safely within the original one.[51]

Aristotle calls this kind of addition the "reverse" of infinite division. It may even be said to be the same process, merely considered from another point of view.[52] As Simplicius in another context says, if you

---

[47] III,6.206b3ff.; note b5, ἀντεστραμμένως.   [48] *Ibid.*, b7–9.

[49] *Ibid.*, 9–12; cf. b20–24, 7.207b15–21.

[50] 206b7–12 (the word ὡρισμένον in b7 probably is meant to indicate a fraction which sets the ratio for the additions). Infinite division needs little explanation, though the potential quality of this infinity must be made clear (206a18ff.).

[51] See b18–20 (the point is repeated in 207b3–5).   [52] 206b3,5.

divide the magnitude of an ell into two half ells and then leave the one half undivided yet cut the other in a constant ratio into progressively smaller parts, you have in this half infinite division going on; at the same time, by adding the parts here successively cut off to the other half you make it constantly larger.[53] As Simplicius puts it, there are two kinds of infinity "locked up" in the ell, the one proceeding in the direction of the large, the other in that of the small. These are the two infinities which Aristotle establishes in our section. Simplicius assures us that his deduction of the dual Infinite figured also in Plato's lecture "On the Good." If one could believe this, his statement would throw interesting light on the origin of Aristotle's doctrine of the twofold Infinite. However, Simplicius here relies on the authority of Porphyry, and he admits at the end of his report that Porphyry provided in effect an interpretation or "articulation" of Plato's "enigmatic" utterances.[54] Thus we had better not assume that Plato made the same use of his "large and small principle" when he derived the numbers, and presumably at the same time fractions. Aristotle's stipulations about infinite addition reflect his own concern that nothing infinitely large should be reached. If he pays homage to tradition by providing infinite division with a counterpart—its "reverse," as he says—he could not go back to the more generous and less anxious fashion in which, for instance, Anaxagoras had done the same: "Of the small there is no smallest . . . yet also of the large there is always something larger." [55] It is difficult to see what prevented Aristotle from holding with Zeno—and Plato's *Parmenides*—that if something is divided into smaller and smaller parts the whole becomes infinitely large (or "enormous," as Plato says) with reference to its parts.[56] Whatever the reason, Aristotle did not see fit to revive this ap-

---

[53] *In Phys.* I,453.36ff. Diels. For a similar point see Ross, *Physics*, "Introduction," 50.

[54] Simplicius *In Phys.* I,453.36ff. and 454.17. The report by Alexander of Aphrodisias on Plato's lecture which. Simplicius cites next is less close to Aristotle's doctrine; it includes no reference to a ratio. J. Stenzel, *Zahl. u. Gestalt bei Plato u. Arist.* (Berlin, 1924), 63ff., uses Porphyry's report with great confidence for the reconstruction of Plato's doctrines. See also P. Wilpert, *Zwei aristot. Frühschriften über die Ideenlehre* (Regensburg, 1949),199ff. Aristotle himself when in this context he refers to Plato's twofold conception of the *apeiron*, 206b27ff., does not suggest agreement in details. Nor can anything closely corresponding be found in the *Philebus*.

[55] *Vorsokr.*, 59B3.

[56] *Ibid.*, 29B1; cf. Plato *Parm.* 164cf., esp. d3f. where καὶ . . . ἐξ αὐτοῦ almost certainly refers to size (as does the preceding part of the clause to number). In the last sentence of Zeno's fragment (B1) I take μεγάλα and ἄπειρα to describe each

proach. The only infinitely large that he admits is to be found in numbers, where there is no limit to our counting. Here it is true that every given quantity can be exceeded in the direction of the "more," whereas in magnitudes this exceeding is possible only in the direction of the "less." [57]

---

of the πολλά in relation to the decrease ad infinitum of its parts which the progressive division brings into existence. For a current alternative explanation ("sum of an infinite series") see Vlastos' recent and exhaustive discussion in *Gnomon*, 31 (1959), 196ff.

[57] See esp. III,7.207b1-21. Actually the same bisections of a magnitude which make this smaller and smaller force us to resort to larger and larger numbers without limit to keep pace with the progressing bisection. Yet even this infinity exists according to Aristotle only potentially, like the infinity in division (*ibid.*, b10ff.). Aristotle's attitude to the mathematical concept of space has been the subject of some inquiries. Where he limits the scope of his investigation, he excludes mathematics from his purview (5.204a34ff.). Later, however, having made his decisions and in particular rejected the idea of an infinitely large, he returns to mathematics for a brief consideration of its concern in the matter. Here (7.207b27ff.) he assures the practicing mathematicians that his negative conclusion does not interfere with their legitimate interests, since they do not actually need infinite lines. True, they did not "need" them for their constructions, but their σκέψις, which Aristotle professes to respect, included parallel straight lines capable of being extended without meeting. Cf. F. M. Cornford, *Essays in Honour of Gilbert Murray* (London, 1936), 230ff., 232; see also Sir Thomas Heath, *A History of Greek Mathematics* (Oxford, 1921), 342ff., and the reply of Ross in *Physics*, "Introduction," 52.

9

The Doctrine of Movement

IN contrast to the first half of the *Physics*, the latter half is entirely concerned with the investigation of one large subject. Because of its history, the concept of movement had a strong claim on such an exhaustive discussion, and this claim had become particularly acute since Plato had made movement the general denominator of all physical changes. Plato had studied movement both as physical fact and as concept; he had defined its status and philosophical significance, had identified the source of its existence in the Cosmos, and had concerned himself with the physical as well as with the logical interrelation of its species of "forms." It is but natural that all these diverse interests should reappear in Aristotle's treatment of movement, and perhaps no less natural that he should give least effort to defending its reality and securing it philosophical status. This had been done once and for all; the subject now has its assured standing. In Book V where the discussion of movement begins Aristotle can dispense with solemn prefatory remarks concerning the desirability or necessity of examining this subject. In the much briefer account of movement in Book III he does offer a few words of justification which culminate in the striking assertion: "If movement is not known, nature [*physis*] is not known." [1] He can allow himself such peremptory language because nature is "the principle of movement and change." This is the essence of its definition with which we have become acquainted in Book II.[2]

[1] III,2.200b14.
[2] II,1.192b20; see above, p. 95. This definition is quoted in the opening sentence of Book III (200b12). For a phenomenological exegesis of Aristotle's views on movement see Walter Bröcker, *Aristoteles* (2d ed.; Frankfurt, 1957).

THE SPECIES OF MOVEMENT: GENERAL PROBLEMS

For the logical organization of the subject Plato's attempts at dividing and classifying the movements provided the obvious point of departure. Yet as far as we can see, Plato's efforts had remained tentative
and undogmatic—witness the recognition of qualitative change as a
species of movement in the *Theaetetus* and *Parmenides,* its omission in
the apparently complete enumeration of species in the *Laws.*[3] It stands
to reason that Aristotle when reading this "catalogue" was aghast at
finding species of motion and of locomotion (which in strict logic ought
to be subspecies) put side by side. His sense of systematic tidiness would
also rebel against the application of heterogeneous and overlapping criteria of differentiation; for Plato does not hesitate to put self-motion
and motion from outside on a par with forward movement, circular
movement, growth, decline, and so forth.[4] It seems that a final ordering
hand was still needed to get these things into shape.

Aristotle retains the distinction between self-motion and motion
caused from the outside. It becomes important when the relation between mover and moved comes to be investigated,[5] yet it need not be
taken into account when the different "forms" of change are set up in
Book V. A distinction between natural movement and movement contrary to nature (i.e., under compulsion) was to prove helpful in establishing the fundamental doctrines of Aristotle's cosmology; in the
Physics its role is very restricted. None of the major theses makes use
of this distinction, and it is only here and there in the course of his
arguments that Aristotle occasionally resorts to it.[6] Aristotle does not
allow differentiations of this kind to enter into the basic scheme of
qualitatively different kinds of change. These kinds are (1) locomo-

---

[3] *Theaet.* 181c–d (cf. 182c6); *Parm.* 138c1; *Legg.* X,893bff. Cf. above, pp. 30–34.

[4] *Legg.* X,894bff. It should not be supposed that Plato was unaware of the
objections to which his procedure in *Laws* X was open. The *Laws* is not a systematic or scientific treatise. We may regard it as close to certain that Aristotle's
basic classification of "changes" was fixed before he read the *Laws* (published
after Plato's death); indeed, it may have been so before Plato wrote Book X. The
principal division of changes into local movement, qualitative change, and growth
and decline may easily have emerged and become consolidated in Academic discussions, where it may have shown itself more immune to criticism than alternative attempts.

[5] See esp. VIII,4.

[6] E.g., IV,7.215a1ff. (in the discussion of the void); VIII,4 *passim.* The distinction
also enters into the question what movements may be considered as contrary to
one another (V,6.23a18ff.).

tion, (2) qualitative change (as from warm to cold), (3) growth and decline, (4) coming into being and passing away (about the problematic position of the last pair we shall speak presently).[7] In Book V the first three kinds are treated as corresponding to the categories of place, quality, and quantity;[8] this treatment, which amounts to a new "deduction" of the three forms, may confidently be regarded as Aristotle's own contribution. Locomotion is later (in Book VIII) subdivided into movement in circle and movement on a straight line, a division which is approximated by Plato when he gives movement in a circle a place apart from the other forms of locomotion.[9]

Both Plato and Aristotle use the concept of self-motion to arrive at the first source of all changes, i.e., the divine principle on which the ordered operation of the Cosmos ultimately depends.[10] Although Aristotle was to find some difficulty with the concept of self-motion, we may take it that initially he accepted Plato's division of all movements into those caused from outside and those arising within the moving object. To have the principle of movement in themselves is for him the distinctive characteristic of "natural" objects which sets them apart from the works of craft.[11]

---

[7] See pp. 178–181.

[8] V,1.225b5ff. Having eliminated coming into being and passing away, which could correspond to the category of substance, Aristotle relates the other changes at V,2.226a23ff. to the three categories mentioned. In view of what Plato had done to establish the status and clarify the problems of *genesis* there is no obvious ground for wondering (as Cherniss does, *Presocr.*, 116f.) why Aristotle would wish to distinguish it from qualitative change. He had inherited *genesis* as something unique and inviolate. *Alloiosis* too had been known in the Academy where it had been set up as a "Form" of movement (see above, Note 3. Cherniss, *Presocr.*, 107 n.441, refers only to *Theaet.* 157b). A more meaningful question would be whether Aristotle could have any motives for wishing to abandon the Platonic differentiation. To this the answer should probably be negative. One reason why Aristotle would wish to maintain the differentiation is, needless to say, again the continuity of problems, including the *genesis* of the elements which engages him in *De caelo* and *De gen.*

[9] See esp. *Phys.* VIII,8.261b28ff., 9; Plato *Tim.* 34a; *Legg.* X,893cff. It is hardly necessary to say that Aristotle too knows the division of noncircular locomotion into (1) to the right and to the left, (2) ahead and back, and (3) up and down; see, e.g., *De caelo* II,2.284b1ff. where it is suggested that the proper place for them is in the theory about the movements of animals (cf. *De anim. inc.* 4ff.). This may also be in Plato's mind in *Tim.* 34a where the Cosmos—treated throughout this section as a ζῷον—is denied these six movements. In *Phys.* III,5.205b31ff. Aristotle treats these six concepts as differentiations of "place."

[10] *Legg.* X,894cff.; cf. *Phaedr.* 245cff. and *Phys.* VIII,5 (see, e.g., 256a4–21, 257a27–31; for a closer study of this chapter see below, Ch. 10).

[11] *Phys.* II,1; see also VIII,4.

Plato nowhere in his dialogues offers a subdivision of movements coming from the outside, but it would be rash to conclude that he—or other members of the Academy—had never attempted one. Thus we cannot decide whether the fourfold division put forward in Book VII of the *Physics* is Aristotle's original contribution. The four kinds here enumerated are pulling, pushing, carrying, and rotating.[12] Aristotle is at pains to show that all conceivable varieties of locomotion may be traced back to these four "forms." In the last analysis, he goes on to point out, the four forms may be reduced to two, namely pushing and pulling.[13] From the mover's point of view one of them is motion toward himself, the other away from himself.

It is noteworthy that Aristotle, while studying these subdivisions of locomotion, protests against the idea that aggregation and dissociation form a separate and additional class of movement.[14] All aggregations and dissociations, except those which occur in the processes of coming to be and passing away, should be understood as forms of "pushing" (ὦσις) and placed in this class. Aggregation and dissociation are the devices which the later Presocratics had used to explain the formation and the passing away of compound substances;[15] in this way they had steered clear of the prohibited concept of *genesis*. Yet the primary target of Aristotle's criticism is not these thinkers but Plato. For although he is tolerant of these concepts as such, he rejects the attempt to set them up as a separate genus of movement. It had been no part of the Presocratics' achievement to establish genera and species or to provide logically valid classifications of the various kinds of movement. Plato, on the other hand, not only availed himself of aggregation and dissociation to explain the actual formation of physical entities in the *Timaeus* but also incorporated both concepts in his final classification of movements. In Book X of the *Laws* they represent the third and fourth form of movement [16] and are treated as an essential prior condition for the materialization of other forms, such as growth, decrease, and destruction. Yet if Plato could go so far in endorsing the Presocratic approach, Aristotle refuses to follow suit. He knows how important a part these two concepts had played in the earlier physical systems and seems on this and other occasions prepared to appreciate their

---

[12] VII,1.243a16ff; a17 makes clear that the division is meant to embrace all local motions. In *Legg.* X,893d Plato distinguishes two kinds of motion from place to place: gliding and rolling.

[13] VII,1.243b16ff.   [14] *Ibid.*, b10.   [15] See above, Ch. 1.

[16] *Legg.* X,893e; cf. above, p. 000.

help in the explanation of *genesis*. But such passages should not be read as a serious or final commitment. Even when he elsewhere says that coming to be and passing away happen by means of aggregation and dissociation,[17] he merely performs a courtesy bow to the *opinio communis* which provides him with a convenient argument, but he does not accept this opinion as the last word on the question. How he himself proposes to account for *genesis* and destruction without this Presocratic pair of concepts he does not disclose in the *Physics*. Their final and unqualified repudiation is reserved for the treatise *On Coming to Be and Passing Away*.[18] For the time being it must suffice that Aristotle refuses to set up aggregation and dissociation as species of movement. His criticism need not be directed against the passage of the *Laws* but may just as well refer to a similar division of movement which Plato had propounded within the Academy.[19]

Genesis poses a special problem. Is it really one of the movements, or is it something different and *sui generis*? It has long been noticed that Aristotle's attitude on this question is not consistent throughout the books of the *Physics*.[20] In some sections he does not hesitate to regard *genesis* as one of the species of movement and to give it a place beside the other three (qualitative change, growth and decrease, and locomotion); in others he sticks to the three species of movement yet employs at the same time another generic concept, change (*metabole*), which is

---

[17] Cf. VIII,7.260b7–15; note the references to Presocratic doctrines in 9.265b17–32.

[18] *De gen. et corr.* I,2, esp. 317a17ff.

[19] It should be noted that the rejection of association and dissociation as species or "forms" of movement occurs in Book VII, which for good reasons is dated in the Academic period of Aristotle. The *Laws*, however, was published after this period had come to an end. Were members of the Academy familiar with Plato's works while they were in process of composition? We have no right to suppose this. Nor is it easy to regard 243b10–12 as a later addition by Aristotle's hand (for it seems that Book VII was replaced by the "maturer" Book VIII, and so far no instance has been found of Aristotle's bringing the content of VII into line with later discoveries or conclusions). Did Aristotle not have other ways of knowing Plato's views? Movement would seem to be an obvious subject for the Academic practice of *diairesis,* and it is hardly farfetched to think that on such occasions Plato came forward with the suggestion that association and dissociation were species of movement. Curiously the other version of Book VII (243b29) has the statement that all local movements are associations and dissociations.

[20] Cf. P. Tannery, *Arch. f. Gesch. d. Philos.,* 7(1894), 224ff., and 9(1896), 115ff. (republished in his *Mémoires scientifiques,* 7 [Paris, 1925], 179ff., 195ff.); G. Rodier, *ibid.,* 8(1895), 455ff., and 9, 185ff.; Ross, *Physics,* "Introduction," 7ff. I agree with Ross that a study of Aristotle's varying usage yields little gain for the chronology of his works. On the relation of "change" and "movement" cf. Léon Robin, *Aristote* (Paris, 1944), 130.

large enough to comprehend movement (with its three species) as well as *genesis* and its opposite, φθορά (passing away). Of the arguments which in Book VIII secure for locomotion the primacy among the movements, some treat *genesis* as a species of movement; but one proof definitely ignores it.[21] The first chapter of Book V excludes absolute as well as relative *genesis* from the realm of movement. If *genesis* is the way from not-being to being, it cannot be movement because "not-being cannot be moved." [22] Another argument to the same effect takes the form that, while movement must take place between contraries, substance, the product and end result of *genesis*, has no contrary.[23] In sharp contrast with this decision, the first chapters of Book III in which Aristotle gives us his basic definition of movement include *genesis* as a matter of course among the movements.[24]

Aristotle's inconsistent attitude has its roots in the antecedent development of these concepts.[25] Movement had flourished in later Presocratic speculation while *genesis* was under a ban, and the rehabilitation of *genesis* in Plato's later works has no obvious connection with the incorporation of movement into his system and the subsequent elaboration of its doctrine. When in the *Timaeus* Plato proves the necessity of never-ceasing *genesis*, he places it beside being and the receptacle as the third eternal reality. Movement cannot be put on the same plane, even though the entities that here arise in the receptacle immediately set up a movement which adumbrates the shape of the Cosmos. As a matter of fact, however different their past history, movement and *genesis* have so many points of contact that they could not for long remain

---

[21] VIII,7 (the first argument operates on the assumption of three movements only, 260a26ff.).

[22] V,2.225a20ff.; see esp. 25ff. Although on the whole I accept the text as presented by Ross, it would seem desirable not to include the statement that *genesis* cannot be a movement in the parenthesis (which might as well begin in a27 with the words εἰ γάρ). In relative *genesis*, like the change of a man from not-white to white, the substratum persists, as we have learned in I (and as Aristotle here too seems to recognize, a27–29); yet the radical decision which Aristotle here formulates makes no allowance even for relative *genesis*.

[23] V,2.225b10ff.

[24] III,1.201a9–15. Book VII ignores *genesis* when establishing the proposition that mover and moved must be in contact (since Aristotle in ch. 2 shows explicitly that the proposition applies to qualitative change and growth, the absence of *genesis* cannot be accidental). Ch. 4 deals with a matter unrelated to the content of chs. 1–3 (to wit, the question whether movements of different kinds are comparable to one another), yet no more than they does it give attention to *genesis*.

[25] What follows is a summary of developments traced in Chs. 1 and 2.

strangers to one another. The constant movements into which the *Theaetetus* dissolves everything are invariably creative of some new entity, however floating and unstable. The basic cosmic movement of the *Timaeus* sets up a large commotion of the elementary particles which results in the formation of new physical entities and the breaking up of others [26] (what Plato has in mind is changes from one element into another, as good a case of *genesis* as can be found). Finally the classification of movements in Book X of the *Laws* includes destruction as well as *genesis*. To be sure, Plato keeps the latter from the all-powerful grasp of "congregation," yet though it is *sui generis*, he does incorporate it in the catalogue of movements.[27]

To a large extent, then, the situation which we find in the *Physics* corresponds to the relation (or lack of it) between movement and *genesis* that had developed in the Academy. The principal difference is that whereas in Plato this relationship must be "distilled" from a study of his works Aristotle actually discusses it. Sooner or later the question whether *genesis* was a movement had to come into the open. If Plato's "published works" never formulate this question, they yet embody situations which suggest it, and as it would be foolish to believe that Plato repeatedly dealt with the question and found an answer to it without being aware of what he did, we may as well say frankly and plainly that Plato knew the question.

One subject—also common to Plato and Aristotle—could not be effectively discussed if *genesis* was denied a place among the movements. Which kind of movement should be regarded as the first and as the antecedent cause of the others? Plato and Aristotle are at one in assigning the first place to locomotion and holding that the other changes presuppose the prior realization of a local movement. In this context the "other movements" definitely include *genesis,* and the point of the entire elaborate physical and cosmological construction would be lost if *genesis*, the coming to being of physical entities, were not also shown to depend on the rotation of the heaven. If the soul, the first mover, were ever to perish, Plato says in the *Phaedrus*, all *genesis* would break down and come to a standstill; and there would be nothing whence it could be set in motion and arise again.[28] Other dialogues give more concrete form to this thought. All movements in the Cosmos that lead to new formations are traced to that of the outermost heavenly

[26] *Tim.* 58a.   [27] *Legg.* X,894a; see, however, above, Ch. 2, Note 62.
[28] *Phaedr.* 245d7ff.

sphere which soul keeps going. The catalogue of movements in Book
X of the *Laws* suggests causal connections between the different kinds
and in effect makes local movement the first in this causal sequence
(though it must be admitted that *genesis* here holds somewhat aloof
from the sequence). The myth of the *Statesman* traces connections between *genesis* and the basic cosmic movement.[29] Aristotle too has a
scheme by which he makes all *genesis* depend on the movements of the
sun, which in turn are caused ultimately by the rotation of the outermost heaven. The details of this scheme will engage us later; quite
properly they are not expounded in the *Physics* but in the treatise *On
Coming to Be* [30] in which Aristotle shows greater readiness to be specific. Yet the *Physics* too has to vindicate the primacy of local movement and succeeds in doing so even without resorting to cosmological
arguments. In the case of an individual—so the argument runs—it is
correct to say that it must first come into being before it can grow,
change, and finally develop also the capacity of motion; but whatever
brings it into being must go through some movement. In this way the
priority of local movement over *genesis* is safeguarded, while the cosmic
scheme, the actual locus of this sequence, is kept out of the discussion.[31]
Surely the first mover would not fully deserve this designation—nor
the place which Plato and Aristotle assign him—if he were not also the
first cause of all coming into being.[32]

As for the nature of the first mover, it is not enough to know that
local movement is the first of all changes. For not local movement as
such but only that form of it which can be eternal may be associated
with the first mover. This again is a Platonic doctrine. What new proofs
Aristotle furnishes for it and what other Platonic concepts and conceptions he preserves in his own theory of the first mover we shall see later
when we pass from the general study of movements to the investigation
of the first movement.

Beyond all details, the fact that Aristotle presents his entire doctrine
of changes under the heading of "movement" (the word which primarily designates local movement) shows his intimate connection with
Plato's approach to the world of changes. It would be worth while—

[29] *Tim.* 58a; *Legg.* X,893c–894a. In *Polit.* 269cff. opposite movements of the
Cosmos as a whole determine opposite directions for everything that comes to
pass in the *physis*. It does not seem irrational to find underneath the mythical
embroidery a causal scheme which persists in the later constructions of Plato himself as well as of Aristotle.
[30] *De gen. et corr.* II,10ff.   [31] VIII,7.260b29–261a12.   [32] See below, Ch. 20.

though it is beyond the scope of this study—to scrutinize the extent to which doctrines and arguments of these books are devised with local movement primarily in mind. To be sure, there are propositions which are successively established for all three or, as the case may be, even all four "forms" of movement; [33] yet where Aristotle contents himself with speaking of "movement" plain and simple, there is reason to believe that local movement is uppermost in his mind. Even the arguments proving that whatever is in motion is moved by something [34] are no exception.

Not for every topic that Aristotle takes up can we be certain that it had already been formulated or investigated in the Academy. But it is hard to think that only Aristotle should have been interested in generalized questions such as "Which movement is contrary to which?" [35] Surely Plato and his fellow workers would often find themselves under the necessity of dealing with, or constructing, contrary movements. A few illustrations culled at random from the later dialogues will suffice to make this evident. Even the Platonic classification of movements includes some that stand in this relation to one another: decrease is the contrary of growth, passing away of coming into being. In the outer regions of the Cosmos the rotation of the entire heaven takes place in the opposite direction to that of the planets; the former moves to the right, the latter to the left, and the one movement is said to represent the principle of the Same, the other that of the Other. The changes undergone by the elementary particles include movements up as well as down, associations as well as dissociations. The *Parmenides* in one of its hypotheses develops the paradox that "the one" becomes simultaneously older and younger than itself. According to the myth of the *Statesman* nature and life change the direction of their processes

---

[33] This point may again be illustrated by III,1, where the definition of *kinesis* is shown to apply to all four kinds, and VII,2f., where the necessity for mover and moved (or agent and patient) to be "together" is established successively for local movement, qualitative change, and growth.

[34] VIII,4. Ch. 5, however, which from the position reached in 4 leads to the concept of a first mover, makes effective use of the different "kinds" of movement (e.g., 257a3ff.; cf. 24). It is interesting to find Aristotle, in V,6.230a18ff., wondering whether his favorite distinction between movement according to nature and contrary to nature has analogues in qualitative change, growth, and *genesis*. See, further, Aristotle's "rediscovery" of the basic meaning of *kinesis* in VIII,9.266a1ff. (cf. 265b17ff.), where this fact serves him as an additional argument for the primacy of locomotion.

[35] V,5f.

with alternating cosmic periods and proceed now in this way and then again in the contrary.[36]

We certainly do not overestimate the Academy's capacity for "abstract" thought if we suppose that it was aware of the general question implied in these specific doctrines and constructions. Nor need it be argued at length that Plato and the Academy knew movement and rest as contraries. Actually Aristotle's question is not whether movement and rest are contraries but what particular movement is the contrary of what rest. He also wonders whether one kind of rest may be regarded as the contrary of another (e.g., "rest" in health as the contrary of "rest" in illness). Further complications result from the distinction between natural movement and movement under compulsion; as Aristotle sees it, there is contrariety, for instance, between conditions of rest not in accordance with nature and movements in accordance with it.[37] The distinction between movement contrary and according to nature is one of his special favorites and is marked out for a large role in the cosmology of the books *On the Heaven*. The more the differentiations that are introduced, the greater becomes the need of clarifying the mutual relations between all of them. Among relations contrariety had commended itself to Aristotle's particular attention. Throughout his works he applies it to a large variety of subjects.[38] If we bear this in mind, we shall not overstress his debt to Plato. In truth, the question from which we started—whether Aristotle's discussion of contrary movements owes much to Plato—merges in the larger one whether his interest in, and concept of, contrariety reflects Academic interests. The answer, it seems to me, is definitely affirmative. Granted that the interest

[36] *Legg.* X,893e–894a; *Tim.* 35c, 58b; *Parm.* 152af. (also, e.g., 156e7ff.); *Polit.* 269cff. (where the word ἐναντίον occurs frequently, 270b8, e1, and *passim;* note the word also in *Parm.* 157b: "going from small to large and to equal" καὶ [εἰς] τὰ ἐναντία).

[37] V,6.229b23ff., 230b10ff. That movement according to nature and movement under constraint form a pair of contraries seems to be taken for granted in 230a18ff. where this distinction makes its appearance in our context; Aristotle at once turns to specific problems connected with it.

[38] It would be pointless to give a complete enumeration of these subjects which, as students of the *Politics* will remember, include even forms of government (*Pol.* V,6f.). Mention may, however, be made of the important role which the question of τὸ ἐναντίον plays in the discussion of the categories (*Categ.* 5,3b24ff. and *passim*). On the whole I refer to Bonitz' *Index, s.vv.* ἐναντίον, ἐναντιότης, ἐναντίωσις. The earliest recorded use of ἐναντίος and its adverb includes instances of movements which meet, coming from opposite directions (ἐναντίη ἤλυθε *Il.* 6.251 *et al.*), while in other cases the sense of opposition (or hostility) is present.

in "opposites" is as old as Greek physical (and ethical) speculation, the concern with generic concepts of this kind is characteristic of the Academy and of the higher level of abstraction to which thought had here advanced.[39] Thus although questions concerning contrariety between movements were rife in the Academy, it would yet be shortsighted to isolate this problem. In a subject like this, where we have to reckon with cross-fertilization of larger and smaller problems, the continuity of the latter is of secondary importance. In point of fact, Aristotle's actual treatment of movements contrary to each other does not recall any specific propositions that could be quoted from Plato's dialogues.

Before studying this relationship of contrariety, Aristotle in Book V discusses a question which may or may not be of the same type. Under what conditions is it correct to regard movements as identical or to speak of *one* movement? [40] It is evident that here the same capacity for precise logical discrimination and definition is called into play and that identity and contrariety of movements are similar problems. For identity the different uses of the word "one" must be borne in mind. Movements may be called one (and the same) because they belong to the same genus, or to the same species, or because they are actually and numerically one; yet to be considered "one," in the full sense of the word, a movement must meet certain qualifications: it must be continuous and uniform.[41] These criteria are invoked again in the last book of the *Physics* where Aristotle has to decide what kind of movement the first and unmoved mover inspires. Here he proceeds by "elimination," ruling out all changes but locomotion and then within the species of locomotion ruling out motion in a straight line as well as mixed forms.[42]

[39] Not surprisingly, Parmenides is the Presocratic in whose fragments (28B8, 55.59) τἀντία actually occurs. Heracl. B10 and 67 are interesting for the occurrence of the term in the paraphrase but not in the authentic wording. A glance at Kranz's Index, *s.v.*, shows a noteworthy discrepancy between the A and the B sections. Some credit may have to be given to the Sophists for bringing the term into fashion; see, e.g., Gorgias 82B80. As for the usage in Plato's dialogues, the important passage in *Tim.* 50a3 has already been mentioned (p. 43); we may further note the discussion of τὰ ἐναντία and their mutual relation in *Phaed.* 102dff. It is possible that for stylistic reasons Plato denied himself as frequent an employment of the term as the subjects taken up might suggest.

[40] V,4.227b3ff.; cf. b2off. Another topic similar in type is studied in VII,4: to what extent and in what way are movements that belong to different species or genera yet comparable in point of speed, etc.?

[41] 227a19ff., b15ff.

[42] VIII,7–9; see esp. 7.260a20–26; 8.261b27–262b8; 264b9–265a12; 9.265a27–b16.

For it is axiomatic that the movement in question must be "one," and "continuity" is from the beginning associated with this "one." In the end only the circular movement can qualify. Should we then suppose that in our chapter of Book V amidst seemingly harmless and purely theoretical qualifications the ground is quietly laid for a doctrine of much larger import? This would give our chapter a function far transcending that of other and on their face comparable inquiries into the various aspects of movement. Yet when Aristotle in Book VIII tests all changes by the requirement of continuity and finally accepts circular motion, the expectations are higher than in our section. The "continuity" which belongs to the revolution of the outermost heaven is one that knows neither beginning nor end; it is, in one word, "infinite," and although infinity is treated as an additional stipulation, there are passages in which continuity as such is understood to entail it.[43] In a similar fashion the standards for "uniformity" have become higher. Movement in a straight line, which in Book V comes up to the mark, is now dismissed on the ground that it is bound to have a beginning and an end and that its speed increases as it approaches the end.[44] Finally, granted that τέλειον in both books may by itself denote nothing more exalted than completeness, the definition of it in Book V is more generous and less exclusive.[45] On the other side of the ledger, the definition of numerical identity which we have found in our chapter is cited in the disquisitions leading to the selection of the circular movement.[46] And on general grounds it is unlikely that Aristotle ever meant to confine his study of movement to the rather restricted scope of Books V and VI. Their topics are important but not of ultimate importance. And if an analysis of these books does not show them to point beyond themselves, reflection upon the intellectual environment and climate in which Aristotle's investigations developed suggests larger goals. The *Timaeus*, the *Phaedrus*, and the *Laws* embody the conceptions of a self-mover who is the fountainhead of all other cosmic movements, and two of these works lay stress on the regularity and circular-

---

[43] Cf. VIII,7.261a31–262a17; 8.264b9–28; 9.265a27–b8.

[44] VIII,9.265b11ff. (a rather special case of movement in a straight line is here used for comparison and elimination); V,4.228b17, 20f.

[45] VIII,8.264b27ff.; 9.265a16ff. (22ff.); V,4.228b11.

[46] VIII,8.261b36ff.; cf. V,4.227b21ff. and esp. 228b1ff. A somewhat different definition of a movement which is numerically one is found in VII,1.242b37–42. Yet here too there is a reference to what "has been said before," and the section thus referred to can only be V,4.

ity of the first cosmic movement.[47] Aristotle did not invent the doctrine of the first mover; he only revised it, giving some of the Platonic thoughts that are fused in this grandiose conception a more precise form and bringing them together in a new pattern. Should it really be the case that Aristotle, when composing his treatise "On Movement," considered the noblest and sublimest phase of the subject as beyond his capacity? Such self-imposed restraint would hardly be of long duration. Thus, if there is restraint in connection with a topic which would invite higher flights, it is likely to spring from a feeling for methodical tidiness. Although aware that a precise definition of "one continuous movement" had to support the last and crowning part of the whole edifice, Aristotle refrained from slanting his inquiry toward that end. To do so would have stultified the general applicability of its results. As matters stand, the results, though generally applicable, prove too lax on the occasion when they ought to be especially useful.

Kinds of movements, mutual relationships between movements, and the supremacy of the self-moving principle clearly struck Aristotle as subjects that stood to gain from a new and more systematic investigation which would take its stand on purely physical ground, allow nothing from the outside to interfere, and regard logic as the sole arbiter. The subjects as such were not new but had in one way or another come into the Academic discussion after Plato had made the decisive turn of including "all that is moved" along with "all that is unmoved" in the scope of philosophic investigation. Yet Aristotle may well have felt that the endeavor of the Academy, concentrating as it did on certain facets of movement, had slighted some basic questions and that this neglect had serious consequences, inasmuch as it left the entire theory of movement without carefully laid foundations. What was still needed was, on the one hand, a precise definition of movement—was it not agreed that every inquiry should start with a definition of the subject to be examined? [48]—and, on the other, an analytical study of the nature and inherent property of every movement. The definition Aristotle supplies in Book III: movement, or change, is the actualization in any given object of the potentiality to change in this particular way.[49] Book III is not a part of Aristotle's comprehensive theory of movement; but

---

[47] *Phaedr.* 245c5ff.; *Tim.* 34b10ff., 36d8ff., 58a4ff.; *Legg.* X,894cff.; see also *Legg.* X,898af. For the first movement as self-movement see also *Polit.* 269e5.

[48] See, e.g., Plato *Phaedr.* 237cf., 263d.

[49] III,1.201a9ff. In the definition ἡ τοῦ δυνάμει ὄντος ἐντελέχεια ᾗ τοιοῦτον κίνησίς ἐστιν the words ᾗ τοιοῦτον are capable of different interpretations. I understand not "of the potential as such," i.e., as potential, but "in what respect it is potential."

this definition is recalled in Book V where the systematic study of this concept gets under way. And the definition was to prove helpful even in the final inquiry [50] which rises above the common varieties of movement to investigate the nature of the self-moving principle and find the way to the ultimate mover.

CONTACT, CONTINUITY, AND RELATED CONCEPTS

For a deeper penetration into the actual nature of movement Aristotle prepares the ground in the third chapter of Book V. Immediately after distinguishing the principal forms of movement he lays down definitions for a number of concepts. The significance of these concepts for a theory of movement is not immediately apparent, yet Aristotle must regard them as crucial, if so early in this treatise he wishes to make sure of their precise meaning. These concepts are "together," "apart," "to be in contact" (or "touch"), "between" (or "intermediate"), "successive," "contiguous," and "continuous." [51]

Clearly these are concepts applicable to the mutual relation of physical objects. We might speak of them as determining the relation of things in space, yet as they stand in no explicit connection with either Plato's or Aristotle's doctrine of space (and place) we must be on our guard when using this term—to avoid it completely would be awkward.[52] The important role which the concepts play in Aristotle's own physical system will gradually come to light. Anticipating our conclu-

---

This means here "in what respect it is changeable." This idea is elaborated and illustrated by the examples that follow. Simplicius paraphrases the words by ἐνέργειαν . . . τοῦ κινητοῦ ἡ τοιοῦτον (I do not wish to defend the reading ἐνέργεια which his text had instead of ἐντελέχεια; but this does not affect the point that "of the changeable as such" brings out Aristotle's meaning). Cf. also VIII,1.251b9; 5.257b6. It may be argued that the absence of a formal definition of κίνησις in Plato's dialogues is no proof that none had been attempted in the Academy. This possibility cannot be gainsaid, yet some statements of "others" about the nature of movement which Aristotle mentions slightly later (201b16ff., 19) do not give the impression of being formal definitions. They recall passages like *Tim.* 57e6ff. (to which Ross refers in the commentary *ad loc.*). Aristotle does not use the word "definition" in describing these statements. They may be said to approximate definition inasmuch as they appear to indicate the genus in which movement should be put.

[50] VI.224b10; VIII,1.251b9; 5.257b6 (note here the entire argument b6–13). Individual passages hardly give a full impression of the benefit which Aristotle in Book VIII derived from his habit of thinking of the moved in terms of potentiality.

[51] V,3.226b18. The Greek terms are ἅμα, χωρίς, ἅπτεσθαι, μεταξύ, ἐφεξῆς, ἐχόμενον, συνεχές.

[52] For a recent experiment which applies some of these concepts to Aristotle's doctrine of place see H. R. King, *Cl. Q.*, 44 (1950), 81ff.

sions, we may say that "contact" is an essential condition for the mutual interaction of things—"acting and suffering" as the Platonists call it—and that continuity is the basic characteristic of every movement and, with one exception, of every change. As every continuum is infinitely divisible, movement combines in Aristotle's scheme the principle of "the one" and infinite plurality. It is not by accident, then, that most of the concepts with which we are now concerned are also found in the *Parmenides*. To begin with, we may try to understand Aristotle's interest in these "spatial" terms as reflecting his Academic environment.

In the *Parmenides* "contact" is among the relationships between "the one" and the others that Plato takes up for scrutiny.[53] In accordance with the procedure generally followed in this dialogue Plato proves both alternatives: the one is and is not in contact with other entities (also, as a matter of fact, with itself, though for our purposes we may disregard this facet). In the course of his argument Plato gives us not so much a technical definition of "contact" and "being in contact" as a statement of certain essential conditions that must be met if contact is to materialize: "Must not everything that is to touch something find itself next [successive] to that which it is about to touch [occupying the place which comes after it]? . . . And the one too if it is to touch itself must find itself next to itself occupying the place contiguous to where it is?"[54] Here we may note the use of the terms "next" (which is identical with Aristotle's "successive") and "contiguous." Again Plato says: "[The one will not touch the others], for, we say, what is about to make contact must while being apart be next [i.e., successive] to what it will touch, and there must be no third thing between them."[55]

This sentence too uses the term "next" or "successive" yet also refers to spatial "apartness" and stipulates that if there is to be contact nothing should be "between" the objects involved in it. Plato does not explain why apartness is a necessary qualification. In the remainder of

---

[53] 148d5. Cf. A. Diès in his edition of the *Parmenides* (*Platon: Oeuvres complètes*, vol. 8, pt. 1 [Paris, 1923]), ad 148e and also "Notice," p. 33.

[54] *Ibid.*, e4–10.

[55] 149a4–6; cf. Cornford, *Pl. and Parm.*, 168 n.1. It is immaterial that Plato for "between" uses the words ἐν μέσῳ instead of μεταξύ, Aristotle's word (see, however, ἀνὰ μέσον, 245b2 et al.). A more serious difference may be that Aristotle (226b23ff., 227a7ff.) defines τὸ μεταξύ with reference to change (between contraries) rather than to position. He uses it, however, in the latter sense; see, e.g., VII,2.243a34, 244a6.

the section we find him particularly anxious to show that the contacts that are possible between entities must always be one less in number than the entities themselves. He does not see fit to give a precise definition of the term "to be in contact," which might show how this concept differs from "next" and "contiguous."

Thus we here have the same cluster of terms as in the third chapter of Aristotle's treatise "On Movement." More precisely, we have five of the seven concepts which Aristotle defines, namely, "contact," "successive," "contiguous," "apart," and "between." This can hardly be accidental. The agreement may be explained in more than one way. It is possible that Aristotle during a careful reading of the *Parmenides* realized the importance of the distinctions and relationships there set up and that he, either at once or later, decided to utilize the same concepts for his physical inquiry. Yet it may also be supposed that these concepts figured frequently in the philosophical conversations and discussions of the Academy. Opportunities were certainly not lacking; for, as we begin to see, the concepts have a bearing on several large subjects. They not only govern the relationship between one object and others but may also be steppingstones toward developing the concept of the one, in the sense of a "continuum" (συνεχές). In fact, Aristotle uses them for both purposes.

However, before we study Aristotle's use of these concepts, a few more words should be said about the details of his definitions. As we know, the list includes "together," "apart" (or "distinct"), "in contact," "between" (or "intermediate"), "successive" (or "next"), "contiguous" (or "adjacent"), and "continuous." The first and the last item are absent in the section of the *Parmenides*. Their inclusion in the list of the *Physics* is amply justified by their importance. For continuity is one of the principal subjects of our treatise, and by exploring the meaning and the connotations of this concept, Aristotle is able to push on to significant new positions. It is through "continuity" that the many become one [56]—a point of view which could only have interfered with the relationships considered by Plato.

"Together" is not destined to play a role of great consequence. Still, in this chapter of definitions it fulfills a useful purpose; for with its help Aristotle does what Plato had omitted to do, i.e., he tells us precisely what is meant by being in contact: "Things are in contact if their extremes are together." [57] In referring to the *Parmenides* we see that Plato

---

[56] See below, pp. 198–199.   [57] 226b23.

uses "apart" of an object which does not yet touch. Aristotle defines the "together" in a way which makes it the exact opposite of "apart" ("things are said to be together in place if they are in one and the same primary place, apart if they are in different" (scil., primary places).[58] That Aristotle defines "apart" is the more noteworthy as he nowhere in the following definitions makes use of this concept (in fact, he never refers to objects that are capable of being, but are not actually, in contact). Evidently the reason why "apart" is defined, along with the other concepts, is that it had a fixed place in this "catalogue."

Regarding Aristotle's definition of the two other concepts, a few observations will suffice. For the "successive" it is essential that nothing of the same kind should come between it and that to which it is successive. The point that "nothing should come between" is the same that Plato makes in the sentence in which he speaks of an object as "about to be in contact" (but not yet actually in contact) with another and describes it as "successive" to what it will touch.[59] The definition of the "contiguous" is a trifle less close to Plato's; for Aristotle, to be contiguous is actually to be in contact ("contiguous is whatever being successive is in contact"). Plato, on the other hand, uses this term (like "apart") of a situation in which objects are about to touch; in this case they occupy "contiguous" places [60] (yet nothing in Plato's phrasing rules out the possibility of objects still being contiguous when the contact has materialized).[61]

If we trace the use to which Aristotle puts the terms here defined,

---

[58] *Ibid.,* 21ff.; the passage of the *Parmenides* is quoted above, p. 188. The "primary place" of an object is that immediately occupied by it, in contrast to a larger spatial unit of which the primary place would be a part (see IV,1.209a31ff).

[59] 226b34ff.; *Parm.* 149a4ff.

[60] 227a6; *Parm.* 148e7. The definition in the *Physics* is followed by a sentence which elaborates the definition of the μεταξύ. Cornford realized that the sentence is out of place. He and Ross have shifted it to 226b23 (after the definition of "contact"), where it would prepare the ground for the definition of the μεταξύ which is given immediately afterward. However, in this list of definitions Aristotle's habit is to begin his sentences with the term to be defined (he follows the same principle also elsewhere in corresponding situations, e.g., 222b7ff.; see also *Anal. Pr.* 70a3ff., with or without Ross's change of the sequence). The transposition violates this "stylistic principle." The sentence in question as well as 226b26f. has the character of notes made by Aristotle with the intention of elaborating his definition of the μεταξύ. The best way of treating them is probably to put both at 226b25 (where one of them is found in the MSS), marking them as later additions.

[61] Note that Plato adds the word χωρίς in 149a5 to make clear that contact has not yet taken place.

we can understand why he is anxious to settle their meaning at this early stage. In the *Physics* itself the "continuous," the "together," and "contact" are assigned important functions; the other concepts have to content themselves with making occasional appearances, mainly to serve as a foil for these three.

The dominating role which the concept of continuity plays in Book VI will claim our attention very shortly; for the present we turn to Book VII whose leitmotif is announced in the first brief sentence: "Whatever is moved must be moved by something." Starting from this proposition, Aristotle works up to his proof for the existence of a first mover. If there were no "first," an infinite number of movements would be interconnected, each of them being caused by the preceding one, and the number of the moving and of the moved objects would be infinite too.[62] This would create difficulties because if the whole series of these infinite movements is considered as a unit we should arrive at one infinite movement, an idea difficult to entertain, especially if the time in which this movement should be carried out is to be finite. For the entire extremely complex movement should be simultaneous with that of any member of the series, and Aristotle assumes that the latter materializes in a finite time.[63] The argument as here put forward has its weak points, and Aristotle himself is not yet satisfied by it. What clinches it, in his opinion, is one further proposition which he now proceeds to introduce: "If that which directly causes a local and physical movement must be either continuous or in contact with the object which it moves (as we see it to be the case in all instances), the movers and the moved [scil., of this series] must be either continuous or in contact with one another so as to form one thing composed of them all." [64]

This leads to the result of one coherent infinite movement produced in finite time, Aristotle evidently still clinging to his initial assumption that the entire movement should not exceed the time needed by one link in the infinite chain. If the argument even in this form retains some of its weaknesses and unwarranted suppositions, we may console ourselves with the thought that Book VII is not Aristotle's last word on these matters and that the proofs and theories embodied in it were later replaced by the "maturer" insights of Book VIII. For the time being,

[62] See VII,1.242a54–b50 (the alternative version of Book VII contains the same arguments).
[63] *Ibid.*, b50–53.   [64] VII,1.242b59ff.

however, the firmest basis for the necessity of a first mover is the thesis that any moved object must be "in contact or continuous" with its direct, or proximate, mover. This, he has assured us, is "the case in all instances." Clearly, however, a mere assertion will not suffice. In the following chapter Aristotle returns to it, repeating his statement that it applies without exception, and launches into an exhaustive examination of the entire variety of "changes," satisfying himself in each and every instance that his thesis holds good.[65] Such is his eagerness to leave no stone unturned that he carries the subdivision of local movement, especially of movement from outside, farther than elsewhere, including pushing and pulling with their subordinate species or varieties, and that, while examining qualitative change, he even investigates psychological processes which may be classed under this heading.[66] Everywhere he finds that mover and moved are "together" and that nothing could have its place "between" them.

As we have indicated, the hypothesis of infinite movers and infinite moved entities in touch with one another and forming "one thing" did not satisfy Aristotle in the long run. It had been worked out as a *reductio ad absurdum;* by showing that an infinite series of transmitted movements is impossible, Aristotle believes himself to have established the opposite thesis, that there must be a beginning, i.e., a first mover. The definitive deduction of the first and unmoved mover in Book VIII dispenses with this *reductio* and reaches its goal in other ways. New proofs and arguments are advanced which, we may note, make very little use of "contact" and "together." This is the more noteworthy as one of the main achievements in this book is the separation of the first mover from the "first moved," which makes the relationship of mover and moved and the operation of the former upon the latter once more an acute problem. Should not the rule which Aristotle has proclaimed to be universally valid apply here once more? Aristotle had formulated it with reference to "physical movement." [67] The movement caused in this instance is the revolution of the outermost heaven which should be in this category even if the mover himself is not a "physical" entity. There seems to be some need at least for clarification; yet Aris-

---

[65] VII,2. The inquiry begins with the consideration of locomotion (243a11), next moves to qualitative change (244b2), and finally subjects growth and decline (245a11) to the same scrutiny.

[66] 243a15–244b2; 244b9–245a11.

[67] σωματικὴν κίνησιν, 242b60. The expression may have been chosen with a view to excluding "psychic" movements and changes; see, however, 2.244b9–245a11.

totle's partiality for the concepts which were so essential in Book VII has evidently decreased.

Still, they are not completely forgotten. "What moves itself must embrace a mover which is itself unmoved and something moved which need not necessarily move something else; they must be in contact either reciprocally or one with the other." [68] The sentence immediately following indicates the serious problem here involved: "If the mover is continuous," i.e., an extended body, "each of the two will be in contact with the other." [69] As a matter of fact, the unmoved mover is not a continuum but, as Aristotle in the final chapter of the treatise proves, without extension and parts. Thus we should not expect reciprocal contact. Yet can there be contact at all, if the first mover has no parts and is not a material entity? The *Physics* provides no answer to this question. An answer is finally forthcoming in the famous statement of the *Metaphysics* that the first mover moves the outermost heaven "like the object of love." [70] This solution avails itself of a peculiar and rather unexpected meaning of "touch" to which Aristotle alludes in a passage of *On Coming to Be:* "It is possible that as we sometimes say only the mover touches the moved . . . ; for we sometimes say that someone who causes us grief 'touches' us but not that we touch him." [71] Now, surely, Aristotle when he laid down the law that mover and moved must be "together" had a more spatial and material kind of "touching" or contact in mind. He would hardly have created this difficulty for his first mover if he had not been thoroughly convinced that "together" and "contact" are the *conditio sine qua non* for the relation between

[68] VIII,5.258a18–21; cf. Ross's commentary on 20. There is an incidental reference to the ἅπτεσθαι of mover and moved in 5.256b19.

[69] *Ibid.*, 21ff. The main clause of the sentence consisting of the three words ἅψεται ἑκάτερον ἑκατέρου is preserved in only one MS (Vat. 241), from which Ross has restored it to the text. It represents a considerable gain.

[70] *Metaph.* Λ7.1072b3; see also a25ff. As for the *Physics*, the qualification made in VII,2.243a32f. may be intended as an escape clause for the first mover.

[71] *De gen.* I,6.323a28ff. Here we also read that "if something moves while being itself unmoved it touches what is moved yet nothing touches itself." Even before this passage Aristotle has emphasized that mutual contact holds good between objects which have extension and place (and which move one another mutually; see a3ff., 22ff.). Cf. Ross, *Physics*, "Introduction," 100, and on 258a20; for the passage in *De gen.* cf. also Joachim's commentary on 323a22ff. and Jaeger, *Aristotle*, 357 n.1, who refers to *De anim. motu* 3.699a15 and concludes rightly that Aristotle found the problem baffling and tried different solutions. Joachim's parenthesis (a30–32) is very unfortunate; the worst of it is that it severs the ὥστε clause from a28–30.

mover and moved. As the catalogue of concepts from which he started —we may call it the expanded Platonic catalogue—was basic for the correct notion of a continuum, so it also seemed to hold the key for the relation and interaction of objects. Yet although it works well enough where material objects are concerned, it refuses to work in the instance of transcending importance. Aristotle's solution in this case is imaginative and brilliant, but it is nevertheless perhaps a tour de force. His less imaginative and, it would seem, more literal-minded pupil Eudemus found it difficult to acquiesce in the master's solution. He insisted on discussing the question whether physical contact was possible between the unmoved mover and the entity moved by him. Alas, there was no possible way in which this might work out. For the first mover is "partless," what is partless has no extremities, and without extremities contact is not possible. These mildly embarrassing propositions may have been self-evident to Aristotle. In the end Eudemus decided to limit the principle of contact to movers who are themselves in motion.[72]

Indeed, it is possible that on occasion the concept of contact did not repay the trouble which Aristotle had taken about it or the confidence which he had placed in it. In the treatise *On Coming to Be* he finds it necessary, before actually tackling the subject of *genesis*, to define some concepts which he intimates will help toward a better understanding of this process. The concepts are "acting" and "suffering" (which form a pair) and, again, contact. Contact must be defined because "things that are not able to come into contact with one another cannot act and suffer nor can things mix without having first somehow made contact."[73] The actual discussion of contact which follows refers to, and develops, the definition given in the *Physics*. It also makes some new points, in particular one which is never brought out in the *Physics*, to wit, that in the case of an unmoved mover contact is not reciprocal but one-sided (only the mover touching the moved, not vice versa).[74] Yet when Aristotle sets forth his doctrines regarding the *genesis* of the elements as well as of composite bodies, it does not appear that "contact" contributes anything material to it. Aristotle does need "acting" and "suffering" and in deducing his elements selects as their constitutive qualities hot and cold, moist and

---

[72] See Eudemus, frgs. 123a, b, with Wehrli's comments.
[73] *De gen.* I,6.322b22ff.   [74] *Ibid.*, 323a20ff.

dry, because "the former are spoken of as being active, the latter as passive." [75] Moreover, when he describes the change from one element to another (which is a *genesis*), we see these qualities proceeding to action and undergoing no small suffering, inasmuch as they are overcome, conquered, or destroyed—and it is probably not too much to say that we can visualize the same processes continuing in mixture, even if they are not quite so dramatically put before us.[76] Yet contact, though perhaps still assumed, seems to be rather irrelevant. It certainly does not help Aristotle anywhere toward developing or refining the aspects of his theory on which he cares to dwell.[77] Should it be the case that the Academic concept on the list that Aristotle so eagerly embraced proved for practical purposes either useless or positively embarrassing?

The great store which Aristotle set by the concept of contact (and by the related one of "between") may account for another piece of doctrine which does not, however, have its proper place in his physics but is incidental to his psychology. In the treatise *On the Soul* Aristotle defines the sense perceptions as "movements" that take place in the sense organ and are caused by the perceived object. This time the salient point is not that mover and moved are in contact; on the contrary, Aristotle takes considerable pains to show that in each of the five kinds of sense perception something must come "between" the mover, i.e., the object of the perception, and the organ that responds to it by being set in motion.[78] In the case of some sense organs the air fulfills this function of being "between" and acting as medium; yet Aristotle goes to the length of postulating an intermediate entity even for the sense of touch—though the Greek word for "touch" (ἀφή) is that which we have consistently rendered by "contact." Aristotle's linguistic sense does not rebel against the postulate that "touch" should not come about by "touch"; unflinchingly he carries his argument to the conclusion that the flesh, far from being the actual organ of touch, really is the intermediate factor.[79]

Now although in these sense functions there is an agent and a patient

---

[75] *De gen.* II,2.329b24ff.   [76] For details see below, Chs. 18 and 19.

[77] II,2–8 (the references to ἅπτεσθαι in 330a1f. are irrelevant to the main argument).

[78] See esp. *De an.* II,7.419a13ff., 18ff., 25ff., 32; 8.418b34; and *passim*. In *De sensu* some further developments of the theory are put forward (438a12ff. and *passim*).

[79] *Ibid.*, II,11, esp. 423a15ff., b7; 26; and *passim*.

(as well as a mover and a moved), we may yet wonder whether they are sufficiently like those for which the doctrines about mover and moved and their "togetherness" had been devised. Moreover, Aristotle's doctrine of movement definitely provides for cases in which one thing moves another, and this moves a third.[80] Thus one might see one's way to identifying the "medium" of the psychic processes with the second item in this sequence of movements—if it is at all advisable to bring the theory of movements and that of sense perception so close to each other. One might indeed feel hesitant if it were not the case that Aristotle himself in the *Physics* includes sense perceptions in the "changes" for which his proposition that mover and moved must be "together," and nothing "between" them, is meant to hold good. Discussing them under the generic heading of qualitative changes, he satisfies himself that they are no exception to his rule. Actually he shows how in the different kinds of perception—though touch is here omitted —the "last" mover is in contact with the moved object, i.e., the sense function or sense organ, and nothing can come "between" them.[81] The last mover is of course the air or whatever else is supposed to function as intermediary agent; in other words, the last mover "between" which and the moved object nothing can intervene is identical with the medium (i.e., the "between") of the psychological treatise. Evidently Aristotle's thinking here works in a different direction, and the facts are forced into a different scheme. This need not worry us particularly. What interests us is the inclusion of sense perceptions among the "changes" to which the law that agent and patient must be "together"applies. For the use which Aristotle here makes of "together" and "between" establishes a presumption that the psychological doctrine too owes its origin to the strong hold which this set of concepts had on his thinking. Contact or no contact? This was a cardinal question which he liked to see answered wherever the relation or interaction of two objects was the issue. Whereas in physical changes agent and patient must be in direct physical contact, psychic changes of a higher order (for the nourishing process certainly requires direct contact of nourishment and the tissues) have the distinguishing charac-

[80] See, e.g., VII,1.242a49ff.; VIII, 5 *passim*.
[81] *Phys.* VII,2.245a3–11 (cf. 244b3ff., 245a16ff.). Aristotle in these passages speaks of the "last mover," i.e., the one directly operating on the moved object. When in 245a16f. he refers to "the first and last mover," the word "first" seems open to various interpretations. I am not sure what is in Aristotle's mind. Is he trying to find his way back to the "first mover"?

teristic that no direct contact takes place but a third factor must be in the play to mediate the "movement." [82]

In a short paragraph which follows the definitions of the concepts now studied Aristotle offers some additional suggestions regarding the relationship between the "successive," "contact," and "continuity." [83] Contact, he says, presupposes a succession, but not everywhere where we find a successive arrangement of objects may we speak of contact. Similarly continuity, although not possible without contact, is yet not identical with it but designates a higher degree of unity. Evidently Aristotle is here putting these concepts in an order of increasing "oneness" (for objects to be in contact it suffices if their extremities are "together," yet to form a continuum the extremities must become "one"). He is, in fact, working up to a new variety of the one. We may call it the one in extension. As we have seen, the section of the *Parmenides* which deals with the one as being in contact includes no reference to continuity. Plato's interest is here confined to "contact" between the one and the others; he has no intention of carrying his inquiry to the point where the one and the others would be merged in a new one.[84] Cornford, in commenting on this section of the *Parmenides*, reminds us that the Eleatics did have the concept of the "one as continuous." [85] However, they denied plurality. Plato is making a stand against their notions by showing that there can be a plurality of things that stand to one another in the relation of contact without becoming swallowed up in an Eleatic one. This would be an additional reason why Plato would not wish to make the step from contact to

[82] For another problem of the *Physics* (VIII,10) to which Aristotle's views on "contact" give rise see a forthcoming paper in *A. J. Ph.* Aristotle in this instance wonders how the movement of a "projectile" can continue for some time although the moving body is no longer in contact with its mover.

[83] V,3.227a17ff.

[84] Actually Plato's argument returns to the one and its solitary existence by a different route which indicates the conclusion that there can be no contact between the one and the others, since they have no share in either the one or in number whereas contact has been shown to be tied to number (149c4ff.; cf. a7ff.).

[85] *Pl. and Parm.*, 170f. For Parmenides' ἓν ξυνεχές see 28B8.6 and 25. In the latter passage the reason for the ξυνεχές is given in the words ἐὸν γὰρ ἐόντι πελάζει. It may be held that Plato's ἅπτεσθαι, ἐφεξῆς, τὴν ἐχομένην χώραν κατέχον, etc. (*Parm.* 148d5, e5, 8ff.), show how this πελάζειν may obtain without yet implying a συνεχές. I am not sure that I agree entirely with the points made by Cornford; in particular, Plato does not operate with the assumption that the one to be in contact must be a "part" or have "parts." This motif is brought in by Aristotle (see p. 193); and I see no reason for reading it into Plato's argument.

continuity which would have stultified his argument in favor of more liberal relations between the one and the others.

Yet if the Eleatic "continuous one" is not mentioned by name in this section of the *Parmenides,* it is clearly in the offing as the natural terminus for certain lines of argument which Plato did not wish to pursue to their last conclusion. When Aristotle introduced it as the final item of a logically constructed sequence (whose other members are on Plato's list), he did not open up a new perspective but rather put things back into their original context. Still, as an essential part of this context is missing in the *Parmenides,* Aristotle's awareness of it may be explained by supposing that the relation between continuity, contact, the successive, etc., formed a topic of philosophical conversation in the Academy. The *Theaetetus, Sophist,* and *Parmenides* show how acute a problem the comparison between Parmenides' philosophical position and Plato's own had become. Why should the discussion of this problem be confined to works composed for a larger public?

What these—let us suppose, repeated—conversations achieved amounted to a rejection of Parmenides' assertion that being must be continuous. There are various ways in which "being can be near being" without forming a continuous "one." Parmenides' word for "being near" ($\pi\epsilon\lambda\acute{a}\zeta\epsilon\iota\nu$) is not identical with any of the precise terms which Plato and Aristotle employ in clarifying the spatial relations of things. Even if there is, as both Plato and Aristotle would readily agree, no not-being or empty space between things, objects may still be successive to one another or contiguous; in fact, they may "touch" one another and yet fall short of continuity.[86] But if they are to be one, continuity must obtain between them. This qualification of the Parmenidean "one" is reaffirmed by Aristotle.[87] Yet it makes a great difference whether continuity is held to be the only legitimate spatial relation in the world of being or whether it forms the end and climax of a series of terms of which each stands for a relation of things in space and each approximates "the one" more closely than the preceding. How necessary these nuances and differentiations are for a physical system that reckons with a plurality of things is obvious; how important a part some of them play in the interaction of these things has al-

---

[86] See Note 85.

[87] See 227a13ff., also *Metaph.* Δ6.1015b36ff. and *Phys.* I,2.185b7 (cf. the disquisitions about "one movement" which must be continuous, V,4.228a20ff. and VIII,8 *passim*).

ready been seen.[88] Beside them the "continuous" remains a valid and indispensable concept even after its monopoly is broken. However, Parmenides, in addition to claiming too much for it, also misunderstood its nature. It is so far from being indivisible [89] that you may cut it into smaller and ever smaller parts without ever reaching the limits of its divisibility.

CONTINUITY AND INFINITE DIVISIBILITY

Aristotle, we know, welcomes "the one" by continuity. He even makes it a special point that a movement to be truly one must be continuous, and when he finally identifies the first movement of the Cosmos (which must be one and eternal), he insists, above everything else, that it meet the qualification of continuity.[90]

In building up his concept of the continuum Aristotle speaks of it as composed of smaller units which at their extremities either grow together or are fastened to one another.[91] The concept of "extremities" figures also in the definition of "contact," the difference being that in "contact" the extremities need only be "together" whereas to form a continuum they must grow into "one." [92] It is not surprising that Aristotle reminds us of his definition of contact—as well as of the successive—while entering upon his theory of the continuum; [93] for, as we have seen, continuity is for him the final item in a series of terms which approximate "oneness." Yet at the beginning of Book VI Aristotle uses this established sequence for a new purpose. Extremities are parts, and if the smaller units of which a continuum is composed must have extremities, it follows that no continuum can be composed of partless or indivisible units.[94] Does this suffice to establish the infinite divisibility of every continuum, which is the central doctrine of Book

---

[88] See pp. 190–197.   [89] οὐδὲ διαιρετόν, B8.22.

[90] See *Phys.* VIII,8f. Aristotle also knows indivisible "ones" that cannot be in contact, since, as he likes to put it, to be in contact a thing must have parts. (It is on other grounds that Plato in the latter half of our *Parmenides* section denies contact between the one and the others.) Even the prime mover is a partless one, and we have seen that in his case the "contact" motif must be modified if it is to be applied at all. At V,3.227a29 Aristotle allows points to be in contact with each other. As points have no parts and no extremities, the passage poses a problem. One hesitates to have recourse to VI,1.231b2ff., where specifications are given for "contact" which seem at variance with the definition of V,3.226b23. It is perhaps best to suppose (with Ross, *ad loc.*) that Aristotle in 227a29 does not formulate his own opinion.

[91] V,3.227a10ff., 21ff.   [92] *Ibid.*, 226b23.   [93] VI,1.231a21ff.

[94] *Ibid.*, 24ff. What is partless can have no extremities, *ibid.*, 26, 28.

VI? It might seem so; [95] yet "part" is an awkward concept, if the division is to go on without limits; in particular the extremity might have to be regarded as an indivisible "part." Actually the decisive proof for infinite divisibility no longer makes use of the Platonic sequence of terms.

Infinite divisibility as Aristotle understands it holds good equally of movements, of magnitudes (i.e., extended bodies), and of time. By applying it impartially and with similar persistence to these three entities, Aristotle by all odds makes a great advance beyond his precursors. With extreme resourcefulness he avails himself of the advantages inherent in this larger view, playing off the divisibility of time against any attempt to limit the divisibility of magnitudes and conversely the divisibility of magnitudes against the notion that time might be composed of unbreakable units. If a given distance (or magnitude) is traversed by a slowly moving body in a certain time, a body which covers the distance faster will break up this time. Take, then, the shorter time needed by the latter body; the slower body will in it cover only a part of the original distance, thereby breaking up the magnitude. As this ingenious game can be continued ad infinitum, the result is that there can be no limit to the breaking up of either time or magnitude.[96] Aristotle's famous refutation of Zeno, too, rests primarily on the new insight that time is divisible in the same way as magnitudes.[97]

One may suspect that in Aristotle's thought the concept of continuity was primarily associated with magnitudes and that from them he gradually transferred it to time and movement; and in scanning the concrete illustrations in the chapters leading up to "continuity," one may indeed detect a slight partiality—but no more than this—for magnitudes.[98] Still, from the beginning of Book VI Aristotle quite clearly has time no less than magnitude in mind. It is, he says, as impossible for time to be made up of "now's" as it is for a line to consist of points.[99] As for movement, this is where the absurd consequences of setting limits to divisibility are first brought out. If movement could not be divided without limit, it would have to take place in jerks—to say nothing here of other and even more illogical results.[100] We must

---

[95] *Ibid.*, 231b15.

[96] VI,2.232a23ff., esp. b20–233a12.

[97] *Ibid.*, 233a21ff., esp. 27ff.

[98] ἅμα as defined in 226b21 does not refer to movements or time; see also 227a2f., 13ff.

[99] VI,1.231b6ff.

[100] *Ibid.*, 20ff. (see esp. 232a6ff.).

not forget that we are in the treatise "On Movement"; where Aristotle early in this treatise defines the terms that lead up to continuity, he probably has his eye on the continuity of movement (which is practically identical with its infinite divisibility [101]), even if the terms as such refer primarily to magnitudes.

The concept of time had helped Plato to make movement countable, to bring it, as it were, under the control of number and purge it of its inherent irrationality. Aristotle follows Plato's lead while developing his own doctrine of time.[102] Yet both time and movement are by nature somewhat allergic to such rational control. They tend to slip back into the "ocean of infinity" from which Plato had tried to rescue them, and in Book VI Aristotle is determined to follow them into this aspect of their nature. He is deliberately overstepping the limits that Plato had set for rational inquiry, as he ventures into this twilight region.

The refutation of Zeno's paradoxes which forms an episode in the construction of the new doctrine [103] should not blind us to the great debt which Aristotle owes to the Presocratic discovery of infinite divisibility. Whether Zeno meant to propose it in earnest or rather to ridicule it, having ulterior purposes of a very different kind, matters little in this connection.[104] The merit of the discovery is his; and the significance of this new idea was forthwith appreciated by Anaxagoras when he made the infinitesimal divisibility of things one of the axioms on which he built his own system of physical composition. It was to counteract this approach and to escape its supposedly fatal consequences that the atomists worked out their concept of unbreakable minimal units. Not from units that give way and dissolve but only from units that defy all further breaking up can bodies be composed. Aggregation as well as dissociation requires such a unit, the one as starting point, the other as terminus.[105] The issue was clearly defined

[101] Incidental remarks scattered through the *Physics* show how intimately these two notions are associated for Aristotle. They seem for him to be the obverse and reverse of the same coin (see, e.g., I,2.185b10; III,1.200b16ff., 7.207b16f.).

[102] See above, Ch. 7.   [103] VI,2.233a2ff., 9.239b5ff.; see also VIII,8.263a4ff., 11ff.

[104] For the view that Zeno's arguments operate by and large with notions held by contemporary Pythagoreans see P. Tannery, *Pour l'histoire de la science hellénique* (2d ed.; Paris, 1930), 257ff.; Cornford, *Pl. and Parm.*, 53ff. and *passim;* H. D. P. Lee, *Zeno of Elea* (Cambridge, 1936), *passim;* J. G. Raven, *Eleatics and Pythagoreans* (Cambridge, 1948). See *ab altera parte* W. A. Heidel, *A. J. Ph.*, 51 (1940), 20ff., 27; H. Fränkel, *ibid.*, 53 (1942), 203 n.92; G. Vlastos, *Philos. Rev.*, 68 (1959), 532ff.

[105] For Anaxagoras see *Vorsokr.*, 59B3 (cf., e.g., Cornford, *Cl. Q.*, 24 [1930], 15 and *passim*, and Vlastos, *Philos. Rev.*, 59 [1950], 51). In the absence of verbatim

and the battle lines had formed when Plato joined the fight, giving strong support to the partisans of "limit," though prepared to concede to the Infinite whatever it could justifiably claim. The *Timaeus* embodies his own brand of atomism, a revision, in fact even if not in intention, of that of Leucippus and Democritus.[106] Material bodies are composed of elementary particles which have the form of solid geometrical figures. If the bodies are destroyed, these particles may break up into plane figures (triangles) to which they owe their existence (rather than their material composition). In the constant process of formation and re-formation these triangles are the *pièce de résistance*.[107] Here, to be sure, it is a mathematical rather than a physical limit. Plato's doctrine of indivisible lines was perhaps another essay in setting limits to the breaking up of magnitudes.[108] The Demiurge fashions the Cosmos by introducing "numbers" and "forms." Without them there can indeed be no Cosmos.[109] Pursuing this line of thought, we are tempted to think that in the receptacle—"before" the Cosmos —infinity reigned unchecked; yet Plato does not use this concept in describing the precosmic condition of things. Thus we had better rely on the *Parmenides*, where Plato makes quite clear that there is unlimited plurality and an unlimited breaking up of the "others"—as long as they have no share in "the one" which by its presence, and in accordance with its nature, provides limit.[110] Here Plato definitely gives the Infinite and the infinitely divisible a place, though it is below

recorded statements of Leucippus and Democritus we may refer to some of Epicurus' arguments in support of the atom which reflect the original situation remarkably well (see *Ad Herod.* 56 and Lucr. 1.551ff., 577ff., with C. Bailey's comments on the former two passages, *Lucretius De rer. nat.* [Oxford, 1947], 2.691).

[106] Interest in possible connections between Democritus' and Plato's "atomism" received a strong impulse early in this century from the studies of Ingeborg Hammer-Jensen, "Plato and Democritus," *Arch. f. Gesch. d. Philos.*, 23 (1910), 92ff., 212ff. and Eva Sachs, *Die fünf platon. Körper* (Berlin, 1917), 185ff. It is not necessary here to list the later contributions; for a careful review of them see Thomas F. Gould, "Plato and Democritus" (diss., Cornell Univ., 1953), who finds that the case for influence or direct connection is not fully made out. Of outstanding interest is P. Friedländer, "Structure and Destruction of the Atom according to Plato's *Timaeus*," *Univ. Calif. Publ. Philos.*, 16 (1949), 225ff. (republished in *Plato*, 1 [New York, 1958], 246ff.).

[107] See esp. *Tim.* 56c8ff.

[108] For a different approach to this doctrine see J. Stenzel, *Zahl u. Gestalt in Pl. u. Arist.* (Leipzig, 1933), 77ff., and A. T. Nicol, *Cl. Q.*, 30 (1936), 120ff.

[109] *Tim.* 53b4f.

[110] See esp. *Parm.* 158b-d, 164c-165c. For connections between this section and Zeno's original argument see H. Fränkel, *A. J. Ph.*, 63 (1942), 6f., 198.

the threshold of being and outside the Cosmos of order, Form and number. Number, however, although by itself absent from the Infinite, is capable of mediating between it and "the one." This idea which is developed in the *Philebus* underlies also the arguments of the *Parmenides*.[111]

When Aristotle concludes his first proofs for infinite divisibility with the words, "It is clear from what has been said that neither a line nor a plane figure nor anything at all that is continuous is indivisible," [112] he is passing judgment on Plato's efforts to enlist geometry in his fight against the infinite divisibility of cosmic entities. From the position here reached the fight seems as hopeless as the effort was ill advised; for as soon as you have any continuum, whether geometrical or physical, it is by its very nature divisible ad infinitum. You can never have the one quality apart from the other. In the continuum "the one" and infinity coincide [113] (the only geometrical entity to which divisibility does not apply is the point, which is indeed something entirely *sui generis;* yet no aggregation of points could ever build up a continuum).

Viewed from the *Timaeus*, Aristotle's decision is indeed radical. On its face it amounts to a return to Zeno and Anaxagoras. But it is well to bear in mind that Aristotle is not here working up to a new conception of matter or laying the foundations of a physical system. His main concern is, after all, with movement. When—in another treatise —he has to define the role of matter in the *genesis* of elements and other physical entities, the infinite divisibility of all extended things

---

[111] *Phileb.* 16c–18d, 24eff. In the *Parmenides* (164cff.) the others, when having no part in the one, become inevitably infinite, refusing to be counted. We may in this connection again refer to the definition of time in the *Timaeus* (37d). Being an image of eternity which μένει ἐν ἑνί, time itself moves κατ' ἀριθμόν. This is Plato's way of rescuing it from the *apeiron.*

[112] *Phys.* VI,2.233b15ff.

[113] In a sense it is still true that when we have a line, i.e., a continuum, infinity is not actually present and that, to describe the situation, the concepts of potentiality and actuality must be used—something that Plato in the dialogues never does. There may be something arbitrary in comparing Aristotle's position with the *Timaeus* when the *Parmenides* shows that Plato "recognizes" infinite divisibility. Moreover, the *Timaeus* deals with things as they are in the Cosmos whereas in *Phys.* VI Aristotle has no intention of laying the basis for a cosmological system. Yet for Aristotle there is no difference between the purely physical condition of things and their cosmic condition; least of all would he admit that physical entities when part of the Cosmos have mathematical configurations and thereby limits to their divisibility. On the other hand, their infinite divisibility matters as little in his cosmology as in his theory of *genesis.*

does not help him. It would be an exaggeration to say that it is a stumbling block, and he does not actually find it necessary to go back on the doctrine so painstakingly worked out in Book VI of the *Physics*. For the infinite divisibility is, fortunately, only a potentiality. It does not really happen (in fact, it could not happen) that a physical object breaks up ad infinitum. Moreover, the theory of *genesis* should not really operate with the concepts of breaking up and coalescing (dissociation and aggregation). It should think of larger units as coming into being and changing from one element into another and should think of them as "wholes." [114] Thus Anaxagoras has not said the last word on the formation of physical entities—but neither has Democritus.

TECHNICAL PROBLEMS RELATING TO THE CHANGE BETWEEN REST AND MOVEMENT

The intimate connection between time and movement which Aristotle keeps in view throughout Book VI may remind us of the fact that when studying time per se in Book IV Aristotle also needed the concept of movement. We recall his definition that "time is the aspect of movement which is amenable to counting." [115] Obviously the relation between time and movement on which Book VI dwells is not covered by this definition; here no aspect of movement matters less than its countability. When discussing the theory of Book IV, we referred to Plato's definition of time in the *Timaeus*. This definition suggests— and Aristotle confirms—that the Academy's interest in time was incidental to its study of movement. This should be borne in mind, even if on the task which Aristotle has set himself in Book VI Plato's definition has no more direct bearing than Aristotle's own.

At the present juncture it may be well to study another Platonic precedent. Two sections of the *Parmenides* throw light on the relation between time on the one side and movement, rest, and change on the other. In one of them "the one" is envisaged as growing older in time,[116] and time is considered essential for being as well as becoming.

---

[114] This conclusion is reached in *De gen.* I,2 where it is preceded by a new discussion of the arguments for and against infinite divisibility and where the advantages and disadvantages of the atomist doctrine are once more weighed in the balance. See esp. 317a17ff. (cf. below, Ch. 16).

[115] IV,11.219b2; for the next points cf. Ch. 7.

[116] *Parm.* 151e2ff. Plato is at the same time interested in the fact that the one, while growing older "than itself," is also growing younger than itself. This point may here be left aside. However, the difficulties connected with any attempt to

"To be" means precisely "to participate in existence in conjunction with time present," as "was" or "will be" means "to participate in it in conjunction with time past or future." [117] Now time is advancing constantly, and whatever is in time grows older. This is a process of "becoming." And this "becoming" goes on all the time; yet if one focuses on the moment "now," which lies between the past and the future and which cannot be skipped, one may think of the object which becomes older as here interrupting this process. For the "time being," i.e., in the "now," it *is* older than it was, but does not become older.[118] Thus becoming would seem to keep pace with, and be tied to, the advancing and constantly moving time, while being—some form of it at least—finds a foothold in the now.

For Aristotle, too, the now and its relation to time are among the most important questions to which an examination of time and movement gives rise. Both his general physical treatise and his inquiry into movements contribute much to the elucidation of this relationship. He would agree that the now is placed between the before and the after, but in his opinion it does not separate them so much as hold them together. In fact, he carefully shows that one and the same now is the limit of the past and the beginning of the future.[119] Moreover, he would emphatically disagree with the notion that in a now a movement or process comes to a halt, as it were, and that being may here for a moment interrupt the process of becoming. Explicitly he disproves the possibility of anything being at rest in a now.[120] His arguments against this notion rely partly on his new conception of the now as

---

find Plato's own "position" in an argument of the *Parmenides* must be kept constantly in mind.

[117] *Ibid.*, e7ff. (Cornford's translation has been used).

[118] 152b6: ἆρ' οὖν οὐκ ἐπίσχει τότε τοῦ γίγνεσθαι πρεσβύτερον, ἐπειδὰν τῷ νῦν ἐντύχῃ, καὶ οὐ γίγνεται, ἀλλ' ἔστι τότ' ἤδη πρεσβύτερον; c6: εἰ δέ γε ἀνάγκη μὴ παρελθεῖν τὸ νῦν πᾶν τὸ γιγνόμενον, ἐπειδὰν κατὰ τοῦτο ᾖ, ἐπίσχει ἀεὶ τοῦ γίγνεσθαι καὶ ἔστι τότε τοῦτο ὅτι ἂν τύχῃ γιγνόμενον. Diès in his note *ad loc.* (b6; cf. above, Note 53) reminds us of Aristotle's νῦν.

[119] The νῦν holds time together (220a5ff.; 222a10) though it also divides it and is a "limit" as being the end of the past and the beginning of the future (*ibid.*); comparing the now to the point, Aristotle says that if one takes the point, which connects parts of a line, as beginning and end and on this ground regards it as two there must be a pause (ἵστασθαι, a standstill in the movement, 220a12f.). He does not seem prepared to allow the same for the now, and even if he did, his ἵστασθαι would not be the same (and not be seen from the same angle) as Plato's ἐπίσχειν τοῦ γίγνεσθαι, 152b6. See also VI,3.

[120] VI,3.234a31ff.

belonging at once to past and future; if in the past there was movement and in the future there will be rest, the now would be simultaneously at rest and in movement. Yet Aristotle also, here as elsewhere, makes use of his definition of rest.[121] If rest materializes when
an object which has the capacity of moving does not actualize it, then,
he argues, by showing that there can be no movement in a now, it is
also settled that rest cannot obtain in it either. Where he says this, the
possibility of movement in a now has already been disproved; it is in-
admissible because the now is indivisible, whereas even the shortest
movement needs an infinitely divisible time.[122] Now, if rest is here
merely the nonactualization of movement, it is not strong enough or
autonomous enough to support being. Aristotle's arguments do not
involve being. Moreover, what kind of "being" is it that the *Parmenides*
section connects with a now? Although it is contrasted with "becoming," we are certainly reluctant to equate it with Plato's true and
eternal being.[123] In fact, we cannot here compare doctrine with doctrine—at any rate, who would have the naïve courage to find Plato's
"ultimate" philosophic position in any of the alternative hypotheses
of the *Parmenides?*

What Plato and Aristotle have in common is to be sought on a
different plane. Both realize that it is impossible for a process—whether
becoming or movement—to go on in the now. Although the now is
time,[124] time yet does not flow on in it. Zeno had used this now to
argue that the flying arrow is at rest in every now. Plato's suggestion
that the movement stops in the now is meant to remind us of Zeno;
and to Plato's deliberately provocative way of describing the situation
Aristotle does justice by allowing the now, alone of all temporal
concepts, to remain undivided or indivisible. Clearly the relation between time and the now—the refusal of the now to participate in the
processes that go on in time—is a problem which Aristotle shares
with Plato. Both bring Zeno's paradox up to date, formulating it in the
language and concepts of the Academy. And both think of the now

---

[121] *Ibid.*, 32; cf. for this definition of ἠρεμεῖν 226b13ff.   [122] 234a24ff.

[123] Note, e.g., *Tim.* 37e5ff., where Plato, perhaps with Parmenides in mind, insists
that only ἔστι may be predicated of true being but does not, like Parmenides in
B8.5, include νῦν in this statement (cf. Cherniss, *J. H. St.*, 77 [1957], 22 n.46).

[124] Note κατὰ τὸν νῦν χρόνον in *Parm.* 152b3; see also 155d1f. Plato's now is the
present (παρόν), but it is everywhere present to "the one," accompanying it
throughout its being (152b2ff., d8ff.). The latter point is in Stenzel's opinion
a strong reason against identifying this now with the ἐξαίφνης of 156d (*Meta-
physik d. Altertums* in *Handbuch d. Philos.*, I D [Munich and Berlin, 1932], 136f.).

as occurring everywhere in the flow of time even if Plato—in the *Parmenides* passages at least [125]—gives slightly more attention to the now in the sense of the "present" moment. For Aristotle the division between past and future may be made anywhere in the movement of time since we may mentally break the flow of time wherever we like.[126] Another point of divergence is that Plato does not speak of infinity or infinite divisibility with reference to time. However, he describes time as "moving" ($\pi o \rho \epsilon v \acute{o} \mu \epsilon v o v$) and by using the same word for the process of becoming [127] suggests an analogy between the nature of time and that of a process, while also pointing to a characteristic of time which the now does not share. Becoming is tied to time which moves, not to the now—we may understand that Zeno was quite right in denying movement in the now's; on the other hand—this must be said with caution because we do not have Zeno's actual text—the relation between the now and time is probably more complex than he imagined.

For the rest, it makes a considerable difference whether the now is thought of as lying between past and future or whether it belongs to and participates in both. When something that has been in Plato's now moves beyond it, it is, as he puts it, simultaneously in touch with the now and the later (i.e., the future).[128] It touches both and is—or, more precisely, "comes to be"—"between" them. It seems to be passing a division, and Plato speaks, in terms somewhat reminiscent of Zeno, as though one could think of this body as occupying a particular place—a place in time [129]—even while it is moving. For Aristotle the

[125] See Note 124. *Tim.* 38a5 may perhaps be compared. Aristotle refers to this $v\tilde{v}v$ as $\tau\grave{o}$ $\pi a\rho\grave{o}v$ $v\tilde{v}v$ $\check{a}\tau o\mu o v$ $\mu\acute{e}\rho o s$ (scil., $\chi\rho\acute{o}v o v$, 222b7). In 222a20, where he distinguishes two meanings of $v\tilde{v}v$, he does not mention this $v\tilde{v}v$ at all. What does Plato mean when he says that "the one" while moving on could not be "caught" by the $v\tilde{v}v$ (c2)? That there is no now in a movement (i.e., as Aristotle would put it, no movement in a now)? And what is Plato's conception of $\chi\rho\acute{o}v o s$ in the *Parmenides* section? It is hardly the $\chi\rho\acute{o}v o s$ of the *Timaeus* which has been tamed and brought under the control of number. There is no telling how definite a view of time as a continuum may be behind these sentences.

[126] This raises the question whether the now is always the same or always a different one; see IV,11.219b10ff.; cf. 10.218a6-30.

[127] $\pi o \rho \epsilon v o \mu \acute{e} v o v$ $\tau o\tilde{v}$ $\chi \rho \acute{o} v o v$ (152a3; cf. b4).

[128] 152c3-6.

[129] Plato does not say that the later touches the now, but merely that "the one," while moving onward, touches (or "lays hold of") both, and is between them. The "between" suggests not so much a straddling as an intermediate position. If this is correct, the now would not touch, or be continuous with, any other section of time (which would correspond to Aristotle's views). Plato's words

indivisible now could not form a part of a continuum, and movement itself is so absolutely and inexorably divisible that it is impossible for it ever to be in or move out of the indivisible now. (Moreover, as we shall presently see, there simply is no first time in which a movement begins.) This should dispose of every attempt to "locate" the moving body between the now and the later.[130]

In another section of the *Parmenides* [131] Plato has more to say about the transition from rest to movement and from movement to rest. When anything leaves the one condition and enters upon the other, there is a "change" from rest to movement or vice versa. This change lies between the two conditions, and Plato treats it as something different from either. While the object goes through this change, it is neither at rest nor in movement.[132] Presumably rest and movement are both in time, and this would seem to be the reason why Plato says that a body which is in neither condition cannot be in time.[133]

What, then, operates instead of time, if time has lost its power? The transition takes place "at once," "in an instant," "suddenly" (ἐξαίφνης); and this "curious thing," the instant, intrudes between rest and movement and gives the object its chance of abandoning the one condition and settling in the other. Time may move on continuously; yet the "instant" is certainly not in time, and no more is the "change" which in this instant comes to pass.[134]

The "instant" which Plato here brings into play cannot be the same as his now (νῦν). A priori it is unlikely that Plato should in his hypotheses have used two different terms without pointing out that they coincide in their meaning. Moreover, he clearly employs them for different purposes, and by contrast to the now which is time—a form or phase of time—the "instant" is definitely not time. On the other hand, Aristotle's now is of all concepts that fall within the orbit of time the only one to which infinite divisibility does not apply. It remains as indivisible as a point (these are the two concessions which Aristotle has to make to atomism) with the result that as little as points

---

are undoubtedly chosen with the utmost care, and yet one cannot be quite sure of their precise meaning.

[130] In connection with the "place" motif note κατὰ τοῦτο in c7 (cf. *Phys.* VI,8.239a25).

[131] 156c1–157a3 (or b5).

[132] See esp. 156c8f., e5ff. The word which Plato here uses for "change" or transition is μεταβολή.

[133] 156c6, c9f.   [134] 156e1, e6.

can build up a line can the now's compose time. Thus the now might well recommend itself to Aristotle as the time, or part of time, in which the change from rest to movement comes about. Has he not been at pains to tie past and future together in the now [135] instead of, as Plato appears to do, placing the now between them?

Aristotle, as we know, uses the term "change" not to denote the transition from rest to movement or from movement to rest but as a generic term comprehending movement, growth, qualitative alteration, and even becoming and passing away.[136] This makes it difficult to compare his views with the suggestions of the *Parmenides*. Still he clearly takes a great interest in "transitions." He never polemizes against Plato's "instant," yet it is difficult to escape the impression that some doctrines of Book VI are intended to take care of the crucial situation for which Plato introduced the "instant."

First of all, we may note that Aristotle applies his concept of divisibility not only to extension, movement, and time but also to the thing which changes.[137] Something that is "partless" cannot change at all and has no way of getting from the one condition into the other. While it is in the former, it does not yet change; while in the latter, it changes no longer.[138] The *Parmenides* too teaches with the help of similar, if not entirely identical, arguments that the partless "one" cannot move and that only things that have parts can be with some of these parts in the new place and with some still outside it.[139] Correspondingly Aristotle thinks of the changing object as having parts and transferring them, as it were, successively from condition A into condition B.[140]

Each of the parts must at any time be either in A or in B, because

---

[135] See above, Ch. 7, Note 33f. Simplicius *In Phys.* 982.2 equates Plato's ἐξαίφνης with "what we call νῦν" (Cornford, *Pl. and Parm.*, 202 n.1). Plato goes on to show (156e7ff.) that the transitional condition (to which the "instant" applies) occurs in changes of every kind. He refers explicitly to *genesis* and its opposite—in fact, to two forms of it—to growth and decrease, as well as to some other changes which would probably come under Aristotle's concept of qualitative alteration.

[136] See above, pp. 178–179.

[137] Cf. for this paragraph VI,4.234b10–20. It is worth observing that Aristotle speaks of the changing object as "divisible," not as infinitely divisible. In fact, he takes no account of the possibility of infinite gradations in the change from white to black, by which he illustrates his point. The infinite is only later brought to bear on these problems (235a13ff.; note especially b3ff. with its reference to the preceding as well as the subsequent investigation).

[138] VI,10.240b8–9, 17–31 (cf. 6.234a11–15). [139] *Parm.* 138d5–139a3.

[140] 234b10–20.

they cannot be in both conditions or yet in neither.[141] It was the latter
contingency which Plato had envisaged and of which he had tried to
take care by his "instant." [142] If a thing changes part by part, the
process surely must cover time and there can be no place for the
"instant." One may wonder what kind of "change" Aristotle here has
in mind, and he himself supplies an answer that may remind us of the
Platonic change: "I am speaking of the proximate degree of change;
from white to grey, not from white to black." [143] Thus in this first
phase a part of the changing object is grey, another still white. It may
be argued that, before the first part became grey, there was an instant
in which this part was between grey and white. Yet Aristotle says
that it cannot be neither white nor grey, and though he does not here
speak of a transition from a stationary condition to movement but
of change from one quality into another, it is difficult to see where
Plato's "instant" of neutrality should come in.[144]

Our problem, however, is whether Aristotle finds a place for his
own "now" in the change from rest to movement. In chapter 5 of our
book he makes clear that "the first time in which something has
changed" may have two different meanings: either it is the first time
in which a change has been completed, or it is the first time in which
change has taken place [145] (would the latter be the situation for which
Plato resorts to the "instant"?). Yet even before making this important
distinction between two meanings of the Greek perfect tense,[146] Aris-

---

[141] 234b16.

[142] *Parm.* 156c6. Cf. Simplicius 963.20f. for the observation that the "neither"
here ruled out by Aristotle would correspond to a μεταξύ. The "neither" is similarly ruled out in *Parm.* 138e3f. for the "other," scil., partless "one."

[143] 234b17ff. Did Aristotle mean this at the beginning of our paragraph where
he states that, when a thing is in the condition into which it changes, it changes
no longer (b11f.)? Perhaps he means no more than that it no longer changes
from white to grey, though this is not the obvious interpretation of b10–12. This
in connection with the point noticed above (Note 137) may suggest that Aristotle
is not yet quite sure of his ground.

[144] Plato too knows in the *Parmenides* that nothing that has no parts can move
(138c4ff., esp. d8ff.); but in our section he does not think of his "one" as having
parts which successively "change" (passing either into movement or into the
neutral condition).

[145] 236a7ff.

[146] It is probably correct to equate one of these perfects with what J. Wackernagel in his classical study (*Studien zum griech. Perfekt* [Göttingen Univ. Progr.;
1904], 4ff.), of which H. Fränkel kindly reminded me, calls the "Resultativper-
fekt," used for actions completed in the past whose effects still persist. The other
perfect of our text I should tentatively identify with Wackernagel's second type,

totle examines the "first time in which something has changed" and examines it without taking account of the ambiguity.[147] If one looks at what he here says, one is driven to conclude that he is studying the first time in which a change has been completed. This first time he allows to be indivisible, and he reaffirms this point after making the distinction between the two meanings.[148] It is a "limit," and a limit should indeed be indivisible. As we know that the now is limit with reference to past as well as to future [149] and as it is the only indivisible entity in the realm of time, we suspect that Aristotle here thinks of his now as the "first time in which the change has been completed," even though he does not actually mention it by name. In the function here assigned to it the now would lie at the point of transition from one condition to another (say, from movement to rest), yet not, as Plato's "instant" does, between the two conditions.

There remains the question what to do with the "first time in which change has taken place." Here Aristotle's answer is that there simply is no first time. If there were a "first," it would indeed have to be an indivisible time-atom (i.e., a now); yet it would also have to belong to the period of rest which precedes the change; and though Aristotle's now binds past and future together, Aristotle cannot get himself to let it simultaneously belong to rest and movement.

Thus there is no alternative: the infinite divisibility of all movement must be assumed to apply also to the initial phase of movement or change, and no possibility remains of seizing anywhere a "first."

The beginning of a change is thus certainly in time, but every chance of singling it out is lost in the infinite divisibility. Plato's attempt to place an "instant" "between" the one condition and the other and to keep this instant outside the flow of time was a hopeless undertaking. We may take it that what Aristotle says about the beginning of change covers at the same time the last stage of the condition from which a

---

in which "das Perfekt das Befinden in einem Zustand bezeichnet" (*ibid.*). In Book VI Aristotle is decidedly very "tense conscious." Because of its different nuances of meanings the Greek perfect is a dangerous tense for philosophical purposes. Plato, if I am not mistaken, does not operate with specific meanings of this tense, and I am not sure that Aristotle has succeeded in avoiding its pitfalls.

[147] 235b32–236a7.

[148] See esp. 236a4, a10. That Aristotle in the former passage refers to the terminal stage follows from his argument where he assumes the "first" of which he speaks to be preceded by the process of change (235b37).

[149] 236a10ff. For the νῦν as πέρας see VI,3 and IV,13.

thing changes. There could be no more a real "last" of that condition than a "first" of the change.[150] It is not necessary to suppose that Aristotle is at every point conscious of what Plato had said in the *Parmenides*.[151] As for the issues with which both of them deal, the more general the terms in which we formulate them, the safer we shall feel (for apart from everything else, we must never forget the peculiarly elusive character of the *Parmenides*). When the relation between movement and rest which had been set up in opposition to one another was investigated in the Academy,[152] there arose, along with other problems of a more "logical" order, also the "practical" question how to conceive of the transition from one to the other. And, since it was understood that rest and movement were both in time, the relation of this transition to time needed to be defined. Is it outside time? asks Plato teasingly. Does it take place in an indivisible time? Aristotle wonders. In either case, it would not be engulfed in the constantly streaming flow of time.

As has been seen, Aristotle denies that there is anything indivisible at the beginning of change, yet at least he allows the end of change to materialize in a now.[153] Here then the flow of time is, if not stopped,

---

[150] The difficult passage 236a16f., where Aristotle says that the "first" beginning of change cannot be indivisible since otherwise the now's would be contiguous, is perhaps best understood with Themistius (194.30) as referring to the now which is the last moment of rest and the now which is the first of movement. See also the interpretation of the Oxford Translation. It is interesting that Themistius in this connection rejects the idea that there could be a μεταξύ between the two now's, yet, in contrast to Plato, his point is that no time could be placed between them.

[151] Aristotle in IV,13.222b15 gives a definition of the ἐξαίφνης. It is that "which has departed [scil., from its previous condition] in a time imperceptible on account of its shortness." The words ἐν ἀναισθήτῳ χρόνῳ διὰ μικρότητα are noteworthy in view of Plato's attempt to treat the ἐξαίφνης as οὐδεὶς χρόνος (*Parm.* 156c2, e6). Cf. Diès' brief but illuminating note (*op.cit.*, 100).

[152] See esp. *Soph.* 249cf. (cf. above, pp. 25–28). Needless to say, this background is more clearly discernible in the *Parmenides* than in the discussion of the *Physics*. I assume throughout my discussion that the *Parmenides* was composed before Aristotle worked out the arguments incorporated in *Phys.* VI. To do so is in any case convenient, and I have not found that any difficulties result from this assumption. It would add to the interest of the *Parmenides* section if it could be ascertained whether Plato knew some of the thoughts regarding the infinite divisibility of time that are incorporated in Aristotle's chapters. Our uncertainty is the greater because we have no right to assume that Aristotle elaborated all refinements of his theory in a coherent and uninterrupted struggle with the problem. One may well think of his efforts as successive rather than continuous, ἐφεξῆς rather than συνεχεῖς.

[153] VI,5.236a7ff.

yet somehow debarred from making every event disappear in its infinitesimal divisions. If the passage where Aristotle describes the end
as a genuine limit were his last word on the subject, the divisibility of
time would indeed not operate. But it is far from being his last word.
In a later section Aristotle comes forward with a new suggestion.[154]
When a thing is "coming to a stand" (ἵστασθαι), it must still be moving;
for it is not yet actually at rest. This implies that the process happens
in time (as every movement does), and again it holds good that there
can be no "first time." Wherever you might try to get hold of a "first"
it eludes you and dissolves into an infinity of smaller subdivisions.[155]

Is not this "coming to a stand" the last event in a change? And does
not the doctrine just summarized dispose of the notion which Aristotle
earlier in this book favors—that this last stage is merely a now, or a
limit, not a process? On second thoughts he does seem to turn it
into a process in which the now would be lost. It may be argued that
if the "end" of the change has now become a process, this process itself
must have an end. If the emphasis is not so much on standstill as on
coming to it, with the result that another movement enters the picture,
does this not simply remove the end of a change one stage farther?
One may regret that Aristotle, instead of telling us that there is no
first time unit of "coming to a stand," does not make clear whether or
not there is a last. He may himself have felt that the matter was not
completely settled; for after proving that coming to a stand is in time
and that there can be no "first" time for it, he takes up one more
concept which again brings us a step nearer to the end. This concept
is "entering upon rest." [156] For this too Aristotle establishes that it
must be in time and that there can be no "first" time unit. If "coming to

[154] In ch. 8. Ch. 7 has no very close connection with these questions. Ch. 6
may be held to work along a different line toward the conclusion (just discussed)
that there is no first time in which a thing begins to change (see 237b); for Aristotle explains that every situation in which a thing has changed requires a previous changing and every changing a previous "having changed." Thus there can
be no "first."

[155] See 238b23–239a10.

[156] 239a10–22. The aorist ἠρέμησε which Aristotle uses (a10, 11) may also be
translated "begin to be at rest" (ἤρξατο τῆς ἠρεμίας, Simplicius 1009.16). Not a
few arguments of Book VI depend for their validity on the exact meaning of the
Greek tenses; the use of the aorist here is the more noteworthy because in the
preceding section (dealing with ἵστασθαι) Aristotle has not felt the need of using
it (still earlier, 236a15, where the aorist could be used, some of the MSS have
it and others have the imperfect). Aristotle's arguments leave no doubt that an
object "entering upon rest" is for him at rest; for he operates with the infinite
divisibility not of movement but of rest (see esp. a11).

a stand" did not quite lead us over to the condition of rest, "entering upon rest" certainly does so.

Could Aristotle have gone farther? He seems to be determined to follow the unfortunate "indivisible" into every conceivable hiding place and to deny it even the smallest toehold in the transitional phase from movement to rest. If the "first time" of coming to a standstill and of entering upon rest is not indivisible, the position of the now at the end of movement, where it previously had been fixed, becomes rather precarious. And yet Aristotle even in these later sections at which we have looked never declares in so many words that there is no "indivisible end" of movement, and none of his pupils or commentators (so far as we know) understood him to have gone back on his earlier statement that, while there was no beginning of movement, there yet was a definite and indivisible end. "There are astonishing things about the very nature of movement," exclaimed Theophrastus, "for instance if it has no beginning but has an end." [157] We may well share his amazement, and not only on account of the inherent incongruity of this view but also because difficulties are bound to arise, if the end of movement is to be thought of as coinciding with the beginning of rest and if it is precisely the function of the now—one and the same now!—to bind past and future together.[158] Should there then be "things successive to the now," i.e., a continuum directly hanging on to an indivisible? It is hard to see how this could be avoided. For to Plato's suggestion that something should intrude "between" the end of the one condition and the beginning of the other Aristotle has nowhere in the discussion given quarters.[159] Still, though Aristotle makes life very difficult for his "indivisible at the end," his intentions may not have been so murderous; he may not have fully realized what his last proofs amount to. If we adopt this view—perhaps the best that we can do—we leave unanswered Simplicius' question: why does he who is usually so sparing of words take up the subject of coming to a stand at all? [160] One thing, however, is clear and from a historical

---

[157] Frg. 25, Wimmer (*Theophr. Eres. opera*, 3 [Leipzig, 1862]) = Simplicius *In Phys.* 986.5, where Diels rightly limits the quotation from Theophrastus to the sentence rendered in the text (his "emendation" is less felicitous); see also Themistius 195.8ff.

[158] See esp. VI,3.233b35ff.   [159] See *ibid.*, 234a6ff.

[160] Simplicius 1008.21. Even if Aristotle does not intend to do away with the πέρας of movement, it is still true that he is particularly interested in the "transitional" stage. Along this line an answer to Simplicius' question may be found. As for the incongruity, if it is correct that the now and infinite divisibility are

point of view perhaps more important than the (after all somewhat unsatisfactory) solution: The transition from rest to movement (or vice versa)—for which Plato had introduced the "instant"—gave Aristotle one of the worst headaches in his *Physics;* this is shown by his repeated return to the subject for the purpose of adding another and still another refinement. Whether this outpost, too, of the finite was finally engulfed by the Infinite whose waves are pounding against it from every side or whether it remains as a solitary landmark in the surrounding flood, it certainly called forth an extraordinary application of argumentative energy on Aristotle's part, spurring him on to efforts the outcome of which still has the character of a compromise rather than of a victory.

On the whole, Aristotle throughout these sections shows himself partial to the Infinite rather than to the finite. He appears bent on extending the former's domain. Still the now remains; it is present everywhere in time, defying every attempt to divide it. Surely, time cannot be composed of the now's (if Zeno attempted this or implied it he was wrong); yet though Aristotle has made inroads upon its territory, he never questions the existence of this last survivor and stronghold of the finite. Even in the paragraph in which he moves on to the refutation of Zeno's paradoxes he says that in a now a body can neither move nor be at rest yet that it is correct to refer to the body as "not moving." [161] This may again for a moment remind us of Plato's attempt to set up the "instant" as an entity in which a body—more precisely his "one"—is neither in movement nor at rest. Yet there is a difference of intent. Aristotle's purpose is negative; he denies to the now both movement and rest, whereas Plato chooses the "instant" for a positive function, wishing it to take care of the "change" from movement to rest and from rest to movement.[162] At least this is what

---

different but not conflicting approaches to the problem of time, we may suggest that Aristotle when he allows an end but no beginning has unawares slipped from the one approach into the other. Clearly the perfect participle μεταβεβληκός suggested to Aristotle completion—and completion in an instant. See also 236a2ff., and note that Aristotle in 236a20 rejects the idea that in an "indivisible" time an object could be at rest and μεταβεβληκός. This word begs the question; for it would not denote the *arche metaboles*.

[161] VI,8.239b1.

[162] We have already (above, Note 130) referred to the section of the *Physics* (239a23–b4) in which this statement occurs: In no part of the time in which an object is moving can it be said to be "over against" a particular place or thing. In a now the object is over against something, but the now is not a component part of time (Zeno's mistake).

he says; whether he means it is another question. Yet even if we discount the content of Plato's suggestions, they still offer evidence of the problems that presented themselves to the Academy, of the form in which they appeared, and—be it cautiously said—of possible solutions. For it is with possibilities that Plato here plays. It is not recorded that Zeno paid attention to the transition from rest to movement. Yet the Academy clearly did, and it clearly discussed this problem with reference to time.

As has been said, while Aristotle makes the points that we have studied he is about to come to grips with Zeno. According to Aristotle, Zeno had argued that the flying arrow is in every part of its flight over against something of equal extension as itself, and this means that it is at rest.[163] One premise of this argument Aristotle would be ready to grant: in every now the flying arrow is in fact over against something and thus "not moving." [164] The error which Zeno (or, as some scholars today would prefer to say, his opponents) [165] committed lay in supposing that time was made up of the now. This is impossible because for Aristotle it is axiomatic that indivisibles cannot build up a continuum.

Here it is interesting once more to refer to the *Parmenides* where Plato speaks of "the one" as interrupting the process of becoming when it meets the now.[166] Plato gives the impression of welcoming this situation which in the flux of time offers being a foothold. But he does not take up the question whether time is composed of the now's. And it is well to note that he uses the motif of infinite divisibility only in connection with physical objects, not with time or movement.[167] Plato knows the now as the "present now" which lies between past and future, yet is a time; and he also knows the "instant" which is no

---

[163] VI,9.239b5–9.

[164] 239a35 (μένον in this line causes difficulties, and if it is read as two words, μὲν ὄν, as in Prantl and Ross, the clause—with two μέν—is not satisfactory either. Perhaps it must be excised; nor am I sure that ἠρεμοῦν, in 239b2, can be saved, even if κατά τι is read before it, as Ross does with E² and as in any case seems necessary).

[165] See above, Note 104.   [166] *Parm.* 151e–152e.

[167] Nor does Plato speak of time (or movement) as a continuum. For Aristotle it is understood that τὸ ἄπειρον ἐμφαίνεται πρῶτον ἐν τῷ συνεχεῖ (III,1.200b17), and he reports that the definitions of the συνεχές—Academic definitions or those of the mathematicians?—make use of those of the ἄπειρον (*Phys.* III,1.200b16ff.). Note that Plato groups on one side: one, being, now; on the other: one, becoming, time. We may add on the one side the point (often compared to the now), on the other magnitudes.

time—or, more precisely, not "even in one time"—and which intrudes at the transition from rest to movement.[168] It will be clear that Aristotle, along with taking up again Zeno's general question of the relation between now and time, also tries to cope with the more specific problems which Plato had singled out because they seemed to him to throw light on being and becoming or on rest and movement. In fact, through large sections of Book VI Aristotle is engaged in a fight on two fronts. Neither Plato's nor Zeno's suggestions satisfy him completely, yet he has to make concessions to both. Although the now cannot build up time—Aristotle is probably the first to bring this out—it must yet be recognized as being everywhere in time. It cannot, like other temporal concepts, be allowed to melt away into the "all-powerful time" which carries so much away into a new kind of infinity.[169] This infinite divisibility had been implied in Zeno's paradoxes. Aristotle makes it explicit, relates it to the infinite divisibility of magnitudes, and applies it in particular to the crucial situations at the beginning and end of a movement. Naturally enough he would not be enticed into suggesting connections between the now and being. The "present" departs rather empty-handed, yet we must not overlook that Plato in the *Parmenides* on the one hand relates being to the present now, yet on the other affirms that the now is present to "the one" "throughout its entire being." [170] This points to Aristotle's proposition that the now is to be found everywhere in time.[171] Finally in the matter of transitions—a Platonic problem, it would seem, rather than a Zenonic—we have admired the untiring energy which Aristotle applies to the solution of this thorny question; in the end, however, he winds up in a compromise, giving both the indivisible and infinite divisibility a place at this juncture. When Plato says that transition materializes "in no time at all" or "not even in one time," he seems almost to point forward to Aristotle's alternative—and, for our feeling, conflicting—solutions. For if one remembers (as one well may and perhaps even should) [172] the process character and flow of time, the now is in fact "in no time," and in the unlimited divisibility of the time flux the time of the transition likewise disappears

---

[168] *Parm.* 156c–157b (μηδ' ἐν ἑνὶ χρόνῳ, 156c2).

[169] Soph. *O.C.* 609 and *Ai.* 646; see above, p. 156.   [170] *Parm.* 151e7ff., 152d8ff.

[171] Especially if it is taken into account that being itself is here defined by Plato as μέθεξις οὐσίας μετὰ χρόνου (τοῦ παρόντος), 151e7.

[172] Cf. Cornford's note on μηδ' ἐν ἑνὶ χρόνῳ (156c2; cf. e1), *Pl. and Parm.*, 200 n.1; see also 201 n.2.

—wherever we may try to grasp this "first time," it escapes and eludes us and no "one time" is to be found.

The reconstruction of Zeno's paradoxes concerning motion and time suffers from the fact that no passage relating to these subjects has reached us in Zeno's own wording. That the two subjects were connected is obvious. We may also say that in the "Achilles" time, movement, and magnitude (distance) are brought into mutual relation.[173] Yet this helps us little as long as we do not know what words Zeno used for this relation. It is more or less certain that the "stadium" paradox showed the absurd consequences resulting if movement is thought of as composed of (a limited number of) jerks while the "arrow" brings out the impossibility of constructing it out of (infinite?) momentary conditions.[174] That Zeno in the latter paradox actually spoke of now's is very probable;[175] whether he explicitly called them indivisible or said that an infinite number of them were to be found in the arrow's flight remains in doubt (the emphasis may well have been on the point that in the now the arrow is not in movement). He need not even have stated clearly that time was composed of now's, though to Aristotle this implication was obvious and gave him the handle for saying that Zeno had built up time out of the wrong kind of infinites. The right kind of infinite divisions of time—moving time —Zeno seems to have approached most closely in the Achilles paradox, which Aristotle solves by taking as a whole the distance and the time in which Achilles reaches the turtle and then explaining in which

[173] For the texts see H. D. P. Lee, *Zeno of Elea* (Cambridge, 1936), 50. They report that Zeno spoke of ἐν πεπερασμένῳ χρόνῳ in which, as he showed, the ἄπειρα of a distance could not be traversed (see *Phys.* VI,2.233a23; VIII,8.263a16, 19; also *De lin. insec.* 968a18f). Ross (*Physics*, "Introduction," 73) is inclined to accept ἐν πεπερασμένῳ χρόνῳ as authentic, because Aristotle later states that the arguments which he has directed against Zeno, although not adequate to the issue, were satisfactory *ad hominem* (263a15). I cannot entirely share Ross's confidence; for even where Aristotle thinks he has done justice to Zeno, he may quite well state the problem in his own terms. First he regards what Zeno "meant" as the real issue; later he sees that more is involved.

[174] Lee (p. 100) well speaks of the movement performed by the bodies in the "stadium" paradox as "cinematographic." Note that Aristotle refutes this view of motion (actually using the word κινήματα instead of κινήσεις) early in his discussion of movement (VI,1.231b29ff.; see esp. 232a8ff.). He does not, however, appear to have Zeno here in mind. For the texts see Lee, 52ff., 54ff. Cf. Note 175.

[175] I should infer it with confidence from *Phys.* VI,9.239b6 in conjunction with the attention given to the νῦν in the *Parmenides*, whose purpose it is to develop Zeno's paradoxes.

sense both are finite and in which infinite.[176] Yet again we do not actually know how Zeno himself here handled the time factor. It is very difficult to believe that he would ever have said in so many words: "If the continuous is one, then since the continuous is always divisible, the products of the division can always be divided into further divisions." [177] For all we can tell, Zeno did not believe in the objective reality of the propositions embodied in his paradoxes, but worked them out to confound the pluralists.[178] The infinite divisibility which he brought to light was not meant to live peacefully side by side with Parmenides' "continuous" and "indivisible one"; nor would there be for him an alternative one, ready to come to terms with plurality.

What would be important for our purpose is not how Aristotle or later thinkers understood Zeno, or to what extent Zeno played with notions held by others, but precisely what he himself said and what suggestions he, whether in jest or earnest, put forward. If we knew this, we could form a fairly precise judgment as to the degree to which Aristotle advanced beyond him. The subject for which we have the best and most authentic information is magnitudes (or physical objects). Here we have some of Zeno's own sentences and can see that he formulated their infinite divisibility with all desirable clarity.[179] Yet this is the subject that interests Aristotle least in Book VI of the *Physics*. With regard to time and movement we have no material of comparable authenticity. Still, the arguments by which Aristotle in chapters 1 and 2 of our book establishes the mutual interdependence of the infinite divisibilities give every impression of being his own.[180] We shall not go far astray if we say that Aristotle put the subject which he found implied in Zeno on the entirely new basis of his own reasoning. In particular, originality may be assumed for the very

[176] See above, Note 173. *Phys.* VI,9 contains relatively little in the way of counterarguments. VI,2.233a21ff. and VIII,8.263a4ff. go deeper into the nature of the problem. Cherniss (*Presocr.*, 155ff.) takes a more positive view about the reconstruction of Zeno's precise meaning and has a less favorable opinion regarding the progress achieved by Aristotle.

[177] The words form part of a testimony (Philop. in *Phys.* 42.9ff.; *Vorsokr.*, 29A21 = 8 Lee) which Lee, p. 27, on other grounds considers open to suspicion.

[178] Plato *Parm.* 128cf.

[179] See *Vorsokr.*, 29B1-3 (9-11 Lee); for the interpretation see H. Fränkel, *A. J. Ph.*, 63 (1942), 3ff., 15ff., 193ff.

[180] VI,1.231b18-2.233a12. Note the use made of perfects in 231b28ff.

elegant argument which operates successively with the faster and the slower body, making the faster produce an infinite series of divisions in time, while the slower does the same for distance.[181]

The infinite divisibility of magnitudes and physical bodies was a discovery of which the physicists who came after Zeno took account. Whether they welcomed it as an essential help for their own constructions, as Anaxagoras did, or rejected it as a threat to a rational understanding of the physical world, as the atomists did, or finally—as Plato does in the *Parmenides*—carefully circumscribed the area where it holds good, they certainly are familiar with Zeno's discovery and testify to its importance. The mathematicians too accepted the infinite divisibility of magnitudes as a basis for their geometry and were as a consequence able to recognize irrational quantities.[182] If Zeno also "discovered" the infinite divisibility of movement and time, the complete lack of any response in the preserved material[183] would contrast strongly with the extraordinary degree of success which attended his proclamation of infinite divisibility in the realm of magnitudes. Did it remain for Aristotle to make up for the stepmotherly reception of these discoveries and to combine the neglected and the appreciated phases of Zeno's doctrine once more *sub uno aspectu?* Or was it Aristotle himself who completed Zeno's discovery by extending the principle from magnitudes to movements and to time? The balance of probability seems to be in favor of this alternative. After all, Plato's *Parmenides*, which is an unambiguous witness for the infinite divisibility of "bodies," does not incorporate a parallel doctrine with reference to time. To be sure, this work points to the peculiar position of the now in relation to time and processes in time, suggesting perhaps, or even implying, that the now cannot build up time. In fact,

---

[181] See above, p. 200.

[182] Cornford, *Pl. and Parm.*, 60, points out that this development led to a separation of arithmetic from geometry. See also Michel H. Hasse and H. Scholz, *Die Grundlagenkrise d. griech. Mathem.* (Charlottenburg, 1928).

[183] When Epicurus taught that magnitudes, movement, and time consisted alike ἐξ ἀμερῶν (frg. 278, Usener), he did not repeat Democritus but formulated a new doctrine in conscious opposition to Aristotle and accepting views that Aristotle had ruled out (see Simplicius *In Phys.* 934.23ff. and Themistius 184.9ff.). Cf. Bailey, *Atomists*, 315f. How close he keeps to Aristotle's thought—while turning it upside down—may be seen from his thesis that in every indivisible minimum of time the moving object "has moved," i.e., the movement is completed in an instant; see Aristotle's repudiation of this idea in *Phys.* VI,1.231b28ff. For the use of the perfect tense see above, Note 146.

Plato's statements may have suggested a great deal to Aristotle. Moreover, they are likely to reflect a considerable amount of thinking and experimenting with these concepts that went on in the Academy; and it need not have been Plato's intention to "publish," even in the tentative form of his alternative hypotheses, everything that had been found out. No explicit parallel between the now and the point is drawn in the *Parmenides;* still less is there an approximation to the idea that, as the line is infinitely divisible yet not into points, so time is infinitely divisible yet not into now's. As has been said, minds—not necessarily only Aristotle's mind—may have been seeking their way in this direction. And it is well to note that what is needed to complete the discoveries still absent in the *Parmenides* is not the concepts of potentiality and actuality, which we incline to regard as Aristotle's individual contributions to Academic discussions. However often Aristotle elsewhere uses them in connection with "divisibility," [184] Book VI of the *Physics* makes its essential points without resorting to them. Rather, the most notable absentee in the arguments of the *Parmenides* is the "continuum." Yet we have found it very difficult to believe that this Parmenidean concept, in some sense the *fons et origo* of Zeno's paradoxes, should have slipped from sight. Is there some hesitation to "lay" once more "violent hands on Parmenides" and to declare outright that every continuum is by its very nature divisible? Aristotle perpetrates this "parricide," which is as hideous as or more so than the rehabilitation of not-being and of movement. Knowing the one—the "one by continuity"—which is at the same time infinitely many, he can operate without paradoxes and without alternative hypotheses, even without "potency" and "actuality," when he proceeds to extend the range and scope of this infinity. He is moving with delight and wholehearted dedication in a region which Plato had kept below the threshold of reality and philosophy.

[184] The most notable instances are probably *Phys.* VIII,8.263a27ff. and *De gen.* I,2.316b19ff.

10

The Unmoved Mover

THROUGHOUT most of the *Physics* Aristotle gives us the impression that he regards the nature and the properties of movement as worth studying for their own sake. Yet the source of movement had with Plato become the first cosmic principle, and Plato's pupil, knowing that the right understanding of movement furnished a clue to the structure of the Cosmos, would not lose sight of this ulterior objective. Sooner or later[1] he would make the turn from the physical theory of movement to its cosmological implications. Book VIII of the *Physics* presents Aristotle's version of the first cosmological principle, a Platonic topic even if, for Aristotle, this principle has become broken up into two. New insights into the nature of movement have necessitated revisions which at times cut rather deep into the inherited fabric. Some Platonic tenets, however, have been incorporated with little or no change.

Whereas Books V and VI and the latter part of Book VII (chs. 3, 4, and 5) consider movement so to speak in the abstract, regardless of whether, where, and when it exists, Book VIII begins by proclaiming the eternity of movement. The first sentences of the book take us into the realm of cosmology and in doing so at once establish contact

---

[1] Reasons suggesting for *Phys.* VIII a later date than for the other books of the *Physics* are set forth by Jaeger, *Aristotle*, 237ff., and Ross, *Physics*, "Introduction," 10. Book VIII seems to have been intended to replace Book VII where Aristotle makes an early effort to find his way to a first mover. The differences between the two books are well stated and the correct conclusion is drawn by Simplicius in his commentary (1036.9ff. Diels). He reports that earlier commentators tended to slight Book VII. Cf. also Ernst Hoffmann, *De Arist. Phys. Libri VII origine et auctoritate* (diss., Berlin, 1905), 24ff.

with Presocratic thought. The reality of movement, Aristotle states with satisfaction, is generally recognized by the physicists and cosmologists [2] (designations which, needless to say, do not include the Eleatics). As for its eternity, the consensus is not so complete, and Aristotle finds it pertinent to specify the mistakes made by those who assume alternations between complete rest and movement. His criticism is directed against Anaxagoras,[3] whom he rightly understands to start with a condition of "no motion," and Empedocles, whom he perhaps less rightly—and certainly on the strength of false inferences [4] —supposes to believe in periodic alternations between rest and movement. The cosmological motif here introduced remains latently present in the book. Although Aristotle avoids being specific about the cosmic entities which he deduces, it is clear (and generally agreed) that his deductions must be understood in cosmological terms.

Plato too asserts the eternity of movement, yet not per se. His statements declare that only the self-moving soul can guarantee eternal motion; if this principle were removed, the physical world would collapse into an utterly static condition. Like Aristotle, he imagines, in purely hypothetical terms, a condition of things in which everything would be at rest; but he immediately goes on to declare that only the self-moving principle could get things out of this condition "since there would be no change in them before." [5] Not so Aristotle. When he contemplates a state of universal rest, he is driven to deny that this can be the first condition. Before it comes to this, there must already have been change. For one thing, the objects supposedly at rest must already be there. If they have come into being, we have *genesis.*[6] If they are eternally there and at rest for some time, yet later begin to

---

[2] VIII,1.250b15ff. For a logical analysis (and a critique) of Aristotle's arguments in this chapter see G. Verbeke, *Revue philosoph. de Louvain,* 46 (1948), 137ff., who believes that the chapter presupposes the conclusions of *De caelo* I.9–12.

[3] 250b24.

[4] *Ibid.,* 26. For Aristotle's misinterpretation of Empedocles B17.9ff. (= B26.8ff.) see Ross, *ad loc.,* and Cherniss, *Presocr.,* 175 n.130. Whether Empedocles actually assumed periods of rest to intervene between the coming together and the dispersing of his four elements depends on the meaning of the word μονίη in B27.4, 28.2. It used to be understood as "solitude." Jaeger (*Theology,* 141) convincingly argues that it means "rest." See also Wilamowitz' opinion as recorded by E. Diehl *ad* Tyrt. 1.15 (*Anth. Lyr. Gr.* [Leipzig, 1923]. The reading is, however, now in doubt; see 3d ed. [Leipzig, 1954], Tyrt. 1.54). Incidentally, Eudemus, frg. 110, Wehrli, suggests that he disagreed with Aristotle regarding the occurrence of rest in Empedocles' cycle. Eudemus' own interpretation is closer to the modern view.

[5] *Legg.* X,895b; cf. *Phaedr.* 245d–e.   [6] 251a8ff., esp. 17ff.

change, they must possess in their nature the potentiality of change. In this case something must have brought them to rest and something must be responsible for their beginning to change again.[7] This would suggest a principle of movement which was at work before the condition of universal rest materialized and which causes both their rest and their movement. However, Aristotle is not here concerned with such a "principle." The conclusion to which he steers the argument is that change must have been operating and that the stationary condition of all things cannot possibly be regarded as their first condition. He sees his way of establishing the priority, and with it the eternity of movement, without bringing his own, or any, principle of movement into the discussion. By this his argument gains considerably in intellectual tidiness. Only when the eternity of movement has been settled on independent grounds does he allow himself to make contact with another line of reasoning which shows that there is an ultimate and unchanging source of movement. Now it becomes possible to be more specific about the eternal movement and to disclose that it is caused by the unchanging first mover who keeps the world forever functioning in its ordered way.[8]

Obviously to prove that there is eternal movement is not the same as to demonstrate that one and the same movement goes on forever. As Aristotle himself says, the assumption of eternal movement underlies some of the Presocratic systems. Let us grant that this is substantially correct.[9] But it is also the case that the eternal movement which the Presocratics know would antedate and outlast the existence of this or any other Cosmos. Nor would the eternity of movement imply for them that it must always be of the same kind and operate in the same direction. Formation and disintegration of the Cosmos would be phases but contrary phases of this movement; nor can the

---

[7] *Ibid.*, 20–b10. Rest, according to the view here taken by Aristotle, is not the normal condition of physical things. Here as elsewhere he regards rest (or the coming to rest, if ἠρέμησις is the correct reading in a226f.) as a privation of movement, implying that movement would be the normal condition.

[8] Chs. 6 and 7; see below, p. 235. Verbeke (*op.cit.*, 151) has found reasons to think that "la dissertation sur l'éternité du mouvement" (i.e., VIII,1) was originally an independent treatise. It is correct that ch. 3 does not make use of the conclusions reached in ch. 1. Yet are not the opinions combated in ch. 3 sufficiently different from those opposed in ch. 1? The question of ch. 3 is no longer whether movement had a beginning.

[9] For a closer study of this question see my paper in *H.S.C.P.*, 63 (1958), 265ff., esp. 275ff.

changes and processes within the Cosmos be identical with those outside it and before it. To identify the eternal movement with one
particular physical—even visible—movement of this Cosmos and to
insist on its numerical oneness and sameness would probably strike
the earlier thinkers as an act of appalling literal-mindedness and very
limited vision. The Academy did precisely this. Imprisoning as it were
the eternal movement within the confines of the Cosmos, it abandoned
the idea of a cyclical law, which for Empedocles and others had
regulated the alternations of movement and transcended the existence
of our Cosmos. Instead of it, there was now the one eternal circular
movement, which is performed by the sphere of the fixed stars. Behind
this momentous departure lies a new religious feeling for the divinity
of the Cosmos, as well as, perhaps, a new mathematical concept of
perfection; in addition the solemn words by which Plato extols the
eternal self-identity of the heavenly rotation suggest that he found in
it something comparable to the never-varying sameness of the Forms.[10]

As long as Aristotle contents himself with asserting the eternity of
movement, he defends a position on which the Academy found itself
in agreement with the majority of the Presocratic thinkers (the most
notable dissenters being the Eleatics). He does not yet find himself on
specifically Academic ground but moves on to it as soon as he makes
the further step of identifying the eternal movement with a particular
cosmic movement, the revolution of the outermost heaven.

As we shall see later, Aristotle takes great pains about proving that
of all the changes which his system recognizes circular movement
alone can be eternal. Measured by these pains, the logically prior step
which would lead from the proof for eternal movement to its identification with one eternal movement is taken rather quickly. One
syllogism stripped down to the essentials of the first figure and using
"eternal" as its middle term proves that movement must be continuous:
"It has been shown that movement must be eternal. If eternal it must
be continuous. For what is eternal is continuous, whereas the successive is not continuous." [11] This syllogism is followed by the statement:
"If it is continuous it must be one." For this no proof is needed, because the point was settled in the general disquisitions of the first book

---

[10] Note, e.g., the emphasis placed on "sameness" in *Legg.* X,898a8. Cf. my *Plato's
Theology* (Ithaca, N.Y., 1942), 86ff., and A. J. Festugière's excellent discussion in
Personal Religion among the Greeks (Berkeley and Los Angeles, 1954), 46ff.

[11] 259a16–18 (the words "it has been shown" refer to ch. 1).

on movement.[12] Remarkably enough Aristotle does not even stop to underline these all-important conclusions. At the juncture where he enunciates them, they are steppingstones toward something more fundamental on which he has had his eyes all the time: if the eternal movement is "one," there must be one first mover and one first moved.[13]

To us the transition from the one position (that there must always be movement) to the other (that there must be one continuous and eternal movement) may seem less simple and unproblematic. For when Aristotle in the first chapter proves the eternity of movement, his arguments do not rule out successive or even alternating movements, nor do they favor one particular movement (or change) above the others.[14] Why then does Aristotle make so little of the step which from the eternal existence of movement leads to the eternity of the heavenly rotation?

We must assume that some antecedent conviction is here operating. That eternal movement was numerically one was settled when Plato had identified self-mover, first mover, and eternal mover and associated this principle with the never-changing celestial movements.[15] Aristotle accepts these ideas and thinks in the same terms with the one difference that he divides the "self-mover" into two entities and afterward no longer employs this concept. When he has proved that only

[12] V,4.228a20–24.

[13] 259a18–20. From the beginning of ch. 6 Aristotle's concern has been to show that the oneness of the prime mover is, if not absolutely necessary, decidedly preferable to the alternative of several prime movers. 259a13 is his first proof for the "necessity" of one first mover and one first moved. That the eternal movement (established in ch. 1) must be one eternal and continuous movement is a proposition which Aristotle never discusses or proves per se; the only proof that he gives is in the syllogism of our passage where, however, it is not the *telos* of the syllogism. At the beginning of ch. 7 (260a20ff., esp. 24, 26) the continuity and oneness of the eternal movement are stated without proof, perhaps on the strength of our passage.

[14] Cf. Ross in his *Physics*, "Introduction," 91f. Simplicius on 259a13ff. makes the interesting point that the eternity proved in ch. 1 was that of successive movements; if we are now to understand that only continuous but not successive movement is eternal, the proofs of ch. 1 are invalidated. This he regards as an *aporia*. He offers the substantially correct explanation that in ch. 1 Aristotle has his mind on things and changes in the sublunary world whereas in the meantime he has shifted to the celestial realm.

[15] Plato *Legg.* X,894d3ff.; see also *Phaedr.* 245c7ff. The cosmological scheme of the *Timaeus* (34b10–39e2) implies the same identifications, except that it may be more strictly correct to think of soul as causing cosmic movements "for all time" (36e4f.), rather than for eternity.

circular movement can be eternal, he does not linger over this point to explain that therefore one particular circular movement—that of the outermost heaven—must be the first movement of the world and the outermost heaven itself the "first moved." The reader's mind must draw this momentous inference and must integrate the various conclusions of the book into a coherent world picture. One way of effecting this integration is to recollect doctrines elsewhere set forth by Aristotle which give body and substance to the cosmology here drawn as a rough sketch.[16] This is a good systematizing procedure. Under a more historical aspect, however, the frame of reference in which Aristotle's conclusions fall into place is the cosmological scheme of the late Platonic Academy. Anyone brought up on the views that we know from the *Timaeus* and other dialogues of this period could not miss the "ulterior" significance of the arguments which show that only circular movement may be continuous. He would combine this conclusion with the previously introduced concept of an eternal "first moved" and recognize circular motion as the movement of this entity. He would also—going beyond what Aristotle actually says—realize that this "first" and eternal movement is that of the outermost heaven. Operating as he does against the background of an established cosmic scheme, Aristotle could afford to leave his conclusions unconnected or, as the case might be, indicate the connection incidentally and almost casually. Long before he actually specifies the one eternal movement as the circular, he expects his readers to understand the concrete meaning of such cryptic phrases as the "eternally moved" and "something moved by the unmoved." [17] The readers would hardly identify the eternal motion of which he speaks with the movement of the Democritean atoms or that set up by Anaxagoras' cosmogonic mind. Some sentences at the beginning of chapter 7 are welcome to us because they tie together the threads of the argument; yet those

---

[16] The cosmological significance of the doctrine is taken for granted also in *Metaph.* Λ7. In Λ8 it had to be made a good deal more explicit. The exegetical tradition (including the commentators of the *Physics* and *Metaphysics*) has undoubtedly done much to keep the readers aware of the cosmological reference of Aristotle's physical propositions. It is often assumed that Aristotle in the oral presentation of his *methodoi* would interpret his austere arguments and improvise some elaborations. Actually we know nothing about his habits of presentation, and it would be unwarranted to think that he took such opportunities to give charitable assistance.

[17] See, e.g., a section such as 259b32ff. where in addition the notion that the planetary spheres are moved by the outermost heaven is presupposed (260a5ff.).

for whom Aristotle wrote would not have missed his points even if he had not here spelled out that if there is an eternal movement it must be caused by the first mover.[18] Nor does Aristotle consider himself obliged to label some of his conclusions as "new" and set them apart from those that reaffirm Platonic doctrines. The task which he had set himself was to find out which Platonic propositions regarding the origin of cosmic change and movement could survive his merciless scrutiny and which had to be recast in a more precise and logically more satisfactory form.

In the chapters which follow the initial proof for the eternity of movement we may distinguish three theses which are successively established: (1) that with reference to movement things fall into three categories, (a) things always in motion, (b) things always at rest, and (c) things alternating between movement and rest; (2) that everything engaged in motion is moved by something; and (3) that all movements are to be traced to *one* ultimate source and originator.[19]

Although setting up the three categories covered by (1), Aristotle in effect provides arguments only for the reality of the third, i.e., of things sometimes in motion and sometimes at rest. He says, however, that it is the "goal" of his inquiry to establish all three categories,[20] and we therefore read the following section with the expectation of finding two other types, i.e., things eternally in motion and things eternally at rest. The proof for their existence is contained in the arguments which lead us to the ultimate originator of all movements; for in the course of these arguments the originator does not remain a unit but resolves himself into two entities, the first mover who must be unmoved and thus eternally at rest and the first moved which is always in uninterrupted and identical motion.[21]

Plato had never given entities that are sometimes in motion and sometimes at rest a place in his scheme. The obvious fact that there are such things was probably for him without philosophic interest, and

[18] 260a23ff.

[19] The theses are established in chs. 3, 4, and 5–6 respectively. It is, however, worth recording that although ch. 5 arrives at the concept of a self-mover and an unmoved mover little attention is given to that of a "first mover." In this point the argument in Book VII (ch. 1.242a49–243a31) is much fuller and much more elaborate. VIII,5.256a4–21, which operates in this direction, cannot seriously be compared with the circumspect discussion of Book VII. It is conceivable that Aristotle was for once satisfied with the achievements of Book VII and therefore treated the same matter rather lightly in VIII.

[20] 254b4–6.   [21] This emerges in ch. 5; see below, p. 234.

attention to it could only have interfered with his conviction that movement was the central phenomenon in the realm of nature. No matter whether the objects of the physical world are *de facto* always in motion or alternate between motion and rest, movement is their distinctive characteristic.[22] Aristotle's introduction of the "mixed" class makes the system neater, but this is not all that he expects to gain by it. For he differs from Plato also by what he has in mind as "things at rest." In his system this phrase designates not the Forms but the prime mover. Unlike the Platonic world soul which is defined as always moving,[23] Aristotle's prime mover is eternally unmoved. Inasmuch as the movement of the world soul never varies, it may be called unchanging. There is some difference between "unchanging" and "unmoving." Both predicates implement the postulate which Greek thinkers had upheld since the day of Xenophanes, to wit, that the deity should undergo no change;[24] but they implement it in different ways, and in some respect—and probably for Aristotle's own feeling—the unmoved mover meets the ideal demand more fully and unambiguously.[25] In contrast to Plato, his study of movement culminates in the realization that an entity completely unmoved and at

[22] See *Soph.* 248eff. and *Tim.* 57d–58c. *Legg.* X,893b is different inasmuch as Plato here divides πάντα into what remains at rest and what moves; the former category can hardly refer to the Forms since the next sentence states that (what moves and) what stands does so ἐν χώρᾳ τινί, whereas the Forms are not supposed to be "in space" or in a place.

[23] *Phaedr.* 245c5 (where the ἀείκίνητον would be emphasized, see c8, even if the reading αὐτοκίνητον were to be accepted from *pap. Oxyrh.*, 1017; ἀείκίνητον is rightly defended by P. Maas, *Textkritik* [3d ed.; Leipzig, 1957], 23; see also my *Entwicklung d. arist. Logik* [Berlin, 1929], 284). See, further, *Legg.* X,894b9 where ἡ. αὐτὴν. ἀεὶ . . . δυναμένη (κινεῖν) indicates eternal power, not eternal potentiality in Aristotle's sense of the word.

[24] Xenoph. B26; it seems noteworthy that local movement in particular is here ruled out; cf. Jaeger, *Theology*, 45, who besides pointing out the historical connection with Aristotle's concept of the unmoved mover refers to Aesch., *Suppl.*, 96ff. (the μίμνειν in *Ag.* 1563 which E. Fraenkel, *Aeschylus' Agamemnon* [Oxford, 1951], III, 831, compares is different). On Empedocles see above, Note 4.

[25] In *Rep.* II Plato does not, like Xenophanes, insist that the God should not move but that he should not change (380dff.); neither his appearance nor his moral quality should undergo any alteration (cf. his statement about the Demiurge in *Tim.* 42e5: ἔμεινεν ἐν τῷ ἑαυτοῦ κατὰ τρόπον ἤθει). For a closer comparison of Plato's unchanging world soul and Aristotle's unmoved mover some further points should be taken into account. As specified and enumerated at *Legg.* X,896e8ff., the movements of the soul are entirely of a "psychic" character. So is the activity of Aristotle's God (*Metaph.* Λ7.1072b14ff.; 9.1074b15ff.), who is inactive only in the sense of experiencing no physical change or movement.

rest is needed to keep the movements in the Cosmos going. And whether or not it is "numerically" one, this is the only entity at rest that Aristotle knows. The Platonic dichotomy between the physical world as the world of movement and the "nonphysical" as that of rest [26] thus gives way to another pattern. Now the physical system as such embodies entities at rest and entities in movement, but having become a tripartite scheme, it also includes the objects in the sublunary region which are defined as alternating between movement and rest. One may feel that Aristotle has stretched the concept of rest, if it is to describe on the one hand the condition of the unmoved God and on the other the cessation of movement which most physical things experience at times. Perhaps he himself regards the word "unmoved" as more solemn and in the last resort better suited to indicate the characteristic state of his God than the word designating "at rest," which is used for the infinitely less exalted temporary condition of objects in the physical world. Yet he does employ this word (ἠρεμία) with reference to the highest entity.[27]

As has been said, the section which introduces us to the trichotomy proves only the reality of the mixed class. The deduction of the two other classes is left to the following chapters. One may expect Aristotle to use the class of whose reality he has made sure as basis for the theses (2) and (3) which he next endeavors to prove. And indeed the proposition that "everything in motion is moved by something" certainly holds good of the class which by definition alternates between rest and movement. More than this, all objects in this class need as ultimate source of their movement the dual entity one part of which is always in motion and the other eternally unmoved.[28] Everything thus gets its due and finds its place (although the integration is again in large measure left to the reader). But we may as well note that the proposition "Everything that is moved is moved by something" has its validity and importance quite independently of any tripartite or other scheme of things. It is a Platonic proposition, and

[26] At *Soph.* 249b what is in motion and movement itself are admitted into τὰ ὄντα; see also *ibid.*, 249c10–d4.

[27] In the context of the tripartite scheme it is natural for Aristotle to use the word ἠρεμεῖν also where the reference is indubitably to the one being eternally at rest (e.g., 254b5); on the other hand, the use of ἀκίνητον suggests itself, e.g., in ch. 5 where the movements of all moved objects are traced to something itself "unmoved."

[28] Aristotle comes back to class (c) in ch. 6 (e.g., 259a23ff. and 260a3ff.), yet he does not use it in deducing his source of all movements.

there is evidence that for Plato too it was backed up by a good deal of specific reasoning.[29] Aristotle on his part fortifies this Platonic doctrine by an exhaustive argumentation, which remains undaunted even before the most recalcitrant facts, but he does not bother to fit it tightly into his own system and provides no link (easy though it would have been) with the mixed class of his immediately preceding tripartite scheme. Plato's thesis "Whatever is moved needs a mover" would be no less true and no less helpful in preparing the next step of the argument if there were no trichotomy and no class of things that change between rest and movement. It suffices that there are things in motion, and, like Plato,[30] Aristotle argues from things in motion to a first source of all motion. Of the three theses embodied in *Physics* VIII,3–5, the second and third are inherited and even (as we shall presently see) inherited as a sequence, whereas the first, Aristotle's own contribution, lacks an original and organic connection with these two. The second and third of our propositions dovetail beautifully as long as we accept the second in the form in which it presents itself in the end: "Everything that is moved is moved by something." [31] From here we proceed at once to the situation sketched in the following paragraph—that which moves may again be moved by something else or may move itself. With the second alternative we have reached the self-moving principle, yet the first too will lead us there after a time, for the simple but good Aristotelian reason that there cannot be an infinite number of moved movers.[32] A self-moving source of all changes and movements is under all circumstances needed. We find essentially the same alternative in the *Laws*: either things receive movement from something else and pass it on, or the movement originates

<hr/>

[29] See esp. *Tim.* 57e3ff., and for the "chain" of movements *Legg.* X,894e4ff.

[30] See the emphatic sentence in *Legg.* X,894e7ff. Aristotle (256a4-21) argues that there cannot be an infinite regress in movements caused by something else. There must be a "first," and this "first" must be a self-mover (a19ff.; cf.21-b3). Admittedly the self-mover is not Aristotle's last word on the subject, but some of his arguments aim at nothing beyond establishing the reality of this Platonic concept.

[31] VIII, 4.256a2f.

[32] See Note 30. Observe that Aristotle here in 256a17-19 quite briefly and peremptorily rules out the possibility of infinite links in the chain of moved movers. This is the same point which he argues at great length and with desperate energy in the first chapter of Book VII (242a49-243a31). Book VII represents his first attempt to find the prime mover. In Book VIII Aristotle never refers to Book VII, but the arguments there advanced may still be in the back of his mind and give him confidence.

with them (in which case soul must be present in them). There is no doubt that Aristotle in his second and third propositions elaborates a Platonic conception: in every movement you can distinguish the active and the passive factor,[33] and in tracing the former back you arrive, no matter through how many intermediate stages, finally at the self-moving principle as the source of the movement.

This time Aristotle has so faithfully preserved the Platonic line of thought—and how could he help it if he wished to find the first mover?—that he does grave harm to one of his own new doctrines. As we know, Book II defines nature as "a source of movement" and natural objects as "having a source of movement in themselves." [34] What in Plato was reserved for soul has in Aristotle become the property of all nature. Yet that which has the source of movement in itself should certainly be able to initiate its own movement and not be in need of receiving the impulse from a remote principle. Evidently in Book VIII Aristotle is developing a legacy of the Platonic world soul which conflicts with his own doctrine that all natural entities have their source and principle of movement in themselves. Soul as Plato conceived it may indeed be the cause of the first cosmic move-ment—the revolution of the heaven—and at the same time of all movement in the world. The attempt made in the *Timaeus* [35] to trace all cosmic changes to the heavenly rotation is one facet of this thought. It is considerably harder to keep up the belief in *one* source of move-ment when everything that belongs to nature has been so lavishly en-dowed with the self-moving capacity.

Was Aristotle aware of the difficulty which results from developing Plato's suggestive conception in two different and to some extent contradictory directions? He can hardly have regarded them as

[33] Cf. again *Tim.* 53e3ff. The relationship between mover and moved is essential for the two last classes of the ten which Plato sets up in *Laws* X,894b8ff. The distinction between the active and the passive factor and their relation dominate Aristotle's relatively brief account of movement in the first chapters of Book III. This account stands outside the comprehensive theory of movement presented in the latter books (V–VIII).

[34] II,1.192b8ff. When we read that the difference between things that are *physei* and those that are not lies in the former's having ἐν αὑτῷ ἀρχὴν κινήσεως καὶ στάσεως (as well as of other changes), we cannot be expected to understand that they have the potentiality of change which is actualized if something outside them moves them. In fact, Aristotle uses the words ὁρμὴ μεταβολῆς ἔμφυτος to show what he means by ἀρχὴ κινήσεως. See above, pp. 95ff.

[35] 58a2ff. (see above, Ch. 2, Note 169).

fundamentally incompatible, for even while arguing for the second proposition, i.e., that whatever is moved must be moved by something, he once more puts on record his belief in nature as principle of self-motion, quoting (if we like to put it thus) what he has affirmed in Book II.[36] In deference to this definition of nature the thesis that everything is moved by something takes on the form of an alternative: everything is moved either by itself or by something other than, and outside, itself (in either case it is moved by something).[37] But in the end the first part of the alternative has for practical purposes disappeared from sight; the "moved by something" seems to be after all "moved by something else"—and even when the concept of "being moved by itself" reappears in the first source and principle of all movement, it proves necessary to regard mover and moved as distinct entities. In effect nothing moves itself.

Does Aristotle, in order to find the way to his first principle of movement, actually ignore his own new definition of nature? Does he minimize it? Are some arguments that we find in this section meant to render it irrelevant? This may not be their intention, but in effect they come close to doing just this. He himself distinguishes here between living beings and inanimate objects. For the former the idea of self-motion remains valid, provided one distinguishes even in them one part which moves and one which is moved. In the case of the latter, the cause of their motion is found outside them and all that is left to them is a very carefully limited and circumscribed potentiality. This category of inanimate objects includes entities such as the heavy and the light, which presumably are identical with earth and fire and thus should, according to Book II, most certainly have a principle of

[36] VIII,4.254b16–17; cf. II,1.192b13f.

[37] See again 254b12ff. Taking up his definition of nature as source (or principle) of movement, Aristotle argues at 255b13ff. that the elements have this principle only in a "passive" sense (30f.). This hardly agrees with the impression which either II,1 or the theory about the natural movements of the elements in *De caelo* creates. As for living beings, Aristotle still treats them as self-movers yet insists that we must distinguish between one part of them which moves and another which is moved (254b27ff.). This is in line with what he has to say about the cosmic "self-mover" (and also agrees with his doctrine in *De anim. motu*); yet on this argument living beings would still have "the source of movement in themselves." See, however, below, p. 245 for other passages which go farther. The difficulties here mentioned are also formulated by Léon Robin, *Aristote* (Paris, 1944), 125f., who views them from a broad philosophical perspective but does not help matters when he cites *De caelo* II,7.289a26ff. as offering a solution.

motion in themselves. Quite obviously much of what Aristotle in that book so lavishly bestowed on nature is here taken away and treated as beyond the capacity of natural objects.[38] When he refutes his own opinions, Aristotle is as merciless as when he criticizes the doctrines of his predecessors; the only difference is that he does not accuse himself of superficiality, vagueness, or obscurity.

As we have seen, Aristotle is determined to trace movements back to one cosmic source—which is now somewhat remoter than Plato's—and to do this by way of the Platonic "chain" pattern of movements: A is moved by B, B by C, and so forth. In actual fact, some of the arguments put forward in support of the *third* proposition arrive at the Platonic concept of the self-moving principle and aim at nothing further.[39] Side by side with them are others which show that this principle cannot be one entity but must be two, the unmoved mover and the "first moved," which can and does move other objects but cannot impart the impulse to itself.[40] The Platonic concept is clearly a steppingstone on the way to Aristotle's own new entities. It is tempting to think that the arguments which content themselves with establishing a "self-moved" entity reflect a stage when Aristotle himself still acquiesced in it and had not pushed on to the differentiation;

---

[38] For living beings see VIII,4.254b12ff., 27–33; for inanimate objects see b33–256a2, esp. 255b13–256a2. Cf. II,1.192b8–15, 32–193a1. On these points I find myself in agreement with H. von Arnim, *S.B.W.A.*, 212 (1931), 5.11f.

[39] On a corresponding occasion Eudemus (frg. 118, Wehrli) points out that the concept of the self-mover is a Platonic legacy (Aristotle, who does not mention this, could probably assume that his pupils knew it). Eudemus himself does not eliminate the αὐτοκίνητον from his own doctrine (frg. 120), though it is possible that his argumentation was tighter and headed more directly for the concept of the unmoved mover (cf. Wehrli's comment on frg. 120). Simplicius (1220.29 Diels) appears to think that the αὐτοκίνητον could be dispensed with; like Eudemus (frg. 115), whom he here follows, he regards it as a concession to the past history of the problem.

[40] The arguments in 256a4–21, 21–26 aim at proving the existence of the αὐτὸ αὐτὸ κινοῦν. The same seems to be true of b3–13, which is followed by a piece of reasoning not organically connected with it. At 257a31 Aristotle appears to make the step toward closer investigation of the self-moving principle (cf. 26f.). Actually, however, arguments to the effect that the κινοῦν must be ἀκίνητον have been given before (256b13–27, b27–257b14). The textual problem here involved was recognized by Cornford (*Aristotle, Physics* [Loeb Lib.; London and Cambridge, Mass., 1932–1934], *ad loc.*) when he shifted 256b13–27 to a later place. I agree that where the MSS have this section it is not in place, but I am not sure that transposition of this or other sections—a device already adopted by ancient critics (cf. Simplicius 1224, 26)—is the remedy. The question must be left to further study.

but matters being as uncertain as they are, little is gained by experimenting with this hypothesis.[41]

Plato extols the circular movement as being eternally the same. The rotation of the heaven will continue and the planets will move in their spheres as long as the Cosmos is in existence, which means, presumably, forever. Circular movement is for him the first in the order of value and also the first in the sense of being the source of all other cosmic changes.[42] Again we find Aristotle in complete agreement. What he works out in chapters 7–9 is that the circular movement is the first, that it is perfect, and that it is the only movement that can be continuous, i.e., eternal. The arguments for its continuity proceed apace with those securing it the first place. This movement is, of course, that of the first entity in motion, the outermost heavenly sphere. That it causes all other movements in the Cosmos is taken for granted; the detailed substantiation of this point has to wait for another occasion.

Let us follow Aristotle on the way toward his goal. Having satisfied himself of the existence of an eternal first mover (and an eternal first moved), he makes a "new beginning." [43] He can now leave aside all differentiations on which he has up to this point concentrated—between movements self-caused and not self-caused, between first mover and first moved. Instead he addresses himself to the dual task of finding the "first movement" and of determining whether or not there can actually be a "continuous," i.e., eternal, movement. This is not exactly a turn from a speculative mode of inquiry to an empirical but rather a return from the consideration of the first entities to the general theory of movements, to a study of their mutual relations and a comparison of their respective properties. The juncture at which Aristotle finds himself corresponds to the passage in the *Laws* where Plato, having proved the existence of a first mover and self-mover, wonders what actual cosmic movement can be assigned to this divine being; [44] for Aristotle too embarks on the new inquiry with the intention of identifying the first and continuous movement with that pro-

[41] The temptation is strong because there is a self-mover in Aristotle's cosmology, to wit, the first body of *De caelo* I which does not owe its circular motion to any "stronger" power.

[42] See *Tim.* 37e–39c; the regularity of these movements (each of which is "time") imitates the μένειν of eternity. Cf. also *Legg.* X,898a. See, further, *Tim.* 58a4ff. for the τοῦ παντὸς περίοδος as source of the other movements.

[43] 260a20.   [44] *Legg.* X,897d, eff.

duced by the first mover.[45] In other words, the steps of Aristotle's procedure parallel Plato's. First the distinction between self-caused and not-self-caused movement leads to the concept of a first mover. His existence having been deduced, consideration is given to his specific nature or characteristics (Aristotle's chief concern is that he must be unmoved). And finally, among the various types and "forms" of movement actually existing, one is singled out as being appropriate to this newly discovered mover. (Needless to say, in Aristotle's scheme this movement is understood as being caused or inspired by the first mover, not as actually performed by him.) The entire procedure is logical enough; for the initial differentiation between movements self-caused and movements induced from the outside stands in no obvious relation to the general classification of movements into locomotion, growth and decline, etc., but these classes are needed when the first and continuous movement must be found. In fact, even subdivisions must here be taken into consideration; for in the end movement in a straight line and movement in a circle, two forms of locomotion, emerge as the principal competitors.[46]

Plato does not keep the criteria of differentiation as consciously distinct as Aristotle. He begins by giving us a general class-division of changes, enumerating altogether eight, with circular motion at the head of the list. After this he adds as ninth and tenth classes movement caused from outside and self-induced movement.[47] To put it crudely, Plato's second kind is movement in a straight line, his fifth is growth, his ninth is movement caused from the outside. Quite heterogeneous criteria are employed, but the classes are put side by side. This leads to the result that the movement of soul is identical with

[45] More precisely it is that produced by the first mover and performed by the first moved (this is implied when at 260a25 Aristotle refers to the active function of the first mover). For Aristotle's tentative consideration in VIII,6 of a plurality of unmoved movers (to provide for the movements of the planetary spheres), see Jaeger, *Aristotle*, 358ff. This line of thought which leads to *Metaph.* Λ8 must here be disregarded.

[46] VIII,8, esp. 262a12–b8, 264b9–28. The elimination of all other movements, including locomotion in a straight line, is presupposed in *Metaph.* Λ6.1071b10f., where Aristotle states briefly that only local movement and in fact only cyclical locomotion can be continuous. A proof for an eternal physical substance, scil., the first heaven (Klaus Oehler, *Philologus*, 99 [1955], 20ff.), can with the best of will not be found in this passage.

[47] *Legg.* X,893bff., 894bf.

the tenth of these classes, namely, self-caused movement, yet when it comes to the question how soul actually manifests itself, its movement must also be identified or at least closely connected with the first class, circular motion.[48]

As we have seen, Aristotle arrives finally at the same conclusions as Plato, yet he does so by a different route. He, too, operates with the classification of movements—which was the only way of finding the "first"—but he never puts self-caused and not-self-caused movement on a par with the other classes. He begins by deciding the issue of priority between the three basic classes of change.[49] Locomotion must be prior to qualitative change and to growth and decrease. If (as some arguments here assume) coming to be and passing away are to be included in this inquiry, they too must yield the first place to locomotion. Indeed, from every point of view, but more precisely by three different conceptions of priority, locomotion carries the day.[50] Next comes the question which kind of locomotion holds the primacy. It is here that Aristotle resorts to the criterion of continuity.[51] The movement that can go on forever without any intervening phase of rest must be the first of all movements—not only of all local movements. Actually the circular is the only one that meets this qualification. We need not be astonished that Aristotle takes great pains to settle this point; for the result is worth his energy. He finds at once the answer to both questions which he formulated at the beginning of this inquiry. Motion in a circle is the only continuous and eternal movement, and it is the first of all movements. Evidently these two topics overlap, and it is not possible for Aristotle to settle the question of the first movement without bringing continuity into play. If there is one further concept that has a bearing on priority among locomotions it is "perfection," yet even of the perfect quality of the circle and circular

---

[48] *Ibid.*, 898aff.; note also Plato's "self-correction" in 894d which corresponds to the introduction of a new point of view late in the classification. Probably the conversational tone of the *Laws* and the avoidance of "scientific" pedantry go far to account for the use of overlapping criteria.

[49] 260a26. The inquiry is concluded at 261a27.

[50] 260b16ff. (the word "first" is used in different senses: as that without which the others could not be, in the sense of temporal primacy, b29ff., and finally in a qualitative sense in which what is last in the order of becoming is first in that of being, 261a13ff.).

[51] Ch. 8. The inquiry as to which local movement is the first begins earlier (7.261a28).

movement Aristotle cannot speak for long without again referring to
the continuity of this movement.[52]

"Continuity" (συνεχές) is a less exalted word than "eternity," yet it
describes the same fact. We may call it a physicist's approach to
eternity, and it is surely characteristic that as soon as Aristotle begins
his search for a continuous movement he finds himself thrown back
into the maze of problems regarding continuity with which he had
struggled in Book VI, and he cannot resist the impulse to examine
some of them once more.[53] Still the upshot of all these painstaking disquisitions is a reaffirmation of the illustrious place which circular
movement had in Plato's later thought. As in Plato, it is the first in
all respects—in an ontological-axiological sense, in the sense of temporal priority, and also as the prior condition for the other changes;
it is the only eternal movement, and it alone is worthy to be caused
by the divine inspirer of all movement. A relatively minor point in
Aristotle's argument for its primacy, though again one common to
him and Plato, is that it is uniform. Already in the preliminary discussion of "one movement" in Book V uniformity had emerged as essential for this concept. Now in Book VIII, where the principal
characteristic of continuity is found in the absence of any halt or interruption, uniformity makes a momentary but significant appearance
when Aristotle argues that only circular movement, but never linear
movement, may be uniform. Plato's eternal circular movements are
uniform too. For him, however, uniformity is a part or aspect of the
eternal sameness and somehow merged in this broader and more
comprehensive idea.[54] Still another peculiarity of circular movement
which Aristotle here points out is that it exhibits a unique combination of rest and motion. Since the center of the sphere keeps its place,
the entire figure remains stationary even while performing the rotation. Aristotle is clearly delighted by this coincidence of opposites,
although it does not have for him the same significance as for Plato.

[52] At 264b9 Aristotle has proved that no other motion can be continuous
(συνεχές). For the *teleion* motif see 264b27ff., also 265a13ff. where the topic of
primacy is resumed.

[53] In making clear that movement along a limited straight line and back must
stop when turning at the end of the line (and thus cannot be continuous like
movement on a circle), Aristotle in ch. 8 shows once more why the line, although
infinitely divisible, can be traversed in finite time and answers once more one of
Zeno's paradoxes (263a4ff.).

[54] V,4.228b15ff.; VIII,8.265b11ff.; cf. again Plato's κατὰ ταὐτὰ. καὶ ὡσαύτως . .
καθ' ἕνα λόγον καὶ τάξιν (*Legg.* X,898a8ff.).

Where Plato describes circular motion as "holding in its center the power of things standing," his words remind us of the two basic classes of things, rest and movement.[55] For him circular motion acquires its special worth by partaking of both great realms into which the sum of things has been divided.

Throughout the long and triumphant argument of Book VIII Aristotle breaks up the complex Platonic concepts into their component parts and disentangles the closely interwoven strands of Plato's thought. In Plato the eternity of movement was tied to the conception of the world soul, its originator and preserver. Aristotle first establishes that there is eternal movement and later identifies it with a particular kind of physical movement (the circular), being most scrupulous about the proofs that this movement can in fact be eternal. The first movement was for Plato that of the self-mover.[56] For Aristotle too the circular movement is the cosmic manifestation of the deity; yet before it can be raised to this supreme dignity, its intrinsic perfection and its primacy among the movements must be shown quite independently and on good physical grounds. His admiration for this movement is as complete as Plato's, yet he seldom allows his enthusiasm to break through the progress of his sober and restrained reasoning. Words like "undying" (*athanatos*) and "unending" (*apaustos*) occur rarely,[57] and the term which he generally uses as antonym of movement (*eremia*) has not as solemn a ring as the corresponding word (*stasis*) in Plato's scheme. Not even the perfect movement is hailed in language comparable to Plato's celebration of the sphere as moving "the same way and in the same fashion, in the same, around the same, and with reference to the same, according to one law and plan." [58] We should

---

[55] 265b1ff.; cf. *Legg.* X,893c4ff. In VI,9.240a29–b7 Aristotle takes a much less sympathetic view of this alleged coincidence. Cherniss' learned comments (*Presocr.*, 161 n.79) are helpful in giving us historical perspective. I doubt, however, whether it is necessary to go outside the "school" to identify Aristotle's "opponents."

[56] 897dff.; note that the circular movement is here identified not primarily as that of soul but of mind, i.e., of the mind associated with the "good world soul." In Aristotle it is the movement caused by mind (though not performed by mind; see 260a23ff.).

[57] For movement as *athanatos* and *apaustos* see 250b13 and 259b25; cf. *Phaedr.* 245c5 and *Tim.* 36e4, where the words are used of *psyche.*

[58] *Legg.* X,898a8ff. Following W. Schadewaldt's suggestion (*Satura Otto Weinreich dargebracht* [Baden-Baden, 1952], 112), we may bear in mind that Plato here declares circular motion to be the best image for the movement of mind. The *Physics* does not bring out any connection with mind, but *Metaphysics* Λ,

not, however, forget that the *Physics* is after all a scholarly treatise; in his dialogue *On Philosophy*, where the same questions were treated, Aristotle was under no necessity of imposing a check upon his stylistic powers.[59]

Several times we have mentioned the central conception of Plato's cosmic theology, of which very few traces are left in Aristotle's discussion and none at all in his own theory. Evidently the doctrine of the world soul could not survive the differentiation between the first mover and the first moved. The first moved must, like any object in motion, be a continuum, i.e., an extended physical body (the propositions regarding continuity which Aristotle has so carefully established in Book VI brook no exception).[60] The first mover, on the other hand, not only may but in fact, as the final chapter of the treatise proves, must be without parts, since neither a body of infinite nor one of finite extension could cause a never-ending movement.[61] This means that the first mover must be nonmaterial. With this statement the *Physics* ends. Everything regarding the ontological place, the peculiar mode of being, and the activity of this nonmaterial entity must be left to the "First Philosophy."

As the physicist sees it, in the Cosmos body works upon body and there is no place within the cosmic organism for the presence or activity of a nonphysical entity. Nor is there need for it; for not even the circular motion—and thus *a potiori* no other motion—is the

---

which rests on the conclusions of our book, describes God as mind and speaks of him as νοητόν and of the movement which he causes as that inspired by the νοητόν. νοῦς δὲ ὑπὸ τοῦ νοητοῦ κινεῖται (*ibid.*, 7.1072a32). And if the Platonic *nous* motif is still active and associated with the first heaven, we may be able better to understand the *orexis* which obtains between the first heaven and its mover, and may even read *De caelo* II,12.292a14, which speaks of the εὖ ἔχειν and ἄριστον of the heavenly spheres, with fuller appreciation. For the rest, I believe that what Aristotle in *De anima* III,10 says about *nous* and *orexis* goes far to solve the difficulties which Schadewaldt (*ibid.*, 112–115) has found in the chapter of the *Metaphysics* and correspondingly to reduce the probability of his hypothesis that Aristotle here writes under the influence of Eudoxus.

[59] Passages such as *De caelo* II,283b26ff. (which Jaeger, *Aristotle*, 301ff., traces back to *De philosophia*) may serve as samples.

[60] See esp. VIII,5.257a33ff., which refers back to VI,4. The same conclusions reached in VI are also presupposed and accepted in VIII,6.258b18–20, 24–26 (cf. VI,10). The sentences give the impression of having originally been continuous. As they stand, a statement referring to the mover of the planetary spheres has been inserted between them. On additions of this kind see Jaeger, *Aristotle*, 358ff. The original arguments of Book VIII were not meant to cover the planetary movers.

[61] VIII,10.

motion of soul. What kind of body performs it Aristotle does not tell us in this treatise in which the fifth element is either unknown or persistently bypassed; all we need to know is that circular motion is eternal and first and that this is the kind of movement that the first mover actualizes in the world.[62]

Plato's Cosmos owes to the world soul much more than its first movement. Soul gives it its divine and lasting status, endows it with life, and is the ultimate cause of all change; at the same time it is more directly responsible for the harmony, perfection, and beauty of its celestial regions.[63] Only through the presence of something non-physical, of something belonging to the order of the eternal, could the Cosmos acquire divine quality and be removed from the domination of mechanical forces whose operation bears no relation to the good. The introduction of something nonphysical into the physical world creates scientific and logical difficulties. For Plato they were irrelevant because his Cosmos was not meant to be a purely or primarily physical organism. But sooner or later the difficulties were bound to make themselves felt. When Aristotle insists on carrying the physical point of view to its last conclusions, he is obeying the promptings of his scientific conscience and trying to guard the realm of physics against the intrusion of foreign concepts. But he also is confident that the essential qualities of Plato's Cosmos—order and law, eternity and even divinity—may be deduced from physical hypotheses and safeguarded by purely physical arguments.[64]

In a passage of the *Laws* Plato faces the difficulties connected with

[62] It seems obvious to identify the "first moved" in regard to its material nature with the *aether* or fifth element. Nothing prevents us from regarding the doctrine of the prime mover in *Phys.* VIII as later than the *aether* theory of *De caelo* I. And it is indeed tempting to think (as Guthrie argues, *Cl. Q.*, 27 [1933], 162ff., and Ross too holds, *Physics*, "Introduction," 98ff.) that the doctrine of the first mover "completes" the theory of *De caelo*. Still we have found reasons for regarding the "natural movements" of the elements (and this would include that of the *aether*) as an extension of Aristotle's view that nature and natural objects have the source of movement in themselves. In view of what has been set forth above, p. 232, I should hesitate to say that the theory of one first mover "completes" this approach to nature (though Ross, *Physics*, 85, takes this view). There is certainly nothing in *De caelo* I that demands such completion (cf. Guthrie, *op.cit.*, 169ff.). See also Cherniss' (*Pl. and the Acad.*, 583f.) reference to *Metaph.* Θ.1050b4–6 in close proximity to b20–30, which embodies the alternative approach.

[63] *Tim.* 34b10ff.; *Legg.* X,898a–899b.

[64] In this respect, the theory of the first body, as developed in *De caelo* I, is quite comparable to the achievements of *Phys.* VIII, a fact all the more noteworthy as the two treatises differ in their first assumptions as well as in their final conclusions.

the introduction of *psyche* into the world of bodies: "The sun's body is seen by every human being but his soul by none. . . . There is much reason to think that it [the soul] enfolds us in a way utterly imperceptible to all bodily senses but that it may be grasped by Mind." [65] The difficulties exist only because we are in the habit of making the senses supreme arbiters. On matters of mind Plato will be guided by mind alone: "By pure mind and thinking let us get hold of something like this" (Aristotle would probably protest that his investigation of movements was as "mental" as Plato's, for his references to the evidence of the senses are few and far between).[66] Now "mind" suggests three possibilities as to the way in which soul may act upon bodies. It may operate within the body and direct it from the inside. It may operate on the body from without through the intermediate agency of a body particularly qualified for this function—a "kind of air or fire." Or it may, again from without and being itself "free of body," act through specific and peculiar powers "surpassingly wonderful." The last of these three hypotheses would obviously remove soul from a "place" within the world and leave to it a form of influence not unlike that possessed by Aristotle's God, whose nature is mind. Actually Plato's soul has at this stage of the argument already "taken" mind "to itself" as its guide and inseparable partner,[67] and even Aristotle's divine mind cannot cause the first movement of the Cosmos without employing a power "surpassingly wonderful." Aristotle's final pronouncement on its mode of operation is that it acts "like an object of love." [68] Thus he too goes outside of physics to explain the acting of his nonmaterial God upon the first material entity.

Something may be said about the reasons why Aristotle would think of the first mover, who acts upon the world from without, as a mind rather than as a soul. True, we do not know for certain what doctrine of soul he held at the time when his theory of the first mover took shape; yet, whether it incorporates nutritive and sensory functions or is conceived as the *entelecheia* of the body, it is not the right

[65] 898dff. (borrowings have been made from A. E. Taylor's translation).

[66] Such references to *aisthesis* are found—and are more in place—in the polemic early in the book against thinkers (scil., the Eleatics) who maintain that everything is at rest (see esp. 253a32ff.). See also 254a6ff., a30ff.

[67] *Legg.* X,896eff.

[68] *Metaph.* Λ7.1072b3. Cf. Jaeger, *Aristotle*, 142, who compares this statement with the third of the three possibilities indicated by Plato.

concept to describe the nature of the first mover. On the other hand, it made excellent sense to identify the first mover with the highest function of the soul. That God was mind had been proclaimed by a distinguished line of thinkers beginning with Xenophanes and including Anaxagoras, to whom Aristotle gives special praise for having kept mind "unmoved." [69] Plato's Demiurge, whether mythical or not, is mind and acts as mind would act. Moreover, there appears to have been a tendency in the Academy toward regarding only the highest soul functions as compatible with the nature of the deity. We have reasons for believing that the conception of a scale of beings originated in this school. [70] This conception implies that at each stage of the way from plants via animals to man a higher soul function is added to the already existing lower ones: plants have only desires, animals have also spirited impulse, and man besides these two functions has mind. And it seems to have been a part of the same scheme that, as we proceed from man to demons and finally to God, the lower soul functions disappear. [71] God should be free of desires, and spirited impulse is as unbecoming to God in Plato's scheme as are the nutritive and sensory functions in Aristotle's. Still it would be superficial to think that such lines of thought sufficiently account for Aristotle's negative reaction to the concept of a world soul. After all, since the Cosmos functions in its normal and orderly way and from the elements to man everything in it lives up to its *physis*, why should it be absurd to speak of its *entelecheia?* We have seen that Aristotle's own concept of nature owes not a little to Plato's world soul. [72] Whenever he endows "nature" with characteristics that in truth befit a living entity and would be more convincing if nature were frankly described in such terms, he is drawing on the legacy of this Platonic conception. But it is one thing to transfer characteristics of the world soul to a new concept of nature, and another to treat the world soul itself as a valid idea.

If we look for the motives from which Aristotle discarded this idea,

[69] 256b24 (cf. Anaxag. B12; Xenoph. B25; Heracl. B41, etc.; Emped. B134).

[70] Cf. my paper "Antecedents of Aristotle's Psychology and Scale of Beings" (*A. J. Ph.*, 86 [1955], 148ff.).

[71] Cf. in this connection also D. A. Rees, *J. H. St.*, 77 (1957), 116, who discusses the differences between the wholly rational star souls (of the *Epinomis*) and the souls possessed by men and animals.

[72] See above, pp. 96–100. It should not be overlooked that in the first sentence of our book Aristotle speaks of the eternal movement in the physical world as οἷον ζωή for all natural entities. Cf. Plato *Legg.* X,895c.

we should not attach much weight to the highly technical arguments by which he effects the separation of the first mover from the first moved.[73] No direct references to the world soul are found in these sections. A reader of the *Physics* may easily receive the impression that it was for Aristotle no longer a live issue. Still we should think twice before we yield to this impression. Although Aristotle when composing Book VIII may no longer have been a member of the Academy, it is unlikely that his connections with it belonged to the remote past.[74] For, as we have seen, the book re-establishes without the help of the world soul a number of propositions that Plato had promulgated with its help and kept closely associated with it. Probably Aristotle felt that the conclusive logic of the book spoke for itself. There was no need for an explicit rejection of Plato's world soul when the book as a whole proved that it was a misconception and could serve no purpose. If doubts remained, the few passages of the book where reference is made to living beings ("beings with souls") would show how unsuited the concept of soul was for the cosmic role that Plato had assigned to it. What had recommended soul for that role was its never-ceasing activity, thanks to which it could be regarded

[73] Ch. 5, 257a33ff. As for the evidence of other treatises, *De caelo* II (284a27ff.) includes a scathing rejection of the notion that a world soul should be responsible for the eternal duration of the world. To my mind the rejection is unqualified and unambiguous, and it should not be argued that Aristotle merely protests against a soul working by *ananke*. Rather, what he appears to say is that soul, if credited with such a function, would have to operate by *ananke*. Elsewhere the same book (2.285a29) asserts ὁ οὐρανὸς ἔμψυχος, a significant statement, no doubt, and yet, in view of its uniqueness, its significance should not be overworked. It should not be interpreted as saying that the Cosmos has a soul but merely that it is "alive" (so Guthrie) or "animate," which is anything but trivial. To be sure, Aristotle does not otherwise know of entities that are alive but have no soul, yet we may safely leave the responsibility for this contradiction to himself. René Mugnier in his book, *La théorie du premier moteur* (Paris, 1930), has to rely on speculative inferences for his thesis that throughout a "période immanentiste" Aristotle considered the first mover as the soul of the first heaven. The texts nowhere lend support to this view.

[74] On the "relative chronology" of Book VIII see above, Note 1. Even Book VII, which is regarded as earlier, contains nothing that could be understood as reference to Plato's doctrine of the world soul. Guthrie (*op.cit.*, 169) suggests that "when he [Aristotle] had given up the Ideas, he started to work on the notion that the heaven had a soul because it moved itself." Aristotle certainly accepted (in *De philos.*) Plato's views of the stars as having souls; yet with regard to the heaven as a whole I can find no evidence (and would hesitate to take it for granted) that Aristotle took this Platonic doctrine as starting point. Cf. Jaeger, *Aristotle*, 348.

as eternally in motion. In sharp contrast to this notion Aristotle treats souls and "beings with souls" as entities sometimes in motion and at other times at rest. Living beings that alternate between states of sleep and activity cannot, he argues, provide a good illustration (still less, of course, a proof) for eternal motion; on the contrary, they might be used as argument that motion may cease for a while and then again suddenly and spontaneously arise, a conclusion which if correct would be fatal for the basic doctrine of this book, i.e., the eternity of movement.[75] But it is far from correct, and in discrediting this inference Aristotle also points to serious errors inherent in the definition of living beings (and by implication of souls) as self-movers. Only in a very limited sense does a living being move itself. For of the four kinds of movement it actually originates only one, locomotion. And if a living being is now asleep and after a while once more bestirs itself to motion, it is wrong to attribute this change to the operation of a spontaneous self-mover (soul) within it. The change may be due to influences of the environment or, alternatively, to the food which we have consumed and which as long as it is digested induces sleep, yet when it is distributed to the body causes us to wake up.[76] From these arguments it must be evident that soul should not be considered for the role of a principle and originator of all movement.[77]

From Plato and the Academy Aristotle inherited the idea of a classification of movements and with it the conviction that locomotion occupies the first place among the classes. We have studied his use of

---

[75] 252b17ff., 254a7ff.; cf. 254a35.

[76] Ch. 2, 253a7–20. For the similar argument in 6.259b1–20 and the implied polemic against Plato see Jaeger, *Aristotle*, 360. I am unable to convince myself that VII,1.241b37–242a37 is directed in particular against Plato's conception of the soul as self-mover; the opinion referred to in b40 is hardly applicable to soul at all. Polemics in other treatises (such as *De an.* I,3) do not concern us here; see on these especially Cherniss, *Pl. and the Acad.*, 391ff.; see 589f. on some interesting passages of the *Topics*.

[77] One of the arguments here adduced (against Plato), to wit, that by itself a living being originates only local movement (259b6; cf. 265b34 and Simplicius 1258.12f.), may suggest the comment that after all Aristotle too regards this as the first movement and source of all others. In fact, as the theory of movements has now been worked out, Aristotle finds himself in a position from which more or less at will he can either operate with all four movements as equal or play out the primacy of locomotion. It may be said that Plato, when formulating his famous definition of soul, was primarily thinking of local motion (cf. Arist. 265b32ff.); but it seems unfair to confront him with this question at all. The differentiation of movement was at the time in its incipient stage, and no need was felt for applying it rigorously to every statement concerning motion.

this twofold legacy and have found him deriving new returns from it. He himself maintains that on the primacy of locomotion Plato is in agreement with him (the passage where he states this[78] is the only one in the entire work where Plato's doctrine of soul is explicitly referred to). Yet his claim extends farther: the Presocratics generally hold this view and could not help holding it.[79] When a good part of this claim has been discounted, there remains a residue which seems correct. Even the later Presocratics (whom he primarily has in mind) did not differentiate as strictly as he would like them to; they did not have a concept of qualitative alteration, and they did not discourse on coming to be and passing away but on association and dissociation. For the latter point Aristotle, as a matter of fact, makes the necessary allowance. For he argues that if mind in Anaxagoras' system works by dissociation, these processes should be regarded as local movements. In the atomist system the primacy of motion is even more evident, since the atoms move through empty space before they coalesce and all other changes are subsequent to the coalescence. We need not hesitate to accept this interpretation of the atomist system as substantially correct.[80] As for Anaxagoras, he himself says that the rotary movement caused by mind produced the separation (and formation) of things;[81] thus in his case, too, Aristotle's statement is borne out. Empedocles presents less definite evidence; still, he too speaks of a commotion (a "shaking") set up by Strife—presumably as bringing about the separation of the previously fused elements—and makes things "come together" when Love begins to assert herself against Strife.[82] Nevertheless it is highly improbable that he actually wished to bring out a primacy of locomotion. This motif may have emerged

[78] Ch. 9, 265b32ff.   [79] *Ibid.*, 17–32.

[80] See, e.g., Democr. B37, 43. We know rather little of the steps by which the atomists went from the movement of the atoms by way of their σύγκρισις to the *genesis* of natural objects. At Lucr. 2.164 this topic seems to have disappeared in a lacuna, and in the *Letter to Herodotus* Epicurus deals with it so briefly that here too a loss may have occurred in the textual transmission (Usener and Bailey assume a lacuna in 43; Von der Mühll, in the Teubner edition [1923], does not).

[81] B12; see also 13–16.

[82] B17.3ff., 31, 35 (the correct place for B35 seems not yet to have been found; I agree with W. Kranz that Diels misplaced it, yet his own attempt, *Empedokles* [Zurich, 1949], 144, to assign it to Book II of the poem *On Nature* is highly problematic because Simplicius *In Phys.* 32.11 clearly states that its place was before B98, which, since it cannot be separated from B96, must like this belong to the first book).

with increasing clarity in the successive systems (there would be little point in following Aristotle into his interpretation of Anaximenes, which makes the twofold assumption that condensation and rarefaction are association and dissociation and these in turn local movements). [83]

All in all not much is gained by translating the agreement on which Aristotle here insists into a historical continuity or a historical development. For the context in which the late Presocratics gave movement its primacy is the formation of the Cosmos or the conditions preceding it. In Aristotle even the "temporal" priority of locomotion has become completely divorced from speculations about the origin of the Cosmos.[84] The one antecedent that really matters for his own doctrine is clearly the movement of the Platonic world soul. This movement has no significant connections with Presocratic thought. To be sure, it is not without interest to find Plato suggesting to the Presocratics that if precosmic conditions were as they picture them nothing but the world soul could introduce motion into this lifeless and amorphous agglomeration. But Plato's point is that only a self-moving principle would work a change in things that are "all together" and at rest.[85] No more than Aristotle does he think of securing a cosmogonic function for his prime mover. So far, then, the similarities are remote and the historical continuity with the Presocratics tenuous to the point of nonexistence.

What remains, as a link between Aristotle's theory and the Presocratics, is the concept of movement as such—provided we admit that they are seriously concerned with its existence and that Plato is right in considering it the common denominator of their systems.[86] Beyond this, we may find continuity with the later Presocratics (Empedocles and Anaxagoras) in the motif that movement must have an originator.

[83] 265b30–32. Ross is surely right in identifying the unnamed author of these doctrines as Anaximenes. Something might be said for incorporating the passage in *Vorsokr.*, A13. On the other hand, there are reasons for being skeptical about Simplicius' (1319.17ff.) attempt to refer the words also to Thales, Anaximander, and Heraclitus. Theophrastus found "eternal motion" in Anaximander (12A9). The historical correctness of his interpretation is called into question by John B. McDiarmid, *H.S.C.P.*, 61 (1953), 142 n.62.

[84] See esp. 260b29–261a12.   [85] *Legg.* X,895a (cf. *Phaedr.* 245d7ff.).

[86] *Theaet.* 152d. Movement, which by the early Presocratics was perhaps simply taken for granted, is a serious, though by no means insoluble, problem after Parmenides' denial of its reality.

The substance of Book VIII is Platonic. To Plato it owes the intention, which it shares with the earlier efforts of Book VII,[87] of tracing all movements in the world to one source; and from Plato has been taken over the pattern of a chainlike transmission of movement—and has been inherited the belief in the supreme worth of circular movement. The Platonic distinction between the active and the passive factor in movement has been applied relentlessly, with the result that in the end even the Platonic concept of an eternal self-mover had to be broken up into two components. Plato's idea of a first mover had already in Book VII been reaffirmed on grounds of logical necessity. Book VIII is less preoccupied with this idea; it aims, instead, at doing something corresponding for the self-mover—another aspect of the same Platonic conception—and in the course of a persistent scrutiny of his nature there emerges the unmoved mover, Aristotle's own divinity. What separates Aristotle's approach from Plato's is not merely that he discards the self-moving soul. First and foremost it is his determination to make the study of the prime mover an integral phase of a physical system. The nature and the properties of movement must be completely understood, every concept pertaining to it must be entirely clarified before its origin can be investigated. When the goal is finally within sight, the preliminary analyses must be supplemented by new differentiations, and new arguments must be found to take care of problems which had not presented themselves before; but the results of the earlier analyses are now applied and prove useful—although perhaps not quite so useful as Aristotle may have hoped.[88] Along with his definition of movement as the realization of a potentiality, the distinction between mover and moved remains an effective conceptual tool. So does the proposition that whatever is moved must be a continuous entity, i.e., a body (whereas the mover need not be of this description). As long as it is at all possible, Aristotle

[87] It would be conceivable that the posthumous publication of Plato's *Laws* gave Aristotle the impulse for a renewed concentration on the problems connected with the first mover. In other words, *Phys.* VII may have been written before, VIII after, he read *Laws* X. But hypotheses of this kind become problematic and unnecessary when allowance is made for lively discussions of these matters within the Academy—discussions in which Plato himself may well have taken part (cf. Jaeger, *Aristotle,* 14ff.; W. D. Ross, *Plato's Theory of Ideas* [Oxford, 1951], 142ff.; per contra, Harold Cherniss, *The Riddle of the Early Academy* [Berkeley and Los Angeles, 1945], 6off.).

[88] Cf. in this connection our observations (pp. 192ff.) about the difficulties caused by the notion of mutual contact between mover and moved.

continues to think in physical terms; even of the self-mover he speaks as though it were a body and had extension and parts.[89]

A study of the kind had never yet been undertaken; in spirit and orientation it is neither Presocratic nor Platonic but only and decidedly Aristotelian. Aristotle breaks a large amount of new ground by developing the implications of Zeno's paradoxes, yet when he moves on to the consummation of his efforts, it is not this new ground that provides him with his *locus standi*.[90] The nature and the properties of the first mover must be discovered through relentlessly precise analytical operations, and Plato is the only thinker who has furnished him with material for the exercise of this logic.

[89] See esp. 5, 257a33–b6; b26–258a5. Cf. Note 90.

[90] Ch. 5, 257a33ff. The *primum mobile* must, like everything moved, be infinitely divisible, whereas the first mover is in ch. 10 proved to be indivisible and partless. Thus it is nonphysical, like Plato's world soul. One feels that Aristotle's proposition "Everything that is in motion must be infinitely divisible," i.e., an extended body, was bound to be fatal to the world soul; yet, as has been said, he nowhere in the *Physics* tells us precisely on what grounds he rejects this conception. It is quite possible that other reasons were even more decisive (e.g., 257b5ff. to the effect that the mover must already be in a state of actuality, whereas the moved is brought from potentiality to actuality).

Part Three

THE COSMOLOGY OF THE BOOKS
ON THE HEAVEN

11

Natural Movements as First
Assumptions

IN spite of the prominent place which Plato had conceded to movement his theory of the physical elements as set forth in the *Timaeus* pays little heed to this concept. On the whole it is an essay in becoming and in "forms." Now becoming (*genesis*) is a Protean concept, yet to some of its phases the elements are so closely linked that Aristotle too is bound to take this connection into account. In the treatise *On the Heaven* he accepts this situation and in fact makes an attempt to define with some precision the relation of the elements to *genesis*. But his major achievements lie elsewhere, and the new insights on which his cosmology ultimately rests spring from his concentration on the question which the *Timaeus* neglects. Nature being defined as a principle of movement, the elements as the first and basic entities in the realm of nature should conform to this definition. To study them in their relation to movement is the prime object of *De caelo*. Bringing together two fundamental concepts of Plato's physics, movement and the simple bodies, the treatise establishes and develops a connection which, Aristotle may have felt, had not received its proper share of attention in Plato's system. That movement is a central phenomenon of the physical world and must be a central concept of a physical system needed no longer to be argued. Aristotle himself recognized this by making it the subject of a thorough and systematic investigation, and when he—let us suppose side by side with the treatise "On Movement"—worked out another set of physical inquiries, the para-

mount importance of movement asserted itself also in these.[1] His
definition of nature in Book II of the *Physics* expresses his conviction
that movement is an immanent tendency of nature and of natural
objects. No external force, no supranatural agent, like the world
soul, is needed to account for its presence throughout the realm of
physis. He had stronger reasons than Plato for studying the elements
from this point of view, and unlike Plato he was committed to no
doctrine that could militate against its application. In the end this new
approach to the elements proved eminently fruitful.

Thus the elements out of which Aristotle builds up his Cosmos
differ from one another not primarily in material substance, still less
in form and shape, but in their natural movements and their tendency
to occupy different places. If Aristotle knew of material differences,
he treated them here as irrelevant to his main purpose; with regard to
shape, we shall presently see that he refutes at some length earlier attempts, and most of all Plato's, to use it as a principle of differentiation.
To be fire is to have a certain movement, namely, toward the circumference of this world; to be earth is to settle in the center. Actually
the fact that there are these "simple"movements is Aristotle's proof
that there are simple bodies, i.e., elements, and if the simple movements
are limited in number, so must be the elements.[2] If "we call light what
moves upward and to the circumference" and "heavy what moves
downward and to the center," it follows that as soon as we have
identified bodies that behave in these ways we have found the two
basic elements. The bodies which meet this requirement are fire and
earth.[3] Whatever else Aristotle may have known about the elements,
this is the deduction of their existence on which he relies in the work
On the Heaven. The relation of his new element to the other four will
engage out attention later; for the moment it suffices that Aristotle
derives its existence too by an argument of this type: as in addition to
the movements in a straight line up and down there is also movement
in a circle, we must assume that there is an element whose nature it is
to move in a circle.[4]

---

[1] See below, Note 20.

[2] *De caelo* III,3.302b5–9; 4.303b4–8. See also I,3.270b26–31.

[3] IV,1.308b29–33; 4.311b13–312a8. On Aristotle's deduction of the two other
elements of the sublunary world, air and water, see below, pp. 283ff.

[4] I,2.268b14–269a9. This is followed by an argument that the circular motion
of this element must be "natural" to it, not contrary to its nature (269a9–18).
See also 269b2–6.

As the four Empedoclean elements had been accepted by Plato, who uses them in his cosmological and physiological account, Aristotle's debt to him is obvious. Here was one fundamental doctrine to which he assented, though he did find it necessary to provide a new deduction of these elements, to work out new definitions, and to complete the doctrine by introducing a fifth primary body. The fifth body is that which has the circular motion—unless it is again better to say that the circular motion, being one of the simple forms of motion, demands an element that corresponds to it.

It is indeed astonishing how persistently Aristotle comes back to the proposition that elements or, as he likes to call them, simple bodies must have their simple and specific movements. This seems to be the one basic and indubitable truth, the firm foothold from which he can move on to further positions. The second chapter of Book III establishes this pivotal fact and, having hammered it home, proceeds to prove the complementary thesis that everything must have either weight or lightness.[5] Immediately afterward Aristotle takes up the question whether there are *genesis* and bodies (i.e., elements) that are involved in it; here he briefly notices the opposition between Empedocles' and Anaxagoras' views regarding the elements, yet before plunging into the details of this controversy he reaffirms the proposition on which he himself takes his stand: physical bodies have their specific movement, and the existence of simple movements proves the existence of simple bodies.[6] The chapter which follows shifts the issue from the nature of the basic bodies to their number—they may be one, several, or innumerable; and it broadens the scope of the polemic by examining in addition to Empedocles and Anaxagoras the doctrines of the atomists. Again after criticizing their doctrines on account of their inherent difficulties, his last word is that since elements have their specific and simple movements and simple movements are not infinite in number (but fundamentally two) it is also from this point of view impossible to admit an unlimited number of simple bodies.[7] This statement still leaves open the question whether there are several elements or only one and thus leads to a discussion with those who favor a single element. Here too Aristotle, after rejecting their theories

[5] See esp. 301a20ff. Here and in our subsequent discussion it is difficult, yet necessary, to disentangle Aristotle's own conclusions from the extensive polemic against his precursors.

[6] III,2.301b31ff.; 3.302b5ff.

[7] Ch. 4; see especially the concluding words, 303b4–8.

on other grounds, winds up by pointing out that they fail to do justice
to the natural movements. The "mistake common to all of them" is
that by assuming one element they (in effect) limit the natural movements to one, a supposition which is at variance with the facts. The
plurality of natural movements makes it imperative to assume more
than one element. This is the point at which Aristotle here leaves the
matter.[8] He does not now press on toward a final decision regarding
the number of the elements—it would in any case be difficult to infer
from the existence of two movements that there must be four elements.
Aristotle will reach this conclusion later with the help of his definition
of heavy and light.[9] Now he prefers to study the relation of the
elements to *genesis;* he decides that they must participate in it and that
the only way in which this is possible is for them to arise out of one
another. Finally he shows that the efforts so far made to explain this
process have fallen short of success.[10] Only in these last sections of
the book, where Aristotle's entire concern is with the *genesis* of the
elements and where neither their nature nor their existence is any
longer at issue, do we find no reference to their natural movements.

The first book of our treatise is more interested in the new element
than in the four of the Empedoclean tradition. It also differs from
Books III and IV in that it takes up and solves a number of central
issues, such as the following: Is there an infinite Universe (or only
one bounded Cosmos)? Has the Cosmos come into being or is it
eternal? Is there one Cosmos or are there several, perhaps even innumerable ones? Yet in spite of different objectives and a somewhat
broader basis of operation this book confirms our impression that the
concept of natural movements is the *pièce de résistance* of Aristotle's
cosmological system. That he uses it in his derivation of the new
element, the first body, we have already seen. It may now be added
that he also falls back on it when he wishes to discredit the idea of an
"infinite body." On this occasion he uses rather emphatic language. If
there is an infinite body it would have to consist either of a finite or
of an infinite number of elements. But the notion of infinite elements
cannot be seriously entertained "if someone will allow our first assumptions to stand." [11] These first assumptions state that the simple
movements are limited in number; given the correlation between

---

[8] Ch. 5, 304b11–22.
[9] On the final derivation of the four elements in Book IV see below, Ch. 13.
[10] III,6–8.
[11] I,7.274a33ff. Aristotle calls these assumptions αἱ πρῶται ὑποθέσεις.

simple motions and simple bodies, it is evident that the elements of the Infinite too would have to be limited in number. One alternative being thus ruled out, the other is now considered more closely and is soon found to conflict with several tenets of Aristotle, including once more the first assumptions; for if the elements are limited in number, each would have to fill an infinite place and to perform an infinite move-ment whereas the first assumptions specify finite movements, to the center of our Cosmos, to its circumference, and around the center.[12]

Similar arguments and similar language are used to disprove the existence of more than one Cosmos. If there were other Cosmoi, they would have to embody the same elements as ours because, again, there are only the few basic movements that have been mentioned and these movements determine the nature of the elements.[13] But the elements fire, earth, etc., would have the goal of their movement in *this* Cosmos—this is again implied in the first assumptions, yet Aristotle adds some special arguments to fortify the proposition. In any case, as he says at the end of this paragraph, either the assumptions must be given up or there can be only one center and one circumference, which implies one Cosmos.[14] To give them up would be tantamount

[12] *Ibid.*, 274b10ff. In subject matter Books III and IV are close to the two books of *De generatione*. But their first assumptions connect them with Book I of *De caelo*, and all attempts to separate them from this and to reconstruct a treatise consisting of *De caelo* III,IV and *De gen.* I,II (e.g., E. Zeller, *Philos. d. Gr.* [3d ed.; Leipzig, 1921], II,2.87, and more recently Léon Robin, *Aristote* [Paris, 1944], 17) make the fatal mistake of ignoring the methodological motif. For an admirably balanced and entirely correct opinion see Paul Moraux, *Les listes anciennes des ouvrages d'Aristote* (Louvain, 1951), 81f. and n.184.

[13] I,8.276a30ff.; note especially b7–10 (for a totally different argument see *Metaph.* Λ8, 1074a31ff.). The motif of natural movements figures also in the criticism of the atomist doctrine in 7.275b29ff. (see esp. 276a1f.) and in the arguments advanced in 276a6ff., a12ff., a18ff. (cf. a30).

[14] 8.276b11ff.; note esp. 18ff., 21ff., 29ff., and the emphatic statement at the end, 277a9ff. I see no need for supposing (with P. Duhem, *Système du monde*, 1 [Paris, 1913], 232ff., 234) that Aristotle considers the behavior of the elements in other hypothetical Cosmoi so carefully because Heraclides Ponticus had declared each planet to be a Cosmos with its own earth and air (frg. 113, Wehrli). Aristotle's *reductio ad absurdum* does not read as if it were directed against such theories (or for that matter against any theories actually propounded). Even in II,8 and II,13f. Heraclides does not appear to be the immediate target of Aristotle's polemic. As for Cherniss' very learned and ingenious interpretation of II,14. 296a34–6, which leads him to regard Heraclides' theory as the object of Aristotle's criticism in this section (*Pl. and the Acad.*, 546ff.), I confess myself impressed by some of his arguments but cannot get over the difficulty that on this view 13.293b32 ὥσπερ ἐν τῷ Τιμαίῳ γέγραπται should form a part of an indirect statement (and, to make matters more complicated, of one which, according to Cherniss,

to rescinding the entire system of this treatise, which is predicated on these assumptions and the closely related one of natural places. The latter enables Aristotle immediately afterward to prove that the sum total of the elements is present in our Cosmos and no material is left for others. For if each element has its natural place in this Cosmos, no part of it could be outside.[15]

However, in the course of his proofs Aristotle resorts also to arguments of a different complexion. He uses, for instance, the concepts of weight and lightness. Yet these concepts are intimately connected with his hypotheses of natural movements,[16] and it is no exaggeration to say that these hypotheses dominate alike in premises, arguments, and conclusions. It may still be mentioned that although in Book II the first assumptions are somewhat less conspicuous they enter with decisive effect into the discussion of one important problem here treated. The position of the earth in the center of the Cosmos should not be explained with the help of any argument devised specifically for this purpose.[17] Aristotle spends some time in examining arguments of the kind, but in the end his patience gives way—this is "no quarrel about particulars but about something whole and universal" (the meaning is: about a principle of universal application). "From the beginning it must be decided whether bodies have a natural movement or not, and

---

Aristotle himself would not endorse, although he neither here nor elsewhere makes this clear). The great majority of interpreters who have read this clause as a direct reference to Plato's own opinion have certainly the good excuse that this is the most natural way of understanding it. The "analogy" between planets and earth in 296a34ff. may seem pointless; but does Aristotle's argument actually rest on it? His point is, rather, that to have *one* movement is the peculiarity or privilege of the first sphere (scil., of the outermost heaven; ἔξω τῆς πρώτης in b1 indicates just this, since ἔξω does not mean "apart from" but "except," so that either φορᾶς or σφαίρας would be a correct noun to πρώτης, even if I agree with Cherniss that both are interpolations). Even though bodies near the center need not have the maximum number of planetary movements (II,12), Aristotle rebels against the notion that such a body should share the significant characteristic of the first sphere. I may add that, contrary to Cherniss, 550, I can find no reference to Heraclides' theory in II,8.289b1-7, where Aristotle begins a disquisition by briefly setting forth the whole variety of possible—rather than actual—hypotheses. I admit, however, that Cherniss has the support of Themistius' paraphrase (549) and that his interpretation makes Aristotle's argument both more subtle and less a priori than mine does.

[15] I,9.278b21-279a11.

[16] For the connection between weight-lightness and natural movements see below, Ch. 13. For an argument in our sections which uses both motifs see 7.276a6-12.

[17] II,13.

if no natural movement whether an enforced movement." [18] If the assumption of natural movement stands—and Aristotle would not for a moment allow it to be questioned—it is clear that no particular explanation or device, no whirl or anything else, is needed to account for the place of the earth. It is in the center for the same reason that every particle of earth moves toward the center and on the same principle on which the fire is at, or moves to, the circumference. Moreover, some other traditional questions relating to the earth, e.g., that of its shape, are also to be settled on the basis of the unshakable "first assumptions." [19]

In founding his cosmology to such an extent on the specific movements of the four elements and on (what fundamentally comes to the same) their weight or lightness, Aristotle has achieved something that by all indications must have been a matter of great concern to him. He has constructed an essential part of his system from purely physical premises. For movement is decidedly a concern of physics and a distinctive characteristic of physical entities, while heavy and light are physical qualities of the elements.[20] In this point of principle his procedure contrasts sharply with that adopted by Plato, and Aristotle himself is conscious of his divergence and feels strongly about its necessity. The hypotheses on which the scientific treatment of a subject is to rest should, as he puts it, be "homogeneous" to the subject; if one deals with an "eternal" subject (as, for instance, mathematics), one needs eternal principles, if with perishable and sense-perceived subjects one should for one's first hypotheses choose principles of such nature.[21] The cardinal mistake which vitiates Plato's construction lies

[18] 294b30ff.   [19] See esp. 295b1ff., b19ff., 14.297a15ff., 21ff.

[20] The second half of Aristotle's *Physics* (Books V–VIII) is a treatise on movement; see also *Phys.* III,1–3 and the statement there made that as long as movement is not known nature is not known (III,1.200b14). On the relevant definition of *physis* in *Phys.* II,1 (esp. 192b13ff., 20ff.), see above, pp. 95–96. In *De gen.* II,2 heavy and light are included in the "contrary qualities" of "sense perceived," i.e., physical bodies (329b18ff.). Their physical character should be self-evident.

[21] See *De caelo* III,7.306a5–11; also 11–17. The term which Aristotle here uses is πρῶται ἀρχαί; this corresponds to the designation of his own principles as πρῶται ὑποθέσεις. It is relevant to recall Plato's own use of the words ἀρχαί and ὑποθέσεις in *Rep.* VI,510b–511d; but it should not be inferred from that passage that for Aristotle ἀρχή represents something more fundamental or that it is impregnable in a sense in which ὑπόθεσις is not. For Aristotle's use of both terms in his "methodological" treatise *Anal. Post.* I see ch. 10 of this work (for ἀρχή also chs. 2, 3, 9, and *passim*; cf. my *Entwicklung d. arist. Logik* (Berlin, 1929), 92ff., and W. D. Ross, *Aristotle's Prior and Posterior Analytics* (Oxford, 1949), 18ff. Incidentally Aris-

in the introduction of mathematical first principles into the realm of physics. Actually Aristotle rejects Plato's attempt not solely on the strength of this vital principle of method; he presents many specific reasons why the triangles and regular solid bodies out of which Plato constructed the elements fail to offer a satisfactory account of *genesis*. Relentlessly and with merciless persistence he points out the difficulties and impossible consequences entailed by Plato's construction.[22] One may wonder whether his awareness of these difficulties led him to formulate the methodical axiom or whether, conversely, the conviction that principles must be germane to the subject inspired his first misgivings about Plato's attempt and sharpened his eyes for its specific weaknesses. In any case, by formulating this methodological tenet Aristotle provides us with his own description—and justification—of what strikes his students as the distinguishing characteristic of his scientific work, to wit, its departmentalization. Although put forward as a regulative principle of all scientific inquiry, it is in fact a self-revelation of Aristotle's *forma mentis*. What he here formulates is a conviction in which he never wavered, a rule from which he never deviated.[23]

---

totle speaks of ὑποθέσεις later in our context (306a30) while still referring to Plato's construction of the elements out of mathematical entities. That Plato's construction (besides introducing into physics principles not germane to it) does violence also to the ὑποθέσεις of mathematics itself is another matter (III,1.299a2–6).

[22] Polemic against Plato is found not only in our chapter (III,7) but also in III,1.8, in some sections of 5, and *passim* in IV. At times (e.g., III,5.304a9ff.) also other members of the Academy who had given the elements geometrical shape come in for criticism; cf. Cherniss' penetrating analysis in *Pl. and the Acad.*, 129ff. In *De generatione*, where Aristotle briefly returns to his criticism of the Platonic theory, reference is made to the fuller polemic of our treatise (see I,2.315b30f. with Joachim's notes). For comparable judgments passed by Aristotle elsewhere on the methods of his predecessors cf. R. P. McKeon, *J. Hist. Ideas*, 7 (1948), 8.

[23] In *Phys.* II,2 Aristotle has important things to say about the difference between the mathematician's subject matter and that of the physicist. We may note his point that the mathematician is justified in considering his objects in abstraction from movement (193b34ff.; cf. also the distinguishing characterization of the respective subjects of mathematics, metaphysics, and physics in passages such as *Metaph.* E1.1026a11–16 and K7.1064a30–b3, for which see Philip Merlan, *From Platonism to Neoplatonism* [The Hague, 1953], 56ff.). This chapter of the *Physics*, however, includes no opinion as to the legitimacy of using mathematical principles and hypotheses in physical inquiry. The suggestion may be ventured that the use of mathematical concepts, propositions, and methods in Aristotle's physics is incidental rather than essential. Still, the question is largely one of definition. Thus one may wonder whether Aristotle would think of himself as operating *more mathematico* when, e.g., he uses the concept of ratio in proofs like *Phys.*

The historian of science may justifiably regard the decision which cuts physics off from mathematics as a "fatal step"; and as two thousand years were to elapse before a new bond could be forged, one may sympathize with this historian if he inclines to burden Aristotle with the full responsibility for blocking promising developments and steering Greek science in a direction which in the end proved sterile. In the history of Greek scientific thought the alliance between mathematics and physical science is in fact confined to an episode—or two episodes, if we wish to distinguish between the Pythagorean school as such and the *Timaeus*, whose mathematical construction of the elements probably falls outside the scope of the Pythagorean tradition. Broadly speaking, astronomy and optics were the only Greek sciences that remained attached to mathematical ways of thinking. Neither of them has a place in Aristotle's philosophical pantheon. Still, it is certainly rash to suppose that if the Platonic tie between mathematics and physics had not been severed ancient physics would have developed in a similar direction, arrived at similar discoveries, and by and large entered upon the same triumphant career as the renewal of this tie in the time of Kepler and Galileo opened up for modern science. In any case, the forces that kept ancient science on a different road must have been strong; however powerful the impulse that Aristotle gave to subsequent research, the personal idiosyncrasies of an individual genius can hardly account for the persistent disinclination to use mathematical methods and concepts in the realm of physical or biological inquiry.

Seeing that the edge of Aristotle's methodological proclamation is turned against Plato and his mathematical derivation of the elements, one may be tempted to look upon this "purification" of physics as heralding a return to the ways of the Presocratics. This view, however, would not be correct even if we were to ignore the Pythagoreans and certain Pythagorean motifs in Empedocles and other early thinkers. For though the Presocratics by and large thought in terms of physical entities and their properties, their primary concern was to find eternal principles for perishable things and temporary conditions.[24] Moreover, their physical principles (and key concepts) were

---

IV,8.215a24–b22 or in his various *deductiones ad absurdum* of the idea of an infinite body (e.g., *De caelo* I,7.274b33ff.).

[24] For their conception of these "principles" as divine, unageing, etc., see especially Jaeger, *Theology*, 28ff., 137ff., 165ff.

chosen with a view to accounting for as many phenomena as possible; far from entailing a departmentalization, they enabled their proponents to unify the world of physical phenomena and to comprehend a great variety of seemingly unrelated matters under identical denominators. To this situation Aristotle cannot find the way back. Not only are there now, as he himself admits, other subjects besides physics which would have to be built up from other "first assumptions"; but even the principles which he uses in our treatise—the natural movements of the elements and their qualities heavy and light—would not serve him in other phases of physics. To understand the changes that pass between the elements, to account for the *genesis* of physical substances, to penetrate the nature of meteorological processes and phenomena, different sets of principles are needed. And if the Empedoclean continuity between physics and biology is by no means given up, Aristotle does make certain assumptions in the latter field which are hard to square with the principles enunciated in his general theory of becoming and passing away.[25] Thus the declaration of independence by which he puts physics on its own feet and rescues it from the embrace of mathematics points the way to the splitting up of physics itself into various autonomous or semiautonomous compartments. Another question is whether Aristotle's physics is so completely cleared of eternal principles as he here would have us believe. There is an eternal source of movement, an eternal and unchanging element;[26] the Cosmos itself is eternal—and, perhaps we should add, the species are. The eternal has certainly a place in Aristotle's physical system, though indeed not the same place as in the Presocratic pattern.

As our study has led us to deal with autonomistic tendencies of Aristotle's science, we may for a moment glance at another manifestation of these tendencies. The first book of the *Posterior Analytics*, which is an essay in the scientific method of demonstration, makes a determined effort to disentangle scientific subjects from one another. In view of the great importance which first principles are bound to

---

[25] In his studies *On the Parts of Animals* and *On the Generation of Animals* Aristotle, in addition to operating with the elements, makes extensive use of the "powers" hot and cold, solid and fluid. Their role in these works does not fully agree with that mapped out for them in the treatise *On Coming to Be and Passing Away*. Cf. below, pp. 347-348.

[26] It may, however, be said that the fifth body is generally neglected in the discussion of Books III and IV; as we shall see, it is possible that Aristotle, when writing our passage in III,7, did not yet know this "imperishable" element.

have for the structure and intrinsic coherence of a subject, it is natural
that these efforts should come to a head when Aristotle defines his
views about the right choice of such principles. True, the book moves
within the orbit of the mathematical subjects and rarely looks beyond
them; when it states that the only correct way of proving something
is to derive it from its own specific first principles,[27] Aristotle's immediate intention is to exclude the possibility that theorems belonging to one branch of mathematics might be demonstrated by first
principles belonging to another. For geometrical demonstrations we
have to find our starting point in geometrical concepts and definitions,
for arithmetical in arithmetical, for astronomical in astronomical. The
only "common factors" that Aristotle is prepared to recognize are
"the so-called axioms," yet even they are truly useful only in the form
in which they apply to a particular field.[28] If the axiom says that
"equals deducted from equals leave equals," what the arithmetician
really needs is "equal numbers deducted from equal numbers, etc.,"
and the same holds good *mutatis mutandis* in the other branches. Even
axioms being thus restricted, everything else must certainly be most
rigidly kept "within the family" (the genus or the subject on hand).
"It is difficult to be sure whether one truly knows or not. For it is
hard to be sure whether the knowledge derives from the principles
of each given fact or not. This [alone] is knowledge. We think we
know when we have a syllogism which starts from true and first
premises; yet this is not real knowledge. The premises must belong to
the same family." [29]

[27] See *Anal. Post.* I,7–9; 28; 32.88a30ff., and *passim.* Cf. on Aristotle's doctrine of
"first principles" J. M. Le Blond, *Logique et méthode chez Aristote* (Paris, 1939),
109ff.; R. P. McKeon, *J. Hist. Ideas*, 8 (1947), 41ff.; and the historically oriented
analysis of K. von Fritz, *Archiv f. Begriffsgeschichte*, 1 (1955), 13ff. A number of
passages in the *Metaphysics* (B4.1000a25ff. *et al.*) which Cherniss in *Pl. and the
Acad.*, 149, compares with *De caelo* III,7.306a5ff. put less emphasis on the methodological aspect of the problem. Ultimately, however, the methodological and the
ontological issues coincide.

[28] *Anal. Post.* I,10.76a41–b2. The very restricted κοινόν which the sentence in
9.76a15 admits for the first principles of different subjects may here be left out of
consideration.

[29] *Ibid.*, 76a26–30 (I have on purpose omitted the last two words from my
translation; the thought becomes more compact if they are regarded as an interpolation which was prompted by a misunderstanding of the word συγγενῆ; as I
understand it, συγγενῆ δεῖ εἶναι refers to the principles, not to the conclusion; however, elimination of the two words does not change the thought materially, but
only renders it clearer). For Aristotle's concept of *archai* as employed in these
sections cf. Ross's comments on 76a34.

Thus Aristotle refuses to dignify by the name of knowledge anything that does not have its basis in "kindred" premises or principles. The situation for which he attempts to legislate is comparable to that in Book III of *De Caelo* where he likewise insists that the principles and first assumptions of physics must be chosen within the subject. At least the impulse and the over-all orientation are the same. To demand that each branch of mathematics should stay within its own precincts and have almost no traffic with the others is simply to carry the idea of autonomous foundations one step farther. Aristotle never formulates a corresponding postulate for the various parts of physics; yet it is easy to see that they actually have different sets of first principles. Principles which are basic for his cosmology have no place in his theory of becoming, and his meteorology is established on first assumptions that are unknown in the two other treatises. Thus his practice in physics accords with his theory as worked out for mathematics.[30]

Nothing suggests that in the *Posterior Analytics* Aristotle had the *Timaeus* particularly in mind. But can there be any doubt what judgment he would pass on the Platonic scheme in which the units of the elements are identified with regular solid bodies, and these traced back to triangles, while for triangles in turn still "higher" principles are envisaged "which God knows and whoever of men is dear to him"?[31] Clearly this would to his mind be an excellent illustration of how not to proceed. The scheme would violate the laws laid down in the *Posterior Analytics* as hopelessly as it is at variance with the methodical tenets enunciated in the books *On the Heaven*. In both treatises we see Aristotle revolt against Plato's vertical integration of the realms of human knowledge; in both he is bent on cutting the "bond" by which Plato had tied them into unity.[32] The treatise *On the Heaven* represents in all probability the first sustained attempt to

[30] *Anal. Post.* I pays no attention to the methodical requirements of physics. For the *archai* of Aristotle's meteorology see below, pp. 400–405; for those employed in his biology, Ch. 17 *passim*, esp. Note 44.

[31] *Tim.* 53c4–56c7; see in particular Plato's comments on the ὑποτίθεσθαι of the right ἀρχαί 53d4ff. (also 6f.).

[32] For the idea of a "bond" (δεσμὸς . . . εἰς) cf. the *Epinomis* ("deren Verfasser doch mindestens gute platonische Tradition vertritt," Stenzel, *Zahl. u. Gestalt*, 91), 991b5ff., esp. e5ff. An exhaustive review of the arguments for and against the genuineness of the *Epinomis*, with ample bibliographical references, will be found in the recent edition of E. des Places (*Platon* XII,2; Budé edition [Paris, 1956], 97ff.). Des Places himself has long been a firm believer in Plato's authorship.

apply the new methodical creed to a specific research project. Here the new freedom which Aristotle has secured for the branches of mathematics bears its first fruits. It allows a new and, Aristotle feels sure, more successful approach to the central issues of cosmology. It is attractive to think that the certificate of independence which Aristotle issued for the mathematical sciences and his own essay in an independent physics belong to the same period of his scholarly life.[33] They are early landmarks in his own struggle for intellectual independence from the authority of an uncongenial system in whose shadow he was still carrying on his work.

[33] It may be well to state that this agreement in outlook is not per se an argument for the early origin of substantial parts of *Anal. Post.* I. For this problem cf. Ross in the "Introduction" to his edition of the *Analytics*, 6ff., and my review in *Philos. Rev.*, 60 (1951), 563ff.; see also *Entwicklg. d. arist. Logik*, 37ff., 78ff., and *Philos. Rev.* 50 (1941), 410ff. Cf., further, Glenn R. Morrow, *J. of Philos.*, 48 (1951), 132ff.

12

Natural Places and the Eternal Cosmos

IN Aristotle's cosmology some other equally simple propositions are closely bound up with those relating to the natural movement of the elements. As the elements have by nature the tendency to move in one particular direction, either to the center or away from it, so they also have their natural places in the Cosmos. It is natural for fire to be in the upper regions of the Cosmos, and natural for earth to be in the center.[1] In what sense this principle applies to the other elements (including Aristotle's cherished fifth or "first") is a question which we must postpone. Yet we can no longer afford to ignore another item of his doctrine, to wit, the close and causal connection of the natural movements with the qualities heavy and light. "By these terms [scil., absolutely light and absolutely heavy] I mean a body whose nature it is to move always upwards, and one whose nature it is to move always downwards, unless prevented. There are bodies of both sorts . . . For we see . . . that earthy bodies sink to the bottom of everything and move towards the centre. . . . If then there is a body which rises to the top of everything else" (as fire is observed to do) "it is clear that this body is moving towards the extremity. It cannot therefore possess weight . . . nor earth lightness." [2] The sentences here quoted contain not only Aristotle's definitions of heavy and light but also his deduction of the two basic elements (from

[1] See, e.g., I,7.276a12ff., 8.276a22ff., 277b13ff.; II,13.295b25ff.; see also IV,4 and 5 *passim*.

[2] IV,4.311b14ff. (Guthrie's translation).

which, by a few further steps, he arrives at two others, water and air).[3]
It will now be necessary to consider how far these subjects—elements,
natural movements, natural places, and weight and lightness—had been
brought into mutual relations even before Aristotle's day.

If we refer to the *Timaeus*, we find that Plato has little to say of
specific movements inhering in the nature of his four elements. Constructing them as he does out of regular solid bodies, he points out that
the element which is built up of pyramids, fire, has the greatest mobility whereas earth, which consists of cubes, is least mobile.[4] Prima
facie this is the only connection between elementary bodies and movement which receives consideration in Plato's scheme.

When it comes to the question of natural places, we find Plato less
reticent. Even before the Cosmos is created, the elements into whose
form or appearance the receptacle has been molded take up different
"seats" just as "when things are shaken and winnowed by means of
winnowing baskets and other instruments for cleansing grain, the
dense and heavy things move in one direction while the rare and light
are carried to another place and settle there." [5] Here Plato uses the
qualities of heavy and light as determining the place which different
items take up. Yet let us note that he does so in the context of a comparison. To the entities that actually are in the receptacle he does not
in so many words ascribe these qualities. When speaking of the latter, he appears to trace their separation from one another and their
massing or grouping in different places to the principle "like to like."
Every part of an element has the tendency to associate with its congeners and keep apart from substances of a different nature. Still,
whatever the reason, elements come to have places of their own.[6]
This precosmic arrangement and this tendency persist after the creation of the Cosmos. In discussing the experiences of elements within
the Cosmos, Plato emphasizes that when an element has changed into
another it must also change its place. Now the places must, even if
Plato does not say so explicitly, be cosmic regions. When fire has
turned into water, its place can no longer be in the same part of the
Cosmos as before. It will strive to reach the place of "those to which
it has become assimilated." Further references to the natural places

---

[3] See below, pp. 283–284.   [4] *Tim.* 55d1, 56a3; note also a2.
[5] *Tim.* 52e5ff. Cf. Cornford's translation and commentary (*Cosmology*, 197). On
the ἕδρα motif see above, p. 130.
[6] *Tim.* 52e5–53a7 (some apology may be in order for using the term "element"
which is not strictly in place; see 53b1ff.).

of the elements occur in the section dealing with heavy and light.[7]

Is it legitimate to regard the movements that take the elements to "their places" as natural movements in the sense—or approximating the sense—in which Aristotle uses this concept? To decide this question we must once more turn to their origin in the receptacle. As we know, Plato calls the Forms the father and the receptacle the mother of whatever floating, unstable things appear in it.[8] And if these entities owe their movement to their mother in a fashion which reflects the mother's own condition, it cannot be entirely fanciful to argue that these movements are a part of their nature (*physis*). Actually the movements arise because the entities have different "powers," cannot keep up a condition of equipoise in the receptacle, and thus produce a swaying movement in the receptacle—and this swaying movement of their mother is in turn imparted to themselves. Plato does not specify the "powers," nor does he say whence the floating entities derive them.[9] Yet the powers are clearly part of their nature; and as the entities are after all semblances of fire, water, etc., one may guess that their inherent "powers" reflect the nature of their begetter, the Forms.[10] It would not be wise to press this point. If we cannot quite precisely assess the respective contributions that intrinsic quality, birth, and heredity make to the origin of these movements, this is hardly a cause for regret. In Greek all of these factors would anyhow come under the heading of *physis*, and thus we can say that the movements of the elements originate in their nature. No agent, no whirl created by Strife or Mind, is needed to separate them and make them show differences of behavior. The parents who have at this very moment produced them are certainly closer to their "nature"

[7] 57b7–c6 (c3, τόπον ἴδιον), 58b6–c2 (b8, πρὸς τοὺς ἑαυτῶν τόπους). On 62c2–63e8 see below, pp. 278–279. Note also 81a4–6, a6–b4 (the distribution of the elementary particles in our food "imitates" the movements of the Cosmos inasmuch as here too like joins like).

[8] 50d2.

[9] The expression δυνάμεις ἰσόρροποι may seem to carry connotations of weight (and lightness); yet, as we have seen, Plato actually mentions the qualities heavy and light only by way of comparison (immediately afterward, 53a1). The only qualities or powers that Plato specifies in this part of the *Timaeus* are hot and white, 50a2; if he here adds "or any of the contraries," we can still not be sure whether he meant to include heavy and light among these. I notice that Cornford, who is on the whole inclined to overemphasize the role played by the "powers," thinks primarily of hot, cold, dry, and moist and makes no reference to the qualities of weight (*Cosmology*, 199).

[10] See 50c3ff., 51a2, 52a4f.; cf. also 51b4ff.

than Strife or Mind or the conditions of a whirl could be. Moreover, the mother has a decidedly spatial character, so that it befits her to cause spatial separations.

The movements thus created contribute a great deal to the formation and structure of the Cosmos; for it is thanks to them that the elements distribute themselves in the proper fashion, each taking up its cosmic region and place. It is all the more remarkable that the Demiurge takes no hand in their separation or distribution. Whatever else he does for the elements, from their original selection to endowing them with their appropriate shape and capacities, he never has a thought to spare for their movements. This important phase of the cosmic structure owes nothing to him but is evidently a result of antecedent tendencies. In fact, it is a continuation of precosmic conditions.[11] Thus much nature itself and the primeval factors of *genesis* contribute to the Cosmos. In the *Timaeus* there is a definite cleavage between the precosmic and the cosmic state—a cleavage which cannot be minimized as being inherent in the mythical form which Plato has "chosen" for his exposé.[12]

Aristotle is in a position to say frankly and with a maximum of emphasis that the movements of the elements are a part of their nature. As we know, his concept and definition of nature call for such movements. Of the definitions advanced in the second book of the *Physics*, one fits the needs of his cosmology so nicely that it seems almost designed for them: "nature is a principle of movement"; natural things have an "inborn urge to move." [13] This definition provides a new scientific basis for the tendencies of the elements which Plato saw taking shape in the receptacle, and it discards not only mythical imagery

[11] See again the passages adduced in Note 7. Cornford (*Cosmology*, 246) says pertinently: "It is not explicitly stated . . . that the main masses of the primary bodies form four concentric spherical layers, with fire on the outside . . . and earth at the centre. This is no doubt assumed as an obvious fact, recognized in other cosmologies." It surely is assumed, but also, as Cornford seems to imply, played down. As the emphasis is (after 53c4) on the Cosmos with its form, order, and purpose—and on features directly traceable to the form of the elements— the contribution still made by "raw" nature is not particularly stressed or elaborated. Precisely the traditional aspect of cosmology which the *Timaeus* takes for granted is in *De caelo* treated as the central problem requiring a new solution.

[12] Plato says that the elementary movements began and the elements took up different places "even before the whole was shaped into order out of them," i.e., shaped into the form of our Cosmos (διακοσμηθέν, 53a7).

[13] *Phys.* II,1.192b12ff., 16ff., cf. also b35ff.; *De caelo* I,2.268b14–16; IV,3.310b16ff. (esp. 24).

but also genetic connections between the elements and space.[14] In Plato only soul—the soul which, being allied to mind, is in control of the Cosmos—is explicitly credited with a movement appropriate to its nature. Now that nature itself has succeeded to the place of soul, the "first bodies" of nature can be given their own specific and characteristic movements.[15]

This new concept of natural movements has implications that are apt to revolutionize the entire cosmological outlook. We have already seen that it furnished Aristotle with strong arguments in his fight against a plurality of worlds.[16] Our Cosmos is unique because in it the elements have the goal of their movements. Here are their natural places. Another, no less important, inference from the same first assumption is that the elements by themselves and in accordance with their own nature build up this Cosmos. It is normal for fire to be in, or move to, the circumference, and the other elements are likewise where it is natural for them to be. This notion implies a radical break with the Presocratic and Platonic approach, and Aristotle is not slow to perceive the significance of this fundamental departure. Essentially what it amounts to is that an origin of the Cosmos can no longer be conceived. There was no process or event; nothing happened to the elements, making them behave as normally and without special impulse they would not behave. In truth, the Cosmos exists precisely when the elements are left at peace and nothing interferes with their natural inclinations. Even the prime mover (who rather surprisingly appears in Aristotle's argument) would not interfere, since the movements of the elements remain "natural." [17] This new idea destroys the basis of the traditional distinction between a precosmic and a cosmic state of things.[18] Aristotle, however, does not proclaim the conclusion that all who have embarked on a cosmogony were fundamentally mistaken. He is content to correct their notions concerning the natural condition of the elements and to put the orderly cosmic arrangement in the place of one disorderly and precosmic. Re-

[14] On Aristotle's severing of this connection see above, Ch. 6.

[15] Cf. especially *Legg.* X,897b–898c. For Aristotle's new concept of *physis,* and the aspect of it in which it succeeds to the place of Plato's soul, see above, the section "Nature and Soul" in Ch. 5.

[16] I,8. 9. Cf. above, pp. 257–258.

[17] III,2.300b1of., 12, 13f., 19f., 22. Cf. for this section Note 24.

[18] For this and what follows cf. especially III,2.300b8–301a20. Aristotle's debt to Heraclitus' eternal Cosmos will be discussed below, in Ch. 21.

ferring in particular to the movements of the atoms in infinite space and to the "disorderly motion" in the receptacle, he suggests that such movements would of themselves distribute the elements in the cosmic pattern.[19] He knows what gives him the advantage over his predecessors. It is his novel and superior conception of nature and of movements in accordance with nature. Being innocent of the Aristotelian concept of nature with all that it implies, the earlier physicists had probably never spoken of either the cosmic or the precosmic condition of things as "natural." In their terminology and conceptual scheme such an assertion would make little sense. With Plato matters are somewhat different. In his scheme disorder is inevitable as long as the elements are left to their own devices. Although Plato approximates the concept of natural movements and natural places, allowing the elements in the receptacle to take up separate places, he denies them the capacity of creating a Cosmos. Blind forces operating without design cannot build up something so perfect.[20] As long as "the god is absent," there is not order but disorder. Still, we have observed that Plato does not actually need his divine craftsman for the distribution of the elements in the Cosmos. Even when he is dealing with the Cosmos in its actual and perfect state, the tendency of the elements to move to their proper places is something that they have brought along from their precosmic habits.[21] The forms with which God has endowed them account for their mutual acting and suffering, for their transformation into one another, and for a good number of

[19] *Ibid.*, 300b8–301a4. The reference to Empedocles in 300b25–31 indicates that although Aristotle singles out Plato and the atomists for special criticism they are not the only ones whom he finds at fault. In the sentences 301a11–20 Aristotle does not seriously suggest that the Cosmos should be constructed from a state of rest or from the elements in a state of fusion. It is tempting to read this passage in the light of 300b21f. and Plato *Legg.* X,895a6ff. and to understand that a first mover is needed to get the elements moving. But Aristotle's point seems to be different: once the elements are in motion and have separated from one another you can no longer construct a *genesis* (*scil.*, of the Cosmos), for the Cosmos is already formed (see a18f.). Cf. Alexander's and Simplicius' explanations in the latter, *ad loc.*

[20] See above, Note 12. For the ἀταξία prevailing before the Demiurge applies his ordering hand see *Tim.* 30a, 53a–c, 69b. On 53aff. and an allusion to the Aristotelian concept of "natural places" see Léon Robin, *Les rapports de l'être et de la connaissance d'après Platon* (Paris, 1957), 60, 62.

[21] See *Tim.* 57b7–c6; 58b8–c4. From the latter passage it may be inferred that ἡ τοῦ παντὸς περίοδος and with it the world soul are needed to establish the elements in their cosmic regions. And in the scheme of the *Timaeus* the world soul belongs to the order fashioned by the Demiurge.

more specific phenomena; yet on the arrangement of the elements
in the Cosmos his work has no bearing. As in Aristotle, the elements
find their places by themselves—aided, it is true, by their mother, yet
how could we regard the mother as alien to their nature? It was for
very different reasons that Plato retained the distinction between a
precosmic and a cosmic condition and identified the one phase with
disorder, the other with order. Thus it remained for Aristotle to
show that order is the natural and normal state of the elements. His
eloquent pronouncements on this point, while resting directly on his
original concept of natural movements, are at the same time inspired
by an entirely new confidence in nature. Nature can be trusted; even
if left to itself it will not produce chaotic conditions. In a concentrated form, the words "The right order [or arrangement, τάξις] is
the nature of physical things" express this "teleological" confidence.
The sentence has its corollary in the statement that disorderly motions
or conditions—like those prevailing in the receptacle—would not be
in the nature of the elements but contrary to their nature.[22] If nature
for Aristotle incorporates purpose and form, it may also incorporate
order; and if for the realization of purpose it no longer depends on
mind, it does not need mind any more for establishing order and
the orderly cosmic pattern. Plato had needed a divine mind to create
order. Anaxagoras had used mind even to effect the separation and
distribution of the world stuff.[23]

The concept of nature here suggested is thoroughly static. It has
rid itself of even the smallest residue of *genesis*—that venerable component of it to which Aristotle in other contexts does ample justice.
The "nature" with which Aristotle here operates knows neither change
nor gradual evolution toward an end or goal; nor would it for a period
be in a state of erratic behavior and have to wait for the development of special conditions before it can attain its proper "form."[24]

In the *Timaeus*, the section which introduces the receptacle and

[22] 301a4–6. Aristotle's use of the words τάξις and άταξία (cf. Note 20) brings the
contrast between his own approach and Plato's into focus. Cf. also 300b31–301a4,
301a6–11. The sentence rendered in the text seems open to more than one grammatical construction and is in fact differently understood by Simplicius, Bonitz
(*Index, s.v.* οἰκεῖος), Stocks, and Guthrie. I am not convinced that my own rendering is correct but do not think that this uncertainty affects the conclusions
here drawn.

[23] For Anaxagoras cf. *Vorsokr.,* 59B12, 15. In Plato the Demiurge motif is pertinent; see also *Phileb.* 28d and *Legg.* X,897bff., XII,967aff.

[24] Note also the definition of "nature" as the condition in which most things are
and in which they are "most of the time" (301a7f.). Although on the whole Aris-

shows *genesis* as coming to pass in it fulfills a dual function. It puts us in mind of two subjects which Presocratic thinkers discussed before advancing to their cosmogonies. While on the one hand it acquaints us with the fundamental and enduring entities in nature, it also shows, on the other, the condition of things "before" the Cosmos came into being.[25] Plato had no reason for separating these two subjects as Empedocles and Democritus had done. For him they coincide. In Aristotle's system one of these subjects has disappeared. The province of physics has become more restricted. It is limited to an investigation of the basic entities and basic concepts of nature and to a study of *genesis* and of movement in their general and universal aspects. To these subjects Book VIII of the *Physics* adds the doctrine of the first mover, but of the first mover as maintaining the Cosmos, not as creating it. A precosmic state of things is no longer a legitimate topic.

---

totle in our section operates with the natural movements of the elements, there is one passage (300b21) where he brings the first mover into play. This passage seems at variance with the first assumptions; it is also curious for another reason— the first mover is here described as "being itself in motion according to nature." (I prefer the reading αὐτό to αὐτό, because it accords better with the whole argument in which Aristotle operates with something "first" that moves the other entities; see 13f., 15.) As Aristotle is here speaking of the motions in the receptacle of the *Timaeus* (52eff.), it is possible to think that he is taking his stand on Plato's own ground (Guthrie, "Introduction" to the Loeb edition, xxif.) and that he regards either the receptacle itself or the world soul as the prime mover in Plato's scheme. But this reasoning does not take us far. For even before turning to the *Timaeus* and while dealing with the atomists, Aristotle has worked up to something κατὰ φύσιν κινοῦν πρῶτον (a15; cf. a13f.), and when he returns to them later, he again refers to entities—one or infinite in number—that cause the motions (a32f.). Moreover, the argument (a14ff.) that "we shall go on to infinity" if there is not a "first" in the series of movers recalls the procedure by which Aristotle in *Phys.* VII,1 (242a49ff.) deduces the necessary existence of a prime mover. Guthrie's opinion ("Introduction," xix) that "one of the main topics" of *De caelo* "is the natural or internally caused motion of bodies" and that "there is almost complete silence" about external movers may still be accepted, but the word which operates here is "almost," and it must be said that Guthrie was not justified in isolating 300b18ff. from its surroundings. As we have seen, Aristotle has developed the Platonic doctrine of movement in two different and at times conflicting directions (above, pp. 95-102). The *De caelo* carries the concept of nature as source of motion to new conclusions and concentrates "almost" entirely on this aspect of movement. Still, the alternative development—the first mover as cause of all movements—although on the whole eclipsed, occasionally enters the picture; and this is obviously such an occasion. Another inference which seems to me inescapable is that Aristotle here thinks of the first mover as "moved" (cf. H. von Arnim, *S.B.W.A.*, 212 [1931], 5.21f.), and this in turn supports the theory that he has not yet reached the position embodied in *Phys.* VIII.

[25] See above, pp. 49-51.

One may wonder why Aristotle, since the stage for it seems to be set, does not in our passage of the third book administer the *coup de grâce* to the evolutionary approach. Why does he limit himself to proclaiming that the elements, if behaving in their natural way, produce order, not disorder, and why does he not so much as allude here to the large question (which occupies him in Book I) whether the Cosmos is subject to becoming and passing away or exempt from all symptoms of mortality? If the discussion of Book I is presupposed, why is there no reference to it; if it is not, why is the issue as such not formulated? The thoughts embodied in our section seem to lead directly to a proof for the eternity of our world, to the doctrine of *one* Cosmos of forever-identical structure. Were some of the arguments that reflect the position here reached incorporated in the larger demonstrations that we find in Book I? Or did Aristotle here deliberately stick to the subject of elementary movements? These questions are hardly capable of a satisfactory answer. What we know of the dialogue *On Philosophy* goes far to show the religious motive and religious quality of Aristotle's belief in the eternity of our world.[26] To speak of religious convictions in a treatise on the nature of the elements would indeed, to put it mildly, be a "transition into another subject" (*metabasis eis allo genos*). Moreover, Aristotle is able to prove the eternity of the Cosmos by arguments of a purely logical—in fact, extremely logical—complexion, by a linguistic analysis of the concepts "created" and "uncreated," destructible" and "indestructible." The results of these analyses are embodied in the last chapters of Book I.[27] All that we can suggest here is that Aristotle's new physical concepts point to the same conclusions to which his religious convictions and his logical analysis were taking him—independently, it would seem, if there were not limits even to the most determined departmentalism.

[26] Cf. frgs. 12–15, 18 (Ross, Walzer). See Jaeger, *Aristotle*, 138ff., 159ff., 163ff.

[27] I,11f. (the arguments of I,10 are somewhat less καθόλου and Aristotle himself regards them as "physical"; cf. 280a32; see also 12.283b17ff.). Clearly what Aristotle here seeks to disprove as thoroughly irrational is the notion that something that has come into being may yet continue to exist forever. This he found set forth in the *Timaeus*, where it is also suggested that the Cosmos will be eternal, although it is φθαρτός (38c, 41af.; cf. Simplicius 351.15ff.). The alternative (Presocratic) doctrine—that the Cosmos has come into being and will disintegrate again—seems in the light of pure logic much sounder. Aristotle here makes no effort to refute it, probably because it was no longer necessary to waste good ammunition on it. Cf. *H.S.C.P.*, 63 (1958), 265f.

13

Heavy and Light

TO associate each of the elements per se with a specific movement
and to study them under this point of view was a bold, new idea which
implied a break with the traditional approach. Tirelessly and with a
certain radicalism Aristotle exploits its potentialities, pushing on to
further conclusions. Of these conclusions some, like the equation of
our Cosmos with the natural order of things, are startlingly novel;
others amount to a reaffirmation, and new justification, of the traditional pattern, embodying as it did the stratification of the elements.
What separates Aristotle's cosmology more than anything else from
the earlier systems is that as a result of his single-minded concentration
on movements he is indifferent to most of the qualities formerly associated with the elements. It certainly does not matter that fire, which
has the nature of upward movement, is hot or that earth, which tends
toward the center, is cold and dry. The qualities hot and cold, dry and
moist are irrelevant in Aristotle's cosmological scheme. We may recall that even with the atomists and with Plato the "powers" had lost
not a little of their time-honored status. On the whole, however,
Aristotle cannot be said to fall in with this trend. In *De generatione*
and in his biological work he rather reacts against it.[1] And even in the
treatise *On the Heaven*, where cold and hot, dry and moist are ignored, one pair of opposite qualities receives careful study and is
given a place of crucial importance. These qualities are heavy and
light. Book IV establishes Aristotle's doctrine regarding them, their
existence having already been deduced in III. That these powers can
on no account be ignored would be evident already from the nu-

[1] See below, Ch. 17.

merous references to them in I and III.[2] As a matter of fact, Aristotle, as soon as he has finally disposed of the Platonic notion that "elements differ by their figures," decides that the correct way of determining their differences is to investigate "their passive and active functions and their powers." [3] It is in this conviction that he undertakes the study of heavy and light in Book IV—for these are the only powers that are pertinent.

Yet we should not suppose that this study leads Aristotle of necessity to a close consideration of the material aspects or the material nature of his elements. To be sure, he points out that the qualities heavy and light reside in the "matter" of the elements and wonders whether it is better to assume for all four an identical matter capable of developing in opposite directions or whether each should be given its own specific matter.[4] This, however, is a side issue which does not affect either the definition of heavy and light or the essential propositions which Aristotle is anxious to defend. As we may expect, the qualities heavy and light are important on account of their relation with the natural movements. "I call absolutely light that whose nature it is to move always upward and heavy whose nature it is to move always downward, if there is no interference." The two qualities may be described as having in themselves the "sparks" of such movements.[5] An indication of the heavy quality possessed by an element is that it sinks below the others, whereas a light element tends to be on top of them. It is in words like these that Aristotle, in chapter 4, actually defines heavy and light, and these functions secure them a central place in his cosmology.[6]

It is not easy to determine the extent to which the Presocratics made

---

[2] IV,3 and esp. 4; III,2.301a20ff. In Book I see, e.g., 7.276a6ff.; 8.277b12ff. See also III,1.299a25ff.; 2.301b16ff.

[3] See the concluding sentences of Book III (307b18ff.).

[4] IV,4.312a17ff.; 5.312a22–33; for an analysis of these sections see below, Note 32. The reasons why I cannot regard these sections as containing "the basic principle which Aristotle seeks to establish" in *De Caelo* III and IV (Cherniss, *Pl. and the Acad.*, 161) are implicit in this analysis. The "unresolvable differences of the four simple bodies" are brought out well enough without the section, which on the whole (i.e., if it is at all a unit) rather shows how the differences can be resolved. What Cherniss calls the "crucial" argument is altogether more germane to the treatise *De generatione*.

[5] IV,4.311b13ff.; 1.308a2.

[6] We can thus understand that Aristotle in IV,1.307b30 speaks of the study of heavy and light as "belonging to the theory of movement." For the definitions see esp. 4.311a16–18.

use of these two powers. There is evidence that they figured among the basic qualitative differentiations of the elements. Parmenides' "Way of Opinion" reckons with two "forms," one of them bright, mild, and light—actually "quick"—the other dark, dense, and heavy; in the Cosmos these forms exist partly in separation from one another, partly in a state of mixture which produces the derivative entities.[7] Anaxagoras too may have spoken of heavy and light powers (though whether they existed in his aboriginal mixture is not quite certain), and it is perhaps not rash to guess that other physicists too knew the fire or the hot which moves to the circumference to be light or "quick" and the cold stuff which settles in the center of the Cosmos to be heavy.[8] Yet it is neither attested nor intrinsically probable that heavy and light as such and through their own action were responsible for the cosmic distribution of the opposites. What little evidence we have suggests rather that the hot qua hot had enough vital power and initiative to embark on the movement which took it to the circumference of our world.[9] In the later Presocratic accounts the separation of the two main masses is effected by a cosmogonic whirl. Quite definitely Anaxagoras and in all probability also Empedocles and the atomists made the separation originate in the same rotating movement which continues in the heavenly revolutions. For Aristotle these revolutions too are movements natural to the element of that region. From

[7] See esp. *Vorsokr.*, 28B8.53–59 (in 57 the reading ἐλαφρόν is not altogether above doubt, yet the balance of probability is on its side; cf. Kranz's note); see also B9–12.

[8] I admit that the evidence is inconclusive. In the case of Anaxagoras doubt may remain whether the secondary evidence of A1.8, 42.2, and B10 (37.10) outweighs the absence of these qualities in fragments like B12 (38.15ff.). By and large, secondary accounts must be suspected of being colored by the Aristotelian theory. Burnet, *E. G. Ph.*, 342, attaches importance to the fact that the *Placita* (see, e.g., *Doxographi* 310) report no doctrines about heavy and light earlier than Plato's. He believes that for the early thinkers weight is never "a thing as, for instance, warmth and cold are." Cornford expressed a similar opinion in *The Laws of Motion in Ancient Thought* (Cambridge, 1931), 37ff. For a different approach see Fränkel, *Dichtg. u. Philos.*, 342.

[9] Perhaps the best clue that we find—yet not really much of one—is Parmenides' reference to the θερμὸν μένος of the stars (28B11.3); if the elements had *menos* in the sense of driving force and urge, this would account for their operations in forming a cosmos. In any case, a concept like this would seem more in harmony with the outlook of the early thinkers than modern attempts to give the whirl a place in the cosmogony of Anaximander (W. A. Heidel, *Cl. Ph.*, 1 [1900], 279ff.; Burnet, *E. G. Ph.*, 61f.); against them see Cornford, *Cl. Q.*, 28 (1934), 15f.

his point of view commotions set up by a whirl would be in the
class of "movements by force" which he considers the contrary of
"natural movements." It would surely be unhistorical to carry this
clear-cut opposition into the Presocratic systems; yet it may be said
that where a whirl is required—and the whirl in turn is produced
by an agent like Strife or Mind—the original confidence in the powers
of the world stuff has weakened.[10] In this respect Aristotle's doctrine
of natural movements is closer to the earlier Presocratics who need no
whirl than it is to the later. The atomists appear to have held that
the atoms form the whirl by themselves and as a result of their own
motions; in the whirl the larger atoms, offering more resistance,
maintain themselves in the center whereas the smaller are thrown off
to the circumference and create the outer regions. In this sense and
with these qualifications we may accept Aristotle's statement that for
the atomists the larger atom is the heavier. Weight and lightness, then,
are not in their scheme inherent properties of the atoms but are acquired in the whirl.[11] Actually with the atomists the powers in general have fallen from their former status and are no longer part of
an atom's nature. Even hot and cold are now an affection of our senses,
an impression made by reality upon the percipient.

This gives us the historical background for the theory of the
powers in the *Timaeus*. Hot and cold, rough and smooth, and also
heavy and light find their treatment in the section which deals with
"the affections concerning the entire body" (as distinct from affections like sweet and bitter, bright and dark, that are limited to a
particular sense organ).[12] What Plato actually says about heavy and
light goes far toward putting them on a par with the sense impressions. Heavy, as he describes it, is a strong resistance which an element exerts against an attempt to remove it from its proper place,

[10] It is of some interest that Anaxagoras speaks of βία (and ταχύτης) as responsible for the separation and rotation (59B9); yet no contrast between it and
nature is implied. Cf. *De caelo* II,1.284a24ff. on Empedocles. See, further, *Vorsokr.*, 31B31, 35; 59A57, B12, 13; 68B164, 167; for other passages see Kranz's
Index, *s.vv.* δίνη, δῖνος. Characteristic of Aristotle's attitude is *De caelo* II,13.295a7-
b9.
[11] For a convincing discussion of the evidence see Bailey, *Atomists*, 143ff.; cf.
De caelo IV,2.309a1f. (Aristotle's statements about determining the weight of composite bodies I discount, in accordance with Bailey, as irrelevant to our question).
[12] For a "chapter heading" of the entire section of *Tim.* 61c–65b see 64a2 or
65b4; for heavy and light see 62c3–63e8. In a sense it is correct to refer to the
entire section as dealing with "touch" and "tactile" qualities, though Plato himself
does not use such terms; for the reason see *A. J. Ph.*, 76 (1955), 159 and n.41.

light a weaker resistance, and such resistance is surely something that we "feel" and that "affects" us.[13] At the same time, however, Plato's discussion suggests a somewhat peculiar status for heavy and light. Although sense impressions, they are, it would seem, sense impressions *sui generis*, since, unlike warm and cold, rough and smooth, they must be understood on a cosmological basis. The sentence which opens this section informs us that "heavy and light may be most clearly explained if we examine them together with what is called up and down" (scil., in the Cosmos).[14] Even though the distinction between up and down soon turns out to be illusory—for in a spherical Cosmos there can be no up and no down—certain cosmological presuppositions remain essential for the correct understanding of heavy and light. These terms can be defined only with reference to the places in which the elements have settled. As we know, Plato has retained the traditional stratification of the elements; the places to which he here refers are the same as those which Aristotle calls their natural places. To an attempt at removing it from its cosmic place every portion of an element will set up resistance, and any such attempt would employ "force" and be "contrary to nature." [15] A small portion, however, would set up relatively little resistance and in consequence of this be called light, a larger would resist more strongly and therefore be called heavy. The tendency of a body to remain in its own place, its reluctance to move from it even under force, is traced to the principle that like tends to be with like; every portion of an element "clings to its kind," to the large homogeneous body (of fire, air, etc.) which occupies a particular zone of the Cosmos.[16]

The differences between this approach and Aristotle's are obvious, and Aristotle himself emphasizes some of them. They should, however, not obscure a feature of Plato's account which recurs in Aristotle's cosmology, albeit in a somewhat different place and in a new function. When an element is not in its cosmic place, it has been removed from it by "force"; the place where it is now is "contrary to

---

[13] Plato does not say so in exactly these words but speaks of the smaller portion as being "more easily forced" (63c1; cf. d1f.). He describes directly the behavior of the element involved and defines only by implication our sensation; but the topic of the entire section is sensations. See Note 12.

[14] 62c3ff.

[15] βία: 63b6ff. (c1, ῥώμη), c4, c8; here also κατὰ φύσιν. Note also the use of these terms in the immediately following section (esp. 64c8) where *physis* clearly denotes the normal condition.

[16] 63e3–7; cf. b2f., d5; see also 57c2.

nature." It is Aristotle's constant habit to employ these two terms and to use them as the alternatives to natural movement and rest in the natural place.[17] In a later passage of the *Timaeus* Plato says that the vital heat or fire in our body tends "in accordance with nature" (or "its nature") to move "toward its kin." Its kin is once more "its nature"; both expressions refer to the large agglomerations of fire in its specific cosmic area.[18] It is not too much to say that Plato here approximates Aristotle's concept of natural movement, even though he makes no mention of weight or lightness. Bearing this passage in mind and considering that Plato in his account of weight refers to "force" and conditions "contrary to nature," we may conclude that the characteristic concepts of Aristotle's cosmology are not his own invention.[19] The concepts were there and had been used. They had, however, not yet become the cornerstones of a cosmological system, and if they were to serve as such, they had to be disentangled from their connection with doctrines that Aristotle did not share.

To us Aristotle's fundamental departure seems to lie in his break with the idea that heavy and light are sense impressions and should be defined with reference to the percipient. Now they are once more qualities and "powers" inherent in the elements—in fact, they belong to their nature and are needed to account for their natural behavior and cosmic role. This essential difference between his conception and Plato's Aristotle curiously enough never points out. Elsewhere too, as we shall see, he quietly restores to the powers their place in the

[17] E.g., I,2.269a9ff.; 8.276a22ff.; III,2.300b10ff., 301a4ff., a20ff., b17ff.; see also II,13.294b30ff., 295a23ff.

[18] *Tim.* 79d5, e6. Cf. my discussion of this passage in *Stud. It.*, 28 (1956), 544ff.

[19] It may be added that Plato in his discussion of the movements that come to pass in the receptacle approximates Aristotle's concept of "natural movement"; see above, pp. 267–269. A different explanation of "lighter" (*Tim.* 59c1) as due to "large interstices" (which should yet not be identified with the atomists' "void") can here be left out of account. Nor is the description of fire as the lightest or quickest element "because it consists of the fewest parts" (56b1) a clue to Plato's final conception of weight or lightness, although Aristotle concentrates his criticism in III,1.299b21ff. on this "chance remark," as Cherniss calls it (*Pl. and the Acad.*, 139; see his illuminating analysis, 136ff.). Léon Robin, *Etudes sur la signification et la place de la physique dans . . . Platon* (Paris, 1919), 40f., tries to synthesize Plato's divergent and conflicting attempts to cope with the problem; besides 56b1 he also includes 57df., although there is no evidence that Plato here has the subject of weight in mind. Inevitably the synthesis is very problematic. Clearly the *Timaeus* embodies a plurality of approaches, and though 62c3ff. is by every criterion the most serious and sustained, there is room for the impression that the "Academy struggled in vain with the problem of weight" (Jaeger, *Aristotle*, 307).

"nature" of elements, without mentioning that he thereby sets himself in opposition to the *Timaeus*.[20]

The other important tenet which separates him from Plato is that some elements are always—i.e., again by nature—light, others always heavy; they do not exhibit these qualities only when removed from their place.[21] For him Plato's comparison between a larger and smaller amount of the same element, both out of their place, would not be a comparison between heavy and light at all but between heavier and less heavy. Yet Plato was not alone in thus misunderstanding the problem; developing this line of criticism, Aristotle finds the other physicists guilty of the same confusion.[22] The further critical point which Aristotle makes is that the distinction between up and down in the Cosmos is correct and that Plato made a mistake in rejecting it.[23] The central area of the Cosmos where earth is situated is always "down," the circumference, no matter of which hemisphere we think, always "up." Important though this divergence is, one might maintain that Aristotle could have driven home his new definition of heavy and light even without affirming the validity of the concepts up and down as used of the Cosmos. Essentially his theory would be the same had he defined light elements as those that move toward (and have their place near) the circumference and heavy as those tending toward the center of the Cosmos.[24] With these cosmological distinctions Plato could hardly have found fault. Still, a deeper issue is in-

[20] See below, pp. 344–347. As has been said in Note 19, Aristotle's criticism of Plato's account is not directed against *Tim.* 62c3ff.

[21] IV,4.311a16ff. and b14ff. Aristotle appeals to empirical observation about the behavior of fire, etc. ("we see," b19; "it is obvious," a19) as the basis for his definition of heavy and light.

[22] IV,1 and 2 (cf. again Note 19 regarding the criticism of Plato).

[23] *De caelo* IV,1.308a17 refers (as is generally recognized) to *Tim.* 62c5ff., d12ff. Plato (*Tim.* 62c6–8) and Aristotle (IV,4.311b16–18) also reject the notion that (by nature; cf. Plato's ἀκουσίως) all things move to the center. Plato's wording would allow us to believe that he is rejecting a popular notion, whereas Aristotle gives the impression of having particular physicists in mind. Probably Simplicius, *ad loc.*, and Stocks (in the note to the Oxford translation) are after all right in thinking of the atomists; if so, Aristotle's criticism would in strictness apply only to the behavior of the atoms in the Cosmos or the cosmogonic whirl, and Plato may be thinking of the same phase in either Democritus' or other Presocratic systems. For the atomists' view of heavy and light see above, Note 11.

[24] Note the use which Aristotle makes of the concepts "center" and "circumference" (literally, "the outermost") in the definitions in 311b18, 20, 24, 26, 29 (also 312a2, 6) and Plato's reference to the "center of the whole," *Tim.* 62d12. (Some doubt may be felt about the authenticity of 311b26, since it is barely possible to keep both ὅ clauses in the text.)

volved. For Plato the particular cosmic region which an element occupies is irrelevant to its weight or lightness—qualities which arise
only when a body is out of its place.[25] In Aristotle, on the other hand,
light bodies have their specific cosmic region qua light, and heavy
theirs qua heavy.

In the *Timaeus* what causes the sensations of heavy and light is the
"traveling of each thing toward its kindred," a tendency which becomes active as soon as portions of an element are kept from their
place. Plato employs the Presocratic "like to like" motif also in other
sections of this work. Ultimately, it seems, the joining of like with like
and the separation of unlike from unlike are due to the swaying of
the receptacle. Yet this new "cause" does not mark a definite break
with the Presocratic use of the motif.[26] For with regard to the motif
the receptacle here has a function not unlike that of the "whirl," and
in the later Presocratic systems it is the whirl which brings like and
like together.[27] The real break comes only with Aristotle's ruling that
the specific movement belongs not only to the nature of the entire
element but also to that of each part or portion of it.[28] Thus each
particle realizes its nature when going to the region where large masses
of its kind are gathered. In its former meaning the "like to like"
motif has no place in Aristotle's cosmic scheme. The only way of
preserving it—as far as he is interested in it at all—is to reinterpret

---

[25] Plato would probably not say that in its own cosmic place an element is
"light." Aristotle, on the other hand, has the theory that in its own place every
element, with the exception of fire, is heavy and would sink "downward" if the
element below it were removed (IV,5.312b2ff.)—a theory which, as Stocks says
(Oxford Translation, note on 312b19), "inflicts some damage on his doctrine of
places" (Guthrie's arguments against the view of Stocks, Loeb edition, *ad loc.*,
suffer from a rather daring interpretation of b6).

[26] *Tim.* 63e3ff.; cf. 53a (receptacle), 57c, 63b.

[27] The fullest authentic statement that we have is Democr. B164, where a whirl
is mentioned, though not a cosmogonic whirl. It is probable that Emped. B37
describes the action of elements when separated from one another in the whirl
set up by Strife. "Like to like" operates also in the distribution of food within
the body; see esp. Emped. B90. Plato too uses the motif in this connection; and
as these movements cannot be due to the action of the receptacle, he says that
the particles in our body are "forced to imitate the movement [scil., pattern of
movement] of the Cosmos," *Tim.* 81b1f. (see also 81a3f.). On the dominating
position of the "like to like" principle in Presocratic speculation cf. Cornford,
Laws of Motion, 31ff.

[28] *De caelo* IV,3.310b5ff. For Aristotle's new conception of the "like to like"
and his opposition to Plato cf. Pierre Duhem, *Le système du monde*, 1 (Paris,
1913), 207f.

it, and this Aristotle actually does in a rather involved passage from which, despite its obscurity, one or two thoughts may with some confidence be distilled. One is that the "like to like" relationship may be said to prevail between one element and its cosmic neighbor. Air and water, water and earth have something in common. By this reasoning the concept of "like" is transferred from the parts of one and the same element to the relation between adjoining elements. Another point of view is that elements stand to one another in the same relation as matter to form. Water is potentially air and thus matter for air. Therefore if water finds itself next to air—and still more if water changes into air—it joins its like (namely, its form). This reinterpretation does not leave the motif much of its original meaning.[29]

A point that has been made before bears repeating. In our treatise heavy and light are the only differences between the elements of which Aristotle takes account. This is the more noteworthy as Book IV proceeds from a recognition of these qualities to a theory of the elements. More precisely it "derives" the elements which Aristotle needs throughout his system. Now it is true that the first body (*aether*) is ignored throughout Books III and IV; yet there remains a curious anomaly, since from the opposite qualities of weight and lightness not four but only two elements can be deduced. These two elements are earth and fire. The former is absolutely heavy, the other absolutely light. Neither the qualities so far assumed nor the theory of natural motions calls for more than two elements. But it is most unlikely that Aristotle ever thought of building up either his cosmology or his physics on the basis of only fire and earth.[30] In view of

[29] The passage IV,3.310a33–b15 remains difficult even after the explanatory efforts of Stocks and Guthrie, *ad loc.* I have tried to use *Phys.* IV,5.212b20–213a10 for its interpretation since in that passage the form-matter relationship is stated more clearly, yet I should not say that thereby all obscurities are removed. The root of the difficulty seems to be that Aristotle does not take one and the same view of the ὅμοιον throughout the passage (its meaning in b5 is different from b10f.). The last five lines add a further complication (on which see Guthrie). One point is very well brought out by Stocks in his note to 310b7: the fact that the main mass of an element is in a particular cosmic place has no influence on the effort of the particles to reach this place; see b3ff. and for contrast *Tim.* 63b2–4.

[30] See below, p. 365. For the derivation of fire and earth in our treatise see again IV,4.311a15ff. and especially 311b13–312a8. On the different deduction of the elements in *De gen. et corr.* see below, Ch. 17. Simplicius *In de caelo* 719.10 calls the deduction in the latter treatise ἀκριβέστερον. For what follows cf. O. Gigon, *Mus. Helv.,* 9 (1952), 124f.

the effort which Aristotle has made to correlate movements, qualities, and elements it is rather astonishing that he passes from two elements to four by arguments which strike us as comparatively slight and perfunctory. Between the two cosmic places which have been essential to his reasoning there must be an "in between." And if there is an in-between there must be, besides the heavy and the light elements, another that is "heavy and light." [31] This argument (if we like to call it so) would be satisfied by the existence of a third element; but a few lines later Aristotle presents another argument which suggests four: "Since there is one body which rises to the top of everything and one which sinks beneath everything, there must be two others which both sink beneath something and rise above something . . . for nothing prevents that there should be one or several intermediates between opposites, as in the case of colors, seeing that 'between' and 'middle' are used in several meanings." [32] Thus we arrive at four elements. It is not unfair to say that "special pleading" was needed to

---

[31] See IV,4.312a8–12; in a11 read διὰ τοῦτο ἔστι τι καὶ ἄλλο ⟨δ⟩ βαρὺ καὶ κοῦφον; so far we have not become acquainted with anything that is both "heavy and light."

[32] *Ibid.*, 28–30, 33–312b2. The points which Aristotle in 312a17–21, 22–27, and again 30–33 makes about the *hyle* of heavy and light and of the four elements interrupt the argument aiming at the derivation of the two additional elements. These passages are probably later additions by which Aristotle brought the doctrine of this book into line with the theory of *De gen. et corr.*, according to which one common matter underlies the elements (see, e.g., I,3.319a33ff., II,1.328a–24ff.). As for the sentences a12–16, they too have no obvious connection with the topics of our chapters, and I doubt whether Aristotle meant them to be inserted here. Stocks and Guthrie rightly refer to the similar thoughts embodied in 310a33–b15, and I should not exclude the possibility that 312a12–16 were originally written as explanatory notes on that section. One has the impression that Aristotle when looking over this book (say, after the completion of *De gen.*) saw fit to add some comments on the *hyle* of the elements and that these comments were later worked into the context. The translators have tried, yet I think without success, to make the best of ὥστε in a17. Actually there is a break and a very abrupt change in the point of view; Aristotle no longer refers to different elements as standing to one another in the relation of matter and Form. Simplicius (718.32) suggests that a step in the argumentation has been left out; and he makes an honest but futile effort to interpret a17ff. in the light of what precedes it. The result is a thought which is definitely not to be found in Aristotle's text (37ff.). As introduced by ὥστε, the sentences a17–21 could follow after a30–33. And if we read a28–30 (ἐπεὶ . . . τινί) as the immediate sequel of a11f. (οἷον ὕδωρ καὶ ἀήρ) and again a33ff. (οὐδὲν γὰρ κωλύει κτλ.) as sequel to a28–30, we get a satisfactory and coherent derivation of the intermediate two elements. I do not maintain that everything can be cleared up and reduced to order; nor do I have anything definite to suggest for 312b19–313a13, a section clearly connected with the discussion of ὕλη or ὕλαι in our paragraphs (in particular, it would seem, with 312a22ff. or a27ff.). But although nowhere sure of the remedy, I am strongly

derive air and water, especially if we consider how often Aristotle makes alternative systems founder on the rocks of his supposedly unassailable position that there are two basic movements, two cosmic places, two opposites connected with weight.[33]

Essentially what this rather lighthearted argument does is to make the new approach consistent with a doctrine settled and established beforehand. One need not be a cynic to deny that Aristotle "discovered" his elements by these arguments. On the four elements Plato and Aristotle are agreed. That Plato decided to accept the Empedoclean doctrine was an event of great consequence for the history of Western science. Still, its course would probably have been different had Aristotle seen compelling reasons for departing in this point from his master's teachings. Evidently he did not, and it is a measure of the hold which this doctrine had gained over his thought that not even the discrepancy between the number of elements and that of natural movements weakened his confidence. What placed this doctrine outside the area of disagreement and controversy was probably its extreme usefulness in biological and zoological studies, both of which had received a strong impulse from Empedocles and were rapidly developing on this basis.[34] It stands to reason that a thoroughgoing revision of the doctrine of elements would have disrupted these studies. The eventual addition of a fifth element had no such effect because it remained safely confined to the celestial region.

Is it pertinent to recall that Plato too "derives" the elements by first proving that the Cosmos cannot exist without fire and earth and then postulating two intermediate entities?[35] In their formal pattern the two proofs seem to have something in common. On the other hand, Plato correlates fire and earth with physical qualities altogether different from Aristotle's heavy and light, arguing that a physical body must be visible and tangible and that the first requirement is satisfied by the presence of fire, the second by that of earth.[36] He also thinks of the two intermediary entities as middle terms of a geometrical proportion. In other words, his derivation operates with

convinced that the end of ch. 4 and the beginning of ch. 5 do not present a coherent sequence of thoughts. On the other hand, Alexander's variant reading (Simplicius 719.28) seems to me irrelevant; it is due to a mechanical corruption of ἑτέρας to πέρας (312a32).

[33] See, e.g., I,8.277a12f.; II,13.295b25ff.; III,4.303b4ff.; IV,1.308a29ff., 3.310b16ff.

[34] Cf. M. Wellmann, *Die Fragmente d. sikelischen Ärzte* (Berlin, 1901), 69ff., 74ff., and Jaeger, *Diokles von Karystos* (Berlin, 1938), 213.

[35] *Tim.* 31b–32b.   [36] *Ibid.*, 31b.

physical and mathematical rather than cosmological concepts. Evidently it was found convenient to treat air and water as "intermediates," yet as Aristotle himself reminds us, "middle and between are used in several meanings." [37]

The roots of Aristotle's cosmological approach are to be found elsewhere, and the difficulties of correlating it with the doctrine of the elements will be seen clearly when we remember that the separation of the cosmic stuff had for two centuries been an integral part of the tradition. Anaximander's grand conception [38] had been faithfully preserved in the later systems. That the hot and bright stuff moves off to the circumference while the dark and cold forms the earth was a doctrine which antedated the four elements. There is no organic connection between these two traditions; when Empedocles introduced the four "roots" he did not support his innovation by a reference to cosmic movements.[39] Plato's correlation between elements and movements is confined to the statement that fire moves most easily whereas earth and water are difficult to move—air is once more a "middle." [40] Aristotle's theory of natural movement reflects (even though the concept as such is new) the traditional dichotomy of the cosmological pattern. It is predicated on a belief in opposites and makes new contributions to this venerable body of doctrines.[41] Small wonder that it leads directly to the deduction of only two elements and that to arrive at the two others the cosmological basis must be modified. Once again the concept of the middle must be resorted to; and as it had already been employed at this juncture, we may be wrong in feeling that the adjustment is made *ad hoc*. Fortunately the "middle" also has more than one meaning; with a minimum of manipulation it will yield two further elements.

---

[37] *De caelo* IV,5.312b2.

[38] See *Vorsokr.*, 12A9 ("the opposites being separated"), 10. Cf. 28B8.53 (Parmenides), 31A49 (Empedocles), 59B15 *et al.* (Anaxagoras), 60A4.2 (Diogenes), 64A6 (Archelaus), 67A1.32 (Leucippus). In Lucretius the dichotomy is somewhat blurred (5.449ff.) inasmuch as the separation of land and sea (453) is not kept clearly distinct from the more fundamental emergence of two main parts of the world; see, however, 480. The earlier accounts treat the separation of land and water on the earth as a secondary development, not directly connected with the original *apokrisis* (12A27 *et al.*).

[39] See esp. *Vorsokr.*, 31B6, 21, 23.   [40] *Tim.* 55e–56a.

[41] On the place of the "opposites" in Aristotle's doctrine of *genesis* and its relation to the tradition see above, Ch. 4.

14

The "First Body"

IT is time that we turned to Book I and gave attention to the most important doctrine of our treatise. Up to this point it has been possible to ignore the *aether*, since the propositions so far considered are independent of its existence. Still, whether the *aether* was from the outset an integral part of Aristotle's system or whether he once was satisfied with four elements, it is certain that the new element is the coping stone of the system in which all emphasis lies on the movement, none on the material substance of the elements. In *De caelo* the existence of the *aether* stands and falls with the new approach,[1] and the discovery of the new element must have been for Aristotle at once

[1] *De caelo* I,2.268b11–269a9; see also 269a9–b17. In the dialogue *On Philosophy* where, in all likelihood, Aristotle for the first time announced the existence of this element (Jaeger, *Aristotle*, 143ff.), it cannot yet have been associated with a specific "natural motion" (*ibid.*, 153). An analysis of the evidence for this dialogue lies outside the scope of our study; nor can we here once more go into the question whether Aristotle is in every sense of the word the "discoverer" of the "fifth element." Philolaus' claims are, in spite of the questions surrounding both the authenticity and the precise meaning of his fragment 12 (*Vorsokr.*, 44B), seriously pondered by W. K. C. Guthrie, *In the Beginning* (London and Ithaca, N.Y., 1957), 128. Actually the Philolaus fragment has neither a mention of the *aether* nor the concept of a fifth physical element, and even if we suppose it to be genuine, nothing would suggest that Aristotle owed his inspiration to the ὁλκάς. A more vexing problem is presented by Xenocrates frg. 53, Heinze, according to which Plato recognized five elements, including the *aether*. This is clearly at variance with the scheme of the *Timaeus*; yet a way may lead from *Tim.* 58d1ff. to *Epin.* 984e (cf. also 981bf.), and if the *Epinomis* here reflects beliefs which Plato held at the end of his life, Xenocrates' testimony would be accounted for. The *aether* as here understood is, however, totally different from Aristotle's. The analysis by Eva Sachs of the tradition about five elements (*Die fünf Platon. Körper* [Berlin, 1917], esp. 41ff.) did much to clear the ground and remains a pioneering study.

a most gratifying reward for his new exploratory venture and a final proof that he had proceeded in the right direction. Without the fifth body or, as he now calls it, "first body," Aristotle's new conception of the simple bodies might have issued in a reaffirmation of the cosmic strata made up of fire, air, water, earth (in this order). It could also have explained, without resorting to cosmogony, why the elements stay in their zones and will do so forever. But it is hard to imagine that the theory of elements moving upward and downward could have thrown light on such crucial questions as the shape and movement of the Cosmos as a whole or on the revolutions of the heavenly bodies. As soon as the fifth element was added, the Cosmos seemed to yield its last secrets. Like the movements from the center and to the center, the circular movement around the center is "natural" to an element. Plato's theological conception which endowed the world soul with this movement is no longer needed to complement the "movements of bodies." [2] From the well-chosen "first assumptions" about natural movements it is possible to deduce the entire structure of the Cosmos. The purely physical approach is triumphant.[3] As for the eternity of our Cosmos, we have seen that the natural places of the four elements could have furnished Aristotle with a proof for it; yet how much better if this sublime idea is associated with the belief in an element which is itself eternally unchanging and exempt from generation and destruction.

We need not linger over the details of Aristotle's proof for the existence of the first body. He does not start from the traditional questions "What movement belongs to the Cosmos as a whole?" and "Why does it have this movement?" but argues from the symmetry of his scheme. His argument is terse and straightforward. The circular movement is a simple movement; thus there must be an element whose nature it is to perform it. However, while asserting that circular motion is as simple and basic a movement as locomotion in a straight line (upward or downward), Aristotle comes forward with another proposition which secures for the new element a status above the others. As a figure, the circle has a "perfection" which the straight line lacks; by this token circular movement is more perfect than linear, and the body engaged in it is "more divine" than the elements

---

[2] Cf. Plato *Legg.* X,897b7ff., 898c6ff. (cf. also *Epin.* 988c4–d4), and Arist. *De caelo* II,1.284a27–35. On the relation between the fifth body and the unmoved mover see pp. 449–451.

[3] Cf. above, Ch. 11.

of the sublunary region. "What is perfect is by nature prior to what is imperfect."[4] Circle and circular movement are perfect because they are complete in themselves, whereas a straight line, if unlimited, lacks this completion or completeness and, if limited, is qua limited of necessity imperfect.

Aristotle has a great deal more to say about the "perfection" of his first body. Having established its greater "worth" on the strength of its specific movement, he proceeds to strip it of attributes that belong to the other elements. For one thing, it is neither heavy nor light[5]— a statement the more remarkable as this pair of opposites was the starting point for Aristotle's new theory of elements. Next Aristotle proves that the first body must be a stranger to generation and destruction. Translated into the affirmative, this means that it is eternal. Although Aristotle for a while avoids using this solemn word, it is sufficiently clear what unique dignity he means to bestow on his new element.[6] Along with generation and destruction he also denies it the possibility of increase and qualitative change.[7] Thus of the four types of change which figure in Aristotle's physical system—locomotion, qualitative alteration, increase, generation and destruction—the first body has only one, local movement. Yet the movement of the first body is of such exalted dignity that, far from being a liability, it confers a claim to divine status. It is the movement which Plato had assigned to mind and world soul.[8] If it is now associated with a physical body, non-physical agents being again eliminated from the Cosmos, this body aspires logically to the same status as Plato's soul.

When Aristotle formulates these conclusions, he speaks of the new element in terms normally reserved for the description of divine beings; while proving it immune from change, he has shown it to be "unageing" and "not suffering."[9] A new divinity has been introduced into the cosmological scheme. We can understand that Aristotle at this point, interrupting, so to speak, the logical course of his argument,

---

[4] I,2.269a18–b17, esp. a19ff.

[5] I,3.269b18–270a12. As the *aether* is neither heavy nor light, its natural motion cannot be motion *toward* a cosmic place (as in the case of the other elements). Instead it is motion *in* its specific area, an incongruity which does not seem to have worried Aristotle. Cf. Cherniss, *Presocr.*, 183.

[6] I,3.270a12ff. The word ἀΐδιον occurs for the first time in 270b1; the ground for it is prepared in a20f.

[7] 270a12ff., 22ff.

[8] See esp. *Legg.* X,898aff. Cf. W. Schadewaldt, *Satura O. Weinreich darge-bracht* (Baden-Baden, 1952), 112.

[9] 270b2.

draws attention to one characteristic which the new deity has in common with the gods of popular belief: Greeks and barbarians alike associate the divine with the "highest region" of the Cosmos, the celestial spaces that are occupied by the *aether*.[10]

Of the solemn predicates which Aristotle uses to celebrate the divine element "unageing" had long been employed to describe the privileged status of the gods.[11] The words which describe it as exempt from becoming and passing away have in his own language somewhat more technical connotations, but we need not doubt that they can acquire a sonorous tone. "Unsuffering" seems to be a new attribute of the deity which takes its place readily beside the traditional epithets of "negative theology." Being an upshot of the new physical interest in the relations of acting and suffering,[12] it is indeed a physicist's contribution to theology. Stylistically, however, it is sufficiently like the other predicates not to create a dissonant note. Beginning with Anaximander, physicists had spoken of their divine principle as indestructible and immortal.[13] They had also defined it as "encompassing everything," a definition which Aristotle later in our treatise applies both to the eternal duration of his new element and to its movement in relation to all other cosmic changes.[14]

To see Aristotle's achievement in the right historical perspective,

[10] 270b4–9; cf. b16–24.

[11] 270b2. Cf. 3.279a18f.; *Od.* 5.218 (*Il.* 8.539, 12.323); Hes. *Theog.* 277 [949, 955]; Anaximander in *Vorsokr.*, 12B3 (Jaeger, *Theology*, 202 n.39); Soph. *O.C.* 607f.

[12] On "acting and suffering" see Ch. 18. ἀπήμαντος is used in Hes. *Theog.* [955] side by side with ἀγήρως of Heracles after he has attained divine status. Aristotle's ἀπαθές has a wider range and is slightly more technical. In the Hellenistic period in which it comes to denote a human ideal it is often used absolutely (as here in Aristotle with reference to the gods; yet see II,1.284a14). This contrasts with the usage in classical authors who like to connect it with a genitive to indicate freedom from specific experiences or evils (see, however, Herod. 9.79 for ἀπαθής = unpunished; cf. L. & S., *s.v.*). Aristotle's ἀγένητον and ἄφθαρτον (270a13) may remind us of similar predicates used by Plato in characterizing the Forms (*Tim.* 52a1) or the soul (e.g., *Phaedr.* 246a1); cf. also Parm. B8.3.

[13] See *Vorsokr.*, A11, 15, B3 (Arist. *Phys.* III,4.203b11ff.). It is hardly necessary here to trace historical connections between the ἀναλλοίωτον of the *aether* (270a14, b2) and the philosophical tradition regarding the unchangeable nature of the deity (note ἀμετάβλητον, I,9.279a32). It may, however, be noted that Diogenes of Apollonia (B5) recommends his principle, the air, precisely on the ground that it is in the highest degree changeable and thereby qualified to operate in a great diversity of ways (for the place of his arguments in the philosophical tradition see K. Deichgräber, *Philologus*, 88 [1933], 353ff.).

[14] Anaximander A15; Anaximenes B2. Cf. Jaeger, *Theology*, 30 and n.39. See *De caelo* I,9.279a23–28; II,1.283b29, 284a6–11.

we should bear in mind the fundamental dualism of Plato's cosmological system. In his scheme the four elements, physical bodies whose substance has no divine ingredients, fill the space between heaven and earth and bring about whatever takes place in this region. The heaven and outer regions of the Cosmos are given over to the operations of the world soul which here holds undisputed sway. The revolution of the outermost heaven as well as the movements of the planetary spheres are its manifestation. Granted that the bodies of the stars consist of fire, their movement is yet analogous—and related—to that of the world soul, and the "physical laws" that govern movements and changes of the elements hardly affect them.[15] On the whole this phase of the Cosmos is constructed by Plato without recourse to the physical properties of the elements. The heaven which for the Presocratics was part of the physical world-scheme—as divine or as little so as the other regions of the world—has been put under a law of its own.

Aristotle does away with this dualism. Having discovered an element to which the movement actually performed by the heaven is "natural," he finds himself in a position to extend physical laws and physical principles of explanation once more to the region which Plato had withdrawn from their domain. Yet the application of physical "hypotheses" to the heavenly areas does not entail a questioning of their divine quality. What happens is rather the opposite. Physics itself now includes a divine element, and the God himself is subject to physical laws and an object of physical studies. The first body takes over many functions of the Platonic world soul, but it can also fill the celestial regions in a material sense (which the world soul cannot do), being at once the stuff of which the heavenly bodies consist and the cause of their revolutions.[16] Plato erred in identifying the origin and agent of circular movement. The difference between this movement and rectilinear ones is not that the former is typical of soul and the latter is performed by bodies, but that the body engaged in the circular movement is of a superior order, immune to the changes and mutual transformations to which the others are liable.

It is curious that Aristotle, who so energetically and at such length polemizes against Plato's mathematical construction of the four ele-

---

[15] *Tim.* 40a; see also b1f. in connection with 34b10–36d7, 38e3ff. We need not in our brief summary consider the relation of soul and heavenly bodies as adumbrated in *Legg.* X,898df.

[16] For the material of the heavenly bodies see II,7.289a11–19.

ments, has only a passing reference to the conception of the world soul.[17] To replace the world soul by a new element was surely as revolutionary a step as to derive the other elements from physical instead of mathematical premises. In fact, it was more revolutionary. The discovery of an eternal entity in the physical world—of a divine "body"—carried dissent beyond the area of "likely tales." Did Aristotle consider it incongruous to discuss religious convictions polemically in a scientific treatise? We have seen that in the *Physics* too he refrains from a direct attack upon Plato's concept of a cosmic soul.[18] Actually in the first two books of our treatise Aristotle crosses the border between science and religion more than once, the crossing being invariably indicated by an elevation of his style.[19] It must be significant that the only polemic against Plato's world soul occurs in a passage whose solemn diction and enthusiastic fervor differ markedly from the language and the purely rational quality of the more technical sections. Originally this passage was written for the dialogue *On Philosophy*.[20] Its style as well as its original place may be indications of the medium which Aristotle regarded as germane to a discussion of the world soul. It is not the medium of scientific reasoning.

That the treatise *On the Heaven* strikes us as compact and intrinsically unified is certainly in large measure the result of Aristotle's success in unifying the doctrine of "natural movements." The same principles of explanation are used throughout Books I, III, and IV as well as in parts of II. If in modern times the revolt against Aristotle's authority took the form of seeking identical laws of motion operating throughout the Universe,[21] Aristotle's own "revolt" against Plato may

---

[17] II,1.284a27–35.

[18] On *Phys.* VIII and its attitude to the world soul see above, pp. 240–245. Regarding the related question of the star-souls, Aristotle's attitude in Book II—the only book where it occasionally becomes acute—seems rather ambiguous. In one chapter (8.292a18ff.) he is emphatic in attributing to them activity and life while protesting against the notion that they should be *apsycha*. In another (12) he deprives them of their activity through his proofs that not the stars (planets) but their spheres move. He appears to be gradually working away from the convictions expressed in the dialogue *On Philosophy*.

[19] I,9.279a17–279b2; II,1. Cf. Jaeger, *Aristotle*, 301ff.

[20] II,1.284a27–35; cf. Jaeger, *Aristotle*, 301ff. Jaeger also claims passages of I,10 for the dialogue.

[21] On this motif and its importance in Galileo see H. Butterfield, *The Origins of Modern Science, 1300–1800* (New York, 1951), 53. Cf. also E. A. Burtt, *The Metaphysical Foundations of Modern Physical Science* (Anchor ed.; New York, 1954), 73ff.; on Newton see *ibid.*, 207ff., 240ff., and *passim*.

be traced to a similar motive. Bent as he was on separating physics from mathematics, the identity does not for him take the shape of mathematical formulas capable of universal application but of a good and purely physical proposition which applies alike to the rotation of the heaven, the revolution of the celestial spheres, and the locomotion of the lower elements.

The first body and its characteristic movement can serve as explanation for questions large and small regarding the phenomena of the celestial region, whereas the natural movements of the other elements cannot so easily be put to practical use. Having established the *aether* hypothesis in Book I, Aristotle can in Book II proceed to complete his account of the heavenly spaces and phenomena and solve the problems partly by means of the new hypothesis, partly on the strength of more specific considerations which he develops as and where needed.[22] The processes and phenomena of the sublunary world are much more complex; not many of them can be understood on the basis of cosmic movements. Their investigation must be left to other treatises.[23] In the books *On the Heaven* Aristotle refrains from considering properties of the four other elements that have no obvious connection with their natural movements. He does, however, in Book III study one aspect which sets them apart from the nature of the heavenly element, to wit, their participation in the process of generation and destruction. Their connection with *genesis* somehow balances the emphasis which Books I and II put on the ungenerated and eternal nature of the *aether*, but there is nothing to balance the inquiry into specific problems that we find in Book II.

Aristotle has linked Books III and IV with I and II by two transitions, one of which stresses a topic common to both sets (scil., "bodies"), while the other briefly points to a characteristic difference between their respective subjects. As we may expect, it is their difference in regard to *genesis*: "*genesis* either does not exist at all or is to be found in these elements" (to be treated in III and IV) "and the bodies compounded of them."[24] To make headway with the problem

[22] See below, Ch. 15.
[23] In particular to *De gen. et corr.* and the *Meteorologica;* yet the biological writings too throw considerable light on the elements and the formation of compound bodies (tissues) out of them.
[24] III,1.298a24–b5, b6–11; see esp. b9–11. The latter passage is a link with Book I, the former with Books I and II. Evidently 298b6–8 is complete as transition, whereas 298a24–b5 cannot stand by itself.

of *genesis* it must be settled how many elements there are besides the
"first" and what they are. As we know, Aristotle's deduction of the
sublunary elements operates with the same first assumption which in
Book I serves him to establish the existence of the celestial. But although the idea of natural movements and places holds good in both
phases of the cosmic system, the alternative "heavy or light" works
only with the sublunary elements. The *aether* is neither heavy nor
light. To put it succinctly, Books III and IV prove that all elements
must have one of these alternative qualities, whereas Book I proves that
the first element has neither.[25] Was Aristotle from the outset prepared
to make this exception? This question is apt to lead us deeper into the
relation of the first body to the elements that Aristotle has in common
with Plato.

It is easy to regard the discovery of the *aether* as an utterly unexpected prize that fell to Aristotle some time after he had embarked
on his novel approach. Having correlated the traditional elements with
the simple movements, he may—gradually or suddenly—have become
aware of the tremendous potentialities latent in the extension of this
approach to one more simple movement, the circular. To go on from
movements in a straight line to the circular would seem a thoroughly
logical and unobjectionable step. A step at the end of which extraordinary rewards were beckoning should certainly be taken.

Yet much may be said for looking at the matter from the opposite
point of view. May not the idea of a celestial element have given
Aristotle the impulse for devising his doctrine of natural motions so
as to bring the theory of the other elements into line with the new-
comer? If the main function of the *aether* is to account for the circular
motion of the heaven—and other movements in the celestial realm—is
not the correlation of the other elements with simple movements a
reflection of this new insight? The insight would be overpowering
enough to suggest a thorough overhauling of the cosmological system,
especially if this system could thereby acquire a remarkable degree of
intrinsic unity. And surely if the remaining phases of the theory were
not brought into conformity with the first body, the latter would not
recommend itself to critical spirits, including Aristotle's own. It would
be an isolated piece of doctrine, out of harmony with the balance of
the system and highly vulnerable to attacks.

On the strength of such considerations a case might be made for

[25] III,2.301a22–b16; I,3.269b18–270a12.

the hypothesis that the major propositions of Books III and IV originated under the influence of the *aether* doctrine.[26] In fact, one may strengthen this case by pointing to certain difficulties and awkward situations that result from making simple movements the basis of the entire structure. One of these awkward results is already known to us, but may now be formulated in somewhat different terms. In the sublunary world Aristotle could find only two natural movements that would correspond to the circular motion of the body in the celestial zone. Yet as he has no thought of reducing the four elements to two, he has in the end to employ arguments of a somewhat different type—ungenerous critics might speak of special pleading—to arrive at the four that the *Timaeus* and the Academy had recognized.[27]

The second difficulty relates to the problem of *genesis*. "Only in these [four elements] can *genesis* be found," says Aristotle when he comes down from heaven to earth [28] and obviously has the best inten-

---

[26] P. Moraux, *Mus. Helv.*, 6 (1949), 157ff., argues on different grounds for a later origin of Books III and IV. In his opinion Book I at one time included an account of the sublunary elements which Aristotle later considered inadequate and replaced by Books III and IV (*ibid.*, p. 160). Moraux does not appear to make sufficient allowance for Aristotle's familiarity with the four elements before he introduced a fifth. I cannot find definite indications for an original discussion of the four elements in Book I. Granted that 268b13f. at first glance seems to promise more than the following chapters provide, does not ch. 2 give the impression that the movements of the other "simple bodies" are known and taken for granted, a situation not at all strange if they had already been set forth in another study? 3.270b26–31 seems a satisfactory sequel to 20–25, and 269b18 to ch. 2 (for 269b29ff. uses the "assumptions" and "proofs" of that chapter so that Moraux' difficulties, p. 163, disappear). 269b21ff. refers to a fuller treatment of the other elements; theoretically the passage may suggest that this treatment was not yet written, but it is also possible that Aristotle found his earlier treatise (now Books III and IV) handy and adequate for the purpose. I agree with Moraux (p. 162) that some passages in Books I and II point to a "redaction" by which they were put together with III and IV. The "redactor" was in all probability Aristotle himself. On 8.277b9–24 (which like 277a12–b9 contributes effectively where we read it to the proof for a single Cosmos) see below, Note 48. Moraux may be right in thinking that 277b24–26 is not the summary of ch. 8 that we may expect (p. 261), but I doubt whether this slight difficulty allows far-reaching inferences.

[27] See above, pp. 293f. When Aristotle makes his transition from the celestial element to the sublunary ones, he actually says: "It remains to speak about the two" (τοῖν δυοῖν; scil., the two other elements). Cf. the commentaries, esp. Guthrie, *ad loc.*, who refers to the pertinent comments of Simplicius and Stocks. As before indicated, I do not infer that Aristotle ever actually recognized two elements only but that in strict logic he could not have recognized more.

[28] III,1.298b10.

tions of penetrating into the nature of this process. Yet hard though he tries, he does not get very far: by tying the four elements to their movements and approaching them entirely from this point of view, he has debarred himself from understanding what really happens when elements change into one another and thus come into being. Neither the concept of movement nor the qualities heavy and light can furnish real help toward this goal. The analysis of matter, in combination with a very different set of qualities (cold and hot, moist and dry) will eventually lead him to it; yet these are the subjects of the treatise *On Coming to Be*, in which the hypotheses of our work are ignored and would in fact be useless.[29] What Aristotle in our books can settle with regard to *genesis* is briefly this: In the sphere of physics, *genesis* is a valid and indispensable concept; the elements are involved in it, and the only convincing way of accounting for their coming into being is to assume that they originate out of, and change into, one another.[30] Aristotle also comes to the point of specifying the four elements that he is prepared to recognize—yet when deducing them (as we know) from the qualities heavy and light, he has nothing concrete to say about their *genesis* out of one another. On the other hand, he succeeds in disposing of the prevailing theories about *genesis*, in particular of Plato's mathematical account.[31] Measured by the theory embodied in the treatise *On Coming to Be*, the results of our books are rather meager. Being committed to natural movements (and to the concepts heavy and light), Aristotle could hardly get farther toward explaining

---

[29] See esp. *De gen.* II,2.329b20ff. This question will receive fuller attention in Ch. 17.

[30] See esp. III,2.301b31–302a9; III,6.7. For what follows cf. P. Moraux, *Les listes anciennes des ouvrages d'Aristote* (Louvain, 1951), 81f. and esp. n.184, where the relationship between *De caelo* III and IV and *De generatione* is described in a few very judicious sentences.

[31] The actual deduction is given in Book IV (4.311b13–312b19). Empedocles, Anaxagoras, and the atomists come in for their share of criticism in III,2, 3, and 7; yet the principal target is unmistakably Plato, to whose geometrical derivation Aristotle returns again and again; 7.306a5–17 states in very strong language the fundamental principles of sound method which Plato has violated. See above, pp. 259f. This is natural enough if these books were worked out while Aristotle was a member of the Academy. If he accepted the Platonic elements and agreed with Plato against Empedocles that they are γεννητά and arise out of one another— extending this principle to earth, which Plato had exempted—it was the more important for him to decide which phases of Plato's account he could not accept and what he wished to put in their place (concerning earth see 306a17ff. and *Tim.* 56d).

genesis.[32] Did he proceed on this unpromising road because it had led him to the discovery of the *aether* and had in connection with the celestial mechanics taken him as far as he could ever hope to go with the help of physical hypotheses?

These arguments may suggest that the concept of natural movements as applied in Books III and IV is an extension or reflection of the *aether* theory presented in Book I. Still, the balance of probability seems to be on the other side.[33] It is natural to think of Aristotle as beginning his work in this field by accepting the four elements which were the basis of Plato's physics, yet revising Plato's theory with a view to eliminating the mathematical motifs and placing the cosmic system on truly physical foundations. If the results fall short of the insights incorporated in the work *On Coming to Be*, why must we assess them with reference to this standard? Taken as an early attempt on the part of Aristotle to clarify his attitude to the *Timaeus*, our two books seem satisfactory and successful. They draw a clear line between Platonic propositions which Aristotle can accept and others which he must reject, and they supply strictly scientific proofs for some of the former, e.g., for the thesis that the four elements are not eternal but

[32] Aristotle does not in our work explain *how* elements change into one another, though in III,7f. he makes clear that his predecessors (including Plato) have failed in their attempts to solve the problem. The last sentences of III express his intention to concentrate on the differences between the elements. This subject has connections with the problem of their *genesis* by mutual transformation. However, as we know, the differences that he actually investigates are heavy and light, and from this investigation Aristotle never finds his way back to *genesis*. III,8.306b20–22 point in the direction in which the treatise *De generatione* actually proceeds; yet how could we take this brief and cryptic statement as an answer to the large question of III,6f.? The statements about "matter" of the elements in IV,4.312a12–5.312a33 would be at best a sketch of an answer, if we could regard them as an organic and original part of the treatise; see, however, above, Ch. 13, Note 32. On the whole cf. Moraux, *op.cit.,* 82 and n.184, with whom I find myself here in complete agreement.

[33] The incongruity emphasized by Cherniss (see Note 5) can hardly establish a presumption for either of the two possible opinions. A refashioning or reinterpretation of the original idea must in either case be assumed, if the first element moves in its place, the others toward their places, and if the one continues in motion whereas the others are in their zones at rest. As far as we can see, Aristotle was not conscious of making these modifications and did not think that he injured the symmetry of his system. Thus the best argument for which one may hope would be that the unconscious remolding would be more likely to operate in one direction than in the other. But any argument of this kind would probably be open to the charge of subjectivism.

come into being and that they can do so only by changing into one another.[34] In addition Aristotle succeeds in finding a closer tie between the cosmic strata and the nature of the elements.[35] His interest in this problem and the prospect of solving it may have made him acquiesce in the shortcomings of his theory—even before the theory produced its most valuable and important results in the form of the *aether* hypothesis. When this hypothesis took shape, it inevitably confirmed Aristotle's confidence in this approach, clear though it must gradually have become that the assumptions which explained the cosmic motions offered no clue to the problem of *genesis*. A different set of premises was needed for this subject; yet Aristotle was ready to pay this price —even the greater price of the resulting rift in his physical system. In our treatise Aristotle makes no actual attempt to use his favorite concepts, heavy and light, for the explanation of the *genesis*, or the changes into one another, of his elements. His last word is that they do originate out of one another;[36] how they do so he cannot now show. Did he realize that he had reached an impasse? Did he try to get farther and give up? The answer to the last question is presumably negative; we have no reason to think that the treatise has reached us incomplete. On the other hand, Books III and IV include no suggestion that another treatise leading deeper into the nature of *genesis* is meant to complete or complement their theory. And when Aristotle did work out the *De generatione et corruptione* he made a new start and did not use our books as an introduction.[37]

As far as their content and arguments go, Books III and IV may once have formed a complete and independent treatise which studied the four accepted elements with reference to their cosmic motions and places and proceeded on the conviction that there are no elements other than these. As Guthrie says, "A[ristotle]'s language often does suggest that in describing the inferior elements he has temporarily

---

[34] See, e.g., III,2.301b31–302a9; 6.304b23–305a15, 305a14–32. Cf. also Note 31.

[35] See above, p. 270, on the significance of III,2.300b8–301a11. Also IV,4 and 5 may be said to arrive at a stratification (see 311b14–312a12; 312a28–30, a33–b19).

[36] See the concluding words of III,6 (305a31ff.). The inquiry to which Aristotle turns next, "What is the manner of this generation out of one another?" (a33ff.), contents itself with negative conclusions regarding the accounts given by Empedocles, Democritus, and Plato.

[37] The *De generatione* begins by developing the differences between *genesis* and the other changes, a topic foreign to our books. On the whole it begins *ab ovo*, though some "negative" points, such as the uselessness of Plato's triangles, are regarded as settled by our treatise (see I,2.315b30ff., 316a2ff.).

forgotten that they are not in his system, as in those of his predecessors, the only bodies in the world." [38] It may be prudent to go thus far and not to push on to further conclusions. Still, the only passage where the *aether* is at all mentioned is in the "transition" from the one set of books to the other, and as soon as the independent origin of III and IV is considered, the transition would as a matter of course acquire the function of integrating an earlier and a later treatise.[39] For the rest, is it mere pedantry to expect that Aristotle, instead of saying "of necessity each body has either a definite weight or a definite lightness" or "the elements must be subject to generation and destruction," should say "each body except the first" or "the elements other than the *aether*"? [40] Patience is a virtue, and we may try to be patient with Aristotle's forgetfulness; but this forgetfulness goes astonishingly far when Aristotle asserts that there are "no more than two simple local movements" (scil., upward and downward). And when we read that a body neither heavy nor light could move only by compulsion and would thereby be carried an infinite distance, our patience is beginning

[38] "Introduction" to the Loeb edition, xiv n. Guthrie (*ibid.*) seems inclined to think that IV,4.312a4, τὸ ἔσχατον τῆς χώρας ἐν ᾗ ποιοῦνται τὴν κίνησιν (scil., the four elements), is so worded as to leave room for the *aether*. This explanation, although not entirely cogent, is probably better than what Simplicius offers. I should also consider it possible that of the two relative clauses in 311b25 and 26, which can hardly stand side by side, one—presumably the second—was put in later and for the same reason, i.e., not to interfere with the existence of the fifth body. (Note the more cautious phrasing in I,3.269b23-26 and also II,14.296b14ff. as contrasted with b29 and 13.295b27f., 296a12ff. On 296b14f. cf. Simplicius, *ad loc.*, and Alexander *apud* Simplicius.)

We have already found evidence of additions in this section, and as it gives us the essence of Aristotle's own theory—whereas most of the other chapters are primarily polemical—it would not be surprising if Aristotle, by a few touches, tried to bring it up to date. However, I should not assert this with confidence so far as the *aether* theory is concerned; my impression is that he did more to adjust the doctrine of this section by way of later additions to that of *De generatione* (see above, Ch. 13, Note 32) than to take account of *De caelo* I. See below, Note 41, on 301a20ff.

[39] III,1.298a25, b6. It has been noted above (p. 293) that the second transition stresses the motif of *genesis* to which the first pays little attention. An explanation would be that Aristotle wrote the first later than the second and at a time when he had solved the problem of *genesis* in other works. Yet if Books III and IV were an independent treatise, it is noteworthy that no part of the original introduction to it has survived. Could it be possible that a part of it is embodied in the first "transition" (a28-b4 or b5; note a30f., which suggests that the entire Cosmos is made up of the four elements)?

[40] III,2.301b16 (this passage may be used to argue that nothing of any consequence should be inferred from the word ἔνια in a22); 6.305a13f.

to be overtaxed. Must we really try to persuade ourselves that there is no contradiction between these speculations and the doctrines of Book I about the natural movement of a body which has neither weight nor lightness? [41] Are we constantly to bear in mind that the laws which Aristotle now lays down hold good only of the lower elements? They certainly make sense only in reference to these. But everything in these books (III and IV) would also make sense on the assumption that Aristotle does not yet know the first element as a body with a natural movement of its own; the "forgetting" might as well be a "not knowing." When Aristotle in Book IV establishes the concept of a cosmic center (μέσον) to which all earthy bodies move, he adds: "Whether it in fact is the centre of the earth or the centre of the Universe to which they move—the two being at the same point—belongs to another inquiry." [42] Actually this problem has been settled in Book II, and a reference to "another inquiry" would be odd and as far as I can see unusual if Book I and II really at the time were part of the same treatise as Book IV. "This has been discussed previously" is the phrase which Aristotle generally uses on such occasions.[43] The passage is the more noteworthy as it is the only one that touches on matters taken up in the other set of books—yet it does not at all have the form of a "reference."

We may read Books I and II as presupposing the doctrine of natural movements and their correlation with the elements, i.e., the content of III and IV; [44] but III and IV never presuppose any of the con-

---

[41] For two simple movements see III,4.303b5. For the movements of a body which has neither weight nor lightness see III,2.301a20–301b1, esp. 301b1–16, and I,3.269b18–270a12. Stocks (*ad* 301a22) observes the contrast between ἔνια in the sentence ὅτι δ' ἔνια ἔχειν ἀναγκαῖον ῥοπὴν βάρους καὶ κουφότητος and the πᾶν (ἄπαν) in 301b16 and b30. His rendering "that there are certain bodies" would be correct on any interpretation. Theoretically it is possible that ἔνια was used by Aristotle in his original draft to forestall a misunderstanding of the later πάντα. Yet it may also be a correction, and not even necessarily Aristotle's own.

[42] IV,4.312a1–3 (Guthrie's translation has been used).

[43] Cf. II,14.296b6–25. As Bonitz says (97b35ff.), an obvious meaning of the phrase ἄλλος λόγος is that *quaestio aliqua simpliciter ab hoc loco removetur*, yet he records no instance in which Aristotle employs it for a question that has actually been treated in the same work (in *De caelo* III,1.299a1 ἕτερος λόγος is used in reference to a matter which falls outside the range of our work).

[44] I,2.268b26–269a9 may be read as a summary of the doctrine of natural movements as developed in III (and IV), this doctrine being now extended to the new element. The discussion of heavy and light in I,3 actually refers ahead (269b21f.) to the fuller theory to be presented in IV. Note also the reference in I,8.277b23f. to IV,4.5 and the identity of the arguments in I,8.277a12–18 and IV,3.310a15–27

clusions reached in I and II. The conceptual pattern of Books III and IV provides the categories which figure in the deduction of the first body. This could perhaps be explained by the supposition that Aristotle was perfectly sure what he was going to say in these books. But if these books are ignorant of I and II, it is better to distinguish two strata in Aristotle's cosmology. General considerations have prepared us to recognize a period in which Aristotle revised Plato's theory under the concept of natural movements but had not yet proceeded to the point of deducing an additional element from this concept. Books III and IV may date from this period and show Aristotle's thought at a stage when he knew only two natural movements, up and down, and had correlated these with the four elements of Empedocles and Plato.[45] We can perceive the same stage of his doctrine in the dialogue *On Philosophy* where he recognized two natural movements—downward on account of weight and upward through lightness—and concluded that the circular movement of the heavenly bodies cannot be natural but must be regarded as voluntary.[46] Here the *aether*, though an element, was not yet included in the "physical" approach to the elements. The *Physics*, which knows the four elements, never mentions a fifth. A passage of this work gives us the stratification of the Cosmos, starting with the earth: although the circumference and the circular motion of the whole are important for the argument, only four elements are enumerated, and the word "aether" is used of the fire—a "misuse of language" for which Aristotle censures Anaxagoras in Book I of our treatise.[47]

(the passages are so close that 310a22f. confirms the addition of the word μεταβολῶν after ἄλλων in 277a13f. which would perhaps recommend itself even without the parallel).

There are obvious reasons why Aristotle, once the theory of the divine body and the heavenly regions was worked out, would put it ahead of the other elements rather than make it a sequel to the books dealing with them.

[45] Professor Gigon's observations (*Mus. Helv.*, 9 [1952], 133) lead him to similar conclusions regarding the relation of Book IV to I. He too believes that Book IV "einmal an die kosmologische Pragmatie angegliedert wurde." The idea of an "Angliederung" has much to recommend it. So far, however, I know of no reason why III and IV should not be regarded as a unit.

[46] Frg. 21, Walzer (24 Rose; Cic. *De nat. deor.* II,44). Cf. Guthrie, *Cl. Q.*, 27 (1933), 166. Note the texts in Walzer, *Arist. dialog. fragmenta* (Florence, 1934), 85 n.2.

[47] *Phys.* IV,5.212b20–22 (cf. Ross, *ad loc.*, who refers among other passages to *De caelo* I,9.270b24 and III,3.302b4, in the former of which Anaxagoras is taken to task). While investigating the Infinite, place, and void in *Phys.* III and IV, Aristotle never brings up the problem of their compatibility or incompatibility

In the large array of arguments which Aristotle in Book I marshals against the belief in an infinite body and in a plurality of worlds there are some which operate only with the sublunary elements, leaving the *aether* out of account.[48] The same book includes passages in which Aristotle says that "there is no other movement" (besides up and down) or considers it fatal for the idea of an infinite Cosmos that not every body in it "would have either weight or lightness"—forgetting,

---

with the existence of a fifth body, though he mentions the sublunary elements and their natural motions—e.g., III,5.205a7ff.; IV,1.208b8ff. (19f.); 8.214b12ff. On the presumable date of *Phys.* I–VII see above, Ch. 3, Note 10. The relationship of Book VIII to the *aether* doctrine is a separate problem, on which see Ch. 12, Note 62, and my comments in *Aristotle and Plato in the Mid-Fourth Century* (ed. by I. Düring and G. E. L. Owen; Göteborg, 1960), 224–234.

Guthrie ("Introduction" to Loeb edition, xxviii) discusses the references to the *Physics* that are found in our treatise and inclines to the view that they are later additions. On the whole I find no difficulty in thinking that both sets of books (I,II as well as III,IV) presuppose the doctrine of *Phys.* I–VII, though I agree with Guthrie that *Phys.* VIII is probably later than any part of *De caelo*. The one exception as far as the references go is IV,3.311a10–12 (which refers to *Phys.* VIII,4). Here Guthrie is right in saying that it is "particularly loosely attached to the argument," that it is an "appendage" (occurring as it does at the end of a section) and "not an apt conclusion to a series of arguments" (*op.cit.*, xxiv). For the preceding arguments operate on the contrary assumption, scil., that motion belongs to the nature of bodies, whereas this passage introduces agents outside them (the first mover?) and the removal of obstacles as the causes of movement. Cf. our discussion above, pp. 232–234, concerning the relation of *Phys.* VIII,4 to the doctrine of nature as a principle of movement.

[48] The relevant sections are I,7.274a19–b25 (for the first assumptions here employed, cf. III,4, esp. 303b3–8, and IV,4.311b13–312a8) and 275b18–8.277b9. The first section is "completed" by a few sentences (b25–29) which bring the new element to bear on the problem. Note the flagrant contradiction between these sentences and b23–25. In the second section circular movement is mentioned, 277a23–26, in a parenthesis (rightly set off by Guthrie, not quite correctly by Allan) whose function it is to bring this movement under a rule which was not devised for it. Aristotle's original argument against an infinite body may have been that there cannot be either infinite weight or infinite lightness; where we read it (I,6.273a21–274a18) this argument forms part of a larger complex of proofs which take account of the element with circular movement and use the "weight and lightness" motif with reference to the sublunary bodies (271b23–274a18). Among the arguments which presuppose the *aether* doctrine, 277b9–25 is remarkable in that it departs from the pattern of opposites in the sublunary world: it treats the *aether* as being without weight, the fire as "having weight," and the earth as heavy (b19), putting a tripartite scheme in the place of the customary antithesis. Had this antithesis which is so essential for Books III and IV lost some of its significance for Aristotle when the *aether* acquired a dominating position in his thought? I should believe this more readily than that the section once belonged to an account of the sublunary elements; see, however, for different inferences, Moraux, *op.cit.*, 161.

it would seem, that he himself knows such a body.[49] Thus our hypothesis that Aristotle at one time operated with four elements only finds support also outside Books III and IV.[50] But although every piece of evidence and corroboratory evidence is welcome, due weight should be given as well to considerations of a more general kind. The thesis that Aristotle began by applying his new method to the four elements of the *Timaeus* and later expanded his scheme by incorporating a fifth has its intrinsic logic and historical probability. A development in this direction is in no way παρὰ φύσιν; on the contrary, it is both rational and psychologically convincing.

[49] I,7.274b23 (the next argument, b25–29, which operates with the circular movement, invalidates the point made in 22–25), 276a15f. The connection of the latter passage with the preceding sentence is problematic (Allan's text strikes me as an improvement over Bekker's, which Guthrie adopts), yet I feel sure that only the translation of Stocks, not that of Guthrie, does justice to the Greek of a15/16. The main question is whether Aristotle here draws an inference from his opponents' views or whether he out of context adds his own mature doctrine to which the argument so far has not lived up (on this view one would have to read ἀνάγκη δὲ—the tradition suggests δὴ—μὴ πάντα ἢ βάρος ἔχειν ἢ κουφότητα, ἀλλὰ τὰ μέν, τὰ δ'οὔ); a third possibility, later interpolation, seems remote. On either supposition the sentence is peculiar and invites thought.

[50] Whether Aristotle actually transferred material from Book IV to Book I, as Gigon suggests (*op.cit.*, 133f.), I do not know; my position is, however, close to his inasmuch as I regard some arguments in Book I as reflecting the doctrines of (III and) IV rather than of I.

15

The Subjects of Book II

AS the *aether* fills the entire heavenly region down to the sphere of the moon, one might expect Aristotle in Book II, where he deals with the phenomena of this region, to bring his new element to bear on as many individual problems as possible. But this is not the case. Not a few problems can be solved without recourse either to the first element or to the first assumptions. Others are entirely outside the competence of the physicist, and as they had been settled in masterly and authoritative fashion by contemporary astronomers, Aristotle's hands are tied and his own contribution must keep within strictly defined limits. Accepting the decisions of Eudoxus and his school, he makes it his task to bring them into harmony with his own cosmological and theological convictions. He would clearly have welcomed it if the number of planetary movements increased in correspondence to the distance of the planets from the "first heaven." [1] Yet the astronomers had ruled otherwise, and the cosmological theory must conform to their findings. Aristotle's explanation is that the capacity of attaining perfection decreases with the distance from the first heaven. Whereas the first heaven reaches this goal by a single movement, the planets relatively near to it do so by a plurality of movements; as the distance increases, perfection is no longer within reach, and a few movements are the maximum effort that the lower planets can make while trying to approximate it. [2] In the *Timaeus* the ratios of the distances between the

[1] II,12.291b28–292a1. Note also the reference to astronomical findings in ch. 10 (291a31,b9). For the contemporary developments in Greek astronomy cf. Sir Thomas Heath, *Aristarchus of Samos* (Oxford, 1913), 190ff., 225ff., 249ff.

[2] II,12.292a18–b25.

planets contribute much to the sublime order and the harmony of the Cosmos. By leaving matters of this kind to "the mathematicians" and theorizing only on a few aspects of their system, Aristotle deprives his cosmological scheme of some great and persuasive manifestations of order in the world. He can find new evidence of order even in the terrestrial phases of the world,[3] but for the celestial region he contents himself with distilling reason and a profoundly meaningful scheme from a system which he does not present in its details.[4]

There is actually only one subject, the substance of the stars, to which the *aether* theory is applied with decisive effect. The stars must henceforth be held to consist not of fire but of the first body.[5] This new theory has the disadvantage that it cannot account as easily as earlier doctrines for their heat and radiance. But Aristotle is not discouraged by this difficulty. The air beneath the heavenly region is ignited by the movement of the stars (since "movement ignites even wood, stone, and iron"), and the heat and light which the stars are commonly supposed to emit are actually this effect of their rotation upon the air.[6]

The question why the outermost heaven moves as it does and not in the opposite direction can be answered without bringing the new element into the argument. It suffices if Aristotle can show that the movement actually performed is the nobler of the two possibilities.[7] The similar problem regarding "right" and "left" in the Cosmos can be attacked only after a good deal of preliminary spadework has been done, since the validity of these concepts in a spherical Cosmos needs to be proved.[8] Yet the element responsible for the sphericity is again irrelevant to the issue.

[3] See below, Ch. 21.   [4] See, besides ch. 12, also ch. 10.

[5] II,7. The doctrines of earlier thinkers are considerably more complex than Aristotle's summary (289a16ff.) makes them appear. For the Presocratic material see Kranz's Index, 78b3ff.; for a discussion of the evidence see Cherniss, *Presocr.*, 184 n.171. Plato states his view in *Tim.* 40a2ff.

[6] 289a19–35; for a good statement of the problems to which this view gives rise see Guthrie's note on the chapter.

[7] II,5.

[8] II,2. Aristotle's answer includes the surprising thesis that the cosmic hemisphere which we see is the "lower." The reason is given in 285b16ff. The notion that "we call right where the movement starts" may also underlie Plato *Legg.* VI,760d1 and a passage in the *Epinomis* (987b5). *Tim.* 36c suggests a different idea (scil., the Pythagorean from which Aristotle sets himself apart). The relationship of these passages is correctly stated by Guthrie, *ad loc.*, and others whom he cites, including E. des Places, *Mélanges Cumont* (Brussels, 1936), 1.135. Des Places's more

That the Pythagorean harmony of the spheres can be rejected mainly on the ground of its intrinsic improbability and that the *aether* does not figure in this refutation is not particularly surprising.[9] A question of much greater complexity—and importance—is whether the heavenly bodies move by themselves or are carried around by their "spheres." Aristotle's answer is that the stars have no movement of their own.[10] The alternative views according to which either the stars alone or stars as well as spheres would move create considerable difficulties which are, however, again in no way connected with the element in which the movements take place. The only passage in this chapter where Aristotle refers to this element is a sentence in which he says that "like the others" he considers it logical to believe in a spherical shape of the stars "since we produce them out of this body," i.e., out of the *aether* to which spherical form and movement are natural.[11] Yet while spherical form is ideally suited to the motion in the same place in which the heaven as a whole is engaged, it is utterly unsuited to the forward movement which the individual stars would have to perform if it were correct to credit them with any motion of their own. Thus in one sense spherical shape is "least adapted to movement." "Nature makes nothing in an irrational way or to no purpose"; to the stars, which perform no movement by themselves, has been allotted no organ of movement and of all shapes that which is least suited to motion.[12] What kinds of motion would be easy or natural for a spherical body and what would not are evidently questions for which the element responsible for spherical form and circular movement need not be taken into consideration. Actually the *aether* could not help Aristotle in his argument; had it been brought in, it would have created a presumption for circular movement of the stars themselves, the opposite of the theory which Aristotle favors.

---

recent discussion of the question in the "Introduction" to his edition of the *Epinomis* (*Platon* 12.2, Budé ed. [Paris, 1956], 103) seems to me no improvement on his earlier position. B. Einarson (*Cl. Ph.*, 53 [1958], 91f.) complicates matters unnecessarily by bringing *Epin.* 984d5, 985e2 into the discussion.

[9] II,9.

[10] II,8 (for the arguments ruling out other possibilities see 289b4–30; for those supporting Aristotle's own conclusion *ibid.*, b30–290b11). It is not completely clear whether Aristotle is speaking of the planets, the fixed stars, or both. The arguments drawn from the spherical shape (290a7ff.) obviously apply to both categories, and so, in all probability, does the conclusion.

[11] *Ibid.*, 290a8 (cf. II,7).

[12] *Ibid.*, 290a7ff., esp. 29–b11; cf. 11.291b11–17.

Two other subjects taken up in this book may be briefly considered. In the *Timaeus* Plato decides that the shape of the entire Cosmos cannot be other than spherical.[13] His arguments are anything but empirical. The sphere is of all geometrical figures the most comprehensive, the most symmetrical, the most beautiful; in one word, it is the most perfect. The same idea informs several of Aristotle's proofs for the sphericity of the heaven. Regarding it as axiomatic that the shape of the entire Cosmos must be the "first" and most perfect geometrical figure, Aristotle proves in a variety of ways that only the circle and the sphere are perfect. It is not too much to say that his chief preoccupation is to establish this proposition.[14] He does not argue that an element engaged in circular motion and below the circumference of the Cosmos determines by this motion the shape of the Cosmos, but, having decided which figure is first and perfect, he assigns this figure to the first element.[15] By thus proceeding he establishes at once the sphericity of the Cosmos as a whole and the spherical shape of all elements insofar as they are cosmic strata (since each must adjust itself to the shape of the outermost). Next follow some further arguments for the spherical shape of the Cosmos. These are of a somewhat different type and without analogue in the *Timaeus*, none being based either on the concept of perfection or on the presence of the *aether* in the heavenly regions. If no void is ever to arise in the course of the celestial rotation, if the movement of the heaven is to serve as measurement for all other movements, if even here in the center of the Cosmos the surface of the water is spherical (and necessarily so; it can be proved), we should not hesitate to infer that the heaven has this shape.[16] Is Aristotle anxious to show that important cosmological doctrines, while fully in accord with his new theory, may yet be proved without resort to it? Does he think that if these doctrines are established independently they will lend additional force to his new departure? Or had he conceived some of the arguments before he had discovered the first body? These questions can hardly be answered. We should, however, note that having demonstrated the sphericity of the Cosmos by so many different arguments, Aristotle in the last sentences of this chapter asserts with

[13] *Tim.* 33b.
[14] II,4.286b10–287a2 (*teleion*, b18; this concept is the keynote of the corresponding section in the *Timaeus*, 32cff.).
[15] 287a2–5.   [16] 287a11–b14.

great emphasis that nothing in our human experience can furnish us with an idea of the utterly flawless rotundity which characterizes the world as a whole; for none of the other elements is "capable of taking such a smooth and accurate finish as the nature of the body encompassing the rest." [17]

It may surprise us to find the regular movement of the outermost heaven among the propositions which Aristotle has to support by careful arguments.[18] For does not the firm conviction of this regularity lie at the root of the entire cosmological and theological movement which is reflected in the dialogues of Plato's old age and in Aristotle's own approach to the Cosmos? Evidently Aristotle thought it desirable to provide new foundations for this central dogma. He draws his arguments partly from certain general propositions regarding the circumstances under which irregular or accelerated motion may obtain, partly from the specific properties of circular movement and eternal movement. In the case of the heaven such prior conditions as would account for a change in speed do not exist.[19] Two arguments make use of the first body, one by referring to its unchanging quality, the other by insisting that the rotation in question is carried out by a simple body which finds itself in its proper place and has no opposite that could interfere with its movement.[20] Let us, however, note that these references to the peculiarities of the fifth body occur in the context of rather complex demonstrations. In both instances they are a

---

[17] 287b14-21.   [18] II,6.   [19] *Ibid.*, esp. 288a17ff., b30ff.

[20] 288a28-b7 (esp. a34ff.), b7-22. The first argument refers not only to the moving body, scil., the *aether*, but remarkably enough also to the entity moving it. On the whole Aristotle develops his cosmological theory in our treatise without taking account of a first mover, and I,9.279a30ff. (and perhaps II,3.286a3-11, even with the reading θεῖον of J in 10) would seem to exclude his existence. See, however, above, Ch. 12, Note 24, and note also II,12.292a22f. The only specific point made about the nature of the κινοῦν in 288a27ff. is that it must be without body (b6); apart from this, Aristotle argues (without reference to anything "previously" established) that it must have the same outstanding qualities as the entity moved by it (simple, eternal, etc.). To justify my reference above in this note to I,9.279a30ff. I add that I cannot follow Cherniss, *Pl. and the Acad.*, 587f., in regarding 279a18-35 as "a long but unified parenthesis." On this view there would be no obvious justification for the statements of 279b1-3 in this context at all; the transition to the first heaven in b1 would be obscure, and the sentence in b1 would lack a grammatical subject. The connection which Cherniss constructs (with the help of the *topos* motif) between a17f. and b1-3 strikes me as forced (not a17f. but b1-3 supplies the reason for b1). As I understand the section, Aristotle returns in a25 to the heaven. The meaning of 279a34f. is not that the heaven does not move itself but that its general condition cannot change either to a worse or to a better status; hence its ἀμετάβλητον (32).

part of the argument, not the entire argument. Thus the last that Aristotle would do was to declare that the movement of the heaven must be regular because it is the movement of a body whose nature does not admit change.

In fact, the type of reasoning which Aristotle uses not just once or twice but again and again in this book operates with the perfect condition of things in the heavenly region.[21] This perfection manifests itself in the circular movements, especially of the first heaven. Although Aristotle feels just pride in having discovered an element that realizes these movements, the conviction that everything here is perfect and the heaven itself divine is even more fundamental. This conviction antedates the new doctrine and has inspired it. It is one of the never-questioned presuppositions that Aristotle's cosmology has inherited from Plato's. Aristotle's arguments have their antecedents in the sections of the *Timaeus* where the perfect "goodness" of the Cosmos helps to establish its uniqueness, its spherical shape, and a number of other cosmological tenets.[22] For Aristotle the eternal regular motion of the outermost heaven is the life of the divine principle. The closer an entity is to the outermost sphere, the higher is the degree in which it participates in the divine perfection.[23] Aristotle cannot, like Plato, represent the perfect condition of these regions as the result of a divine plan ($\lambda o\gamma\iota\sigma\mu\acute{o}s$), nor can he regard the physical Cosmos as the copy of another Cosmos in the realm of Forms and explain what is perfect in the former as approximation or imitation of the latter.[24] The perfection is immanent in the Cosmos, and the belief in it has for Aristotle the force of a religious conviction. The doctrine of the "first element" and some of the propositions which Aristotle proves in Book II substantiate this conviction and give it a more concrete form; but there can be no doubt that the conviction itself is prior to the individual tenets. Again and again it enters as a premise into the arguments that prove the validity of specific proposi-

[21] The deduction in ch. 3 (see below, p. 310) rests on the divine quality of the first heaven (286a10); see, further, 4.286b10ff., 5.288a2ff., 6.288a18ff., 27ff., 8.290a29ff., 12.292a22ff., b28ff. Some arguments simply take the form that nature always realizes the best (e.g., 288a9, 291a24), a point of view which is not confined to the celestial phenomena; but Aristotle gives this argument a specific turn by suggesting that nature, which never operates haphazardly, would certainly not do so in connection with beings of such outstanding worth (290a32).

[22] See *Tim.* 31af., 33b, 33b–d; cf. A. J. Festugière, *Le Dieu Cosmique* (*La révélation d'Hermès Trismég.*, 2 [Paris, 1949]), 104f.

[23] 3.286a9; cf. 12.292a14–b25. [24] See *Tim.* 29e–31b and *passim*.

tions.[25] The teleological criterion, as used by Plato and Aristotle, replaces the principle of justice which had inspired so many cosmological visions in the sixth and fifth centuries.[26]

For Plato's conception it was essential that the Cosmos should be considered as a living being; at the same time, being anxious to guard this idea against "zoomorphic" misunderstandings, he goes into detail to show that the Cosmos needs none of the organs and has but few of the functions that are generally characteristic of living entities. For Aristotle too the Cosmos is alive;[27] yet somehow this quality is for him less essential or less vividly apprehended than its divinity, and the need of protesting against zoomorphic notions is no longer acute. On the other hand, Plato had, in the same early and basic section[28] of the *Timaeus*, "deduced" the presence of the elements from the existence of a physical Cosmos, and it is easy to understand that Aristotle too considers such an a priori deduction desirable. We have already seen that the deduction of the elements in Book IV of *De caelo* has some features in common with that of the *Timaeus;*[29] there, however, Aristotle does not take the existence of the Cosmos as his starting point. Moreover, some of Aristotle's arguments proceed in what one may call the opposite direction: he needs the elements with their natural movements and places to establish his concept of the Cosmos, its singleness and its eternity.[30] Still, a chapter of Book II shows that he too can derive the elements from the existence of the Cosmos, although the specific premise from which he here starts is the existence of a divine element engaged in circular motion. Such motion needs a center, and a center which is at rest.[31] This argument suffices to deduce the existence of the earth, and as soon as the earth has been shown to exist "of necessity," Aristotle can once more use his concepts of contraries and intermediaries to deduce the remaining three elements.[32]

To be precise, Aristotle in this chapter proves even more than the necessary existence of the four sublunary elements as corollaries to

[25] See Note 21; cf. *De philos.* 12, 13, 18 Walzer.

[26] See in particular Jaeger, *Paideia*, 1.216ff., and *Theology*, 33ff., 139ff., and *passim;* Vlastos, *Cl. Ph.*, 42 (1947), 156ff. (cf. also Vlastos, *A. J. Ph.*, 76 [1955], 356 on Heracl. B 80).

[27] See esp. II,2.285a29. For Plato cf. *Tim.* 30c, 32c–34a, and *passim*.

[28] *Tim.* 31b–32c.   [29] See above, p. 285.

[30] I,8.276a18–277a12; 9.278b21–279a11; see also III,2.300b8–301a20. See above, Chs. 11 and 12.

[31] II,3.286a12–22.   [32] *Ibid.*, 22–31.

the existence of the divine first. As the four elements are not eternal but liable to suffer from, and be destroyed by, one another, the same arguments which convince us of their existence in the Cosmos also establish the "necessity" of *genesis*. Now *genesis*, while it may be found implied in the existence of the elements, points to still another set of causes. To operate as it does it requires the existence of more than one heavenly movement. The rotation of the outermost heaven could never account for changes in the sublunary world; yet the planetary movements do have this kind of effect. In particular—as we may interpolate from other contexts where Aristotle is less sparing of detail—the sun through its alternate approaching and receding has the strongest influence on growth, life, and other changes in the central regions of the Cosmos. Thus the existence of the planetary movements follows of necessity from that of the four elements whose own existence is necessarily connected with that of earth, earth itself being postulated as the stable center for the heavenly revolution.[33] One may say that all essential phases of the Cosmos are deduced by this one train of a priori reasoning.

In Plato the existence and the direction of the planetary movements are linked to the structure of the world soul. The movements have no teleological connection with *genesis* but besides contributing to the beauty of the Cosmos are needed to furnish the Cosmos and man with the pattern of time. Although Plato, too, seems to base his account on the prevailing system of the astronomers, he goes farther than Aristotle in providing a philosophical rationale for the astronomical doctrines.[34] Aristotle nowhere in Book II so much as mentions the number of the planets—or the number of their movements. As has already been said, he accepts the system of heavenly movements in the form in which it had been worked out by contemporary authorities, in particular by Eudoxus, with whom he had become acquainted in the Academy.[35] A philosophical rationale is supplied by the state-

[33] *Ibid.*, 21–b9. Aristotle promises in b5 a fuller exposition of the relevant doctrines regarding planetary movements; see *De gen.* II,10.

[34] *Tim.* 35a–36d; cf. Heath's chapter on Eudoxus, *op.cit.*, 190ff., and Cornford's remark that "the system [of Eudoxus] must have been known to Plato and the probability is that he incorporated in the *Timaeus* as much of it as he could accept" (*Cosmology*, 92).

[35] For Aristotle's connections with Eudoxus see esp. Jaeger, *Aristotle*, 16f., 131, 342f. The details of the astronomical system worked out by Eudoxus and his school are particularly important for *Metaph.* Λ8 (Jaeger, *Aristotle*, 342ff.), where Aristotle actually gives a fuller report about them. For the chronology of Eudoxus

ment that more than one heavenly movement is needed to produce *genesis;* but this brief statement determines nothing about the number of the "other movements," nor is it here mentioned that these movements are opposite in direction to that of the first heaven.[36] Still, there is one question which evidently cannot be handed over to the "mathematicians"; when Aristotle examines the alternative explanations available for the movements of the heavenly bodies, he reaches the decision that not the stars themselves but their spheres perform them. This decision differs from Plato's; although Aristotle too thinks of the stars as living beings, he does not regard it as necessary or desirable that they should have a local movement of their own.[37]

The final section of Book II is devoted to a very full discussion of topics pertaining to the earth. There is the question of its place in the cosmic scheme, of its shape, and in addition the problem whether it is at rest or in movement. These are questions of long standing in the history of cosmological speculation, and it is not surprising that Aristotle here has more occasion than elsewhere in Book II to mention, and polemize against, the opinions of his predecessors. Plato, too, had spoken of the earth at the corresponding juncture of his account, i.e., after discussing the planetary movements and the heavenly bodies; briefly and rather dogmatically he had assigned to earth a motion whose nature and rationale have caused the interpreters no end of worry.[38] This time Aristotle's solution springs entirely from his new concept of natural movements and natural places. One and all, his

---

see K. von Fritz, *Philologus*, 85 (1929), 478ff., where it is argued that he died shortly after Plato.

[36] 286b2–4; for a brief reference to the "opposite direction" of the planetary movements see 10.291b2.

[37] II,8.289b31–290b11; cf. Plato *Tim.* 40af.

[38] *Tim.* 40b8–c3. Aristotle (*De caelo* II,13.293b30ff.; 14.296a26ff.) understood correctly that in *Tim.* 40b8 the earth is meant to be at the center of the Cosmos. Regarding the text of 40b8ff. I follow Cornford, *Cosmology*, 120 n.1, and accept the main idea of his explanation (*ibid.*, 131ff.; approximated by Th. H. Martin, *Etudes sur le Timée de Platon* [Paris, 1841], 2.86ff.), to wit, that the earth by a rotary motion of its own must counteract the diurnal revolution of the "same," since if earth were swept away by this it could not be "guardian of day and night." To what kind of impulse Plato would attribute this counteraction I see no way of deciding with confidence, though it is certainly significant that earth is here thought of as a divine being (cf. my *Hesiod and Aeschylus* [Ithaca, N.Y., 1949], 105 n.8). Cherniss' arguments against Cornford are convincing in most points of cosmological doctrine (*Pl. and the Acad.*, 555) but should leave us free to understand that Plato here concentrates on earth's own motion, not on the combined effect of two contrary motions. Inevitably Aristotle's reference (II,13.293b30–32)

precursors have fumbled because they failed to grasp these concepts, and Aristotle's own handling of these questions is particularly triumphant because his "first assumptions" allow him at one stroke to settle all three. The earth is in the center because the natural movement of the element earth is toward the center of the Cosmos; it is stationary because every element—at least each of the sublunary elements—is at rest when it has reached the goal of its movement; and it has spherical shape because each part or particle of earth is anxious to be as near the center as possible; the particles tend to shift their place until they have satisfied this desire, and only when they have arranged themselves in the shape of a sphere can they be content, since every other geometrical figure would leave some of them at greater distance from the center than is necessary.[39] Thus there is no need to adduce one reason, like the cosmogonic whirl, for the place of the earth, another for its shape, and perhaps still a third for its condition of rest or motion; nor should one explanation be given for the coming together of earth in the center and another for its remaining

---

to *Tim.* 40b8 has played an important part in the history of its exegesis. For the cosmological context in the *Timaeus* (scil., the heavenly bodies and their movements) note 39e-40d. The place and shape of the earth are not clearly indicated in the *Timaeus* passage; see, however, *Phaedo* 108ef.

[39] II,13.294b30ff., 295b19ff.; 14.296b6ff., b25ff., 297a5ff. In ch. 13 Aristotle provides much information of great value about the earlier theories regarding the place of the earth in the Cosmos and the reasons why it was held to remain in its place. He also mentions the hypothesis of its sphericity as one of the opinions already in vogue and refers to objections that had been raised against it (293b32–294a10), but he does not record the names of its proponents. The origin of this doctrine has been debated with much zest since Erich Frank (*Plato u. d. sogenannten Pythagoreer* [Halle, 1923], 184ff.) challenged the traditional ascription to Pythagoras and Parmenides and maintained that the theory as put forward by Plato in *Phaedo* 108e4ff. has the character of a novelty. T. G. Rosenmeyer, *Cl. Q.*, 49 (1956), 193, questions even Plato's advocacy of this doctrine. He rests his case in part on the ambiguity of the word περιφερής (e5), while minimizing the comparison with σφαῖραι in 110b7. The most that may be conceded is that Plato does not commit himself unambiguously and beyond every possibility of doubt. As for the element of "novelty," it is indeed not quite clear with which part of the theory it should be associated, but one can hardly with a good conscience deny it to Socrates' "first conviction" (e4 πέπεισμαι; cf. c8). Thus Frank's argument, though repeatedly opposed, retains some force, and the attribution to Parmenides and to Pythagoras (*Vorsokr.*, 28A44) remains problematic. A. Rehm and K. Vogel (in A. Gercke and E. Norden, eds., *Einleit. in d. Altertumswiss.* [4th ed.; Leipzig and Berlin, 1933], 2.5.11ff.) and P. Friedländer (*Platon* [2d ed.; Berlin, 1954], 356) do not succeed in dispelling all doubt with regard to Parmenides; what they do prove is that beginning with Theophrastus he was credited with the doctrine.

there.[40] The correct answer to all questions springs from the same basic insight and reflects Aristotle's new definition of nature as a principle of movement.[41]

With regard to the other problems of our book, the great distance which separates Aristotle's position from that of the Presocratics leaves little room for a direct comparison. The Platonic dichotomy of the cosmic system still makes itself felt inasmuch as Aristotle, while dealing with the celestial phenomena, relies on convictions regarding an intelligent order and an inherent perfection which he would not so readily and without any qualifications apply to the lower elements and their mutual relations.[42] Besides this, the new astronomy had done much to change the outlook and had provided a new framework of thought within which physical or philosophical inquiry has now to move. Aristotle readily accepts this framework because it is inspired by the same belief in order and regularity—perhaps also by the same admiration for the perfect geometrical figures—which he himself holds. Given the paramount importance of this belief, we may understand his desire to make clear in what respect it differs from the Pythagorean concept of harmony. The musical connotations of this concept do not recommend themselves to him at all; going farther than Plato, he cuts every tie between the new idea of cosmic order and this archaic version of it. He finds more value in the Pythagorean distinction between "right" and "left" in the Universe, yet to become incorporated in his own system this distinction must be reformulated with the help of a maturer scientific theory of directions.[43]

[40] See, e.g., 13.295a13ff.

[41] Comparable in elegance is the argument of II,3 which "deduces" *genesis*, the four sublunary elements, and the plurality of heavenly rotations from the eternal movement of the outermost heaven. This movement needs a center which must be at rest, and rest, as Aristotle conceives of it, is clearly absolute so that it excludes also the motion "around the axis of the Universe" which the *Timaeus* assigns to earth. Cf. esp. 286a12–22. At the end of this section Aristotle refers, however, to the more specific arguments in II,13f. for the stationary condition of earth. As in Aristotle's scheme there is no world soul in whose movement earth would be involved (see above, Note 38), he would see no need to provide for a counter-movement.

[42] Without trying to do justice to this complex problem, I refer to *De gen.* II,10.336a23–b9, b23–337a7, and *Meteor.* I,9.346b36–347a8 as giving a good impression of the form and the extent in which these convictions enter into the theory of the sublunary world. Cf. below, *passim* in Ch. 21.

[43] II,9; II,2. According to the doxographers (Aetius 2.10 Diels; cf. *Vorsokr.*, 31A50) Empedocles too expressed a view on "right" and "left" in the Cosmos. See, further, Plato *Tim.* 36c5ff. (yet also 34a4f.).

A radical break with Presocratic ways of thinking is implied in the absence of all questions formerly connected with the "evolutionary" approach to the Cosmos. Since the Cosmos as a whole has not come into being and will not pass away,[44] questions of *genesis* with regard to its parts are no longer legitimate, and Aristotle sees no need to show in every single instance that the questions were misconceived. By and large they have simply dropped from sight. If one judges by Book II, Aristotle never faced any of these Presocratic problems in its original form and as part of an evolutionary context. This is easy to understand since even in the *Timaeus* the "origin" of the heaven, of the stars and planets, and of their movements is no longer conceived as a physical process—in fact, since teleology replaces mechanics, there is no mechanical process and in the traditional sense of the term no origin either. Plato's creator does not reduce disorder little by little.[45] His acts present not so much a physical sequence of events as the unfolding of an intellectual design. God's thoughts and their realization coincide. "Without toil by the thought of his mind he sets everything in motion." [46]

For Aristotle "origins" are no longer a topic. When dealing with the shape of the heaven, the nature of the stars, and the place, rest, and shape of the earth, he finds it easy to ignore the original meaning and reference of these questions; not how they have come to have their shape or nature but what it is and why they must have it are the issues. Occasionally, it is true, he remarks that also those who "produce" the parts of the world would have to come to the same conclusions as himself. Thus, regarding the shape of the earth the truth of his own views can be more effectively brought out if one thinks of the earth along genetic lines.[47] Yet if Aristotle for a moment resorts to this line of thinking, he does so merely for a "practical," that is to say explanatory, purpose.

The cosmologist has no longer to explain the movements of the sun, the moon, and the other planets.[48] How they move in their

---

[44] I,10–12; cf. II,1.283b29–284a2.   [45] Note *Tim.* 34b10.

[46] Xenophanes' idea (B25) is here finally implemented. See also Aesch. *Suppl.* 598f. (and 99ff.). Cf. Paul Shorey, *A. J. Ph.*, 9 (1881), 4ff. I am aware that words suggesting manual work occur in the sections describing the Demiurge's procedure.

[47] II,14.297a12–b17 (note b14–17). Note also the remark in 13.295b3ff. that the differentiation of heavy and light cannot come about in the whirl but must exist prior to it. See also 2.285b5–8. The verb γεννᾶν as used in 8.290a9 has no "genetic" implications.

[48] It seems unnecessary here to display the evidence for Presocratic theories, in-

spheres and what spheres and what number of spheres are needed to "save" the "phenomena" he learns from the astronomer, and how and why these movements originated should not even be asked because the planets always moved in these ways. The philosophical cosmologist has contributed all he can—astonishingly much, as a matter of fact—when he has proved the existence of an element which accounts for the circular movement of these spheres, if not of the planets themselves.[49] For the heavenly bodies two of the time-honored questions are still in order: "Of what kind of material do they consist?" and "What shape do they have?" Needless to say, neither of these questions has any longer a genetic meaning. In his discussion of the former Aristotle says that he agrees with the earlier physicists in holding that these bodies should consist of the material prevalent in their cosmic region (which for them is the fire, for himself the *aether*).[50] He ignores the fact that for the Presocratics the material of the stars was a part of the larger problem: under what circumstances and through the agency of what forces did the stars come to be formed and at what stage of the cosmic history did this happen? [51] The brief

---

cluding those concerning the *tropai* (cf. Kranz's Index, *s.v.* ἀστήρ, ἥλιος, σελήνη); *speciminis gratia*, I refer to Democritus' pattern (*Vorsokr.*, 68A88). See also Plato *Tim.* 34b–36d, 38c–39e, 40a–d.

[49] We have seen, however, that Aristotle in Book II uses the first body with considerable discretion. He nowhere actually says that the movements of the heavenly spheres are caused by it. A full enumeration of the evolutionary ideas and constructions that Aristotle ignores cannot be attempted. It may, however, be mentioned that to the earlier physicists the question whether the heavenly revolution is uniform or not would not present itself in the same form as to Aristotle (II,6). For him it is enough to dispose of the possibility of alternating accelerations and retardations. He has no reason for discussing the notion (Emped. A75, Anaxag. B12; II.38.6ff.) that the heavenly revolution now takes less time than it did in earlier phases of the Cosmos.

[50] II,7, esp. 289a16. The accuracy of Aristotle's historical generalization is open to serious doubt; cf. Cherniss, *Presocr.*, 184 and n.171. One may find it surprising that Aristotle does not say more about the nature of the heavenly bodies. The question whether or not they are living beings is not brought up in this chapter. No more is it in the following, and it is only in 12 (292a18ff.) that his views on this subject are disclosed and brought to bear on the argument—now indeed with telling effect. For anyone remembering Plato's views (*Tim.* 39c and *passim*) and the important place which this question occupied in the dialogue *On Philosophy* (see frgs. 19, 21f., Walzer), Aristotle's silence in II,7 and 8 is astonishing. Does he wish as far as possible to decide cosmological issues without bringing this religious conviction into play?

[51] See, e.g., *Vorsokr.*, 21A11.4 (Anaximander), 28B11 (Parmenides), 31A53 (Empedocles).

chapter which settles the shape of the heavenly bodies includes no references to earlier doctrines. The paucity of our information makes it difficult to gauge the extent of Presocratic interest in this subject; the view that lends itself most easily to a comparison with Aristotle's doctrine and arguments is Plato's. In the *Timaeus* the heavenly bodies are given spherical form "after the likeness of the whole [Cosmos]." This makes it possible for them to move with the heavenly sphere as well as to rotate on their own axis. In our book the same shape is assigned to them on the ground that the sphere is least adapted to movement and that the heavenly bodies do not move by themselves.[52]

There is reason for wondering why some subjects that had been discussed by the Presocratics are ignored in the *Timaeus*. One of these is the size of the heavenly bodies. If we remember the startling doctrines, put forward notably by Anaxagoras, as to the size of sun and moon, we may be surprised that Plato makes no reference to this challenging topic.[53] He may have considered it idle curiosity to wonder about such matters. As for the exciting discovery, made it seems by Parmenides and adopted by others, that the moon borrows its light from the sun, Plato again has nothing to say on it. In the *Republic* he had indicated his approval of this doctrine, but the account of the *Timaeus* would rather suggest that the moon is a shining fiery body not different in nature from either sun or planets.[54] Aristotle knows that astronomical research has shown the sun to be of greater size than the earth, and his favorite example for a particular kind of definition implies that the moon suffers an eclipse when it is "deprived of light" (scil., which it normally receives from the sun) owing to the interposition of the earth. Definitions of this type are discussed in the *Metaphysics* and *Analytics*. Here and in his psychological treatises Aristotle incidentally shows his familiarity with these matters.[55] In

[52] Plato *Tim.* 40af.; Arist. *De caelo* II,11.291b12–15; cf. 8.290a35–b8 (and for arguments against rotation *ibid.*, a7–24).

[53] See Anaxagoras (59A72, 77); note also Empedocles (31A56) and Aetius (2.21).

[54] Note 40a22ff. as well as *Rep.* 10.616e9f. For Presocratic doctrines see esp. 28A42, B14f. (Parmenides); 31A60, B45, 47f. (Empedocles); 59A76, B8 (Anaxagoras). Doxographic reports to the same effect about Thales and Pythagoras (Aetius 2.28 = *Doxogr. Gr.* 358a15ff., b18ff.) are discounted; cf. Heath, *op.cit.*, 19, 75ff., who, however, goes too far in denying the doctrine to thinkers earlier than Anaxagoras (see also Burnet, *E. G. Ph.*, 177 n.1).

[55] *Metaph.* H4.1044b10ff.; *Anal. Post.* II,2.90a15; 8.93a23ff., etc. Cf. also *De gen. anim.* IV,9.777b24f. For the size of the sun see *De an.* III,3.428b3; *De somniis* 1.458b29; *Meteor.* I,8.345baff.

the second book of *De caelo* neither of the topics has found a place.
The size of sun and moon must, like their distances from the earth, be
left to the studies of the astronomers. The great advances after
Eudoxus were made by Aristarchus and Hipparchus, not by Aristotle
and Theophrastus.

The second book of *De caelo* is highly selective with regard to its
topics. If we compare its content with the *Timaeus*, we notice that it
includes no statement about the ecliptic, that it shows only by incidental remarks how well its author understood the nature of eclipses,
and that references to the time and speed of planetary revolutions are
confined to a few passages in which Aristotle refuses to accept the
responsibility for any matters of detail.[56] The actual periods of the
planetary revolutions need not be stated because Aristotle does not
regard time as integral to his cosmology. Plato's discussion of day and
night under the heading of time [57] was from the Presocratic point of
view decidedly unorthodox; but night, in any case, had long been a
subject of cosmology (or cosmogony). Astronomical as well as
meteorological explanations had been put forward for it.[58] Now it
seems to be neither a cosmological nor a meteorological phenomenon;
the subject has slipped through the meshes, as it were, of Aristotle's
system. Aristotle must have known Empedocles' brilliant discovery
that night is the shadow thrown by the earth,[59] but he has no opportunity of indicating whether he accepts it. The *Topics* mentions
this doctrine—or rather a part of it and without the author's name—
to find a "dialectical" flaw in it; [60] but dialectical criticism is not the
same as scientific criticism, and Empedocles' own statement would
have been immune even to the former.

[56] II.292a23ff., chs. 9, 10. See, for contrast, Plato *Tim.* 36b6ff., 40c3-d3; 38e6-39b2.
[57] *Tim.* 39c1f. (see, however, also 40b8-c2).
[58] Astronomical, Anaximenes B14; meteorological, Heracl. A1.11. Aristotle shares
with Heraclitus the assumption of two exhalations as the principal causes of the
meteorological phenomena (see below, p. 409), but in the *Meteorologica* the
power of the exhalations does not, as in Heraclitus, extend far enough to provide
day and night.
[59] Emped. B48; for a new interpretation of this fragment see W. Kranz, *Rh.
Mus.*, 100 (1957), 122ff. See also the "Pythagorean" theory of which Aristotle
gives us an account in *De caelo* II,13.293a21ff. It is evident, and Simplicius' comments confirm, that this theory included the shadow motif.
[60] *Top.* VI,8.146b27f.

Part Four

THE NATURE AND FORMATION
OF PHYSICAL OBJECTS

16

The Philosophical Status
of *Genesis*

THE aspects of the elements that in the books *On the Heaven* are treated as secondary and in the end fade from sight assert themselves all the more vigorously in the treatise *On Coming to Be and Passing Away*. Assuredly the function of the sublunary elements does not exhaust itself in realizing certain movements and thereby contributing their share to the structure of the Cosmos. These elements are also involved in less permanent formations. They must explain the changes and processes that come to pass in the physical world; and in their nature must be found a clue to the most important of all these processes, *genesis*. The large problem of *genesis* in the physical world had actually been attacked in the third book of *On the Heaven*. Yet it had been left unsolved—at least in the sense that no essential advance was made beyond the position which Plato had reached.[1] Our treatise penetrates deeper into it and, in fact, finds the solution.

One initial conviction underlies both works: the theory of *genesis* must begin with the *genesis* of the elements.[2] It is impossible for Aristotle to proceed as Empedocles had done; he could not take the existence of the elements for granted and then make them play their

[1] In effect Aristotle's final conclusion in Book III is that the elements must originate out of one another (6.305a31f.; cf. above, p. 296); how they do so he hardly attempts to show. It becomes clear, however, in the course of this book that Plato's mathematical explanation of their origin must be abandoned and also that earth cannot be exempt from the mutual transformation.

[2] *De caelo* III,1.298b9ff.; III,3.6; *De gen.* I,1.3, 6; II.2 and *passim*.

part in the emergence and the passing from the scene of secondary or compound entities. That this procedure was illegitimate had been emphatically stated by Plato.[3]

In any case it is here appropriate to remember how much Plato had done to rehabilitate *genesis* in philosophical discourse. It was he who lifted the ban and did away with the restrictions under which Parmenides' successors (Empedocles, Anaxagoras, and presumably the Abderites) had labored. Instead of contenting himself with association and dissociation, the philosopher or physicist may again with a good conscience turn to the larger and more fundamental problem of coming into being and passing away. "Being, space, and *genesis* exist" is Plato's new and heartening doctrine.[4]

Plato's physical system makes provision for being as well as for becoming; the same entities that represent being guarantee becoming, since they have an apparently unlimited power of generating offspring in the receptacle.[5] There is no danger that *genesis* will ever give out or that its source will dry up. However, when it comes to showing *genesis* as actually taking place in our Cosmos, Plato is nearer to the Presocratic association and dissociation than one might expect after his energetic reaffirmation of *genesis*. In the actual processes of our Cosmos *genesis* and destruction of an entity come to pass when the elements break up and their parts recombine into the basic particles of another element. This process goes on without interruption; not only the aggregate masses of fire, water, etc., are broken up and dispersed, but also each elementary particle, whether pyramidic, cubic, or of whatever shape, splits into the smaller units that can regroup themselves so as to form the particles of another element.[6]

It remained for Aristotle to rule out this approach to *genesis* and to point out the misconceptions on which it rested. For him *genesis* must have the character of an intrinsic and organic transformation; it works a change in the substance. Mechanical composition, addition, or association could not affect the substance. To be sure, not only *genesis* but other "changes" too, especially growth and decrease, must be redefined; they too are an organic, not a mechanical, process.[7] Yet for the present it is better to concentrate on *genesis*.

As soon as Aristotle in this treatise takes up *genesis* and tries to

---

[3] *Tim.* 48b5ff.; cf. Arist. *De caelo* III,6.   [4] *Tim.* 52d3. Cf. above, pp. 40–42.
[5] *Tim.* 48e–52c.   [6] *Tim.* 56c8–57c6; see also 58a–c.
[7] See below, Note 10; Ch. 17, Note 22; Ch. 19, Note 4.

distinguish it from the other "changes," he discovers that precisely
where he would find *genesis* his predecessors have spoken of aggregation.[8] One might expect him here to review the major varieties of this
approach, yet what he actually does is to take up one crucial problem
inherent in these doctrines: is it necessary to posit indivisible entities?
Both the Abderites and Plato have done so, and it might be held that
if physical objects come into being by aggregation indivisible minimal
bodies cannot be dispensed with, since otherwise the corresponding
process of dissociation would continue ad infinitum, and nothing
would be left that could again be put together.[9] Aristotle gives this
notion what he himself would certainly regard as a fair hearing. However, his conclusion is that there is no real cause for apprehending the
complete evanescence of a physical object and thus no good reason
for positing indivisible entities either. The arguments for and against
indivisibles are set forth at such length that they almost overshadow
the historically even more significant statement which is embodied in
the last sentences of this chapter: breaking up and coalescence of
things are possible and have their place in nature, but *genesis* in the
"simple" and "full" sense of the term does not come to pass in this
way. The subject undergoing *genesis* has its form as well as its matter,
and when either of them changes, then it is correct to speak of coming
into being or passing away. A breaking-up or coalescing may facilitate
changes of the kind, but these subsidiary processes must never be
confused with the basic event. To do so has been the fundamental
error.[10] We recall that Plato too distinguishes between *genesis* and

[8] *De gen.* I,2, esp. 315b15ff.; cf. b20, 316b32ff., 317a12ff.

[9] *Ibid.*, 315b24ff., 28ff. Cf. Note 10.

[10] *Ibid.*, 317a17–31. Note the final verdict on the theory of association in a19;
the whole error (ἐν ᾧ σφάλλεται πάντα) lies in identifying it with *genesis*. I have
isolated this strand of Aristotle's argument from the complex pattern of the
chapter. As for the other strands, the upshot of the disquisition about infinite
divisibility has been taken into account above, pp. 203–204; the distinction between
genesis and qualitative change is not confined to this chapter (315b6–9; 317a17–20;
cf. 1.314a8ff. and the entire ch. 4). From a historical point of view this distinction
seems less significant than the rejection of *genesis* by association. W. A. Heidel
(*Arch. f. Gesch. d. Philos.*, 19 [1905], 333ff.) has shown conclusively that the
Presocratics did not operate with a concept of qualitative change. Aristotle reads
it into their systems; in fact, as Heidel has pointed out, he introduces his own
concept of qualitative change into contexts in which the early thinkers actually
speak of recomposition, *ekkrisis*, condensation, and other "mechanical" processes.
Cf. also Cherniss, *Presocr.*, 105ff. For *alloiosis* as one of the two or four species of
movement in Plato and Aristotle cf. the Index, *s.v.* Aristotle's polemic against
the mechanistic doctrines of the Presocratics is analyzed and criticized by Cherniss,

association (σύγκρισις) and that for him also *genesis* in its true and best sense is something other than the coalescence of parts and the "whole" something over and above the sum of its parts.[11] Although Plato nowhere exposes the errors of the "associationists," he had done much to indicate their limitations. The concept of an organic whole which emerges in Plato is by Aristotle played off against *genesis* by association.[12] Now there is no longer any question of a compromise; association and dissociation cannot be considered legitimate species of the genus change.[13]

It is noteworthy that when Aristotle in this treatise polemizes against Plato's conception of *genesis* he concentrates his fire on the construction of the elements out of "indivisible" triangles.[14] The reason may be that he is here primarily concerned with the *genesis* of the elements and that his elements are the same as Plato's. In the *Physics*, where he establishes more general propositions about becoming, Aristotle does not speak of this Platonic construction at all, but contrasts his own theory which relies on matter, Form, and privation with the Platonic principles, i.e., the Forms and the great and small.[15] From a historical point of view his own theory has its roots in still other Platonic concepts. His formless matter and his Form are "developments" of the indeterminate receptacle and the Platonic Forms. Here, in the notion of the receptacle, is the germ of Aristotle's idea that something entirely devoid of Form and quality underlies the process of *genesis;* here is something ready to receive different and opposite imprints, and here, we have seen, are even hints that qualities enter into and determine this entity which is by itself indeterminate and entirely formless.[16] These are the ideas that come to fruition in Aristotle's conception of matter and *genesis;* they have made it possible for him to overcome the mechanical theories of a coming into being by coalescence and to put in their place a doctrine of organic change, transformation, and becoming.

Presocr., 102ff. However, the contention that in the place of the discarded theories Aristotle puts another mechanism, scil., the "actualization of the potential," is unjust to his achievements. On the subject of *genesis* Aristotle has much more specific doctrines to offer, and in his explanation of mixture he operates, to be sure, with the concept of *dynamis*, but not entirely in the sense of "potentiality."

[11] See above, pp. 52–62.   [12] I,2.317a20–22.

[13] See *Phys.* VII,2.243b11ff. Cf. above, p. 177.

[14] See esp. *De gen.* I,2.315b28ff., 316a2ff. (about the reference in 315a29 one cannot be quite sure).

[15] *Phys.* I,9.192a1–25.   [16] See above, pp. 43ff., on *Tim.* 50a2ff.

The doctrine of *genesis* as presented in our treatise is obviously an extension or application of the fundamental tenets that had been put forward in the *Physics*, for again *genesis* comes to pass when matter that had been informed, say, by hot and moist changes to the opposite, in this case cold and dry, condition (and such contraries may easily be understood as representing Form and privation). On the other hand, Plato's construction of the elementary particles out of indivisible triangles is not an extension of his doctrines regarding the receptacle but an alternative and almost completely unrelated approach to becoming. It cannot astonish us that Aristotle, in this treatise as well as in the books *On the Heaven*, attacks Plato's mathematical theory of *genesis* and that, among other points, he criticizes it as incapable of accounting for physical qualities (which in the other work means especially heavy and light, in ours presumably cold, hot, etc.).[17] Still, by doing so he incidentally obscures the historical roots of his own theory and in effect plays off one Platonic approach against another. In his own theory Plato's "physical" doctrine of *genesis* carries the day over Plato's "mathematical" derivations.

There is one passage in our treatise where Aristotle does remember the receptacle of the *Timaeus*. When about to describe the substratum which is needed for the origin of the four elements he mentions, side by side with Presocratic theories, Plato's "all-receptive" principle. "[Plato] says that it is a substratum prior to the so-called elements." [18] What greater credit could he give to Plato, seeing that this is precisely what he here himself needs as "matter" in his own system? In a comparable passage of *On the Heaven* Plato is said to be right in making his receptacle shapeless and entirely devoid of Form; "for thus it will be best for modeling," i.e., for receiving Form.[19] Here Aristotle ungrudgingly endorses the conception to which he owes so much. In our treatise the recognition of Plato's achievement is buried under strictures. It is not clear, Aristotle complains, whether or not Plato thinks of his principle as existing in separation from the elements,

---

[17] This seems to be the point of the statement in I,2.316a4 that the Platonists do not even attempt to produce a *pathos;* for one cannot by composing triangles produce qualities like hot and cold, etc., which in fact do not for Plato belong to the nature of the elements but are impressions or sensations produced by them. In *De caelo* Aristotle shows that neither the doctrine of triangles (IV,2.308b3ff.) nor that of indivisible lines (III,1.299a25) can do justice to the phenomenon of weight; see also III,1.299a17ff. on the difficulties inherent in an attempt to construct *pathe* out of indivisible principles.

[18] II,1.329a14–24.   [19] *De caelo* III,8.306b18ff.

i.e., whether Plato avoids the mistake of the Presocratics, who regard their first principle as a separately existing entity. Moreover, Plato does not actually make use of the receptacle when it comes to constructing the elements but instead composes them out of triangles; and surely "it is impossible for the nurse and primary matter to be identical with the triangles." [20]

The last comment has its validity. In the *Timaeus* it is indeed difficult to find continuity between the receptacle and the mathematical deduction of the elements which Plato presents next. Plato himself indicates a break, at this point, by bringing his Demiurge into action; [21] and, as we have already said, Aristotle owes much to the physical, nothing to the mathematical, *genesis* of the elements in Plato.

In some way Aristotle misses or misunderstands the intention of the Presocratics when he says that they identified *genesis* with aggregation. Actually those who after Parmenides introduced the concepts of aggregation and dissociation did not believe in *genesis*. When they explained the formation of physical entities Empedocles and Anaxagoras—and presumably also Leucippus and Democritus—were honestly convinced that they were not dealing with a problem of *genesis* but with one of coalescence.[22] Between them and Aristotle lies the rehabilitation of *genesis* which Plato accomplished in the *Timaeus*. This all-important step has been made, and it is typical of the changed situation that Aristotle no longer needs to clear away the fundamental prejudice which had so long militated against any assumption of becoming. He, too, has to "establish" *genesis*, yet in a different sense. He has to find the precise place for it within his own system of categories and other differentiations. More specifically he must make clear the essential difference between *genesis* on the one hand and qualitative change and increase on the other.[23]

---

[20] 329a21–24. In the *Physics* we have noted Aristotle's proneness to identify Plato's *chora* with his own *hyle* concept (above, Ch. 6, esp. Note 24).

[21] *Tim.* 53b.   [22] See above, pp. 6–7.

[23] *De gen.* I,1; 2.315a26ff.; 4; 5. The latter books of *De caelo* do not approach *genesis* as a "species" of *metabole*. As we have seen, it is very unlikely that they were planned as a vestibule to our treatise; nor did they actually offer Aristotle much help toward the propositions now to be established—except in the negative point that, Plato's mathematical deduction of the elements having been sufficiently refuted in *De caelo* III (and IV), this subject need no longer be labored. When working out our treatise Aristotle realized—what in *De caelo* III does not seem to have occurred to him—that his first task was to set *genesis* clearly apart from qualitative change and increase.

There are other differences between Plato's and Aristotle's strategy and strategic situation. If Plato's main concern had been to secure a respected place for *genesis* (by the side, and at the same time as the opposite of, being), Aristotle is equally concerned with *genesis* and its counterpart, destruction.[24] In the context of his theory of changes it was his obvious task to discuss these complementary concepts simultaneously and to bring out their interdependence. As in Parmenides and his successors, the two concepts are once again tied together, though no longer in the sense that they are equally to be admitted or rejected. What matters is that the problems presented by the one may be solved by considering them in conjunction with those inherent in the other.[25] In Plato there are only a few references to the passing away of the phenomena as a correlate to their appearance. His preoccupation is with the metaphysical status of *genesis* and with the two-headed proposition that while *genesis* has full reality the individual γενόμενα are unsubstantial, impermanent, floating, and devoid of true reality. A large, shadowy realm has been brought under the heading of *genesis* and must receive its place in the scheme of being. To problems of a purely physical type, e.g., whether the arising of one physical object always implies the passing away of another, Plato does justice in later sections.[26] Yet these are the sections where coming into being shows again affinities to the Presocratic aggregation (as passing away to dissociation); here the metaphysical questions are no longer acute. In the account of the receptacle, where the metaphysical point of view prevails, it is immaterial whether or not destruction "balances" *genesis;* this is one reason why Plato makes almost too liberal provision for *genesis.* We have already noticed his failure to set limits to its occurrence.

Quite generally Aristotle lays it down that the coming into being of one physical entity is tied up with the passing away of another.[27] To put it in the simplest terms, when water turns into air, the destruc-

---

[24] *Tim.* 49e7ff., 52a6f.

[25] See esp. I,3.318a9ff., 23ff., to say nothing here about the specific doctrines concerning the transformation of the elements into one another (II,4).

[26] See above, pp. 52–56.

[27] One of the subjects of I,3 is τίς αἰτία τοῦ γένεσιν ἀεὶ εἶναι (317b34). For the answer see 318a23ff., 29ff.; cf. also 319a5ff., 20ff. P. Shorey, *Cl. Ph.,* 17 (1922), 352, compares 318a17 with Plato *Phaedo* 72c, which may be profitable if the similarities are not overemphasized. Plato aims at cyclical *genesis,* to which Aristotle finds his way in a different context (II,4, 10). What matters now for him is mutuality or reciprocity; cf. Shorey, *loc.cit.*

tion of water is the coming to be of air. This thesis guarantees that
genesis can constantly go on and also that there is no diminution and
final evanescence of the material in the physical world. As Aristotle
sees it, the only alternative explanation for the constant supply of
material would be the hypothesis of an Infinite, a concept which he—
here and elsewhere—understands as answering a concern for an inexhaustible supply. Actually we happen to know that already Anaximander had made all that comes to be pass away into the same entities
from which it had arisen, and it seems doubtful whether he (or any of
the early thinkers) really needed the Infinite as an inexhaustible source
of supply.[28] That changes in one direction are balanced by such in
the opposite is emphatically stated by Heraclitus, for whom this
balance is a manifestation of the *logos* and of a deep metaphysical
harmony in the order of things. To this harmony and metaphysics
Aristotle cannot find the way back. He keeps the discussion in a nar-
rower and strictly physical frame of concepts.[29] The point at issue is
the eternity of *genesis*, not (as in the *Meteorologica*) the balance of
opposite changes or the stability of the *maxima membra mundi*.

It is likely, if not certain, that Aristotle here and in the corresponding passages has Anaximander in mind. Anaximander does speak of
genesis and destruction, and as Aristotle has returned to these concepts
—which the later Presocratics had eschewed—he would have reasons
for casting a glance at Anaximander. To the later Presocratics it would
not occur to balance *genesis* against destruction, since neither had a
place in their scheme; yet reckoning as they did with certain indestructible entities, they could combine, separate, and recombine
them. A definite, unchanging amount of material would serve their
purposes quite adequately. When they say that nothing new comes
into being (and nothing passes away), they come as near as we may
expect to saying that the sum total of available material is constant.

[28] I,3.318a19f.; cf. *Phys.* III,4.203b18; 8.208a8. For Anaximander see *Vorsokr.*,
12B1. In none of Aristotle's passages is Anaximander named. He is in this connection named in the *Placita* (*Doxographi* 277.19 Diels). For doubts regarding
the attribution to him of the supply argument see Cherniss, *Presocr.*, 21 (who
mentions that Simplicius *In Phys.* 466.30 assigns it to "some of the physicists").
In 208a8 Aristotle says that the assumption of circular change (i.e., destruction of
one entity = generation of another) makes the Infinite unnecessary. On the problem of such change in Anaximander see J. B. McDiarmid, *H.S.C.P.* 61 (1953),
96ff. Note also the appearance of the infinitely small in Aristotle's argument in
318b21.

[29] See esp. *Vorsokr.*, 22B30, 31, 90.

There certainly is no way in which it could diminish. One may fittingly recall Empedocles' statement that his elements are eternal and his questions "What could bring about an increase of this all? Whence should it come?" [30] Whenever a physical entity disintegrates, the portions of the elements thus set free enter into new mixtures—though presumably they may also remain free for a time and exist in an unmixed condition by themselves. In either of these cases we may say, applying Aristotle's terms, that the destruction of one entity is the *genesis* of another. *Mortales mutua vivunt.*

Thus Aristotle's axiom is implicit in the scheme also of the late Presocratics. That it was explicitly formulated by them cannot be asserted with the same confidence. Somehow their statements have a different point, a different orientation; the *mutua* motif is less stressed than in Heraclitus; it may be in abeyance and in need of re-discovery.[31] To say that nothing new comes into being and that there are only association (or mixture) and dissociation of "being things" is not the same as to say that dissociation of one entity corresponds to, and is balanced by, association in the forming of another. We should also bear in mind that the supply on which these thinkers count is very large; more is available than this Cosmos requires, and as the Cosmos knows phases of growth and decrease, its relation to the sum of available matter is variable. In the atomist system, at any rate, new material continues to reach it from the outside.[32] Plato and Aristotle, on the other hand, are agreed that "the frame of the world took up the whole of each of these four [elements]," [33] and already Plato, though in principle he sets no bounds to *genesis,* had shown how the destruction of one elementary body is the coming into being of another. He had done this along the same lines on which the later Presocratics constructed association and dissociation and had, in fact, not emancipated himself completely from the power of these concepts.[34] All of this goes to show that Aristotle had enough precursors for his axiom that

---

[30] *Vorsokr.,* 31B17.32.

[31] Lucr. 2.76. Bailey ("Commentary," *ad loc.,* following Giussani) mentions that for living beings the statement is not quite correct. It would be correct for the ζῷα of Empedocles (B35.14), whose language may have influenced Lucretius' phrasing.

[32] See, for Democritus, *Vorsokr.,* 68A40; for the Epicurean view Lucr. 2.1105ff.

[33] *Tim.* 32c5ff.; *De caelo* I,9 (see above, p. 258). See, for contrast, *Vorsokr.,* 31A47, on Empedocles. In Anaxagoras too (*ibid.,* A59B1, 4) and, needless to say, in the atomists the material far exceeds what our Cosmos can absorb.

[34] See again above, pp. 52–54.

destruction and coming into being play into each other's hands. But he had to translate the insights of other thinkers into the language of *genesis* and destruction, had to face these ultimates from which his immediate forerunners had shied away, and had to come to grips with the possibility that everything might pass out of existence.[35] If this were to happen, *genesis* itself would cease, the most dreadful of all possibilities that a physicist may contemplate (the horror at the mere thought of it is vividly brought out by Plato).[36] Aristotle's physical scheme does not include eternally "being" things comparable to Empedocles' divine elements, Anaxagoras' powers, and Democritus' atoms. Such eternal principles would suffice to guarantee the eternity of *genesis*. If the elements themselves come to be and pass away, the predicate of eternity must be attached to *genesis* as such.[37] It need not be divine; for the physicists had long been in the habit of positing eternal entities without granting them the highest honor in their gift. Even "immortal" seems too good a word—an indication, perhaps, that Aristotle could give more of his personal enthusiasm to movement than to *genesis*.[38] Still it clearly is one of the prime realities in Aristotle's world. We recall that being, space, and *genesis* are the three fundamental realities of Plato.[39]

The invariable interdependence of *genesis* and destruction being established, Aristotle can take the daring step of including the dreaded concept of not-being in this scheme. "*Genesis* is the destruction of not-being, destruction the *genesis* of not-being." [40] It is perfectly legitimate to speak of not-being in physical theory and to assume a constant interchange between it and being. In common parlance we speak of things as "coming into being" in an absolute sense; [41] and Aristotle is here prepared to back common parlance and find sense in the idea behind it. In fact, he sides with it against Parmenides. Things do come into being

[35] I,3.318a13ff.; 16.

[36] Plato *Phaedr.* 245d7ff.; *Legg.* X,895a6ff. (Plato conjures up this hypothetical and utopian possibility with reference to what Aristotle regards as the "other" cause, scil., the moving or efficient cause of eternal *genesis;* see I,3.317b33–318a8).

[37] This accounts for the new emphasis in Aristotle's argument; as we have seen, he makes explicit the mutuality and reciprocity which had been implicit in the Presocratic schemes. For the contributions of II,10f. to the eternity motif see below, Ch. 20.

[38] For movement as ἀθάνατος see *Phys.* VIII,1.250b13; 6.259b25. *Genesis* is called ἐνδελεχής in *De gen.* II,10.336b32. A less exalted word often used of both is συνεχές.

[39] *Tim.* 52d3.   [40] *Ibid.,* 319a28ff.; cf. 317a32ff., b1ff.

[41] 318a27ff., 31f. (on the text of this passage see below, Note 45); see also 318a18ff.

by emerging from not-being. Parmenides' veto could not be violated
more flagrantly. And as if to top this heresy Aristotle declares that this
is absolute *genesis—genesis* pure and simple without any qualifications.
What new conception of not-being lies behind this challenging departure?

As we know, Aristotle had faced the problem of not-being already
in his *Physics*.[42] There too he treated *genesis* from not-being to being
as a completely correct, in fact as a necessary, assumption. The essence
of his doctrine was that *genesis* takes place between contraries, like
white and not-white, uncultured and cultured, and that one of these
contraries was the negation of the other and thus not-being with
reference to it, i.e., a relative not-being. Yet the crucial problem—not
fully solved in the *Physics*—is whether this point of view may also be
applied to substance. In our treatise, for which *genesis* is first and foremost that of elements, this problem must be confronted. What is not-
being in the realm of substances? And how can there be in this realm
a *genesis* out of not-being? The need of solving the problem is the
more urgent since for Aristotle simple (absolute) *genesis* is the *genesis*
of substances, not of qualities or quantities (like a change from not-
white to white, not-large to large).[43] To this embarrassing question
he still owes us the answer.

In his own scheme of categories, then, the question of absolute
genesis would take the form whether substance can come into being
out of not-substance or being out of not-being—a difficult proposition
because where could he find a not-being to serve in this function? [44]
Aristotle does identify absolute *genesis* with *genesis* of a substance,
but he soon finds it necessary to make a distinction even within substances and elements. When certain elements come into being, we

[42] Aristotle himself refers in 317b13 to what he has said in the *Physics* (I,6–9).
Cf. above, Ch. 4.

[43] Cf. 317b18ff. and also *Phys.* I,7.190a32 and II,1.193b20 where Aristotle appears
to have the problem of our section in mind. In ἀπλῆ γένεσις as Aristotle thinks of
it, *genesis* of an οὐσία (or εἰς οὐσίαν) and *genesis* out of μὴ ὄν coincide (see *Phys.*
V,1.225a15). Some arguments which proved helpful in the *Physics* do not reappear;
for instance, it is not again stated that *genesis* is only *per accidens* from not-being.
That elements originate out of one another *per accidens* would be a hard saying.

[44] In 317b19–33 Aristotle discusses "potential being," yet decides that he cannot
use it for the purpose on hand. Surely elements cannot simply arise from "potential
being" and pass away into it. What kind of existence should one assign to such
potential being which in some way must certainly be not-being? What is really
needed (as we gradually learn) is prime matter which never exists by itself and
another element whose destruction makes possible the "absolute" *genesis*.

should regard this process as absolute *genesis;* in the case of others it is a qualified *genesis.*[45] This restricts the concept (and the problem) of absolute *genesis.* When Parmenides issued his interdict against *genesis,* he was innocent of categories and would have spurned any idea of differentiation or qualification. Actually his veto covers even changes of quality and of place, and though some of his successors reinstated change of place (i.e., movement), they follow him in eschewing the *genesis* of qualities; colors, for instance, do not come into being but are present in the elements and merely "mix" in the formation of composite transitory entities.[46]

Aristotle may have felt a special satisfaction when pointing out how Parmenides himself, who made all later physicists shy away from *genesis* and not-being as though these were something unclean, may help toward finding not-being among the substances. In his "Way of Opinion" he treats one of his two basic entities, earth, as not-being and the other, fire, as being.[47] That Parmenides himself branded this dualistic approach as a mistake Aristotle feels free to ignore. As he sees it, it is indeed necessary to distinguish among the elements—these prime substances—between some which have being and others which have not-being. This differentiation may be made in more than one way (and it is not of fundamental importance which is chosen).[48] The common run of people will be inclined to regard air as not-being because it is not visible and to treat solid earth as being. For them it would be sufficient that what changes into air seems to pass away into nothing. A more philosophical approach would be to consider fire and

---

[45] See 317b5; 318a26ff., 31ff.; 318b5: *genesis* of earth is qualified *genesis,* of fire absolute *genesis.* Aristotle treats this difference as identical or comparable to that between a man's coming into being and his "becoming learned" (318a33). This comparison led to misunderstandings even in antiquity (cf. Philop., *ad loc.*)— naturally enough, for the distinction made in this illustration is of a very different type and, as Aristotle himself in effect later admits, his theory of the categories (319a8ff.) suffices to explain it. He was obviously misled by the fact that in either case he could contrast a mere γίγνεσθαι with a γίγνεσθαί τι. I infer from Philoponus' comments on a31 that the text of our passage was originally λέγομεν γὰρ ὅτι ⟨γίγνεται νῦν ἁπλῶς καὶ ὅτι⟩ φθείρεται νῦν ἁπλῶς καὶ οὐ μόνον τόδε. This corresponds better with what follows. Philoponus' lemma was taken from a text in which the omission had occurred whereas his explanation suggests the fuller version.

[46] See Parmenides in *Vorsokr.,* 28B8.40f. (where change of color is ruled out). In Empedocles, as far as we can see, the elements have their specific colors (B21) as well as other qualities; for the mixing see B71.3, and cf. B23. For Anaxagoras see 59B4 (II,31.7f.).

[47] See *Vorsokr.* 28B8.53ff., B9.   [48] For this and what follows see 318b7–319a23.

air as real because they have a higher degree of form [49] (and also because their characteristic quality, hot, is an affirmation, whereas cold is a negation); under this point of view earth would be not-being. Yet whichever of the elements is identified with not-being, there clearly is, as long as the elements can pass into one another, *genesis* of being as well as of not-being, and destruction too catches up with both of them.

It would never have occurred to the Presocratics to use the "hint" in Parmenides' "Way of Opinion" and with its help to escape from his veto of not-being. How could Empedocles have looked upon some of his divine elements as more real than the others or how could Anaxagoras, who rebelled at thinking of not-hair, not-flesh,[50] make some of his powers or homogeneous entities real, others not real? The atomists, to be sure, had brought not-being back into physics, yet they were far from thinking that void could change into atoms or atoms into void (the only *genesis* here possible would be what Aristotle calls local *genesis:* place now occupied by void may later be filled by atoms). And even in Aristotle's own scheme the introduction of not-being into the elements has considerable difficulties of a physical as well as metaphysical order. For all practical purposes his elements are on a par with one another—when Aristotle later in this treatise goes into detail about the formation and transformation of the elements, different degrees of reality, to say nothing of being and not-being, have no place in his account. Moreover, it is one of his axioms that substance has no contrary and that there is no such thing as non-substance.[51] Does Aristotle violate these doctrines here? Is he as merciless with his own vetoes as with Parmenides'? These forbidden concepts and doctrines are not openly employed in our section, yet it is hard to resist the impression that Aristotle is precariously close to them. That *genesis* had its physical locus among the elements was his conviction; this part of the Platonic legacy had remained intact when Aristotle examined the scheme of the *Timaeus* and decided which doctrines regarding the elements he could and which he could not accept.[52] But he obviously felt that *genesis* still carried a large part of the Parmenidean mortgage. Should this mortgage be retained

---

[49] See on this point *De caelo* IV,3.310b14f.; 4.312a15f.

[50] See *Vorsokr.*, 59B10. For the μὴ ὄν in the atomists see *ibid.*, 67A6, 8; 68A37, 38 *et al.*

[51] See above, Ch. 4, Note 22.

[52] Cf. *De caelo* III,1.298b8ff. and 6.305a31f. (in connection with 3.302a10f.).

or could it be cleared? Aristotle's answer is in effect that the mortgage may be kept but that it in no way impairs his freedom of operating with the concept of physical *genesis*. This in any case is the decision at which he here arrives, at the price of neglecting some of his own favorite doctrines. That his specific account of elementary *genesis* in Book II shows no trace of the mortgage has already been said. One may wonder whether Aristotle owes his freedom in all matters of detail to the preliminary struggle with Parmenides or whether he would have and use this freedom in any case. Of the *genesis* of the elements he seems to be certain; it is hard to imagine that he would have allowed metaphysical worries to preclude *genesis* and change between the elements. Still, it is well that the arguments of our chapter can allay these worries. The last sentences of this chapter, incidentally, give an indication that Aristotle is not completely satisfied with his solution. Rather surprisingly they admit that "absolute not-being" has not yet been fully cleared up. Perhaps it should after all be identified not with one of the mutually opposite elements but with matter—an idea which the *Physics* ruled out.[53] Thus on the cardinal question regarding the identity of not-being the last word is still *non liquet*.

In the *Physics* Aristotle had considered it a characteristic of *genesis* that it takes place between one contrary and the other. The chapter of *De generatione* which we have just studied (I,3) is in full agreement with this approach; one of its reasons for introducing the concept of not-being is that if qualified *genesis* comes to pass between well and sick, small and large, absolute *genesis* should lead from not-being to being.[54] As we shall presently see, the specific doctrines regarding the formation of the elements likewise remain faithful to the commitment made in the *Physics*, and at times Aristotle even allows two elements to stand to one another in the relation of opposites.[55]

Another concept which was introduced in the *Physics* and is now slated for a more concrete function is the substratum. Elements may pass into one another and the disappearance of one be the emergence of another because the substratum changes back and forth between the opposites.[56] How this happens and what kind of relation there is between substratum and elements Aristotle does not yet tell us. He is

---

[53] 319a29ff. In the *Physics* the μὴ ὄν is found in the στέρησις, i.e., the contrary, not in the substratum (I,8.191b13ff.). But the μὴ ὄν which Aristotle there recognizes is a relative, not as in our treatise an absolute, μὴ ὄν.

[54] 317a34ff. Cf. *Phys.* I,5-7.

[55] See I,3.318b11ff. (14ff.; cf. also 319a29ff.); II,3.331a1ff.   [56] I,3.319a18-20.

determined to prepare the ground for these subjects with the utmost care and circumspection and also to explain beforehand a number of other concepts that he will later need. These explanations and clarifications fill the latter half of Book I. As we need not yet follow him into these, we may immediately turn to Book II and analyze its more specific propositions about the nature, formation, and transformation of the elements. Aristotle's final decisions on these questions are the core of his theory of becoming. Attempts at their solution he has made elsewhere and earlier; [57] yet only now does he fully succeed.

[57] See above, pp. 295–297, on *De caelo* III and IV.

17

The Derivation of the Elements

TO all appearance Aristotle enters upon the *genesis* of the elements with his mind not yet made up as to their number and identity. He asks: what factors operate in the formation of perceptible bodies [1] (of which the elements are the prototype)? It seems that when the relation between the substratum and "perceptible bodies" is settled it will also be clear what bodies qualify as elements and how many of them there are. For the rest Aristotle's procedure is determined by two basic considerations. Since it has been established that becoming is a passing from one contrary to the other,[2] he must find suitable contraries that can inform the substratum and make it change from one element to another; and as he is dealing with perceptible bodies, these contraries must be found among the qualities that make a body perceptible.

In fact, everything depends on making the right choice between such qualities. Each of our sense functions is associated with its own specific set of qualities, and Aristotle's first step is to declare that only the qualities connected with touch can be taken into consideration as possible principles of a "perceptible body"—for though a perceptible body should perhaps be equally accessible to every sense function, Aristotle has made up his mind that only touch matters [3] (a point to which we shall come back).

This step at once narrows the field of inquiry very significantly.

[1] II,2.329b7; cf. 3f. (but note the first words of II,3).
[2] For the motif of τὰ ἐναντία see here II,1.329a30, 33f., b2, and esp. b8ff. Cf. again Plato *Tim.* 50a2f.
[3] II,2.329b8-10. In 11-13 some ἐναντιώσεις of sight and taste are ruled out. See also 14-16.

Even now, however, a large number of opposites are left, and Aristotle himself enumerates them: hot and cold, dry and moist, heavy and light, hard and soft, viscous and brittle, rough and smooth, coarse and fine.[4] A further narrowing of the scope is clearly indicated. In view of the essential part that heavy and light played in the books *On the Heaven*, where they formed the basic "differences," it is startling to see that this is the first pair here to be ruled out.[5] The reason is that they have no capacity of acting or being acted upon. (Why capacities of the kind are so essential will gradually become apparent.) In this respect the opposites hot and cold, dry and moist are obviously more serviceable because the one pair of them (hot and cold) can be active, the other (dry and moist) passive.[6] Almost the whole of the remainder of our chapter is given over to an attempt to "trace back" the other pairs of opposites to the basic oppositions of hot and cold, dry and moist.[7] If we look at these "reductions" more closely, we see that

[4] *Ibid.*, 18–20.

[5] *Ibid.*, 20–24. Cf. O. Hamelin, *Le système d'Aristote* (Paris, 1920), 361. On the fundamental role of these opposites in *De caelo* see above, my Ch. 13. Curiously, in I,6 while dealing with the subject of contact between bodies, Aristotle says: "All things that are in contact with one another must have weight or lightness or both; and things of the kind have the capacity of acting and suffering" (323a8–10). Joachim (*ad loc.*) may well be right with his suggestion that the objects referred to may yet owe their capacity of acting and being acted upon to other qualities that they likewise possess. It would certainly be most hazardous to infer that Aristotle here still cherished the hope that the qualities on which he had put such emphasis in *De caelo* would also prove usable in the new approach to *genesis* which our treatise embodies. Yet why does Aristotle here mention weight and lightness if they do not contribute to acting and suffering? Is it perhaps because he has just said that things in contact must occupy place and the most important difference in the realm of place is that between up and down, concepts associated with heavy and light? In any case, the reference to these qualities seems to contribute nothing essential to his argument.

[6] *Ibid.*, 24–26 ("active" and "passive," scil., with reference to one another).

[7] 329b32–330a26. Joachim notes (*ad* 329b20) that the pair rough and smooth which is mentioned in the initial enumeration of tactile contraries does not reappear in the sentences which perform the reduction. He refers to Philoponus (214.33) for an explanation to the effect that rough and smooth (like heavy and light) are not active and passive with reference to one another. It is correct that Philoponus has this explanation, yet he presents it not as his own but as Aristotle's (ἀποκρίνει, *ibid.*, 31; scil., Aristotle eliminates these qualities). This seems to indicate that our text is defective, and it should be easy to find a place for rough and smooth in 329b21: βαρὺ μὲν καὶ κοῦφον, ⟨ὡσαύτως δὲ τραχὺ καὶ λεῖον⟩ οὐ ποιητικὰ οὐδὲ παθητικά. Joachim (*ad* 18) also raises the question why the pair dense and rare is not included in the list of tactile qualities. This question too had engaged the attention of ancient commentators. Philoponus (214.22ff.) reports the explanation given by Alexander of Aphrodisias.

actually no pair is resolved into hot and cold but that all of them are understood as varieties of dry and moist.[8] It will suffice here to quote the first of these "reductions": "Since the moist has no determinate shape but is readily adaptable and follows the outline of that which is in contact with it, it is in its nature to fill up" (scil., to leave no corner of the receptacle unfilled). "Such is also the nature of the fine; for the fine consists of subtle particles, yet what has subtle particles will fill up, being in contact whole with whole" (scil., again with its container), "a characteristic which the fine has in the highest degree. Hence it is evident that the fine derives from the moist and the coarse from the dry."

Aristotle concludes these reductions by observing that, even if the other opposites can thus be resolved into hot and cold, dry and moist, these two pairs cannot be resolved into one another.[9] They are irreducible, and this evidently is the reason why the physicist must resort to them if he is to explain the relationship between matter and the four elements. The way in which these basic pairs operate—and co-operate—to the end of forming the elements is well known. "The differences are reasonably distributed among the primary bodies";[10] in every instance one term of the one pair combines with one of the other. Earth is cold and dry, water cold and moist, air moist and warm, fire dry and warm. We may add at once that on this basis Aristotle finds it easy to account for the change of elements into one another. In accordance with his principle that the coming into being of one contrary is the destruction of the other, he makes these opposite qualities which form the elements give way to one another. If, for instance, of the hot and dry which characterize the fire, the hot changes into cold, the resulting body, being dry and cold, will be earth. Corresponding processes account for all transformations of elements into one another. The only difference in these transformations is that in some cases (e.g., the change from water to air) only one quality has to be replaced by its opposite, whereas in the change, for instance, from water to fire both must yield to their opposite. The

[8] This is noted by Joachim (*ad* b32ff.), who, however, thinks (following Zabarella) that these varieties of dry and moist are produced by the action of hot and cold (if this was of interest to Aristotle here, he has certainly given no indication of it). My rendering of 329b34–330a4 and the explanations interspersed in it are indebted to Joachim.

[9] II,2.330a24–29.   [10] II,3.330a20–b7.

latter type of change is more thoroughgoing and complete, consequently also more difficult.[11]

There should be no doubt that Aristotle, in devising his construction of the four elements, kept in mind the necessity of explaining their mutual transformations. He divided the opposites among the elements in such fashion that their mutual replacement would bring about the change from one element into any of the three others. Even cyclical *genesis* is now possible and not only possible but easily accomplished. For the elements in adjacent cosmic strata have one identical and one contrary quality, so that, throughout the sequence fire, air, water, earth, transformation materializes through the exchange of one contrary for the other.[12]

When the four elements were set up by Empedocles as the "roots" of everything else, they were eternal and unchanging, in fact, they were deities, and Empedocles would have considered it absurd that these divine beings should change into one another—or that one god should appear in various forms and shapes.[13] Yet changes ($\tau\rho o\pi a i$) of the kind had been an integral part of the earlier systems—witness Anaximenes' air and Heraclitus' fire—and it was natural that, though ignored by Parmenides and Empedocles, they would come back again. They did so with a vengeance; in Anaxagoras' scheme and with the atomists the elements lose their status as principles and become, like other entities, composed of something more fundamental.[14] They were not to reappear as unchanging gods; but to their place as *physical* principles they were restored by Plato; and it is due to him that they enjoy some of their erstwhile privileges also in the systems of Aristotle and the Stoics. On the question of their mutual transformation,

---

[11] See II,4.331a22ff. Chapter II,3 embodies Aristotle's account of the nature of the four sublunary elements; here the role of the contraries in forming each of them is specified. Chapter II,4 deals with the mutual transformation of the elements; Aristotle observes in 331a14 that the elements have specific qualitative differences which are the contraries of the qualities present in other elements. From this point of view the elements themselves have an $\dot{\epsilon}\nu a\nu\tau\iota\omega\sigma\iota s$ $\pi\rho\dot{o}s$ $\mathring{a}\lambda\lambda\eta\lambda a$ (15).

[12] See II,4.331a23–b4.

[13] We may here ignore that in the *Sphairos* the elements have lost their characteristic identity and that at this juncture another god, scil., the *Sphairos*, comes into existence (*Vorsokr.*, 31B27ff.). For Plato's and Aristotle's qualified acceptance of the Empedoclean elements cf. P. Shorey, *Cl. Ph.*, 17 (1922), 346, 348.

[14] For the relation between "powers" and elements in Anaxagoras see G. Vlastos, *Philos. Rev.*, 59 (1950), 31ff.

however, Plato takes his stand as decidedly against Empedocles as Anaxagoras and Democritus had done before him.[15] Like them, he associates eternity and indestructibility with something different (his *eternal* principles are not even material components of the elements). Only the Forms of fire and of the other elements remain forever unchanged; the fire that we see will when barely yet perceived as such turn into air, clouds, water, earth, and more of the kind (we need not here linger over the fact that in his more specific scheme Plato makes no provision for any transformation of earth).[16] The elements pass into one another. *Genesis* is a cycle, says Plato, and Aristotle repeats it, though with a marked change of tone. In this point there is full agreement between him and his teacher: the Empedoclean elements are to be accepted as the basis for a construction of the physical Cosmos, but the theory must be so framed as to leave room for their passing into one another. This was the task to which Aristotle had addressed himself in the latter books *On the Heaven*. There, however, the attempt remained abortive, and, as we have seen, the premises on which it rested are in our treatise discarded as useless. Still, it is important that Book III of that work affirms one Platonic doctrine: *genesis* of the elements comes to pass by mutual transformation.[17] Moreover, Book IV of the same work includes a deduction of the same four sublunary elements at which Aristotle arrives in our treatise.[18] There cannot be much doubt that the result was—in both

[15] For the formation of the elements in Anaxagoras see *Vorsokr.*, B15f.; for their intermutation *ibid.*, B16, A45. Democritus evidently identified the fire with a particular type of atom (the spherical; *Vorsokr.*, 67A15, 28, etc.), a decision which would interfere with the capacity of changing into another element. On the whole, however, it is likely that in his system elements, like other substances, arose through specific groupings of the atoms—groupings with more or less density, larger or smaller void between them, and also in different patterns. This at any rate is the Epicurean doctrine (see esp. Lucr. 2.98–108), and it is probably safe to think of Democritus as holding substantially the same view (cf. Cherniss, *Presocr.*, 119f.).

[16] *Tim.* 49b2ff. (in b7ff. Cornford, *Cosmology*, 180, notices echoes of Anaximenes and Anaxagoras); see also 48b5. For earth as exempt from the intermutations see *Tim.* 54bf., 56d.

[17] III,6; note the conclusion, 305a31f. Aristotle's arguments are closer to physical theory than Plato's in that he discusses and refutes alternative ways of accounting for the *genesis* of the elements. He disposes of the idea that an element may break up into (and form itself again out of) its specific atoms or other indivisible units; nor can a *soma* arise out of something *asomaton*, scil., the void.

[18] See esp. *De caelo* IV,4f. (311b13–312b19).

instances—far less "new" than the way which leads to it. In the *De generatione* Aristotle selects the right and truly useful qualities for his elements.

As Plato describes the mutual transformation of the elements, it is not a change from one opposite to the other. The particles of one element break up into the triangles that compose them, and these recombine so as to form particles of another. This mathematical construction does justice to the relation of the elements to principles of higher than physical standing. It also implies quantitative relationships between one element and another: the triangles that formed one octahedron, i.e., one particle of air, will build up two pyramids when air turns into fire; and two and a half air particles will form one unit of fire.[19] Aristotle, too, finds a quantitative factor involved in the changes between elements. He knows that the air into which water has evaporated fills more space than the water did. Yet, keeping everything that might look like mathematics out of his physical account, he allows himself no guess about the ratio of the two spaces and absorbs the quantitative—along with the qualitative—aspect of the transformation into his substratum. As the substratum, thanks to its potentialities, accounts for the change from hot to cold, so it also does for that from small to large and the reverse.[20]

Aristotle's own construction of the elements operates entirely without mathematics, it does not connect the elements with principles of higher ontological standing, and it steers clear of the concepts of association and dissociation which had bulked so large in this subject. He may seriously have considered the possibility that different elements should have different substrata.[21] This idea would have had

[19] *Tim.* 56dff.

[20] This is set forth in a section of the *Physics* (IV,9.217a26–b11) where Aristotle's immediate purpose is to show that no void is needed to make possible the change from one body into another which occupies more space (his illustration is that from water to air). See Ross's comments on 217b20 and Joachim's on *De gen.* I,5.321a5ff. Note also *De gen.* I,4.319b31–320a5. That one and the same *hyle* is potentially both large and small is Aristotle's solution of—or alternative to—*genesis* by condensation and rarefaction (cf. Anaximenes in *Vorsokr.*, 13A5–8).

[21] The reason why this is impossible is, naturally enough, that they must change into one another, and Aristotle has already in *Phys.* I adopted the view that when there is *genesis* of one contrary out of the other the substratum must persist. Cf. *De caelo* IV,5.312a32. The cosmology of *De caelo* does not require an identical *hyle* for heavy and light bodies (312a22ff.; the passage and its difficulties and textual problems have been discussed above, Ch. 13, Note 32. It is not possible to

the advantage of widening the gulf between *genesis* and qualitative change—a point in which Aristotle is deeply interested. But he decided that the underlying substratum should be the same for all elements, and thus *genesis* falls short of being a change of the "whole thing," and the difference between *genesis* and qualitative change has its problems, though not for Aristotle himself. In both processes qualities are replaced by other qualities. Presumably hot and cold, dry and moist are more essential and constitutive qualities than black and white or cultured and uncultured.[22]

Of the concepts that Aristotle employs one is known to us—both in itself and in its ancestry, for we have traced the connections between Aristotle's "matter" and Plato's receptacle. The connection is here particularly relevant because the substratum of the elements is "prime matter," so that indeterminateness and formlessness reach their highest degree. They are now absolute, not, as usually, relative. But what are we to say about the other concepts which are here presented as "sense-perceived contraries" of the tactile class? Hot and cold, moist and dry are very familiar characters to students of ancient philosophy, physics, or medicine. From the beginnings of physical speculation they have, albeit with frequently changing status, persistently played important roles. We cannot forgo an excursus into their past.

In Anaximander hot and cold, moist and dry stuff are the component parts of our world—nothing less.[23] Originally they go under the name of "powers" and are very powerful indeed: if we do not see them compete with the elements for the status of principles (or divinities),[24] this is certainly not due to any lack on their part of power,

---

infer from it with confidence that Aristotle at one time seriously entertained the idea of different *hylai* for different elements; the final verdict, a17ff., is identical with that passed in our treatise, I,3.319a33ff.).

[22] *De gen.* I,4.319b10 suggests this difference between *genesis* and qualitative change: in the case of the latter the substratum which remains identical is a visible substratum (the illustration is a man changing from sick to well) whereas when water changes into air the substratum which persists is not in the realm of sense perception (*ibid.*, 15).

[23] See esp. *Vorsokr.*, 12A10, 16; on the "powers" in Anaximander see Fränkel, *Dichtg. u. Philos.*, 342ff. There remains some doubt as to the precise status of the moist and the dry in his system; neither A16 nor A27 gives us fully satisfactory information on this point. Perhaps it is not fanciful to derive from these reports the impression of a cosmic antagonism between these powers.

[24] For what is probably an exception see "Hipp." *De carne* 2. The physician who wrote this treatise introduces the *thermon* as a cosmic *arche* and gives it the attributes of divinity. Having come to know its "supreme" power in his pro-

activity, or substantiality. The early thinkers may have regarded them as less persistent than the elements, as less capable of surviving in their changes. The hot of summer is not present in the cold of winter; the moist, when dried up, does not exert its own specific power in its opposite—or, as Aristotle would say, its contrary.[25] If the relation of the powers to the elements did not constitute a problem in early stages of physical speculation, it was yet bound to become one. Empedocles seems to have "attached" some powers to each of his elements; but he also allowed the powers independent activity when dealing with processes like nutrition. Here the "powers" of the bitter and the sweet, the sour and the astringent, and many others had probably by his time already a firm standing due to the interest taken in them by the professional physicians.[26]

It is nevertheless correct to say that in Empedocles' system the powers recede into the background; but they again come to the fore with Anaxagoras, who used them for the composition of both elements and tissues.[27] Once again they are the basic world stuff, different combinations of them forming the variety of physical entities. But this rehabilitation was short-lived; soon enough the existence and reality of these powers were to be radically challenged, and it became doubtful whether they have a place in the nature of things at all or whether they are temporary sensations experienced by a percipient subject. Democritus correlated specific atom shapes with particular tastes and other sensations. Hot and cold, bitter and sweet have their names by convention; they have no reality in the *physis*, and the atoms which

---

fession, he raises it to such a high status in deliberate opposition to the *archai* introduced by the philosophical physicists (and by other physicians who had joined their ranks; on his relation to Diogenes of Apollonia see Karl Deichgräber in the edition of the work, *Hippokrates über Entstehung . . . des menschl. Körpers* [Berlin, 1935], 30ff.).

[25] See Heraclitus in *Vorsokr.*, 22B126, a fragment whose authenticity is not above doubt but has recently been defended by G. S. Kirk, who also refers to Melissus B8(3), where a common opinion appears to be reported (*Heraclitus: The Cosmic Fragments* [Cambridge, 1954], 149ff.).

[26] In *Vorsokr.*, 31B21, fire (more precisely, the sun) is described as white and hot, water (rain) as dark and cold, and earth in somewhat different words is associated with solid things (cf. the epithets—partly epic, partly physical—in Hes. *Theog.* 107, 736f.; see also Parm. 28B8.56ff.). See, further, Emped. B90. Cf. "Hipp." *De prisca med.* 14 (16.2ff. Kühlewein), a chapter which also throws light on the place of the powers in the medical tradition.

[27] See esp. *Vorsokr.*, 59B4; also 12, 15, 16.

produce these "sensations" by means of their shape are themselves devoid of quality.[28]

To a remarkable extent Plato in the *Timaeus* agrees with this line of thought. Although in the "raw" condition of things—before the Demiurge gave the elements form and shape—the "powers" have liberty to display themselves, as soon as the Cosmos has come into being their liberty and with it their reality have disappeared.[29] In the section devoted to the "sensations of the body as a whole" Plato asks, "In what sense do we call the fire hot?" and answers as follows: "We are all aware that the sensation is a piercing one, and we must take into consideration the fineness of the edges [scil., of the pyramid which constitutes the unit of fire], the sharpness of the angles, the smallness of the particles, and the swiftness of the movement, thanks to all of which [fire] . . . cuts sharply into whatever it encounters." [30] The sensation of cold is explained along analogous lines, except that Plato does not connect it so definitely with one element and its shape but refers to "moist things" which surround and enter the body as producing the sensation.[31] Basically the same principle of explanation is adopted for most of the former "powers." The powers that affect our organs of taste, the harsh, the pungent, the acrid, the sweet are understood as effects produced by elements and their atomic shapes upon these organs; the colors are sensations caused by particles of different size in the organ of vision.[32] Heavy and light are likewise treated in the section dealing with sensations; in the last analysis they are understood as sensations of the resistance—more or less strong—which elements set up against attempts at removing them from their proper cosmic place.[33] Neither the hot nor the cold, neither the heavy nor the light has any independent existence among physical things. Instead of "powers" we are here introduced to sensations which, in accordance with the sugges-

---

[28] The fullest account is in Theophrastus' *De sensu* (*Vorsokr.*, 68A135, esp. 65ff.). See, further, B117, 125. Protagoras' place in the development here sketched is difficult to determine. In the light of Sextus' statement (*Pyrrh. hyp.* 2.216ff. = *Vorsokr.*, 80A14) it is perhaps safe to suppose that he considered qualities as existing in the object. Cf. Cornford, *Theory*, 33ff., who thinks that Protagoras' position was much closer to that of Anaxagoras than of Democritus. See also Cherniss, *Presocr.*, 369.

[29] *Tim.* 52e1f. See the Index, *s.v. dynameis.*　　　　[30] *Tim.* 61d5ff.

[31] *Ibid.*, 62a5ff.

[32] See esp. 65c1ff., 67c4ff. For Plato's distinction between affections of the entire body and such concerning specific organs (the former of these replacing the sensations of "touch") see my comments in *A. J. Ph.*, 76 (1955), 159 and n.41.

[33] 62c3ff.; see esp. 63b2ff., c1ff.

tions of the *Theaetetus*, arise between the objects and the percipient. Plato's doctrine of sensation as set forth in that dialogue may, in conjunction with his own construction of the elements, have led him independently to conclusions that remind us of the Abderites.[34] Although not every sensation is explicitly traced to a particular element, their geometrical construction is the basis of Plato's account; Plato cannot, like Democritus, co-ordinate atom shapes with tastes and colors but has to use his four regular bodies, with their variations and combinations. Agreements with the atomists in points of detail do not go far; whether coincidences with Empedocles' theory of colors are more significant (since Plato owes his elements to him) is hard to decide and need not here be settled.[35]

Some of the "powers," however, demand a different place. Moist, though it probably could be treated as a bodily sensation, is understood as one of the conditions in which the water units may find themselves. If the atoms are of equal size and closely packed, water is in a frozen state; if, owing to loss of uniformity and the action of fire between the units, motion arises, water becomes "moist." [36] Actually the Greek word ὑγρόν might here more fittingly be rendered as "fluid," inasmuch as its opposite is not the dry but the frozen condition of the same element.[37]

The construction of Plato's elements and elementary particles ex-

[34] Cf. Thomas F. Gould, "Plato and Democritus" (diss., Cornell Univ., 1953).

[35] For Democritus' account of colors see esp. *Vorsokr.*, 68A135.73ff.; for that of tastes *ibid.*, 65ff. It is decidedly un-Democritean to trace all colors to fire (*Tim.* 67c4ff.). In treating of the colors Plato speaks of effluences from the object that may be smaller or larger than the μέρη ὄψεως or of the same size as these. Empedocles appears to have made the same distinctions in the size of the effluences though he compared them in each case to the pores of the eye into which they try to enter (see Plato's own account of his theory: *Men.* 67c = Emped. A92; also 86.7). Like Cornford (*Cosmology*, 261) I find it difficult to make satisfactory sense of Theophrastus' statement (*De sensu* 60f.) that Plato, in contrast to Democritus, does not deprive the sense qualities of independent reality; in fact, Cornford himself seems to me to go too far in allowing the elementary particles to possess "powers" (*Cosmology*, 261f.).

[36] 58dff.; 59d4ff.

[37] For "the dry" and "the frozen" as contraries of the moist one may compare Arist. *De gen.* II,2.330a12–24 where "the frozen" is subsumed under "the dry." Hard and soft are in 62b6ff. (cf. 63e10) defined both with reference to our sensations and in relation to one another. For dense and rare (i.e., tightly or less tightly packed) which bear on the organization of the material see 62c2 and also, e.g., 59b2ff. In Anaxagoras the dense and the rare (or "the thin") are powers of the same order as the cold and the warm, the dark and the bright, etc. (see, e.g., B12; 2.38.12).

cludes any thought that the powers could be of use in their formation. On the other hand, "powers" do enter into the receptacle,[38] and this is all the more significant since Aristotle's substratum has succeeded to essential functions of the receptacle. Nor should we while dealing with the *Timaeus* forget the perhaps reluctant yet in any case unqualified recognition of the "hot"—scil., the vital heat—as a substance in our body.[39] In the process of respiration this "hot" enters into a relationship with the (cold) air outside which may be described as "acting" and "suffering." [40] In a medical or physiological context it was hardly possible to do without such entities. For whatever philosophers had decided about them, the moist and dry, the cold and hot remained firmly entrenched in medical theory—there was nothing that could take their place. A physician of Plato's generation, Philistion of Locri, deserves special interest in this connection. Being a follower of Empedocles, he adhered to the doctrine of the four elements, yet developed it in the direction of associating each of them with one of the basic powers: fire with the hot, air with the cold, earth with the dry, and water with the moist. This doctrine—which is well attested [41]—is not likely to have been an isolated *aperçu* in his physiological theory; whether or not he described these "powers" in detail, it stands to reason that he availed himself of them again and again to account for the behavior of the human organism in health and sickness. If it was he who acquainted the Academy with the current version of Empedocles' doctrine,[42] the difference between Plato's and Aristotle's response is certainly revealing. Plato follows him more readily in his physiology and etiology of the diseases than in his physics, where it would not serve his purpose to endow the elements with such powers. Aristotle, on the other hand, although much closer to Philistion's approach, modifies the relationship of elements and powers by connecting each of the former with two of the latter: water is not only moist but moist and cold, fire hot and dry.

---

[38] *Tim.* 50a2.

[39] *Ibid.*, 79d (in d2ff. Plato in effect admits that the "fire" which he has used in the preceding sections [78a–79a; see also 80d] to explain the functions of digestion and respiration is this *thermon;* see also 82a7ff.).

[40] See again *Tim.* 79df., with my comments in *Stud. It.*, 27–28 (1956), 544ff.

[41] Philistion, frgs. 4 and 5 in Max Wellmann, *Die Fragmente der sikelischen Ärzte* (Berlin, 1901), 110ff.

[42] For the relation between Philistion and the Academy, esp. his influence on Plato and Aristotle, see Carl Fredrich, *Hippokratische Untersuchungen* (Berlin, 1899), 47ff.; Wellmann, *op.cit., passim*, esp. 10ff., 69ff., 74ff.; Jaeger, *Hermes*, 48 (1913), 49 and n.4, and *Diokles von Karystos* (Berlin, 1938), 211ff.

Yet he does admit—in the last sentence of our section [43]—that "each" [element] is characterized par excellence by one quality: earth by dry rather than by cold, water by cold rather than by moist, air by moist rather than by "hot"—note the divergence from Philistion in these two instances—"and fire by hot rather than by dry." In any case the traditional powers have been brought back by Aristotle; and whatever term may now designate their status, they are once more essential for the formation and definition of the elements.

It is hard to gauge the extent to which the pivotal role of the "powers" in medical thought facilitated their rehabilitation in Aristotle's system. We need not doubt that he adopted them in the first place because they provided him with the best explanation for the mutual transformation of the elements; yet the doctrine of our treatise also lays the foundation for the biological and zoological works and may well be devised with an eye upon them. The large measure of fundamental agreement with these is certainly not accidental. Philosophical and "practical" considerations may have conspired in Aristotle's mind; in fact, there is no telling how early these "practical" considerations asserted themselves and how strong a mark they may have left on what, at first glance, seems "pure" theory. On the other hand, the relationship between substratum, powers, and elements as spelled out in our treatise is still a trifle too theoretic for ready application in biology. Discarding the nice distinctions of our treatise, Aristotle declares, in the *Parts of Animals:* "The moist, the dry, the hot, and the cold are the matter [substratum] of composite bodies." [44] Although calling them "powers" and relying on their physical powers, he here treats them also as substances. The fact is that biological theory needed the four elements as well as the four powers as its primary data. The latter are throughout Aristotle's zoology and Theophrastus' botany regarded as existing in their own right. For biological—to say nothing of medical—thinking it would be an intolerably awkward complication if the powers were merely qualities of the elements and, to make matters worse, in these elements in-

[43] II,3.33123ff.

[44] See *De part. anim.* II,1.646a14-17. Aristotle here refers to our chapter (II,2) of *De generatione*, yet simplifies its doctrine. An analysis of his (and Theophrastus') biological treatise with regard to the use made of these four powers and to the co-operation or competition between powers and elements is still a desideratum. It will be obvious, after what has been set forth in my present chapter, that Josef Zürcher, *Aristoteles' Werk und Geist* (Paderborn, 1952), 142, errs when he speaks of hot, cold, moist, and dry as Aristotle's "new" four elements and finds them playing this role in the *De generatione*.

variably associated with a second quality. Since in our treatise the powers are something less than substances, Aristotle sees no need to account for their own *genesis* and destruction. Nor do they change into one another. It is not the moist which evaporates and changes into dry, or the hot which undergoes a change into cold,[45] but an element, like water, changes into air by losing its moist and acquiring the dry instead.

Aristotle would of course not deny that the fire, besides being hot and dry, is also red and bright. That it is light he has said over and over again in the books *On the Heaven*. It may have any number of further qualities, but they are not constitutive. Anaxagoras' statement that "there is a portion of everything in everything" seems to imply that he regarded all powers—sweet and white no less than hot and moist—as constitutive of elements and other objects. For him even the opposite powers are present everywhere, albeit in differing mixture and ratio.[46] Compared with Anaxagoras, Aristotle is highly selective. He admits that if there were more elements he would have to use more "contrary qualities" to differentiate them and actually mentions black and white as possibilities; yet the more elements and differentiating qualities there would be, the more complex the process of transformation, and if there were an infinite number of qualities (as there ought to be), the process would never be completed.[47] Four is quite enough for nature's and Aristotle's purposes. As has been said, his selection may have been influenced by his association with physicians of the "Sicilian school"—or by the requirements of his own biology. (These are not real alternatives.) If it is true that the Stoics identified water with the moist, air with the cold, fire with the warm, and earth with the dry,[48] we may regard them as going Aristotle one better in selectivity; whether the agreement of this doctrine with Philistion's is accidental or not is a question which we must leave to the future investigator of their large debt to medical theory.

What, then, is the status which Aristotle gives the four principal powers when he rehabilitates them in our treatise? Since they are tied to matter (or "prime matter") and meant to modify matter, it is clear that they cannot enjoy the same independent existence as formerly. Aristotle introduces them as sense-perceived contraries of the tactile class. Actu-

---

[45] See II,1.329a35–b3; cf. I,6.322b16ff. and indeed Plato *Phaedo* 103b. *Phys.* I,6.189a22–24 goes even farther but is hardly borne out by the theory of our treatise.

[46] See *Vorsokr.*, 59B6, 12; cf. Vlastos, *Philos. Rev.*, 59 (1950), 41ff.

[47] *De gen.* II,5.332b12ff. (20ff.); 333a3ff.   [48] See *St. V. F.*, 2.580.

ally, his concentration on "tactile" powers and his selection of four presuppose still another rehabilitation in the realm of physics, where, as we know, everything is in flux and concepts change their status and "honors" again and again. In the systems of the late Presocratics and in Plato all sensations come about by touch, i.e., touch of the particles or atoms upon the sense organs.[49] As an incidental result of this approach, touch itself is no longer a sense function of distinct individuality; it has no peculiarities that could set it apart from the others. Where Plato in the *Timaeus* deals with the sense qualities that Aristotle calls tactile, he refers to them as "sensations affecting the entire body" (while sight, etc., affect specific organs).[50] It would have been pointless to call them "sensations of touch" because in his scheme taste comes about by touch between the tongue and particles of such and such shape in the food, color by touch of elementary "effluences" with the organ of sight. This curious situation does not seem to have given rise to particularly vexing problems; still it prevailed until Aristotle put the doctrine of the senses and sense impressions on an entirely new basis. In his treatise *On the Soul* he teaches that the sense organs are affected, and can only be affected, by objects that are not in touch with them; the potentialities of each organ are brought to actuality by the working of something remote. To be sure, this remote object needs an intermediary to exert its influence, and Aristotle goes to the length of postulating even in the case of touch an intermediary or "medium" between object and organ. This medium of touch is the flesh.[51] Thus, whereas for the Presocratics all sense functions had become reduced to touch or direct contact, the pendulum now swings to the opposite extreme, and for Aristotle even touch is no longer direct touch or contact. However, his specific doctrines interest us less than his rehabilitation of touch as a peculiar sense function, different from the others. He can speak of tactile qualities as a variety of the "sense-perceived differences." For his present purpose—which is to explain the *genesis* of the elements—it is the only variety that can be of help.[52]

[49] For what follows see my discussion in *A. J. Ph.*, 76 (1955), 159f.
[50] See *Tim.* 64a2ff., 65b3. The section in question is 61d–65b.
[51] *De an.* II,7.418a31ff., 419a18ff., a27ff.; 11.423b2–27.
[52] See again II,1.329b7ff. It may seem curious that Aristotle does not make a greater effort to defend the status which he gives to "powers" in general and to the tactile in particular. If they are more, and have more reality, than sensations (as which they had lately been treated), one might expect him to polemize against the atomists and the *Timaeus*. We have reasons for thinking that the demotion of the "powers" had not been generally accepted; if, in particular, medi-

Why is Aristotle convinced that the qualities which inform matter and mold it into primary bodies (elements) must be found in the tactile group? Is it because bodies cannot act on one another and be acted upon unless they are in touch? This proposition has indeed been worked out in a preceding chapter.[53] Yet "touch" or contact between physical bodies is not the same as the sense function of touch—not for us at any rate and, as far as I can see, not for Aristotle either. To be sure, the capacities of acting and being acted upon appear in our chapter among the considerations that determine the selection of the right qualities; and of the two pairs which Aristotle chooses one, hot and cold, is in truth active, the other, moist and dry, passive.[54] Still, it is impossible to suppose that Aristotle confused the two meanings of "touch" (ἀφή). It may be more to the point to recall what Plato says when deducing the four elements which he needs for the Cosmos. Starting from the affirmation, "That which came into being must be bodily and thus visible and tangible," he proceeds to derive the presence of fire from the visibility of the Cosmos and that of earth by reasoning that "nothing touchable can exist without something solid, nothing solid without earth." [55] Like Plato, Aristotle uses as his starting point the fact that a body is in the realm of sense perceptions; he may even have Plato's precedent in mind when he too concentrates for a moment on vision and touch and then—contrary to Plato—eliminates vision from his argument. The main difference is that he does not merely wish to "de-

---

cal thought still regarded the powers as active *dynameis*, this may have made it easier for Aristotle to treat them as enjoying a higher status than philosophers had lately been willing to concede to them.

[53] I,6.322b21–323a34. Aristotle in 322b29ff. points out that the word *haphe* has more than one meaning. It can hardly be his intention to give us here a complete list of these meanings; yet though he includes a usage barely related to "physical contact" (323a32: what "grieves" us "touches" us), there is no shred of evidence that the sense function of touch and the physical contact of objects are for him closely related meanings of *haphe*.

[54] This, it seems to me, is clearly stated in II,2.329b24–26 (cf. also 26–32). It should indeed not be questioned that "moist" and "dry" are also active and passive in regard to one another, but this is not the point which Aristotle here wishes to make (cf. Philoponus' good comments *ad loc.*, 216.13–217.1; Joachim in his commentary *ad loc.* discusses the reciprocal activity and passivity of moist and dry without making clear that it is irrelevant to, and ignored in, our passage. His translation leaves no doubt about Aristotle's meaning. See, further, his discussion in *J. of Philology*, 29 [1904], 83ff.).

[55] *Tim.* 31b3ff. (see Cornford, *Cosmology*, 43 and n.2); see also 28b. For a comparison of this Platonic deduction with Aristotle's derivation of the elements in *De caelo* IV see above, p. 285.

duce" the elements but is looking for qualities which can actually constitute them and belong to them essentially; as soon as he has found these qualities, he uses them to explain both the nature of the elements and the most important phases of their behavior. In Plato the deduction of the elements with the help of the concepts of visibility and tangibility remains an episode.

The other difference is that Aristotle keeps to the concept of tangibility and exploits it more fully. All qualities that he needs to build up the elements are found within the range of this concept. However, it is the status of these qualities which interests us. The Platonic precedent may help to explain why they are here introduced, and Aristotle would use "touch" all the more readily because he had done so much to restore and clarify its place. For him tangibility is the conceptual bridge between the "sense-perceived" elements and the qualities hot and cold, moist and dry. By no other sense function could he find the way to these qualities, and he had reasons—as well as precedents—for considering these closer to the substance of elements than bright and dark or bitter and sweet. (Imagination does not readily supply appropriate examples of sounds and smells.)

As soon, however, as the four qualities have found their place between the substratum and the elements, their character as "tangible contraries" becomes irrelevant. When they fight one another, yield to one another, and by such "acting and suffering" cause the mutual transformation of the elements, they are constitutive factors of these elements; their relation to touch or any other sense perception has no bearing on their behavior.[56] They shed their credentials, whose only purpose was to gain them admission into the inquiry. Once more, then, what is their status? The truth is that hot and cold, moist and dry have changed their status so often that Aristotle has considerable freedom and can employ them now in one character, now in another.

When Plato in the *Phaedo* establishes that the opposites, such as hot and cold, do not "receive," and do not change into, one another—a thesis of which we have found some echoes in our treatise—these opposites are "forms." Such "forms" and even opposite "forms" had already been known to the medical writers.[57] And not only in medical but also

---

[56] Chs. II,4 and 7.

[57] *Phaedo* 102dff. (cf. 105a, τὸ ἐναντίον τὸ ἐναντίον μὴ δέχεσθαι, and 103cf.). In Aristotle's comparable passages note the use of abstracts like πυκνότης, θερμότης (*Phys.* I,5.189a22ff.; *De gen.* I,6.322b16ff., II,1.329b2). On the Hippocratic εἶδος

in physical thought the opposites are "powers"; [58] as such, they are at times treated as independent of the elements and at others as attached to them. Again they had been defined as sensations with the implication that sensations were devoid of objective reality. And finally in Aristotle's own system they are qualities, and qualities are certainly quite distinct from substances. In the *Categories* qualities like hot and cold do not even represent the "first" type of qualities, since there are others of a more enduring nature.[59]

This may help us to understand that Aristotle introduces these four entities as "sense perceived contraries" but at the same time gives them a crucial place in the material constitution of his elements. Their history qualified them for both roles—and indeed for more. They are used in a third role when they act on, and are acted upon by, one another. "Sense-perceived contraries" are not substantial enough, and normal Aristotelian qualities not independent enough, for such behavior. In the later chapters of our book Aristotle, while developing in detail his theory of the nature, changes, and mixtures of the elements, has much need for acting and suffering.[60] In fact, he there uses hot, cold, moist, and dry once more in two functions, as constituting the elements and as meeting one another in their active and passive capacities. These capacities they owe to their traditional status as "powers," and we shall presently see that, though not originally introduced with this status, they are ready to exert their "powers" very vigorously as soon as they are given a chance.

(and ἰδέα) as offering analogues to Plato's see Jaeger, *Paideia*, III.23f.; cf. also H. C. Baldry, *Cl. Q.*, 31 (1937), 143ff.

[58] On the *dynameis* in Hippocratic writings see below, p. 359.

[59] *Categ.* 8.9a28ff., where also the definition of παθητικός differs considerably from the sense in which Aristotle employs it in our chapter. Aristotle at the end of *De caelo* III (8.307b19ff.) declares his intention to investigate the *pathe*, *erga*, and *dynameis* of the elements. This, he says, is the most promising way— more promising certainly than Plato's mathematical figures—of arriving at their distinctive differences. As we know, the only *dynameis* which he really investigates in the following book of *De caelo* are heavy and light. Yet in some way the discussion of *De gen.* II,2 implements the program of that passage.

[60] See Chs. 18 and 19.

18

"Acting" and "Suffering"

AS we have seen, Aristotle uses the concepts of "acting" and "suffering" to select the qualities which, suitably combined, constitute the nature of the sublunary elements. Yet as long as a particular element is in existence and shows no tendency to change, the qualities which form it live peacefully together and show no inclination to act upon one another.[1] The subjects for which Aristotle really needs "acting" and "suffering" are the intermutation and the mixture of the elements. To these subjects he turns as soon as he has said all that is necessary on the nature of the elements.[2] The ground is well prepared; it will soon appear how circumspect Aristotle was in the derivation of the elements.

Of the importance which "active" and "passive" qualities have in his physical system there can be no doubt. Even in the preliminary general discussion of *genesis* in Book I they come in for extensive scrutiny.[3] Here Aristotle tries (as is his wont in important topics) to distill from the Presocratic systems definite opinions as to the nature and the conditions of physical interaction. However, the doctrines which he scrutinizes for this purpose are somewhat arbitrarily selected. Although the Presocratics certainly made their "powers," elements, and other principles "act" upon and affect one another, Empedocles' theory of sense perceptions or Leucippus' views on the coalescence of atoms are not obvious antecedents of Aristotle's own doctrine.[4] Moreover, it is far

[1] Aristotle does not go into detail about the mode of combination but simply speaks of σύζευξις (II,3.330a30, 34; συνδυάζεσθαι, 31).

[2] II,4; see also II,7.

[3] See I,6.322b9ff. and what follows in this chapter, as well as I,7-9.

[4] I,7.323b1ff.; 8.324b25ff., 35ff. (note 325a32ff., b9ff., yet also b36ff.); 326b6ff. In mentioning Empedocles' theory of mixture (8.324b34), Aristotle does touch on a

from certain that the Presocratics actually employed the concepts of "acting" and "suffering"—or that they employed them in any but the most casual fashion, untouched by any desire to speculate about the conditions of their realization.[5] Now, while trying to find out what use they made of acting and suffering, Aristotle approaches their systems with a very specific question which is to bear fruit in his own doctrine: do early physicists assume acting and suffering to materialize between similar or between dissimilar entities?[6] Needless to say, his ruthless insistence on this question limits the historical value of his findings, yet it leads him in the end to formulate his own stand. To act upon one another, objects must be dissimilar but not too dissimilar; contraries of the same kind that come under the same category are ideally suited for this purpose,[7] because they have the same substratum.

Another doctrine affirmed—or rather reaffirmed—in these chapters is that what "suffers" must do so as a whole if this "suffering" is to cause *genesis* or substantial change. *Genesis*, as Aristotle here once more says, does not come about by a breaking up or splitting, nor is it his idea of "suffering" that another entity settles in the pores, open spaces, or, generally speaking, in limited areas of the thing affected and, as it

---

subject for which he himself needs "acting" and "suffering"; yet one hesitates to accept his statement that in Empedocles mixture generally comes about by way of the pores (it is possible that Aristotle generalizes on the basis of doctrines that did not apply so widely; see *Vorsokr.*, 31B92, in connection with [Philop.] *In de gen. anim.* 123.13ff. = *ibid.*, A87). One may suspect that if Aristotle had found in Empedocles a clear and good physical description (without use of metaphors) as to how earth and water mix he would not have turned to his theory of sense perception, a subject which has no bearing on *genesis*.

[6] Kranz in the Index of the *Vorsokratiker*, *s.v.* ποιεῖν, very appropriately assembles the occurrences of ποιεῖν καὶ πάσχειν under the heading "Doxographie." Aristotle (I,6.322b13ff.) reports with approval a view expressed by Diogenes of Apollonia to the effect that if things were not basically one there could be no mutual "acting and suffering." Here we are in a position to check Aristotle's report: Diogenes actually speaks of ὠφέλησις and βλάβη (B2), which may be an approximation to our pair. In the *Lysis* (214e5) Plato makes use of the same two concepts (ὠφελίαν ἔχειν and βλάβην ποιεῖν) for one part of the alternative; for the other the verb πάσχειν (scil., πάσχειν τι) is all he needs (e7).

[8] I,7.323b1ff. The *De anima* asks the same question when reviewing doctrines regarding nutrition and sensation (*trophe* and *aisthesis*; II,4.416a29ff., 5.416b35ff.). Here too acting and suffering enter into the discussion; in 417a1 Aristotle refers to what he has said in our treatise. Plato *Lys.* 214aff., 215cff. offers possibilities for a comparison with Aristotle's procedure, even though Plato is concerned with friendship and hostility, not with acting and suffering; see, however, Note 5.

[7] 323b31ff. Note also the observation that agent and patient must have the same substratum (I,6.322b18f.).

were, "between" the original material.[8] What he has in mind is whole-sale or organic transformation. Still another conclusion of this section is that in order to act and to be acted upon objects must be in direct physical contact with one another.[9] We may recall that contact—like contiguity, continuity, the successive—is among the concepts denoting spatial relationships that are defined in Book V of the *Physics*.[10] Having in his Academic years become convinced of its importance, Aristotle is on the lookout for situations in which physical contact is a necessary ingredient or plays a decisive role. That mover and moved must be in contact is a case in point, and the doctrine of our section that agent and patient must be so is another (Aristotle himself points out parallels between the two propositions).[11] Yet it seems fair to repeat that the motif of contact is more important in the medium of pure theory than when it comes to practical applications. In Book II, where Aristotle deals in more specific fashion with elementary interchanges and mix-tures, "contact" does not reappear. It is quite conceivable that hot and cold, when one of them ousts the other or when both mix, are in phys-ical contact; but obviously Aristotle, when he becomes engrossed in these processes, regards other aspects as more significant. His partiality for the concept may, however, be illustrated by his affirmation that in Plato *genesis* and breaking-up come to pass by contact. "Contact" be-tween triangles or elementary particles may indeed be found in Plato's account—if one looks for it—but there is no indication that Plato him-self attached significance to this feature.[12]

[8] I,9.326b29ff., 327a14ff.   [9] I,6.322b21ff., 26ff.; 323b6ff.

[10] *Phys.* V,3.226b19, 23; cf. 227a17ff. In *De gen.* II,6 the definition of the *Physics* is presupposed (323a3), but for Aristotle's present purpose further specifications are needed; cf. Joachim's note on 322b29. Cf. also *Phys.* VII,2. For a fuller discus-sion of Aristotle's interest in ἀφή see above, pp. 187–197.

[11] In 323a12 Aristotle substitutes κινητικά and κινητά for ποιητικά and παθητικά. It is again profitable to compare *Phys.* VII,2, although in this chapter the reciproc-ity of acting and suffering does not enter the problem with resulting complications, as it does in *De gen.* I,6 (cf. Joachim's note on 323a12ff.) and I,7.324a24ff., where Aristotle returns to the parallel between mover-moved and agent-patient and works it out to his satisfaction. On acting and suffering in movement see also *Phys.* III,3.

[12] I,8.325b32 (see also 9.327a12). It is not easy to decide what section of the *Timaeus*, if any, Aristotle here has in mind. The concepts—or words—ἅπτεσθαι and ἀφή occur neither in 53c–56 nor in 56c–57c (nor, if this is relevant, in 58c–61c), although there would have been no lack of opportunity for employing them had Plato wished to. The relations between *Parm.* 148d and *Phys.* V,3 have been studied above, p. 188. It would seem that Aristotle, who owes his interest in ἀφή to Plato, uses the concept in summing up Platonic doctrines in which it had no place.

Aristotle's "acting" and "suffering" may have more antecedents and their previous history may be more complex than our limited knowledge allows us to realize, but we venture the suggestion that Plato was the first to give them their standing in philosophical and physical thought. The concepts have the merit of bringing a large number of phenomena under a generic heading, and Plato had both a greater desire and a greater capacity for "abstracting" or finding the "one in the many" than any of his predecessors. We recall the passage of the *Theaetetus* where acting and suffering are described as two "forms [i.e., aspects] of movement." [13] Two other passages in the later dialogues are of particular importance.

In the *Sophist* Plato puts forward a definition of being: "I say that anything has real being which by nature possesses any kind of power either to act upon something else or to suffer even if ever so little, if from the most insignificant agent and if only once." [14] Here we find besides acting and suffering, and closely associated with them, the concept of "power"; and in the next sentence Plato even proposes as a definition of real things that "they are nothing but power." We have already had occasion to suggest that Aristotle's "sense-perceived differences" in which he hopes to find active and passive capacities—the hot and the cold, the moist and the dry—are "powers" in disguise, and although he himself in the larger part of our treatise does not employ this term (*dynamis*), we shall still find passages where his restraint gives way. Now as for Plato's "definition" of being, Cornford issued a strong warning [15] to look at it as no more than a provisional formula, and we should indeed not consider Plato as committed to it. He has in this passage to find common ground between the "idealist" position and the materialists with their very limited conception of reality, and the definition of being serves this purpose. It seems to be primarily applicable to the relation between physical objects, and this is in fact the topic of the section in the *Timaeus* which furnishes us with our second passage.

Here we find ourselves in the midst of a violent battle. An element is pictured as surrounded by others; it fights, it is defeated and overcome,

---

[13] *Theaet.* 156a; see above, p. 37. Note also the further development of the argument here in the course of which our concepts recur at 157a3. Note further the more casual use of the concepts in passages like *Phaedo* 93a, 97d.

[14] *Soph.* 247c8ff.

[15] *Theory*, vii, 234ff., 238. On the concept *dynamis* and its previous use cf. J. Souilhé, *Etudes sur le term* δύναμις *dans les dialogues de Platon* (Paris, 1919), and Cornford, *loc. cit.*

and when this happens it may either flee to its kindred or be dissolved, broken up, and transformed into the victorious element.[16] Plato's elementary particles have sharp edges and angles; they can be as good fighters as the Presocratic powers. Acting and suffering, as we know these concepts from Aristotle, would almost seem too pale and abstract to describe this life-and-death struggle; however, when Plato himself shifts for a moment from the pictorial to the conceptual medium, he avails himself of these terms: "Kinds that are identical or similar cannot work [act] any change in one another, nor can they suffer anything from what is identical and in the same condition." [17]

Here, then, if anywhere before Aristotle, is an account of the mutual transformation of elements which conforms to rules about acting and suffering. Change from one element into another is the topic for which Aristotle, too, needs these capacities. For him too such change is a victory of the element into which the other passes; it is brought about by the victor's own "action"—cases in which the change would be due to the operation of a third element were certainly not unknown but are here left out of consideration.[18] Just as in Aristotle the powers fight, and act upon, one another, so in Plato do the pyramids and other geometrical units of his elements. Moreover, the general rule governing these interactions is that which Aristotle accepts at the beginning of his inquiry.[19] As we have seen, he turned to the Presocratics to find out whether they assume acting and suffering between similar or dissimilar entities. His own decision is not only the same as Plato's but actually recalls Plato's wording; he too denies the capacity of mutual suffering to identical as well as to similar objects. "It is reasonable to assume that things similar and in every respect without difference cannot suffer from one another; for why should one of them have more power to

[16] *Tim.* 56c8–57c6. As is to be expected, Aristotle's account offers no parallels to the breaking up (διαλύεσθαι) of which we find a good deal in Plato's section. This notion is typical of the aggregational approach which he has dismissed. The imagery of warfare may remind us of earlier world systems which knew the elements, or rather powers, as fighting one another and encroaching upon one another (see for Anaximander *Vorsokr.*, 12A27, B1; cf. also Lucr. 5.380ff. with my comments, *A. J. Ph.*, 72 [1951], 13ff.).

[17] *Tim.* 57a3 (cf. *Lys.* 214e3–215a1).

[18] For the "victory" motif (the κρατεῖν) see, e.g., *Tim.* 56e8, 57a5ff., and *De gen.* II,3.331a28ff., 37; for "destruction," 331b1, b8ff. (often). For changes due to action of another element see, e.g., *Tim.* 60c (yet the changes covered in this and the preceding section are not elementary transformations; Plato does not mention that, by the action of fire, water may be made to change into air).

[19] Cf. *Tim.* 57a3 with *De gen.* I,6.323b18ff. (see also b29ff.; 324a5ff.).

act than the other, and if like can suffer from like, it could also suffer from itself." [20] However, Aristotle complements this proposition by another and more affirmative statement to which we find nothing comparable in the *Timaeus:* since utterly different objects cannot act on one another either, those which belong to the same genus yet are contraries within the genus have the best qualifications for mutual interaction.[21] Clearly the powers hot and cold, moist and dry meet these requirements; contrariety is more definitely present between them than between either the elements as such or the geometrical figures which Plato brings into action. In Aristotle's account, where the elements change as a result of actions and passions undergone by their powers, the general rule and the specific doctrines are in complete harmony; yet we can also understand why Plato was content with enunciating only the negative half of this rule. An octahedron can hardly be represented as the "contrary" of a pyramid.

It is logical enough that the power of acting should reside in things that by nature are "powers," and if it remains uncertain whether the Presocratics had abstracted our pair of terms, there can be no question that they in effect made the hot and cold behave as active powers and represented the moist and dry as sufferers.[22] More generally they dealt with many physical processes in a fashion which could be brought under these headings. Even the possibility that Plato encountered the actual terms in their writings should not be *a limine* ruled out. On the other hand, if early physicists thought of cosmic processes in concepts of injury or injustice inflicted by one entity and undergone by another,[23] Plato too would be able to "transfer" two complementary aspects from the moral sphere to the physical. Shall we then amass evidence for the idea of injustice done and suffered or for sin and criminal action expiated by just retribution? [24] This would probably

---

[20] 323b18-20 (for "from itself" cf. Plato *Lys.* 214e5-7).　　　　[21] 323b31ff.

[22] Evaporation or the drying up of the moist and the change of water (scil., the sea) into air and earth under the influence of the sun would illustrate the activity of the *thermon* (see, e.g., Anaximander in *Vorsokr.*, 12A27). In the case of the *psychron* such active power is perhaps less self-evident; yet see Anaxag. B16. Cf. also Plato *Tim.* 46d1ff.

[23] See Anaximander in *Vorsokr.*, 12B1. Cf. Jaeger, *Paideia*, 1.217ff., and *Theology*, 34ff., and also Vlastos, *Cl. Ph.*, 42 (1947), 168ff.

[24] For "correspondence" between acting and suffering in the moral sphere see esp. Plato *Gorg.* 476aff. See further, e.g., *Legg.* IX,859c (and for the relation between δράσας and παθών, 865df.). Cf. Aesch. *Ag.* 1526, 1562, and *Cho.* 144, 313ff.: δράσαντι παθεῖν is the "thrice old word," and Plato uses the more archaic word

be pointless. No amount of evidence would constitute a "proof." If Plato needed help to arrive at the pair, he could find it in many quarters.

One of them he seems to indicate himself when in the *Phaedrus* he appeals to "Hippocrates and the truth" [25] as suggesting valid methods of procedure (in medicine as far as the body is concerned and in rhetoric by adapting their teachings to the soul). Whether the object to be studied is simple or multiform, in either case the proper way is to investigate its natural "power" of "acting upon another" object and of "suffering" from such an object. It is well known that attempts at identifying a particular "source" for Plato's statement in our Hippocratic corpus have fallen short of carrying conviction; yet the last chapters of the treatise *On Ancient Medicine* offer as much evidence as we need for the use of our two concepts in medical thinking. "This too it is necessary to know," the author says at the beginning of the last chapter but one, "which kinds of sufferings in man are due to powers and which are due to structures" (scil., of the organs affected).[26] He has in earlier sections given us sufficient information as to what he means by "powers": "salty and bitter, sweet and acid, astringent and insipid, and a vast number of others, possessing powers of all kind." [27] In the remainder of our chapter typical differences between the organs are pointed out; this is one of the subjects "necessary to know." The next and final chapter begins with the words: "There are many other structures [inside and outside the body] which differ widely with re-

---

δρᾶν also in the important context of *Tim.* 33c8f. (whereas Aristotle in physical topics prefers ποιεῖν). Note also *Legg.* X,894c.

[25] *Phaedr.* 270c9ff.

[26] *De prisca med.* 22 *init.* The word here translated by "sufferings" ("diseases," according to W. H. S. Jones in the Loeb edition) is *pathemata*. For a variety of opinions on the relation between this work and the *Phaedrus* passage see Jaeger, *Paideia*, 3.23; R. Hackforth, *Plato's Phaedrus* (Cambridge, 1952), 151; W. H. S. Jones, *Philosophy and Medicine in Ancient Greece* (Cambridge, 1947), 16ff. Some recent studies attach greater significance to 271c2 with its reference to ἡ τοῦ ὅλου φύσις than to our passage (c10ff.); see, e.g., the widely differing interpretations of M. Pohlenz, *Hippokrates u. die Begründung d. wiss. Medizin* (Berlin, 1938), 74ff., and L. Edelstein, *R.E.* Suppl. 6.131ff. Still other solutions are advocated in the studies of Hans Diller, *Hermes*, 80 (1952), 285ff., and Joseph Hans Kühn, *System- u. Methodenprobleme im Corp. Hipp.* (*Hermes*, Einzelschriften; Wiesbaden, 1956), neither of which can here be discussed. I have referred to chs. 22f. in preference to 20 because, although the subject of acting and suffering is under discussion in both, the later chapters use the actual concepts and use them in relevant combinations.

[27] Ch. 14. Cf. Souilhé, *op.cit.*, 32ff.

gard to sufferings." [28] So much about suffering. The sentence which follows gives us the complement to it: "As has been said before, we must examine the powers of humors as to how each of them acts upon man and how they are related to one another." [29]

Granted that the author does not speak in so many words of a "power to suffer" and that he does not use the words "acting" and "suffering" in one and the same sentence but stays for a while with the "patient" before he goes on to the agent, can we doubt that the two concepts combine in his mind and that he knows "sufferings" in man which result from the acting "power" of different foodstuffs? [30] On a closer study of such interaction he bases his best hope for progress in the intelligent treatment of sick people. As far as antecedents for Plato's "power to act and to suffer" matter, the medical writers may well have approximated this conception more closely than the Presocratic physicists.

The physicians knew many more "powers" than Aristotle saw fit to use in defining the nature of his elements. Even in his biological work, which has contacts—yet after all limited contacts—with medical thinking, Aristotle falls short of employing the entire range of powers which his medical friends knew to be present either in the "nature of man" or in the food and the medicine that act upon this nature. Still Aristotle does look to the "powers" to find the power of acting and suffering, whereas Plato, though aware of close connections between elements and hot and cold, moist and dry, does not give the latter a place in the "nature" of his elements. In the *Timaeus* hot and cold, like bitter and sweet and many others of the kind, do not produce sufferings but are the sufferings, affections, sensations—or at least the names for them.[31] The active factors in these processes are the geometrical entities which compose the elements. These units bear the brunt of the battle between the elements which usually ends in the victory of one and the re-forming of the triangles that belonged to the destroyed enemy into the figure of the aggressor. For it surely is a merciless warfare, and while witnessing its dramatic events, we find it difficult to recall that in an earlier section Plato has described the basic relationship between the elements as one of amity and concord.[32]

---

[28] Ch. 23 *init.* (I have again translated *pathemata* by "sufferings," though it refers here to "experiences" in health as well as in sickness).

[29] *Ibid.* (in some editions this is the beginning of a new chapter).

[30] For a fuller study of the *dynameis* in the Hippocratic writers cf. Souilhé's book (see Note 15).

[31] *Tim.* 61d–62b6.   [32] *Ibid.*, 56c7ff.; cf. 32b8ff.

In Aristotle the imagery of warfare is somewhat paler, yet there is the same readiness to conquer and destroy. "If the dry is overcome by the moist, air will arise [scil., out of fire], and again water will result from air if the hot is overcome by the cold." "If fire is to come into being out of water, both the cold and the moist must be destroyed, and the cold and the dry must be destroyed if air is to arise from earth." [33] A peaceful regrouping or mutual replacing seems to be out of the question. In Anaxagoras "powers" that along with others were present in water may separate themselves out and as soon as they are by themselves enter into a new combination which happens to be earth. The atomists would explain such transformation by a similar mechanism, relying partly on a new "arrangement," partly, one would think, on a change in composition, some atoms departing, others of different shape arriving.[34] Aristotle's hot and cold, moist and dry cannot behave in such ways; if they did, they would be too "substantial." They are not "being things" in Anaxagoras' sense of the word, but merely contrary qualities informing the substratum which underlies the four elements. Nevertheless from the time when they were more they have retained powers through which they are now able to work on one another. If this is more than what "sense-perceived differences" or contrary qualities should do, we can only repeat that moist and dry, hot and cold had brought along a large and varied legacy. Intrinsic consistency is evidently not the only point of view from which Aristotle's physical system should be interpreted; where the systematic interpretation encounters difficulties, the historical may come to its aid. We may once more refer to the biological treatises where "the hot" in particular is treated as an entity in its own right—without being tied to either substratum or element—and where hot and cold employ their specific powers to whatever ends nature directs them.[35] And there are other differences between the functions of these powers in our treatise and in the biological works. In the latter, hot and cold are active and formative—it is they which after conception fashion the fetus out of the material present in the female—whereas moist and dry are confined to the passive role of being worked upon.[36] In our section all four are active and passive, actualizing these capacities whenever changes from

---

[33] *De gen.* II,3.331a28ff., b7ff.

[34] The reconstruction of this mechanism is in part conjectural, since no account gives us precise information as to the use made of διαθιγή. See, however, *Vorsokr.*, 68A38, and cf. Bailey, *Atomists*, 80. For Anaxagoras see *Vorsokr.*, 59B16.

[35] See, e.g., *De gen. anim.* II,6.742a15f.; 743a4ff., 37ff., b26ff.

[36] Cf. again *De gen. anim.* II,6.742a15f.; see also *De part. anim.* II,2.649a30ff.

element to element come to pass. It is true that Aristotle employs throughout this section passive verb forms and when he speaks of the overcoming of one quality by another regularly describes this event from the side of the sufferer; but he leaves no doubt that, e.g., the dry is overcome "by" the moist.[37]

Another point of difference is that in our treatise none of the four exercises its specific power. The hot does not really act as hot; it does not burn, scorch, consume, harden, or exsiccate. These are the functions which had been of interest to earlier physicists and physicians; "active power" as such would have meant nothing to them. Where Aristotle introduces hot and cold into the present discussion, he defines their specific "active" powers as capacities of bringing together (i.e., "associating") the homogeneous or the heterogeneous (presumably in the object on which they work)—definitions which, incidentally, are somewhat reminiscent of the older "aggregational" conception of *genesis*.[38] The moist and dry are in the same passage defined with reference to passive functions of a very general type. Yet neither these nor any other specific powers operate when through their acting and suffering hot and cold, moist and dry bring about the elementary transformations.[39] It seems that the exclusive emphasis on the power to act and to be acted upon is injurious to the more concrete power concept from which it had been abstracted and that Plato's pair of terms has—here at least—had the effect of depriving the four basic powers of their

[37] See esp. 331a28. Beginning with this line, I find only passive forms of the verbs κρατεῖν and φθείρειν in this chapter. Plato in the corresponding section (56c8ff.) likewise looks at the process from the side of the "sufferer," yet note τὸ κρατοῦν in 57b2 (cf. b7).

[38] See for these definitions (and also those of "moist" and "dry") II,2.329b26–32. The definition of the "hot" incorporates a correction of the traditional view about its specific power: it too "associates" (συγκρίνει) rather than "dissociates" (διακρίνει). Joachim (*ad loc.*) suggests that it was the Pythagoreans who had thought of the hot or the fire as dissociating. However, in connection with a later passage (II,9.336a3) where Aristotle once more mentions such views Philoponus vouchsafes the information that Alexander attributed them to οἱ περὶ Παρμενίδην; and this is probably the reason why the definitions are now included among the *testimonia* on Parmenides (*Vorsokr.*, 28A35). Whatever their origin, there are reasons for thinking that these views enjoyed considerable vogue. Democritus seems to have accepted them (A120), and Plato too makes use of them in *Tim.* 61dff. for his explanation of hot and cold sensations. For "homogeneous" Aristotle in our passage uses the word ὁμόφυλον in alternation with ὁμογενές. The former was probably the traditional term, whereas the latter looks like a new and analogous coinage formed from the word γένος.

[39] Ch. II,4.

individuality. The power concept is here as generalized as the concepts of nature and *genesis* are in the *Physics*.[40]

Still, hot and cold, moist and dry fulfill the functions for which Aristotle selected them. In their specific combinations they fashion the substratum into the elements and when overcome by their contraries they make an element change into another. With the latter doctrine Aristotle remains faithful to the fundamental proposition of the *Physics* that *genesis* is from contrary to contrary. Had he, like Philistion, assigned only one quality to each element, this would not have been possible; for a change from dry to hot would not have taken place between contraries.

Here as well as in the treatise *On the Heaven* [41] Aristotle "derives" his four sublunary elements through concentrating on the qualities; yet the qualities this time chosen—and, as we know, chosen with great care—can help toward objectives for which heavy and light proved of little use. The qualities of our treatise are more "intrinsic"; they do not characterize the elements only with reference to their cosmic place. Furthermore, the elements are now once more equals since all are equally defined by the possession of two basic qualities; [42] nothing is left of the discrimination inherent in the alternative derivation which begins by deducing two elements and then, by a kind of special pleading, brings in the other two as necessary intermediaries.[43] But the most important advantage of the new derivation is that the question raised but left unanswered in the *De caelo* can now be solved. This time the same qualities that constitute the elements account also for their mutual changes.

This is a great gain; but there is also loss. The cosmic distribution of the elements is a part of their nature and a definition of their nature ought to be mindful of these cosmological requirements. But Aristotle cannot allot cosmic places with the help of hot and cold, moist and dry. All that he can do about this subject in our treatise is to remind us of its existence. After he has deduced his elements in the new fashion, he adds a brief remark to the effect that two of them have their place in the upper cosmic regions and the other two in the lower.[44]

[40] See above, pp. 87f. and 98.   [41] *De caelo* IV,4.
[42] That according to I,3 (318b27ff.) some elements have a higher degree of form and are nearer to "being" is immaterial in this connection.
[43] *De caelo* IV,4.312a8ff.; 5.312a33ff. See above, Ch. 13. There is no evidence that Aristotle himself saw anything awkward in this procedure.
[44] *De gen.* II,3.330b30–33.

If he ever entertained hopes that identical premises could serve for all aspects of elementary behavior, this hope has been disappointed. The doctrine of elementary changes and mixture rests on one set of premises, that of the cosmic strata on another.

In a different form this dichotomy is present also in the *Timaeus*, where the cosmic distribution results from the motions in the receptacle while the transformation of the elements is due to their geometrical figures.[45] In Empedocles one "extrinsic" agent, Strife, creates the whirl which distributes the elements, and the other, Love, brings them together in mixtures (intermutations being out of the question in this system). Anaxagoras' whirl, on the other hand, seems to cause not only separations and cosmic movements but also formations and mixtures.[46] The atomists too may have avoided the dualism by assuming movement to be always present. Thus the atoms need no special cause or agent to come together in clusters and at times to form a cosmogonic whirl.[47] And indeed Aristotle too knows one ultimate cause of all cosmic movement and all cosmic *genesis;* and as soon as we turn to his "other," or moving, cause, the dualism on which we have dwelt will disappear. Moreover, the possibilities of finding common principles for movement and *genesis* were not yet exhausted; Aristotle's own concepts "active" and "passive" could, if advanced to an even more central place, help toward new solutions. Instead of attaching both capacities to the powers or qualities that modify matter, the Stoics assigned the one to matter as such, the other to the creative *logos* or the evermobile fire, i.e., to the principle which fashions and moves matter.[48]

---

[45] *Tim.* 52eff., 55dff.

[46] See *Vorsokr.*, 31B30f., A37, 52, B35 (and many fragments where Love is described as "mixing," e.g., 71, 73, 75, 96, 98); 59B12 *et al.* I cannot subscribe to the widely held opinion that a Cosmos forms also in the "period of Love"; but this is not the place to argue the case against it. If the opinion were correct, the statement made in our text would simplify matters unduly. Another controversial (and perhaps hopelessly obscure) subject is the precise relation between Strife and the whirl. In Anaxagoras' system many details regarding the formation of physical entities are uncertain, yet there is no doubt that all such formation has its origin in the *perichoresis* set up by mind.

[47] For the place of *kinesis* in the early atomist systems cf. Arist. *De caelo* III,2.300b8ff. (*Vorsokr.*, 67A16, 68A40, and *passim*).

[48] See, e.g., *St. V. F.*, 1.84 (Zeno), 493 (Cleanthes); 2.300ff. (for further testimonies of this basic doctrine see M. Adler's Index to *St. V. F., s.v.* ποιοῦν). For ὕλη as πάσχον in Aristotle see *De gen.* I,7.324b18; II,9.335b29f. Passages from other treatises (e.g., *De gen. anim.* I,18.724b5) are collected and discussed by A. Mansion, *Introduction à la physique arist.* (2d ed.; Louvain and Paris, 1945), 243 and n.23. The debt of Stoic physics to Aristotle's theory of *genesis* needs careful study.

Compared with the earlier systems, Aristotle's has the advantage if not of unity at least of a certain symmetry. Hot, cold, moist, and dry, like heavy and light, belong in an essential sense to the nature of the sublunary elements. The status of both groups is the same, no matter whether it be defined in terms of powers, of sense-perceived differences, of qualities, or of alternative modifiers of the substratum.

Still, the cleavage is now even more patent. The reason for this is not so much that Aristotle's physical system covers more ground than those of his percursors; nor is it simply to be found in his native bent toward departmentalization, i.e., toward severing what he found united and perceiving differences where Plato had found connections. In this instance departmentalism is the result rather than the cause—or the cause only in the sense that physics as a whole has been severed from metaphysics and must now be established on its own principles. This being the situation, Aristotle's philosophical conscience would insist on the most thoroughgoing exploration of these principles, even if it led to the result that cosmology and chemistry cannot be based on the same "first hypotheses." When in his early cosmological study he had tried to explain also the *genesis* of the elements, he had to content himself with proving that they must originate out of one another.[49] For the actual *modus* of this transformation his first assumptions would provide no clue. Now that, with the help of different assumptions, the mechanism of *genesis* and transformation has been discovered, he wisely makes no attempt to rebuild his cosmology on the new basis.

The thoroughness with which Aristotle inquires into the nature and constituents of his elements should not lead us to think that he was completely uncommitted when embarking on this search. As has been said more than once, he bears in mind the two fundamental processes, intermutation and mixture, for which the constituents must be able to account. Nor should we doubt that the elements themselves were fixed in his mind. His belief in the four Platonic elements was unshakable. While it did not prevent him from adding a fifth (which would not interfere with the chemical relationships of the others), it had with remarkable elasticity adjusted itself to cosmological propositions which in strict logic would entail two simple bodies rather than four. We have refused to believe that Aristotle "found" the four elements by the deduction embodied in the fourth book of *On the Heaven*.[50] It would be naïve to think that the deduction of our treatise

[49] See above, pp. 295ff.　　[50] See the analysis of *De caelo* IV, 4f. above, pp. 283–285.

produces results that he did not know beforehand. What is new [51] is
not the conclusion but the premises—the premises (if the word is
here permitted) which are so chosen that they can also explain mixture and transformation. Aristotle maintains that his deduction is in
full agreement with every other argument that has a bearing on the
number and nature of the elements. By selecting the four qualities correctly and combining them in the only possible ways, one arrives at the
four bodies which have every claim to be regarded as primary and which
could not be reduced to a smaller number.[52] It is completely true that
everything is in best agreement, and no loose ends are left anywhere.
Yet this is so because Aristotle, knowing his conclusions beforehand,
fashioned his premises and chose his "powers" with full awareness that
they must build up these particular four elements and provide them
with all they need to behave as elements. "Powers" which cannot
serve or would complicate the theory unduly are ruthlessly eliminated
—on arguments valid perhaps in themselves, yet nevertheless, we may
suspect, found a posteriori.[53]

There may be something presumptuous in looking behind the cur-
tain and trying to reconstruct the working of Aristotle's mind. We may
grant that, if he had not convinced himself that the hard and the soft,
the fine and the coarse, the brittle and the viscous are merely varieties
of the dry and the moist, he would have put up with them as constituents of the elements and would have pictured the coarse as "overcome" by the fine and the brittle as conquering the viscous. Nor would

---

[51] II,2.329b7–3.330b7.

[52] Note especially II,3.330b1–3 and 6f. The comments on earlier elementary
theories which follow (b7–21) appear to have the purpose of showing that four
is the obvious number for the elements and that his precursors arrived at this
number without clearly realizing it themselves. Empedocles, the original proponent of the four elements which Aristotle here once more accepts, is treated in
a far from gracious or grateful manner (330b19–21; see also II,6).

[53] II,2.329b2off. It has already been suggested (above, p. 346) that the fundamental importance of hot and cold, moist and dry in biological (and medical)
theory had some influence on Aristotle's selection of these powers as constituents
of his elements. In a passage of *De partibus animalium* (II,2.648a37–b11) where
Aristotle draws attention to their central place in biology, he again, as in *De gen.*
II,2, eliminates other "powers" and in the end finds it εὔλογον that the same powers
that are "principles" of the elements should have control of life and death, sleep
and waking, etc. (b8). The word εὐλόγως occurs also in *De gen.* II,3.330b6, where
Aristotle stresses the agreement between the results of his deduction and other
evidence regarding the elements. In both instances it is hard to believe that the
agreement is merely the fortunate result of correct reasoning.

a larger number of powers have created unsurmountable difficulties in his theory of mixture. To what extent, then, does Aristotle, in deducing the nature of the elements, follow the argument where it leads him, and to what extent does he lead the argument where he wants it to take him? It is more than probable that Aristotle's mind worked "back" from the conclusion to the supporting propositions.

19

Mixture

EVEN thinkers like Empedocles, who posited unchanging elements, would think of them as mixing and by their mixture creating all other physical entities. Where *genesis* is not a valid concept, mixture takes its place; where it is admitted, mixture is one of its principal forms. Given this close connection, it was almost inevitable that a treatise on coming to be should include a discussion of mixture. The question was not whether this subject should be treated but whether *genesis* and mixture were identical and coextensive; for there were systems in which even the elements came into existence through mixture.[1] This, however, is not Aristotle's approach. If hot and moist combine to give the substratum the form of air, they are "coupled," [2] not mixed. Although Aristotle does not say what prevents them from mixing, we may guess that it is their heterogeneous character.

As soon, however, as Aristotle goes beyond the elements, he finds himself dealing with substances that come into being by mixture. Here transformation no longer has a place. As in Empedocles and in the *Timaeus*, all physical objects that are not elements are compounds of them.

Actually Aristotle discusses mixture twice.[3] In the first book the

[1] Scil., those of Anaxagoras and of the atomists. Precosmic mixtures and a condition in which all things are "together" or even "one" (Emped. 27; see also Note 16) do not interest Aristotle here; but see, e.g., *De caelo* II, 14.297a17 where Aristotle speaks as "cosmogonist." Anaxagoras proceeds from this condition to the mixture in compounds; for Empedocles it is the consummation of Cypris' fusions.

[2] συνδυάζεσθαι, in 330a31, is a term which seems to indicate a logical rather than a physical relationship.

[3] I,10 (there is a good deal in ch. I,6–9, that is relevant and prepares the

discussion is as usual kept in general terms. The intention is here to define the requirements which an object must meet if it is to be regarded as mixed—in the precise sense of the word. At this juncture the elements have not yet been deduced, nor has their relation to matter and the powers been settled. The second discussion is more specific and can proceed on a different basis, since in the meantime all that is needed has been said on these questions.

The conception which Aristotle finds it necessary to combat is again at bottom the same as in the sections dealing with increase, with acting and suffering, and indeed wtih *genesis* itself.[4] Mixture too had been understood as a process of mechanical aggregation in which, to put it crudely, parts of one material join up with parts of another. In the resulting product the parts would be "intermingled";[5] yet they would still lie side by side without having changed their nature, even

---

ground for this discussion; cf. esp. 6.322b6–26); II,7. Aristotle does not say in so many words at the beginning of II,7 that he is returning to the subject of *mixis*; see, however, 334a28, b17, 19.

[4] Cf. I,2, esp. 317a20; I,8f. Note also 9.327a22f. In his discussion of growth (αὔξησις) in I,5 Aristotle overcomes the mechanical and purely aggregational theories by insisting that what grows is the form of the increased object rather than its matter and that this form must grow symmetrically in every part. The situation is here peculiar in that growth does come about by the addition of material. This Aristotle has no intention to deny; on the contrary, he keeps it constantly in view and fashions his theory with full recognition of this fact, pointing out, however, that the absorbed material is not simply added but transformed (321a2ff., 17–29, b16–322a3).

[5] See esp. I,10.327b33ff. Previous to this passage Aristotle has already succeeded in limiting the range of objects between which mixture can obtain. Matter does not "mix" with form, nor can there be mixture between things utterly heterogeneous or falling under different categories. His richly differentiated conceptual scheme makes clarifications of this kind desirable. Earlier thinkers were under no such necessity, and Aristotle here (b19) rejects as impossible Anaxagoras' idea that "everything was mixed with everything." If we had a commentary on this treatise by the hand of Simplicius, we should almost certainly know (in connection with 327a35ff.) which thinker denied the possibility of mixture on the ground that if the mixed objects remain what they were they are not mixed, whereas if they lose their identity "they" are no longer there and can thus not be spoken of as mixed. W. J. Verdenius and J. H. Waszink (*Philos. Antiqua*, 1 [1946], 35) feel reminded of Diogenes of Apollonia (*Vorsokr.*, 64B2). But does his argument about the basic identity of all things as condition of their mixture have anything significant in common with our passage? If, as Aristotle's report suggests, the original argument attacked the idea of mixture from alternative and opposite premises, it may have figured in Zeno's polemic against Empedocles' use of mixture (see *Vorsokr.*, 29A2, with Kranz's note). The argument may have had the same form as 29B4: "things are mixed neither if they are destroyed nor if they are not destroyed." Cf. also Cherniss, *Presocr.*, 141, n.564.

though the two substances mixed may have broken up into parts so small that it is quite impossible to tell them apart in the mixture. Aristotle is ready to admit the impossibility; yet it does not save this conception of mixture from the decisive argument by which he discredits it. The resulting product is not really one new and intrinsically homogeneous substance but rather the two or more original substances, broken up, yet in the particles preserving their former nature unchanged.[6] That one might not be able to perceive these particles and see that each of them is exactly like its original whole is quite irrelevant. For Aristotle has already at the beginning of this section raised the question whether mixture "is relative to perception." [7] Is our vision to be the judge, so that when the original substances have split up into invisible parts we call the product a mixture, whereas if our eyes can still distinguish heterogeneous particles we would speak not of mixture but of composition or juxtaposition? His intention is of course to lead this conception of mixture *ad absurdum*. If our eye can no longer distinguish the original ingredients, a microscope or, as Aristotle himself puts it, the eye of Lynceus could still distinguish them.[8] The solution is not to make the particles as small as possible but to get away completely from the idea of particles and of a splitting up (yet substantial preservation) of the bodies that combine. Every part of the resulting body, whether visible or not, must be a new substance—and

[6] This, Aristotle makes clear, would be *synthesis*, not *mixis*, and the two are not the same (328a1ff., 6f.). He takes notice of the fact that the Greek language uses the word *mixis* also to denote, e.g., the "mixing" of two kinds of grain (a2ff.), but the mixture which interests him is not of this type. Rather it is analogous to the mixing of wine and water for which Greek also has the word *krasis*. The Stoic refinement on this point, involving a distinction of *mixis, krasis,* and *synchysis*, is well known. (See *St. V. F.*, 2.463ff., esp. 471; cf. Max Pohlenz, *Die Stoa* [Göttingen, 1947], 1.72f., 2.41f. For the interest of later Stoics in Aristotle's doctrines see Alex. Aphr. 216,1ff. Bruns = *St. V. F.*, 2.470.) For a comparison of the Aristotelian and the Stoic concept of mixture cf. Harry A. Wolfson, *The Philosophy of the Church Fathers*, 1 (Cambridge, Mass., 1956), 374ff. Wolfson deals in particular with the vogue of these concepts in the Church Fathers (Tertullian, Origen, the Gregorys, Nemesius *et al.*), who use them to define the union of the Logos and the man in the Second Person of the Trinity (*ibid.*, 372-428, 441ff., and *passim*). The Stoic tradition encouraged this surprisingly materialistic approach.

[7] 327b32. For Aristotle's conception of mixture cf. throughout H. H. Joachim, *J. of Philology*, 29 (1904), 73ff.

[8] 4.328a12-15. Not this passage but *Protrept.*, frg. 10a (Ross, Walzer), does justice to the idea that Lynceus' eyes can "penetrate" (scil., *obstantia*, like walls and trees). Cf. Jaeger, *Aristotle*, 99. For the vision motif cf. οὔτ'. διείδεται (Emped. B27.1) and οὐδὲν ἔνδηλον (Anaxag. B1) in the descriptions of precosmic mixtures.

identical with the substance of the new whole. The process should not be a coalescence or juxtaposition but a change in the nature of both participants. Potentially they (and their qualities) may still be there, but in actuality they exist no longer.[9] To anticipate conclusions of the more specific discussion, if one of the original bodies was cold and the other hot, the mixture must in every part have the same new temperature—an intermediate temperature somewhere on the scale between the two original ones.[10] For this new concept of an organic compound which Aristotle here creates he uses a word (*homoeomeres*) which Anaxagoras may have applied before him to the nature of homogeneous tissues like flesh or hair; yet whether or not Anaxagoras had actually used the same term, it is obvious that his conception of homogeneous bodies would fall far short of what Aristotle himself is driving at.[11] In fact, it misses the basic point. Thanks to the infinite divisibility in which he believes, Anaxagoras could allow his powers in the act of coalescing to break up ad infinitum and could assert that, into however small parts you cut, say, a piece of flesh, it would still present the powers in the same ratio of combination as the entire body.[12] Yet this is still a combination—and not in Aristotle's sense a mixture—and the powers present in it have remained what they were; since they are "being things," it would be impossible for them to change or lose their being, i.e., their identity.

Quite clearly, then, Aristotle has, in this chapter on mixture, to oppose the same misconception against which he protested in the earlier chapter on *genesis*.[13] In both cases he emphasizes that the object as a whole must change its character and that there must be nothing of the same kind before and after the process. In both connections aggregation must be rejected—and in the case of *genesis* the complementary concept of dissociation as well. In fact, one might say that while dealing with mixture Aristotle shows somewhat more clearly and trenchantly what is wrong with this approach. This is hardly astonishing;

---

[9] 327b24-26. That potentially the mixed objects are still what they were before the mixture is Aristotle's answer to the argument (mentioned in Note 5) that when mixed the original substances are no longer in existence and that it is therefore not permissible to speak of "them" as mixed.

[10] II,7.334b8ff.

[11] See esp. 328a4 and 10ff. As is well known, the word ὁμοιομερής does not occur in the fragments of Anaxagoras.

[12] See *Vorsokr.*, 59B3, 6 (the latter also for the importance of the *moira* motif; I should think it possible that ἴσαι μοῖραι πλῆθος indicates an identical ratio).

[13] I,2.317a17ff.

in the late Presocratics mixture had actually established itself in the place of *genesis,* and the only way in which all things, or at least (in Empedocles) derivative and compound things, could arise was by mixture. Regarding substances other than the elements, Aristotle fully agrees that they arise by mixture. What sets him apart from his precursors is on the one hand his new idea of organic mixture, on the other his ready identification of it with *genesis* in the case of compound objects.[14] For, as *genesis* has been rehabilitated with all due honors, the concept of mixture should no longer take over its place but fill an area inside it. And as the notion of *genesis* has been thoroughly revised with the result that it is now an organic change, the reconstruction of the concept of mixture must and, as we have seen, does proceed *pari passu.*

When Empedocles and Anaxagoras saw a need for correcting the "usage" of the Hellenes, they did not suggest that instead of speaking of birth or coming into being they should henceforth speak of "association" (*synkrisis*). Their correct alternative for *genesis* is "mixture"; the opposite term, which they recommend in place of "death" or "passing away," is the breaking up of the mixture or, indeed, simply "dissociation." [15] It is by no means certain that Empedocles needed association (*synkrisis*) at all. When his elements mix to form tissues, organs, or even complete animals and plants, there is no purely mechanical settling side by side of quantities representing different materials. Rather, what happens is that divine entities form an intimate union in which they fuse their specific powers and characteristics.[16] Anaxagoras, on the other hand, seems to favor terms like association and dissociation; in his cosmological fragments we read a good deal about

---

[14] II,7. It being settled that the elements arise out of one another, the next question is "how anything besides them can come into being," 334a22.

[15] See *Vorsokr.,* 31B8, 9; 59B17.

[16] Compound verbs beginning with συν- (συνέρχεσθαι, σύνοδος, B17, 47, etc.) occur frequently; yet συγκρίνεσθαι is not among them. It has often been noticed that the words and the imagery describing the operation of Love have sexual connotations. The suggestion made in the text is perhaps too timid. I am strongly inclined to think that the Presocratics knew "fusions" which are much more than a mixture by mechanical association and a lying side by side of particles. Note the disappearance of the elements in Empedocles' *Sphairos* (31B27). Vlastos' comment on Anaximander's *apeiron* (*Cl. Ph.,* 42 [1947], 171), "one in a far more intimate sense than would have been possible for a physicist schooled in Parmenidean logic," gives a good lead for carrying the matter farther. Empedocles' Cypris produces ἓν μόνον and εἰς κόσμος (B26.5, 7; 35.5). Although "schooled in Parmenidean logic," he would certainly not admit any imperfections for his ἕν. To arrive at it he uses the concept of mixture which Parmenides had introduced into the

groups of things congregating or segregating, breaking up or breaking away—all this being expressed by compounds of the same Greek verb (κρίνειν).[17] It stands to reason that the term "association" lent itself to denoting the accumulation of identical powers, atoms, or—in the *Timaeus*—mathematical units of the elements; and such an accumulation is, in fact, necessary whenever an element is to pass the threshold of perception. Where compound objects are under discussion, mixing is a no less obvious term to be used, and Plato does employ it repeatedly, e.g., when defining the composition of gold and other metals. In such cases it would probably also be correct to speak of "association" (σύγκρισις), scil., between the differently shaped particles that represent the elements involved in such mixtures.[18] Tissues too are by Empedocles and in the *Timaeus* described as mixtures of the elements, yet special care is taken to make this mixture very intimate and enduring; one is tempted here to speak of "organic" mixture, and it may be felt that Plato actually goes beyond a mere mixing of fire, earth, and water.[19] In any case it is evident that mixture as well as association bulks large in the late Presocratic systems and that the *Timaeus* preserves much of their pattern. Aristotle, although refusing to operate with association, accepts mixture on condition that it be differently understood. The one concept is hopelessly mechanical and conflicts with the idea that a physical object has its intrinsic unity; the other can be redefined along organic lines. Thus remolded, it is for him, too, the bridge between elements and tissues or, as he likes to call them, primary and secondary formations.[20]

---

account of the phenomenal world (28B12, 16, 18; cf. A37). His *Sphairos*, in which the mixture reaches its final form, corresponds at once to Anaximander's *apeiron* and to Parmenides' being.

[17] For σύγκρισις see *Vorsokr.*, 59B4 *init.* ἀπο- and διακρίνεσθαι occur with characteristic frequency.

[18] See, e.g., *Tim.* 60d5, 61a8, 59a4; for the tissues see Note 19. For the "gathering" of homogeneous elementary units see 56c2; in 58b7 Plato speaks of the συγκρίνεσθαι of such units.

[19] See the account of bone in 73e and of flesh in 74cf. Besides speaking of mixture Plato here uses the verb συναρμόττειν, which is also found in a corresponding passage of Empedocles (71B4). It may be mentioned that fire, in addition to being a component of the mixture, also has the function of hardening the product (bone) and making it insoluble (73e5; cf. Emped. B73, 96). Symmetrical mixture and mixture in specified ratios are again a different matter (Plato assumes this only in the case of the marrow, the most valuable of all tissues, 73c1, whereas Empedocles applied the idea more widely). On the whole subject cf. my paper "Tissues and the Soul," *Philos. Rev.*, 59 (1950), 446ff.

[20] See *De part. anim.* II,1.646a13ff.

Inasmuch as he uses the Empedoclean elements, it is difficult to imagine how he could have departed from Empedocles' conception of the tissues as mixtures of these. He is even ready to follow Empedocles in regarding all bodies on earth as mixed of the four elements,[21] though he would of course not endorse any of the sweeping metaphysical implications of this idea. The place of mixture in his scheme is much more moderate; it is (as already for Plato) simply a variety of *genesis*; and there is no longer any thought that it could be a more valid concept than *genesis* or could in any connection be played off against the latter. Moreover, if for Empedocles tissues, organs, and again entire animals and plants were all alike mixtures, Aristotle knows that these entities represent different degrees of composition.[22] Beyond the formation of the tissues, the concept of mixture offers little help.

When Aristotle proceeds to deal with the tissues, we are aware of passing the boundary between his general physical theory and his biology; it is interesting to see that although the more general disquisition about the nature of mixture in Book I includes no mention of the tissues the more specific doctrine set forth in Book II constantly refers to them. What is here said about mixture, in particular of hot and cold, must prove applicable to concrete physiological instances, such as flesh and marrow.[23] For Aristotle, as for Empedocles and Anaxagoras, tissues are clearly the test case.

The details of the doctrine as given in Book II offer interesting parallels to the process of transformation. Not only *genesis* but mixture too must materialize between contraries, and, as we know, the qualities or powers are more genuine contraries than the elements themselves. Thus they again do the actual work and fight out the battle.[24] The mixing of earth and water is in actual fact a mixing of dry and moist. The fight must this time not lead to a complete destruction of one of them by the other—still less of both; yet they have again to make use of their active and passive capacity.[25] That mixture can only come to pass between contraries possessed of such capacities Aristotle has explicitly stated in the general disquisition of Book I; [26] here he

[21] See II,8.334b31ff.

[22] In the *Timaeus* larger parts of the body are composed of the tissues; yet there is nothing that would correspond to Aristotle's concept of "tertiary composition" (cf. *Philos. Rev.*, 59 [1950], 448ff.).

[23] *De gen.* II,7.334a25, 30, etc.   [24] II,7.334b2ff., 8ff.

[25] For the *phthora* motif (which we have also found in the account of transformations, II,4) see 334b7, 11.

[26] See I,6.322b6–11 and esp. 10.328a31ff., b16f., b20; cf. II,7.334b20f.

does not repeat this point, yet it does not take much imagination to realize that hot and cold, moist and dry must once more employ their capacities of working upon, and suffering from, one another.

If hot and cold are present in equal strength, they will undo or cancel each other, and the result will be simply matter, as undifferentiated as it was to begin with; for if matter is not informed by one or the other of a pair of opposite qualities, it cannot possibly attain the level of an element, still less of a tissue or homogeneous mixture.[27] Fortunately there are intermediate degrees between the extremes of hot and cold. The extremes are in actuality only hot or cold, yet potentially either of them is also the contrary quality. Between them there stretches a scale on which things may, as Aristotle puts it, be "qua warm cold yet qua cold warm." [28] And between the middle position, where qualities would cancel each other out of existence, and either extreme, there are any number—surely an infinite number—of intermediate positions. Each of them presents a different mixture of hot and cold. These mixtures are best described as ratios; Aristotle here speaks of conditions in which the hot is present with twice or three times as much "power" as the cold.[29] Presumably every conceivable ratio between contrary powers may be found on this scale. The quantitative point of view would here have a chance of entering the picture to determine the relationship of qualities; yet Aristotle is no more than moderately interested in it. Only once does he refer to the ratios 1:2 and 1:3. Owing to the lack of precise methods of measurement any attempt to be more specific would end in guesswork. Although Aristotle pays tribute to Empedocles for having conceived "ratios of mixture," he has no intention of following him on this path. As Plato in the *Timaeus* says on a similar occasion, "neither proof nor likely account can be given of these ratios" with even "moderate" confidence.[30]

As far as we can tell, Empedocles had specified ratios of mixture in but a few instances. Anaxagoras generalized this principle, holding that the different ratios in which the omnipresent powers combine account for the great variety of physical objects.[31] Contrary to what one

[27] II,7.334b2–7. Needless to say, the mutual cancellation does not actually arise. Matter has not this kind of reality.

[28] 334b10f., 12ff.   [29] 334b15f.

[30] Cf. *Vorsokr.*, 31A78, B96ff.; Arist. *De gen. anim.* I,1.642a17ff.; *Metaph.* A10.993a17. For λόγος τῆς μίξεως as applied to colors see *De sensu* 3.440b10–25. This is the subject to which Plato's skeptical comments (*Tim.* 68b6; cf. d2) refer.

[31] See Anaxag. B6, 12 *et al.* On the importance of the *moira* motif see Vlastos, *Philos. Rev.*, 59 (1950), 41ff., 45ff., and *passim*. For Empedocles cf. A78, B96, 98.

might expect, this "mathematical" approach did not appeal to Plato.
Apart from one instance, the marrow, where Plato postulates a perfect
or "symmetrical" mixture of the elements, the most that he is prepared
to say is that a given mixture has a "small portion" of a particular element.[32] In the section on colors which reckons with mixed colors
Plato openly professes his reluctance to specify proportions for these
mixtures. His reason for this diffidence has already been quoted. If
painters or merchants in his time tried to find the ratios of mixed
colors by way of practical experiments, Plato has a special word of
rebuke for them: they do not know the difference between divine
and human wisdom.[33] He himself has a different way of accounting
for the great variety of objects in nature. The geometrical figures
which compose his elements are present in different "grades" or sizes.
Such different grades of one element may be mixed with one another
as well as with those of other elements; this yields "an endless variety
which must be studied by one who is to put forward a probable account of nature." [34] Aristotle, it is clear, would prefer Empedocles'
and perhaps even Anaxagoras' principle of ratios to Plato's geometrical
explanations. Yet when it comes to practical implementation, we find
him making no use at all of the Empedoclean idea which Plato applied
once. The resort to ratios in the chapter on mixtures is both perfunctory and unique.

It is startling to see how easily Aristotle's concept of potentiality
can change back into that of "power." That hot is potentially cold and
cold hot are familiar enough, and to make the opposites, partially or
completely, change into one another Aristotle has to avail himself of
these potentialities. Yet in the same context we read of conditions or
objects which are twice or three times as hot "in power" as they are
cold.[35] We have long suspected Aristotle's contrary qualities of being

---

[32] 73c1; 59b7f. On the whole it is more important to indicate what elements and
whether or not several "grades" of an element are present in the mixture.

[33] 68bff.; see esp. b6ff., d2ff. Although he has described colors as sensation, Plato
here takes an "objective" view of their nature; see further, for this approach,
59b3, 74d4 (80e2ff.), 83a5ff. The last passage is taken from the "etiology of diseases" where Plato's estimate of the "powers" differs generally from the definitions given in the physical sections. In the medical section Plato probably could
not avoid keeping close to the prevailing medical views and usages.

[34] 57c8–d6. For a detailed reconstruction of these "grades" see Cornford, *Cosmology*, 230ff.

[35] II,7.334b9ff.; see esp. 14ff. Joachim in his commentary on b8ff. rightly speaks
of the contraries as having "powers of action" (see also his note on b14ff.); yet

"powers" in disguise. Here we see them with surprising quickness change back to their past status. The idea that from a mixture of powers "middle" or intermediate ones arise may not have been unknown to the medical thinkers. Plato too resorts to a "middle power" in a passage of the *Timaeus* where the mixture of flesh and bone in the substance of the sinews gives these a "power" halfway between the soft and pliable quality of the one and the tenseness of the other.[36]

The result of mixture is thus a substance characterized by "intermediate" powers. Only through the new relationship between elements and powers is Aristotle in a position to explain mixture. Still, the powers are far from being the power stuff of earlier systems; if they were, they would settle side by side or between one another, and we should again have the mixture by aggregation or association which Aristotle abhors. In an organic mixture all parts, no matter how small, must have the same temperature somewhere on the scale between hot and cold and the same intermediate degree between dry and moist, soft and hard.[37] The mixture may still be hot—in fact, it must be either hot or cold—yet not in the extreme degree. Unlike substances, qualities can show a "more and less." [38] The *Philebus* teaches us to find this "more and less" in the hotter and colder and other antithetical comparatives and adverbs. In the context of the same argument the "more and less" itself is placed in the "family" of the "unlimited" (or "infinite"). As long as it persists or, as Plato puts it, moves on, there is no possibility of quantitative determination; any quantitative determination (like Aristotle's ratios 3:1 and 2:1) introduces the factor of limit, and we have emerged from the flux of things to a fixed and firm position.[39] In Plato this imposition of limit upon the unlimited leads to nothing less than *genesis* into being (or if this is too much, to a "coming to be," with a good emphasis on "be").[40] We know that for Aristotle too mixture is a *genesis*, and we can see that when in the mixing the proper ratio has been reached the process of amalgamation along the scale has come to a halt and the

---

as he refers to the fuller discussion in his comments on 327b22, it appears that he regards "potentiality" as a satisfactory denominator which would include also this variety of meaning.

[36] *Tim.* 74d2ff. (literally, "a nature halfway in power"). See also *Legg.* X,893e3ff.

[37] Cf. the affirmation in ch. I,9 (326b31ff.) that if acting and suffering occur between objects the latter must take place everywhere in the affected object, not only here and there. The difference between *synthesis* and genuine *mixis* is brought out again in II,7.334a27ff.

[38] Cf. *Categ.* 8.10b26ff. Note the use of the "more and less" in II,7.334b8.

[39] *Phileb.* 24a–e; see esp. d4–7.   [40] *Ibid.*, 26d7ff.

product has been formed. Yet Aristotle does not operate with the limit and the unlimited; the problems of the *Philebus* are not acute, and of its ontological background nothing should be read into Aristotle's account.

In actual fact even the same tissue need not always have the same degree on the scale. Some blood is hotter than other blood, just as some has more of water, some more of earth (strictly the prevalence of either element ought to show itself in a "more" or "less" of dry and moist; yet we need not be so strict, for, as we know, in Aristotle's biology the powers may act independently, not only as representatives of the elements).[41]

[41] Cf. *De part. anim.* II,2.647b29–648a14 and ch. II,4. Aristotle's point may be not so much that blood in which earth predominates is hotter but that it can be more easily heated (see 650b33ff. and for an analogous point about water b27ff.). The sections illustrate well the importance of the μᾶλλον καὶ ἧττον motif. Cf. in general *Philos. Rev.*, 59 (1950), 464ff.

20

The Moving Cause of All *Genesis*

MATTER and qualities which inform and modify matter are surely indispensable for the explanation of becoming, and throughout the first book of our treatise and in the larger part of the second book Aristotle's interest is monopolized by these aspects of *genesis*. But in Chapter 9 of the latter book the whole orientation changes; suddenly our attention is directed to causes and principles of *genesis* that had so far been completely neglected. The beginning of the chapter reminds us that Aristotle's system of causes includes more than matter and form.[1] The two other kinds of causation would be the teleological and the source of movement. In the following chapters the outlines of Aristotle's teleological scheme become visible, but his professed and primary concern is with the moving (or efficient) cause; and since his causal pattern provides not only for *genesis* but for eternal *genesis*, he is soon led to

[1] II,9.335a24ff., esp. 28–32. From II,10.336a13f. it appears that the formal cause has been treated in the preceding sections (simultaneously with the material cause). The reference is clearly to II,9; before this Aristotle has made very little use of the Form principle. We have learned that fire arises when matter is qualified by the hot and the dry; if this approximates a definition, one may argue that the formal cause has been given its due (cf. II,9.335b5–7). Yet prior to II,9 the scheme of the four causes has hardly been used for the analysis and theory of *genesis*.

Could hot and cold, moist and dry, in addition to many other characters, also have those of Form and privation? This would be in keeping with *Phys.* I. Cf. *De gen.* I,3.318b14ff. Is it still permissible to speak of the "presence" and "absence" of a Form, e.g., the hot (see above, p. 86)? Or are we right in feeling that Aristotle has traveled rather far from that position and that *de facto* he has dealt only with the material cause for the origin of the elements, etc.? From his own point of view this would mean that he has returned to the way of the early Ionians. It would be unwise to press this point, yet it is probably true that the *De generatione* is less Platonic in outlook than Book I of the *Physics*.

define the place and rationale of eternal *genesis* in his entire cosmic system. This can most adequately be done by speaking in terms of a divine plan. For a moment we seem to see the Demiurge at work and become, in the manner of the *Timaeus*, acquainted with the train of his reasoning. God did the best that was possible when the conditions of earthly existence ruled out eternal being for the individual entities on earth, and "nature always aims at the better."[2]

We must postpone the discussion of these teleological motifs and return to the moving cause. Aristotle has no intention of exhausting the possibilities of this subject. We learn nothing here about the proximate moving cause—about man begetting man, to use one of his favorite illustrations—or about the frequent coincidence of this type of cause with the formal cause.[3] The only efficient cause that is now considered is the first of all, a cause which, if not identical with, is at least directly traceable to, the first mover and originator of all cosmic movements. That all cosmic changes are predicated on the existence of a first mover who must himself be unmoved had been proved in the final book of the *Physics*. The same book also furnishes indications about the nature of this first mover.[4] But the first mover is and remains remote; the only other entity with which that book brings him into a relation is the "first moved." How the movement which originates in this first cause is passed on, how it actually causes changes in the other phases of the Cosmos and especially "around the central place" was not made clear. For obvious reasons Aristotle felt the need of tracing this influence in a more specific fashion; and the last chapters of our second book do something to bridge this gap. They connect the *genesis* here on earth with the primary efficient cause (or causes). This complements the one-sided account so far presented.

Nevertheless the change in orientation remains abrupt. In addition the concept of *genesis* as used in the next chapters has somewhat different connotations and emphases. We are closer here to birth and death, to the life cycle, primarily of vegetative entities (whose beginning and end are directly related to the approaching and receding of the sun on its annual path) yet by a kind of extension also of the other organic beings.[5] For a moment one may feel attracted by the idea that Aristotle added these chapters later and that originally he was satisfied with the one line of inquiry which he has so consistently pursued. Yet

[2] II,10.336b27ff., 31ff.
[3] See, e.g., *Phys.* II,7.198a24ff. and *De gen. anim.* II,1.732a4f.
[4] *Phys.* VIII, esp. 5–10. [5] II,10, esp. 336b10ff., 15ff.

this tempting idea must be dismissed. For there are passages—in our treatise as well as outside it—that "promise" something in the nature of these chapters.[6] Moreover, we have met an analogous situation in the *Timaeus*. There, too, the "first source of movement" intrudes from outside and, quite as abruptly and unexpectedly, into an account of the elements which up to this point has concentrated on causes of a different and (*sit venia verbo*) "formal" type.[7]

Plato has dealt at length with the *genesis* and transformation of the elements before he remembers that an impulse is needed to keep these processes in continuous operation. It would be unfair to deny Aristotle the right to do the same. A "genetic" explanation is as unnecessary in the one case as in the other. What the abrupt transition in our treatise really indicates is that the different "causes" can be studied in isolation from one another. Around the material cause a set of propositions and theories has developed in which the moving cause is left out of consideration. To tell the truth, the moving and the formal cause do not interlock very closely even in Plato. Is it astonishing that in Aristotle the causes have drifted farther apart?

Aristotle establishes the continuity between the origin of all movement and the becoming and passing away on earth by appealing to one of the most elementary impressions of man, the influence on nature at large of the sun in its yearly approaching and receding.[8] The first motion of the Cosmos, the revolution of the outermost heaven, is indeed the ultimate source of all movements and changes, but as it is eternally identical with itself—always proceeding in the same direction—it can cause changes only in one direction.[9] Yet there are in this world changes

---

[6] I,3.318a1–10 recognizes the need of explaining the material as well as the efficient cause of *genesis* and promises a discussion of the second "later"—a definite reference to chs. II,9ff. If it were necessary, 318a3 (περὶ μὲν . . .) to 9 (εἴπωμεν) or 5–8 (τούτων δὲ . . . αἴτιόν ἐστιν) could be regarded as later insertions. *De caelo* II,3.286a5 promises an account similar to that given in our chapters (I call it similar because there is a certain discrepancy between 286a3f. and *De gen.* II,10.336a27–29; the passage nevertheless creates a presumption for the presence *ab initio* of our chapters).

[7] *Tim.* 57d7–58c4. Cf. above, the last section of Ch. 2.

[8] II,10.336b2ff., 15ff.

[9] *Ibid.*, 336a23ff.; see also b2, where it is stated that this first movement is "the cause of continuity." This probably refers to, or at least includes, the continuity of all *genesis*, though Joachim, if I understand his translation correctly, thinks only of the continuity of the solar movements (which in turn cause all *genesis*). For the priority of locomotion to *genesis* which is assumed throughout these sections (cf. 336a18ff.) see *Phys.* VIII,7, esp. 260b29ff. Cf. in general Pierre Duhem, *Le système du monde*, 1 (Paris, 1913), 162.

in opposite directions; there is destruction no less than *genesis* and they are intimately related. Therefore the more immediate cause of physical changes on earth must have a movement capable of causing opposite processes. The approaching and receding of the sun offer a pattern which satisfies this condition; these are the movements directly responsible for the phenomenon of contrary changes.

According to the system of the contemporary astronomers (which Aristotle accepts and often presupposes), all planetary ways are composite movements, each planet moving simultaneously in several "spheres." These elaborate doctrines are never far from Aristotle's mind when he has occasion to speak of the celestial phenomena. In this chapter, however, all he needs is that the sun moves in the ecliptic circle; omitting all technicalities, Aristotle says that "the movement along the zodiac" is the cause of coming to be and passing away.[10]

There would be no point in calling to mind that Plato too in Book VI of the *Republic* speaks of the sun as the father of all *genesis*.[11] Aristotle surely did not need to learn this from Plato; nor is it at all Plato's purpose to specify the function of the solar movements in a scheme of causations or to find a place for them in a physical theory of *genesis*. The connection of all cosmic changes with the first source of movement must be defined in Plato's scheme as much as in Aristotle's, yet where Plato gives us his solution he does not need the movements of the sun. The passage of the *Timaeus* to which we have already referred introduces no intermediary agent between the rotation of the first heaven and the constant processes of movement and change among the elements.[12] His first mover is the world soul; the rotation

---

[10] 336a31f.; the word ἀνωμαλία seems to refer to the fact that the movement of the sun (or, more generally, movement in the ecliptic circle; cf. Philop., *ad loc.*) is not simply a circle; for a circular movement would be ὁμαλές. But this motif is not developed; in 336b21ff. the reason for the ἀνωμαλία of *genesis* is found in "matter." For the reference to the ecliptic see 336b4; for the difficulties inherent in the words ἀνίσου τοῦ διαστήματος ὄντος (b3) cf. Joachim's note, *ad loc.* An essential idea is that the movement of the outermost heaven is one component in the movement of the planets (cf. *Metaph.* Λ8.1073b25f.); otherwise there would be no continuity between the *primum mobile* and *genesis*.

[11] *Rep.* VI,509b.

[12] In Aristotle's cosmological scheme the outermost sphere of the heaven could not be in direct contact with, or exert a direct influence on, the four "sublunary" elements. Where Aristotle says (336a26ff.) that the πρώτη φορά, the rotation of the first heaven, cannot be the cause of opposite changes, like generation and destruction, he may have *Tim.* 58a4ff. in mind. He certainly rejects the pattern there presented.

of the first heaven is the soul's own movement, and this revolution keeps up a steady pressure—a "constricting" and "condensing" influence, Plato calls it—on the elements within the Cosmos, causing them constantly to move "through" one another and thus preventing any rest or stationary condition.[13] What is thus produced is in the first place local movement (scil., of the elementary particles), yet this leads immediately to new physical formations,[14] and since local movement is for Plato, as for Aristotle, the "first" of the changes, we may infer that every *genesis* is linked to the first principle of movement. It may be argued that Plato's primary concern in that passage of the *Timaeus* is with local movement and change of place, whereas Aristotle aims at tracing the connection between the heavenly movements and *genesis*.[15] But in spite of these and other differences, both schemes are clearly inspired by the same idea. Both show how the movement issuing from the "first principle" imparts itself to the area of the four elements, where the changes are much more diverse and confused than in the celestial region. This is the "downward" path from the first mover to the physical and cosmic realities. In the *Laws* and in the *Physics* arguments of a more abstract type lead us on the "upward" path to the origin of all movements in the first mover.

The *genesis* directly caused by the heavenly movements seems in Aristotle's scheme to be of the biological type; yet he also asserts—though without providing either proof or details—that the transformation between the elements has its cause in the twofold movement of the sun.[16] If this efficient cause were not working, each element would forever, without change, remain in its cosmic region. Since, however, the elements are exposed to this influence, they keep changing into one another, and having changed their form, say, from water to air, they

[13] *Tim.* 58a4–c4. Cf. Cherniss, *Pl. and the Acad.*, 448ff., who rightly says that the world soul, though not explicitly mentioned, must be considered as the ultimate cause of motion. For details of interpretation cf. Cornford, *Cosmology*, 242ff.

[14] *Tim.* 58b4ff.; the changes thus caused are transformations from one element into another (cf. Cornford, *Cosmology*, 245); neither Plato nor Aristotle would go so far as to construct an influence of this first moving cause on the formation of, e.g., the tissues. It suffices if the material cause of their formation has been set forth; to this the biological sections of the *Timaeus* and the biological treatises of Aristotle add the teleological cause.

[15] Aristotle here reiterates the doctrine of the *Physics* that local movement is the first and that *genesis* presupposes it; 336a18ff. refers (as, e.g., Joachim points out) to *Phys.* VIII,7 (260a26ff.). We have dealt with this doctrine above, p. 237.

[16] 337a12ff. The *Meteorologica* substantiates this assertion; see below, Index, *s.v.* Sun.

must also occupy new places in the cosmic scheme.[17] This answers the same question—and answers it in the same way—which Plato had raised in the corresponding context: why have not the elements, distributed as they are between the four cosmic strata, settled down there quietly forever? [18] Why is there still exchange, why intermingling and movement to and fro? The answer is in both cases that movement is kept up from the outside, by an agent either identical or closely connected with the first principle of all movements. As for the question as such, it was bound to arise at a stage of physical thought where the cosmic places tended to become "natural" to the elements. Left to themselves, the elements would show no inclination to enter into relationships of mutual combination or transformation that would take them away from their "natural" and accustomed abode.[19] But if they do not move, life and all cosmic processes will be at a standstill. For Anaxagoras "all things were at rest" while "together," an idea utterly repugnant to Plato and Aristotle,[20] for both of whom it is axiomatic that in the physical world movement continues forever and uninterrupted. Surely the possibility that all things should be at rest while separated would be just as abhorrent to their minds. It is not enough that the movements of fire, air, water, and earth delineate and fashion the Cosmos (which means that Anaxagoras' precosmic condition can never materialize). Preservation of movement is vital also while the Cosmos is in existence.

In the books *On the Heaven* the first mover was irrelevant. It is possible that Aristotle's doctrines about him had not yet fully developed; but even if they had, the first mover has no function since the elements do not need any external impulse to take up their places.[21] Yet to change into one another the elements need an external influence; though the "powers" are active and able to conquer, they are not by themselves aggressive. Something must cause the powers in one element

---

[17] 337a7–15.

[18] *Tim.* 58a2ff.; note Aristotle's reference to this passage in 337b8 by way of the words ὅ τινες ἀποροῦσιν. Joachim, *ad loc.*, says that the "people" alluded to are not known, and it seems to be the case that the identity of Aristotle's problem and *Tim.* 58a had not been noticed before P. Shorey pointed it out in his review of Joachim's edition, *Cl. Ph.*, 17 (1922), 352.

[19] In earlier systems the Cosmos, as soon as completely formed by the separation of the elements, may begin to disintegrate. In Empedocles, after the separation has been effected by Strife, Love sets up a movement in the opposite direction which brings the elements again together and causes their mingling (B35).

[20] See, for Anaxagoras' doctrine, *Vorsokr.*, 59A50, 64, and Arist. *Phys.* VIII,1.-250b24ff. Plato *Phaedr.* 245d6ff. and *Legg.* X,895a6f. are indications of Plato's attitude to it. For Aristotle's criticism see *Phys.* VIII,1.252a14ff.

[21] See above, Ch. 11.

to work on those in another. It is here that the first mover comes into play. The constant change between the elements, the eternity of *genesis* in the world, depends on the eternity of the first cosmic movement. This movement—communicating itself, to be sure, through others of intermediate function—makes it possible here for Aristotle to integrate the two aspects of elementary behavior which he has so far treated separately. Elementary movements and elementary changes have different "principles"—as long as these are to be found in the "nature" of the elements. Yet the approaching and receding of the sun call forth changes of both kinds; for when a substance has undergone alteration, it can no longer keep its former place.[22]

Summarizing the doctrines about the first movement which he has expounded elsewhere, Aristotle finds it desirable once more to state which factor above all guarantees the continuity of this first movement. It is the "body carried in a circle," a description which appears directly applicable to the first element of *On the Heaven* but would also fit the *primum mobile* of *Physics* VIII.[23] In any case both are ultimately one and the same entity. What Plato specifies at the corresponding juncture

[22] 337a11ff. I am inclined to understand μεταβάλλειν in a11f. and a14 as relating to substantial change (i.e., transformation from one element into another); on this interpretation the clause a13–15 (διὰ δὲ . . .) states that change of place is subsequent on change of substance. Joachim takes the opposite view (see his translation and commentary, *ad loc.*). I believe that Philoponus' interpretation agrees with mine but am not sure.

[23] 337a17ff., 25ff. The unfolding of the thought in 337a15–33 is rather complicated. The first series of premises points to the first mover (17–22; cf. *Phys.* VIII,6.258b10–259a6); in 22–25 the argument shifts to the circular movement as representing the συνεχές in movement—here we may compare *Phys.* VIII,8; finally the movement is declared to owe this συνεχές to the object in motion, and thus we arrive at the κύκλῳ σῶμα φερόμενον which recalls the doctrines embodied in *De caelo* I rather than of those in *Phys.* VIII. A helpful analysis of this "gigantic" argument will be found in Verdenius' and Waszink's study *Philosophia Antiqua*, 1 (1946), 75ff. They offer a convincing explanation for the anacoluthon in a18ff. and rightly distinguish in 25–33 two premises (25–30, 30–31) leading to the final conclusion. The same method does not work so well for 17–25. Here the two scholars misstate the "first premise" (17–22), which says or suggests nothing yet about cyclical motion, and simplify the complexity of 22–25. From 22–24 we learn, in the first place, the reason why in 19 movement was assumed to be συνεχές; at the same time this passage prepares the next statement (here Verdenius and Waszink are right) that continuous movement is cyclical. That the "second premise" of the "second syllogism" (30–31, see above) "may be deduced" from the first of the same syllogism is a curious error of interpretation as well as of logic—since when is the second premise deduced from the first? That it follows from the conclusion of the first syllogism (24f.) may be correct, though it is not, strictly speaking, necessary. Aristotle may consider 30f. self-evident or recall the proofs given in *Phys.* VIII; in other words 30f. may be "parallel" to 24f., rather than based on it.

is "the revolution of the whole" (or "the circumference of the whole" [24])—surely not quite the same, and Plato had in fact no "body" which he could, or would have wished to, charge with this function. Still, both are at one in regarding the circular movement of the outermost heaven as cause of the never-ceasing changes in the Cosmos.

Thus the chapters which study *genesis* with reference to its moving cause relate it to principles of high and highest standing. They bring the eternal into view. To be sure, on its material side *genesis* also has an eternal foundation. But "matter" has no independent subsistence or reality and would, moreover, not be the kind of subject to inspire sublime thoughts regarding the dignity and metaphysical status of *genesis*. By contrast the awe-inspiring and immortal entities to which *genesis* is linked through its moving cause suggest reflections about its place in the divine world pattern and in particular about its relation to eternity.[25] As the study of the efficient cause complements that of the material aspects, so the thoughts about the august function of *genesis* in the world pattern complement the vindication of its physical reality that was accomplished in earlier sections.[26] Yet it might appear that *genesis* when considered from a metaphysical perspective loses again the reality which, in the light of physical arguments, seemed safe and impregnable. Metaphysically becoming and being are apart. Entities as remote from the divine principle as everything in the sublunary region of necessity is cannot be eternal.[27] Thus they are debarred from being. "God therefore adopted the remaining alternative by making *genesis* [itself] eternal." Not the objects involved in it but the process as such is on a par with the divine entities of the heavenly region (where *genesis* has no foothold).[28] Aristotle could afford to treat time without reference to

---

[24] Cf. Cornford, *Cosmology*, 243, on the ambiguity of the word περίοδος as used in *Tim.* 58a5.

[25] 336b27ff.

[26] On the "rehabilitation" of "absolute" *genesis* in I,3 see above, Ch. 16.

[27] 336b26–34. In *De caelo* II,3 (286a22–b9) Aristotle shows the necessity of *genesis* in his world scheme. The existence of *genesis* in turn necessitates the existence of more than one heavenly φορά (b2–4; cf. b6f.).

[28] Plato too treats *genesis* in the *Timaeus* (52d2ff.) as in a higher degree real than the individual γιγνόμενα. In *De gen.* II,10.336b33 we read that the coherence of being is safeguarded διὰ τὸ ἐγγύτατα εἶναι τῆς οὐσίας τὸ γίγνεσθαι ἀεὶ καὶ τὴν γένεσιν. It seems to me very hard to construe these words as Joachim (*ad loc.*) suggests, "that coming-to-be should itself come-to-be perpetually" (scil., "is the closest approximation to eternal being"; cf. his translation). Philoponus seems to indicate that the word ἀεὶ also qualifies γένεσις, but this impression may be deceptive. The words καὶ τὴν γένεσιν were probably not in the text which he read, and we too should treat them with suspicion.

eternity and place without a Platonic counterpart of nonphysical objects not in place; but *genesis* cannot be properly understood unless it is related to eternal being. The eternal beings with which Plato connects *genesis* are the Forms. Aristotle finds eternity within the Cosmos and traces *genesis* to the revolution of the heaven, the path of the sun, and the first body.

This eternity of *genesis* Aristotle in our chapter illustrates by the cyclical change of the elements, the subject on whose more technical aspects he has dwelt before.[29] Elsewhere the continuity of the species by way of reproduction is discussed from a similar point of view; this is the form in which biological entities participate in eternity.[30] It too would be cyclical inasmuch as the life of the offspring repeats the stages of the parent's.[31] In the metaphysical perspective this cyclical aspect of *genesis* has a significance which it could not have as long as the inquiry was content to proceed along purely physical lines—in point of fact, the technical phases of the doctrine require only mutual and reciprocal, yet hardly cyclical, change.[32] Now we learn that *genesis* "imitates" being not only through its eternity but also by reproducing in its cyclical nature an essential characteristic of the cosmic bodies that have eternal being and eternal motion. To the cyclical movements in the higher areas of the Cosmos corresponds cyclical

[29] 337a1-6.

[30] See *De an.* II,4.415b3-7; *De gen. anim.* II,1.731b24-732a2. For the "generic" ἀνακάμπτειν of living beings whose substance is perishable and who can be eternal only in their *eidos* yet not individually, see *De gen.* II,11.338b16-19, the last sentences of our treatise. It is very instructive to compare with these and b8ff. Plato *Phaedo* 72af. where the ἀνακάμπτειν is applied to living beings. P. Shorey, who may have been the first to suggest this comparison (*Cl. Ph.*, 17 [1922], 352), believes that Aristotle's aim is to refute the doctrine of the *Phaedo*. But the form in which Aristotle presents his thoughts (b6ff.) does not favor the idea of such an intention. On the whole Shorey appears to overrate the force of verbal similarities between our treatise and the *Phaedo*. To me the value of his article lies in the penetrating remarks about the nature of the treatise and the right method of approaching it. An analysis of ch. II,11 falls outside the scope of our study; cf. the very acute comments of Suzanne Mansion, *Le jugement d'existence chez Aristote* (Louvain and Paris, 1946), 75ff.

[31] Richard Harder, *"Ocellus Lucanus"* (Berlin, 1926), 122f., makes it probable that in the dialogue *On Philosophy* the relation of *genesis* to eternity was treated in the same sense as (and in language similar to) *De gen.* II,10.336b31f. and *De an.* II,4.415a29.

[32] See I,3; II,4. The point of the former chapter is that the *genesis* of one element is the destruction of another. II,4 shows cyclical change to be possible and declares that it is the ῥᾷστος τρόπος (331b2ff.); however, it does not seem absolutely necessary for the elements to complete this cycle. For the motif of cyclical transformation cf. *Tim.* 49b7ff. (c6f.).

genesis "in the region about the center." [33] And this cyclical change would not be possible without the movements whose nature it reflects.[34] Moreover, the cyclical movements of the heaven being time, Aristotle sees fit to reaffirm the doctrine of the *Physics* that time itself is by nature cyclical—and not only time but also life which comes to pass in it.[35] The popular view, which the *Physics* recorded with interest and approbation, that human life is a cycle is thus not only found to be valid but seen to contain a deeper truth. It leads us to understand the metaphysical condition of living beings. In fact, the "periods" of the heavenly revolutions give all physical life its order (*taxis*). As the *Physics* has said, "everything is decided [or even 'judged'] by time," and "time itself is considered a cycle." [36]

Cyclical thinking had deep roots in the Greek mind. For some of the Presocratic thinkers the recurring cycles embraced the formation and destruction of innumerable successive worlds. This particular cyclical conception of time became invalid when the Cosmos was declared to be eternal—more precisely when time was shown to exist only in the Cosmos and as long as the Cosmos. But, though dead for the Academy and the Peripatus, the archaic idea would come to life again with the formulation of the first Stoic system. In the meantime Plato had by the

[33] 337a1ff.; note the imitation motif in a3. Aristotle argues that if eternal *genesis* were not circular but proceeded in an infinite straight line there would be no beginning (*arche*), causes would have to be traced back ad infinitum, and thus no *genesis* could be considered necessary. But what is eternal is also necessary (II,11, esp. 337b23–338a11). The argument presupposes not only that *genesis* is eternal but that certain things (or events) must of necessity come to be.

[34] According to 336b34f. the heavenly movements are the "cause" of the eternity of *genesis*, "therefore" *genesis* imitates their cyclical nature. A section of the *De generatione animalium* (IV,10.777b17–778a9) offers very interesting parallels to the thought of our chapter. In some way it goes farther by pointing to the influence which the periods of sun and moon have on *genesis*—in the first place of the animals, by determining the time of gestation (and of life); but in addition "the behavior of the air and the wind depends on the period of the sun and the moon" (777b33). The cyclical ἀνακάμπτειν of the seasons is probably too obvious to be mentioned; however, see *De gen.* II,11.338a4. *Genesis* is in this section said to be brought about by heating and cooling, processes "whose limits are controlled by the movements of these heavenly bodies" (b28). Again, as in our chapter (336a21), Aristotle looks to "matter" as a cause for the *anomalia* in *genesis* (778a7).

[35] Cf. 336b10–15 with *Phys.* IV,14.223b18–33.

[36] *De gen.* 336b12; *Phys.* 223b26ff. Cf. above, pp. 147ff., and add Eurip., frg. 415, to the passages cited in Ch. 7, Note 50. For more specific statements regarding the influence of the heavenly *periodoi* on life see *De gen. anim.* IV,10.777b17–778a10.

same act which destroyed the traditional form of cyclical cosmology given the cycles and periods a new and pivotal place within the cosmic pattern. The movements of the world soul, of the outermost heaven with the fixed stars, and of the planets are one and all cyclical, and it is they and they alone which constitute the "periods" of time.[37] With this as basis and starting point Aristotle found a way of extending the cycle motif to all *genesis*. His doctrine incorporates both the Presocratic scheme of cyclical changes among the elements and the quintessence of old wisdom that "all things human are a cycle." The conceptual link between cyclical *genesis* on earth and the cyclical *periodoi* of the heaven is "imitation," a Platonic motif which reminds us of what the *Symposium* says about man's desire to approximate the immortality of the gods by leaving behind offspring like himself.[38]

[37] *Tim.* 37b–39e.

[38] *De gen.* II,10.337b3; Plato *Conv.* 206bff. For the participation of living beings in immortality (through reproduction) see the passages cited above in Note 30. For the other form of man's immortality which the *Symposium* describes in glowing colors (207c)—immortality through *arete*—see Aristotle's enthusiastic statements in the *Ethics* (*Eth. Nic.* X,7.1077b24–1178a2; see also *Metaph.* A2.982b24ff.; cf. Jaeger, *Aristotle*, 72 n.1). It may, however, be thought that *Tim.* 90b6–c6 (esp. c2f.) is closest to Aristotle's famous statements. Intellectual excellence, ἀθάνατα φρονεῖν, is the truly Platonic version of this immortality.

Part Five

METEOROLOGY

21

Place and Purpose of the
Meteorologica

ARISTOTLE'S *Meteorologica* may go far toward bridging the gulf between the two large bodies of doctrine into which his theory of the four terrestrial elements had split. Having in one of his previous treatises studied the movements of these elements and in another explained their nature, origin, and mutual transformations, Aristotle now comes to deal with transformations that result in movements—as a matter of fact, in movements identical with those discussed in the latter books of *On the Heaven*. If parts of an element are changed into another, they evidently must go to the cosmic region which is their new home. This truth is amply illustrated by the processes of cosmic interchange on which Aristotle dwells in the *Meteorologica*. When portions of water change from cold and moist to warm and moist, they rise to the higher strata of the Cosmos, and so do parts of earth when instead of continuing in a cold and dry condition they become warm and dry.[1] Moreover, what causes such change in temperature is the sun, an idea entirely in keeping with the role assigned to it in the preceding treatise *On Coming to Be*, where the sun is described as the eternal source of all changes and all becoming in "the place around the center."[2] Underneath the heavenly rotations, Aristotle reminds us early in the *Meteorologica*, is matter potentially hot and cold, dry and moist. When exposed to the right kind

---

[1] See I,4.341b7ff. and 9.346b26ff.; II,4.359b27-35.
[2] I,3.341a13ff. (19ff.); 4.341b6ff., etc.; *De gen.* II,10.

of influence, it will have any of these qualities "actually." [3] We are free
to understand that the action of the sun renders some parts of matter
warm that were previously cold; when thus changed they transfer
themselves to the cosmic zones reserved for the warm elements.

Thus the bulk of the *Meteorologica* seems to provide a bridge between two sets of doctrines which, based on different premises, had
tended to consolidate themselves in isolation from one another.[4] The
fundamental assumptions of both are here respected and applied. Instead
of dichotomy we have connection and interaction.

The essential correctness of this impression is hardly open to doubt.
What is less certain is that Aristotle himself was anxious to close the
gap and that he composed this treatise with any such intention.

The purpose of the *Meteorologica*—always leaving aside Book IV—
may be defined in a variety of ways. One may look upon it as providing
the answer to what Aristotle at the end of the preceding work described as "the problem raised by some," actually meaning Plato.[5] If
every element has the urge, as it were, to move to its own natural place,
why have the four sublunary elements not become completely separated from one another and broken off all connection? The answer, in
the general terms to which Aristotle there confines himself, is that the
elements, under the influence of the sun, change into one another and,
having done so, also exchange their places.[6] We remember Plato's own
solution: the pressure of the circumference thrusts the elementary particles past and across one another, a process in which they are broken
up, regrouped, and finally led to a new cosmic place.[7] From this description it is a far cry to the consideration of specific meteorological
topics and questions, and the *Timaeus* has indeed little thought to spare
for these. In Aristotle's scheme too the passage just referred to is incidental in a more general discussion of the sun and of its movements in
the ecliptic circle which have so decisive an influence on *genesis*. Rather
sweepingly, all *genesis* is traced to the sun as its efficient cause, and

---

[3] I,3.340b15-19. More precisely Aristotle says that the actualization of these
qualities depends on motion and absence of motion. His reference to his earlier
treatment of this subject (*De gen.* II, 10, as the commentators indicate) makes
clear that he is thinking of the annual movement of the sun in the ecliptic. Material
here on earth which remains cold when not "moved" (i.e., affected, changed) by
the sun turns hot when it comes under its influence.

[4] See above, pp. 363-365.

[5] *De gen.* II,10.337a7ff. (discussed above, pp. 383-384).

[6] *Ibid.*, a11-15.   [7] *Tim.* 57d7-58c3.

even the remarks about the mutual changes of the elements are formulated quite broadly. To maintain that Aristotle here maps out the ground to be covered by his *Meteorologica* would make undue demands on our imagination. Having shown that mutual transformation is possible on his hypothesis, all that Aristotle here wishes to do is to indicate its efficient cause. This makes the possibility a reality and gives it concrete form. Still, the "problem raised by some" was a very real one for himself. The books *On the Heaven* had carried the idea of natural places to extreme lengths, the upshot being that each element will be in its place "if nothing prevents it." [8] Evidently these conclusions must be supplemented if we are not to end up with a world picture in which everything is static—this time not while "all things are together" but while all things are separated.[9]

Nor could a physicist who aimed at some degree of completeness be content with stating that the elements, because of their common substratum, can change into one another and that the sun stands ready to help them. The fact is that neither of the two preceding treatises has an opportunity of coming to grips with particular phenomena. Yet precisely meteorology as it had taken shape presented Aristotle with a goodly number of phenomena—recurrent and in some degree regular phenomena—which could illustrate material transmutation and consequent exchange of cosmic places.[10] Here he could make the turn from the static and the general to the dynamic and specific.

He could—but did he actually approach the subject with such intention? On the whole we find him in the *Meteorologica* engrossed by its own particular subject matter. He is satisfied as soon as he has penetrated to the core of the phenomena and in addition has made sure that there is nothing to militate against his strongest cosmological convictions. To fit the facts here covered and the theories here framed into the larger pattern of his physics and cosmology is a task which takes second place. True, he does in the beginning refer to the works in which this pattern has taken shape and summarizes very briefly some of their con-

---

[8] *De caelo* IV,3.311a7f.

[9] See Plato's reference to this Presocratic hypothesis (at *Legg.* X,895a7); cf. *H.S.C.P.*, 63 (1958), 276ff.

[10] E.g., for Aristotle's theory about the origin of the rivers it is essential that inside the earth there is a constant change of air into water (I,13, esp. 349b20ff., 31ff.). Water is a γιγνόμενον, not an ὑπάρχον. This is the salient feature of the theory, and the theory itself is original to the extent to which it is predicated on this assumption.

clusions.[11] He also presupposes the existence of the first body in its own large area and, what is more important, relies on the heavenly movements to serve as efficient causes for some of the meteorological events and formations.[12] Our imagination readily carries us beyond these movements to the rotation of the outermost heaven and to the first mover who inspires it. Yet Aristotle himself does little to encourage such higher flights.[13] It is left to the reader, if thus inclined, to wonder how the *Meteorologica* completes or supplements the more general and fundamental studies. Our own answer as given on the preceding pages is based on inferences and speculations advanced with some confidence that they are tenable and with considerably less confidence that they mattered for Aristotle himself.[14] One's first and last impression is that Aristotle does not aim at more than providing valid and intrinsically coherent explanations for the whole range of meteorological phenomena. Where larger questions of cosmic order arise, he gladly avails himself of the chance thus offered for broadening and enriching his scheme, yet the dualism here overcome is that between the celestial and sublunary phases, not between the basic assumptions of cosmology and chemistry.

Books III and IV of the work *On the Heaven* told us about the upward movement of fire and air and the contrary movement of water. Now we learn why such movements are constantly taking place, and it becomes clear that in particular air and water are not very permanent in their cosmic region but carry on a good deal of mutual exchange.[15] On the whole, however, the earlier treatise left us with the impression that the elements exist as permanent and constant masses and that they keep dividing the sublunary world between themselves.[16] This impression we are now forced to give up. The two upper elements especially

---

[11] I,1 takes stock of subjects so far covered, I,2 of some results. See, further, 3.339a37ff., b17ff., 340b4–21.

[12] See above, Note 3.   [13] He goes farthest in I,2.339a22ff.

[14] For traditional opinions see W. D. Ross, *Aristotle* (5th ed.; London, 1949), 108f. Ross's own view (p. 109) is close to ours. Léon Robin, *Aristote* (Paris, 1944), 135, observes that the dry exhalation changes the element which is cold and dry into the hot and dry and that the moist links the two elements defined by this quality. This is undoubtedly correct, but it is also true that Aristotle has done little to bring out this connection between the *Meteorologica* and *De generatione*.

[15] See esp. I,9.346b21–347a8; II,2.354b24–34.

[16] For a noteworthy exception see IV,3.311a1–6, yet note also 6–8. On the whole cf. Joachim, 138ff. We may also recall that in Book III Aristotle commits himself to the view that the elements arise out of one another but does not succeed in showing how this comes to pass.

are all the time coming into existence—and coming to their places—as the result of a transformation. Some passages of the *Meteorologica* lead us to think that cosmic air and "fire" owe their existence entirely to the exhalations which keep rising up from land and sea.[17]

Moreover, Aristotle finds it necessary to revise a far from unimportant point of his earlier theory. In the *De caelo* fire occupies the cosmic zone beneath the first body; next comes the zone of air, then those of water and earth. In the *Meterologica* the substance which fills the highest stratum of the sublunary world is no longer fire but another kind of air. The exhalation from the earth which reaches this region is "smoky" and "potentially fire"—yet not actually.[18] Already in the *De generatione* Aristotle had felt the need of explaining that the "simple bodies" for which his theory holds good are not fire, air, water, and earth but are "like" them, presumably purer in their composition. Fire in particular is an extreme or "excess" of the hot.[19] The passage where this is stated does not inform us whether the bodies which fill the four strata of the sublunary world are fire, air, etc., or the true and ideal "simple bodies."[20] Now, however, in the *Meteorologica* Aristotle definitely eliminates fire from the cosmic region which it possessed throughout

---

[17] Esp. I,3.340b24–30; 4.341b7–18; 7.344a9ff.

[18] I,3.340b22–30; 4.341b13–24. For what follows cf. Hans Strohm, *Untersuchungen zur Entwicklungsgeschichte d. aristot. Meteorologie (Philologus* Suppl. 28.1 [1935]), 10f.

[19] *De gen.* II,3.330b21–30. Fire is here in 25f. described as an excess of the hot and as a "boiling" of it, in 29 as a boiling of hot and dry. Observe that the entity compared with fire and likewise disqualified as a "simple body" is not another element but a particular condition of another element, namely, ice (25–30). *Phys.* IV,5.212b20ff. should *pace* Strohm (*op.cit.*, 19ff.) not be compared; see Ross's commentary on this passage. P. Shorey, *Cl. Ph.*, 17 (1922), 343, has probably our section (330b21–30) in mind and has here found the Aristotelian "elements in their ideal purity." Correct as this is in itself, it should not make us think of Plato's Forms. The similarities are accidental and superficial.

[20] One would look for the answer in the immediately following section, 330b30–331a3, where Aristotle speaks of the cosmic places; but does Aristotle here observe the distinction which he has just established? If, as I believe, 330b21–30 are a later insertion by Aristotle's own hand, it may well have been prompted by the more precise doctrine of the *Meteorologica;* for also in the passage of *De gen.* the element which really worries Aristotle is the fire. We may compare the additions made in *De caelo* with a view to bringing its theory into line with that of *De gen.* (see above, Ch. 13, Note 32). 331a3–6 has the appearance of a correction due to Aristotle's doubts whether the straightforward identification of each element with a mixture of two qualities really worked out. For doubts as to the nature of the simple bodies (again primarily the fire but also earth) see also Theophr. *De igne* 7f.

the treatise *On the Heaven*. Describing fire again as an excess, he assigns to that region a kind of air mixed of hot and dry.[21] If this is the genuine "simple body," it would, far from being something purely ideal, have a very real existence in the Cosmos. Yet to tell the truth, Aristotle is not now interested in the distinction between true simple bodies and the actual elements, and we had better not press our question. What is evident is that the meteorological theory he is about to propound would not work out if fire were supposed to fill the space next to the first body. The winds which originate there can certainly not be fiery. All, then, that is left of the original doctrine is that the air in that area has the capacity of being set on fire.

These modifications and corrections are anything but slight.[22] In the light of them the cosmic distribution of the four simple bodies, as set forth in the *De caelo*, would appear to rest on assumptions that are both too simple and in some ways incorrect. If the stratum next to the *aether* is not really fire, the correlation of simple bodies and simple movements would lose much of its value—and especially much of its cosmological significance. How much help can the observation that we see fire moving upward [23] provide if there is no actual stratum of fire in the Cosmos? Moreover, it is one thing to hold that earth and water can be transformed into air and fire and another to treat the latter two substances altogether as products of earth and water. Can they under these circumstances still retain the status of elements and be entirely on a par with the other two? It is not quite easy to imagine what would have become of the doctrines embodied in *De caelo* III and IV if Aristotle had seen fit to recast them and bring them into harmony with his new insights. They might have lost not a little of their symmetry, compactness, and simple elegance. Thus it is hardly a matter for regret that Aristotle did not rewrite these two books. What kept him from it

[21] *Meteor.* I,3.340b22–27. This time fire is said to be an excess and "a sort of boiling" of the hot (23), not of the hot and dry (cf. Note 19).

[22] See, e.g., *De caelo* IV,4.311a19, b21ff. Another new and surprising doctrine would be the distinction between different degrees of purity in the "fifth body" (I,3.340b7ff.; the sentence in question is, however, open to a different understanding). Cf. Josef Zürcher, *Aristoteles' Werk und Geist* (Paderborn, 1952), 178. I agree with Zürcher, 178ff., that the *Meteorologica* embodies new features in its scheme of cosmic strata but do not think that he has identified them with sufficient precision. Nothing, so far as I can see, bears out his contention that the *aether* is now for Aristotle a kind of fire, and nothing suggests that the doctrine of planetary spheres (which belong to the area covered by *De caelo*) is abandoned.

[23] See, e.g., *De caelo* IV,4.311a19, b21ff.

was probably not so much dogmatic respect for his earlier ideas but preoccupation with other fields whose data had not yet been brought under the control of his philosophical concepts. As the treatises follow one another, we look to the earlier work in which the outlines of the Cosmos are drawn in the expectation that it will provide the frame for the more specific inquiries of the *Meteorologica*. Unfortunately the frame does not entirely fit the picture which should fill it.[24] The discrepancies must be understood as reflecting Aristotle's transition from one speculative position to another.

In the first chapter of the *Meteorologica* Aristotle defines the province of this treatise partly by reference to its traditional name ("what all earlier thinkers have called meteorology"), partly by pointing out a peculiarity of the subject matter. The events here to be studied have less regularity or order than those connected with the first element.[25] Trying to be more specific, he adds that the phenomena in question come to pass in the region bordering on the movements of the stars, i.e., underneath the *aethereal* region. However, as this description clearly would not cover everything that he means to include, he next refers to phenomena in which air and water are involved.[26] These we know, even though Aristotle does not say it, materialize in a lower cosmic area. Finally, and still more at variance with the original spatial demarcation, he mentions "parts of the earth" and their "experiences." This slightly enigmatic phrase may among other matters cover earthquakes, and earthquakes definitely are within the realm of this study.[27] Yet they can hardly be regarded as "things on high." No matter what criteria may be used, it is difficult to find a common de-

---

[24] The observations here put forward suggest that a certain amount of time elapsed between the composition of *De caelo* III and IV and that of the *Meteorologica*. Exactly how much time it is of course impossible to say; yet from our point of view the dating of *Meteor.* I–III in the period of the Lyceum would be entirely acceptable. Cf. Jaeger, *Aristotle*, 325ff., and Capelle, *R.E.* Suppl. 6, *s.v.* "Meteorologie," 339.

[25] For this and what follows see I,1.338a26–339a3. On the "proem" in general cf. Capelle, *Hermes*, 47 (1912), 514ff.

[26] In 338b24 ὅσα τε . . . is loosely added; so is ἔτι . . . in 25. H. D. P. Lee's translation (Loeb Lib.; 1952) brings out the somewhat rambling way in which one set of phenomena after another is added; see, however, my comments, *Gnomon*, 29 (1957), 132. Cf. Capelle, *Hermes*, 47 (1912), 526.

[27] 338b25ff. (ἐξ ὧν in 26 would seem to be causal and may easily be justified in this sense. Lee's translation [see Note 26], "there follows," is not satisfactory. I agree with him that it is difficult to find a precise reference for γῆς ὅσα μέρη καὶ εἴδη in 25).

nominator for the disparate subjects of his treatise. This difficulty may help us to see Aristotle's own achievement in the proper light. What the phenomena really have in common is the identical cause and origin which Aristotle assigns to all of them. In the introduction it would not have been good form to anticipate the idea by which he later in the work unifies the subject materially as well as methodologically.[28] In Books I–III the whole range of phenomena is traced to the exhalations, i.e., to material changes in earth and water by which portions of these substances are transformed, separated from the main body, and transferred to the higher cosmic regions.[29] One may doubt whether after Anaximenes (who evidently used the air as principal cause for many phenomena) the subject had ever been organized with such single-minded determination under one and the same ruling idea.

Let us briefly consider how Aristotle proceeds in applying this idea. He introduces the exhalation in the fourth chapter of Book I, making at once clear that it materializes in two forms. It is either moist and vaporous or dry and smoky.[30] Having thus defined his *arche*, he immediately turns to developments in the upper atmosphere. Shooting stars, the aurora borealis, comets, and the Milky Way are traced to the inflammable dry exhalation.[31] In chapter 9 there is a change of subject; for some time to come the moist exhalation dominates the discussion. This is the cause of the clouds, rain, hail, snow, and all similar formations. Next Aristotle seems to turn to the winds, yet, allowing himself to be sidetracked, he first sets forth at length his views about the nature of the rivers and the sea, paying special attention to the question of their origin. These subjects are closely linked to the moist exhalation since both sea and rivers contribute to it and in the end, when the exhalation has passed through some changes, benefit from it.[32] Having clarified these processes, and a good deal more on the way,

[28] For a different opinion see Strohm, *op.cit.*, 8ff.

[29] Cf. A. Rehm and K. Vogel, in A. Gercke and E. Norden, eds., *Einleit. in d. Altertumswiss.* (4th ed.; Leipzig and Berlin, 1933), 2.5.36.

[30] I,4.341b6ff. For the following survey Strohm's more detailed analysis (see Note 18) should be compared.

[31] I,4–8.

[32] I,13; note the transition to the rivers in 349b3ff. (cf. a25ff.). For the contribution made by rain and exhalation to the formation of the rivers see esp. 350a7-13. Strohm (*op.cit.*, 74f.) is probably right in holding that chs. I,13–II,3 are not everywhere closely related to the *anathymiasis* principle. Yet we are far from losing sight of it (note 354b24ff.). The thesis that these chapters are of later origin than

Aristotle returns to the winds which again have their origin in the dry exhalation.[33] The same exhalation when not moving upward but turning back into the earth produces earthquakes.[34] The last chapters of Book II and the first of III deal with phenomena such as thunder, hurricane, typhoon, and firewind that are closely related to the nature of the winds; thus they too go back to the dry exhalation.[35] The remaining subjects—halo, rainbow, mock suns, etc.—are in the last analysis likewise due to the exhalations, in fact, it would seem, to both of them, but for their full understanding certain optical laws and mathematical theorems must be taken into consideration. Here the exhalations do not dominate Aristotle's account as conspicuously as in the larger part of the treatise.[36]

Still, the principle works everywhere. And we can even see that Aristotle, perhaps emboldened by his success, contemplated some further uses for the twofold exhalation. In the last chapter of Book III, the discussion of "the effects produced by the exhalation in the regions above the earth" being completed, he turns his eyes to still other spaces in which the exhalations may be at work.[37] Below the earth, he announces, the exhalation, in accordance with its dual nature, produces two kinds of bodies. The dry variety, acting by way of its heat, forms all "fossils," a term under which Aristotle includes "stones that cannot be melted" and also ocher, sulphur, and similar substances. The moist, when pressed together and solidified, creates every kind of metal.[38] Aristotle barely indicates how such compression is brought

---

the bulk of Books I–III has its attractions, and certain textual difficulties at the beginning of II,4 may seem to lend it support (Strohm, *op.cit.*, 44 n.89). Still, the more significant difficulties in I,13.349b2ff., where Aristotle unexpectedly drops one subject to take up another, give the impression of being due to a spontaneous digression rather than to a later insertion. Nevertheless Strohm's book will serve as a good corrective if I have overstated the importance of the *anathymiasis* principle. For Strohm, although fully aware of its great importance, has *data opera* collected all instances in which Aristotle conceivably has broken away from it and prefers a more "empirical" approach. Moreover, Strohm is surely right in arguing (*op.cit.*, 60f. and *passim*) that the heavenly rotations are not consistently treated by Aristotle as the moving cause of meteorological phenomena.

[33] II,4ff.

[34] II,7f. Cf. Strohm, *op.cit.*, 56ff. I am not convinced that the difference between the *pneuma* which operates in earthquakes and the exhalation is as great as Strohm believes. In its basic nature the *pneuma* is clearly identical with the exhalation, which is the cause of all winds (II,4).

[35] II,9; III,1.   [36] See below, pp. 418–420.   [37] III,6.378a13ff.

[38] *Ibid.*, a20-b4. Some of the problems posed by Aristotle's brief and rather sketchy account have been clarified by D. E. Eichholz, *Cl. Q.*, 43 (1949), 140ff. I

about, and he does not try to explain the individual differences between the various metals. Yet he clearly planned elaboration in detail; for the last sentence of the book points forward to an examination of each kind. There is no evidence that he actually lived up to this promise [39]—if a promise it is; for the words might conceivably be read as a program of research for his pupils. In this case the pupils did not see fit to follow his lead. They may have convinced themselves that in the explanation of individual metals and minerals Aristotle's favorite idea was less helpful than his optimism had led him to expect. The metals in particular could after all best be understood as substances and as consisting either wholly or predominantly of water and earth.[40] This is basically the same approach as Plato had adopted in the *Timaeus* where he classes the metals with other "forms" and phases of water, allowing for some an admixture of earth.[41] Aristotle, in a remark

should, however—for reasons which will presently become clear—hesitate to use Book IV as readily as Eichholz for the elucidation of this section and am not fully convinced that his arguments succeed in identifying the dry exhalation as the "efficient" (rather than as the material) cause of the fossils.

[39] Ingeborg Hammer-Jensen, *Hermes*, 50 (1915), 118ff., has pointed out that the treatise which we now read as Book IV of the *Meteorologica* is not the sequel which the concluding section of III leads us to expect. She also advanced a number of reasons against Aristotle's authorship of Book IV. Not all of these reasons are equally cogent; some have been refuted by Ingemar Düring, *Aristotle's Chemical Treatise* (Göteborgs Högskolas Arsskrift 50, sec. 2; 1944), 19ff., and by Lee, in the "Introduction," xvff., to his translation. Both of them regard Book IV as genuine yet admit that it did not originally belong to the *Meteorologica*. In my review of Lee, *Gnomon*, 29 (1957), 131ff., I briefly indicated the grounds on which I should question the authenticity of the treatise.

[40] *Meteor.* IV,10.389a27ff.; see also 8.384b31ff. (cf. Note 43). In Theophrastus, *De lapidibus*, the part played by the exhalations is similarly reduced; for the only reference to them see 50. On the whole I sets the tone: τῶν ἐν τῇ γῇ συνισταμένων τὰ μέν ἐστιν ὕδατος, τὰ δὲ γῆς. Cf. Regenbogen, *R.E.*, s.v. "Theophrastos," 1416ff., and my comments, *Gnomon*, 29 (1957), 132ff.

[41] *Tim.* 59bf. Plato refrains from proceeding very far along this line (59c5ff.). Still, in spite of a somewhat disparaging remark earlier in the *Timaeus* (46d), he shows in these sections (58d–61c) considerable interest in the processes of freezing and melting. It was natural for the Peripatus to embark on a more systematic investigation of them, and indeed there is a priori no reason why Aristotle himself should have been unwilling to do so. The case against his authorship of *Meteor.* IV rests on other grounds (*Gnomon*, 29 [1957], 132ff.). That in a study of the kind the λόγος and the teleological cause have little scope and that συναίτια or, as the Peripatus says, material causes dominate are points on which Plato and the author of Book IV agree (see *Tim.* 46c7ff. and *Meteor.* IV,12.389b27–390b2, with the comments of Lee in the "Introduction," xvf., to his translation).

which may be directed against the *Timaeus*, makes clear that he regards this approach as unsatisfactory, though not as wholly wrong; a real understanding, according to him, can be achieved only by thinking in terms of the moist exhalation.[42] Yet it appears that his pupils gave preference to Plato's method. The so-called fourth book of the *Meteorologica* pays on one occasion lip service to Aristotle's idea, yet in a fashion so clumsy and suggesting so superficial a harmonization of the alternative theories that in effect it rather underlines the departure from Aristotle's program.[43] What the author of this book actually does is to treat metals as *homoeomere*, i.e., on a par with the homogeneous parts of animals and plants.[44] These *homoeomere* are for him mixtures of earth and water. There may have been reasons for blurring the line between organic and inorganic substances, though neither Plato nor Aristotle, nor indeed as far as we know any of the Presocratics, had taken such a step.[45] Yet as the author of this book has chosen to study the action of the hot and the cold on the moist and the dry,[46] he finds himself dealing with chemical processes which apply in the organic as well as in the inorganic realm. The systematic investigation of these processes seems to have been a desideratum in the Peripatus; it was probably biological research—rather than physical—which prompted the idea. It would be worth inquiring to what extent the biochemistry inherent in Aristotle's biological theory contributed to the creation of chemistry as an independent branch of science.[47] Yet a study of this kind is outside the scope of our present investigation.

[42] III,6.378a33ff. There is, however, the possibility that Plato had precursors who are not known to us; see above, p. 9.

[43] IV,8.384b31-385a1; cf. again *Gnomon*, 29 (1957), 133.

[44] See the passage cited in Note 43 and also 10.388a13. The actual procedure adopted in Book IV corresponds to these statements, even if it is the case that in the latter part of it metals receive more attention than in the former.

[45] The evidence for Empedocles and Anaxagoras must be admitted to be inadequate, but as far as it goes, it suggests that their concern was to explain the *homoeomere* in organic beings. The *Timaeus* deals with "mixtures" of the inorganic kind in 58d-61c, with those of the organic in 73b-76e (for the organic Plato seems to have the term δεύτεραι συστάσεις, 82b8); there is no attempt to establish a connection or to draw a parallel. Finally Aristotle appears to use the term *homoeomere* of organic "tissues" only.

[46] IV,1.378b10ff. and *passim*.

[47] See Bonitz, *s.vv.* θερμόν (326b15ff., 52ff.), πέττειν, πέψις, πηγνύναι, σῆψις, under all of which words passages are listed that suggest problems and theories comparable to those of *Meteor.* IV. A study of these connections (for which I hope someday to find the time) should, however, pay equal attention to Theophrastus' botanical treatises.

Returning to Aristotle's physical world picture, we shall now consider the significance of the one and only material cause to which he traces all meteorological phenomena.

Measured by previous achievements in this field, the uniformity may have entailed loss and be a retrograde step; but to Aristotle himself it must have been most gratifying. His methodological postulates had met a test. It was his firm conviction that each scientific subject rested on its own first principles and first assumptions. These "hypotheses" guarantee the subject its peculiar character, setting it apart from others that rest on different and perhaps even heterogeneous first principles.[48]

Aristotle formulates this methical postulate with special reference to the various branches of mathematics, yet it is evident that his cosmology as set forth in the *De caelo* conforms to it. The doctrines concerning the celestial and the sublunary elements rest on one and the same hypothesis.[49] It is not at all necessary that the principles of the various sciences should in the final analysis resolve into one. Evidently the two exhalations of our treatise are as satisfactory first assumptions as the natural movements of the *De caelo*. The situation in the *Physics* is not comparable because throughout it Aristotle is concerned with clarifying and defining the fundamental concepts of this subject— that he also develops some corollaries of these definitions may here be disregarded.

The first assumptions of the *De caelo* had put cosmology on a new basis, but the work as it stands combines the exposition of these assumptions with a study of celestial movements, celestial phenomena, and other matters pertaining to the zone of the first element. As a result meteorology which deals with events below this zone was more clearly and sharply set apart than ever before. For this field a different procedure, resting on different first assumptions, had to be worked out; and as Aristotle in the first chapter distinguishes the area of the *meteora* from that of the first body, so in the bulk of this work he treats the phenomena themselves as differing in type from those of the celestial spaces.

Aristotle must have attacked meteorology "with a will." To investigate it meant to unify it. An adoption of more than one explanatory principle in the sense that the first hypothesis would cover one set of

---

[48] See above, Ch. 11, with the references to *Anal. Post.* in Notes 27ff.
[49] See above, Chs. 11 and 14.

phenomena, the second or third some others, would probably have appeared to him as dilettantish, as a failure to live up to his philosophical calling. It may be argued that his physical system favored a hypothesis which involved transformations from one element into another. Granted the relevance of this argument, it would not automatically exclude the possibility of several, perhaps mutually independent, physical processes each of which could have served in the role of a principle. No doubt there was the precedent of the Presocratics whose search for a root cause had set a kind of pattern. But pattern or not, with the exception, it would seem, of Anaximenes, the Presocratics can hardly have been fanatically intent on tracing all events on high to one and the same operating principle. They had a variety of elements or powers and were under no obligation to explain earthquakes, the rainbow, and the saltiness of the sea at the same juncture in their accounts.[50] Compared with Aristotle's monistic procedure, theirs has a more flexible character. Moreover, if precedent mattered, Aristotle had after all created one himself. A method which had proved so extraordinarily successful in the *De caelo* would recommend itself strongly for the parallel task now to be mastered.

This being the situation, it was probably easier for Aristotle to find his single cause in the central and more familiar parts of the Cosmos. One cannot readily think of a process in the fiery or airy stratum— the upper and lower atmosphere, as we should call them—which could have answered his monistic intentions as effectively as the two exhalations. If Aristotle ever wavered in his choice of principle, the *Meteorologica* as we read it preserves no trace of this phase. On the other hand, as none of the three preceding treatises includes a reference to the exhalations, it is possible that Aristotle's selection of this cause barely antedates the actual composition of the three books.

[50] We have touched on this difficult subject in the "Historical Introduction" (pp. 12–13), but it must be emphasized again that it abounds in pitfalls. Although it is easy to point to some αἴτια in Empedocles (A63–66, 68), Anaxagoras (A8off.), or Democritus (A92ff., 97ff.) which do not converge very readily, such impressions may be due to our inadequate information. Still, there is no reason to suppose that late Presocratics had any common heading for matters as diverse as shooting stars, winds, earthquakes, and the salt content of the sea or that they felt a compelling need to treat them along similar lines and as owing to comparable causes. If Democritus used the atoms for every meteorological *aition*, this in itself would not yet imply a high degree of uniformity. Besides Anaximenes, whose air serves as a ubiquitous principle of meteorological explanation, Xenophanes' handling of such matters strikes us as remarkably consistent. For it seems that in his theory clouds accounted for a great variety of phenomena (B32, A43ff.).

From the proem of Book I we may gather how strongly Aristotle felt about the need of incorporating this additional field in his philosophical domain. As he sees it, the meteorological theory completes his system of the physical world.[51] Going a step farther than he, we may say that without this theory he would have had no system. Integration would have been lacking, and the other treatises would have remained unconnected. By contrast to these other treatises which are self-contained and make no attempt to define their "place," the *Meteorologica* opens with a recapitulation of the previous achievements. The recapitulation indicates that there still is a gap to be filled. Here we may speak of a systematic conception, but we have no right[52] to project it back into earlier years and to think of it as existing before, say, the composition of the *Physics* or the *De caelo*. It is more probable that Aristotle "shaped" his system gradually and over the years. After individual works dealing with more circumscribed problems had come into existence, Aristotle saw the possibility of integrating them into larger bodies, and as the integration proceeded, he realized that these larger units in turn could converge and cover the entire realm of physical problems. What had still to be done was to bring the remaining array of problems under control and, if possible, under compact and unified control.

In a sense, then, the subject matter of our treatise is "what was left" (λοιπόν). After the *De caelo* had carved out a large segment of cosmological problems, others of old standing required scrutiny, it being obvious that the Presocratic solutions would seldom fit into Aristotle's general physical scheme. Thus considered, the unity of the subject would be extrinsic rather than intrinsic. Whether the tradition presented it to Aristotle in a more unified form is a question on which we have tried to be cautious but on which we should, if an answer must be given, incline to a negative vote.[53] As unified as Aristotle rendered it, the subject certainly was not. If it had for some time been centrifugal and liable to break up into unconnected details, we now know the reason why Aristotle rescued it from this condition. However, even for him it remains somewhat peripheral. The twofold exhalation is not an idea as brilliant and original or as fertile and inspiring as the idea of natural motions and places which had built up Aristotle's cosmology and put the doctrine of the heavenly movements on a new foundation.

---

[51] I,1.338a20ff., esp. 26. Cf. again Capelle, *Hermes*, 47 (1912), 514ff.
[52] Not even the reference to the ἐξ ἀρχῆς προαίρεσις (I,1.339a3) would justify this.
[53] See above, Note 50.

The hypothesis of our treatise is something of a stopgap. A hypothesis was necessary—and therefore found. Moreover, it came late, indeed too late to become fully effective and to prompt a thoroughgoing revision of other theories that were beginning to harden into dogmas.

THE HYPOTHESIS OF THE DUAL EXHALATION

If Aristotle looked for one principle and looked for it among terrestrial processes, exhalation undoubtedly had a very strong claim on his consideration. Of its important place in Presocratic physics something will presently be said; for there can be no question that earlier doctrines strongly influenced Aristotle's own choice. Apart from these historical motives, exhalation would recommend itself because it could link events in the "place around the center" with those originating in higher cosmic strata. It implied interchanges between three sublunary elements (earth, water, and air) and confirmed Aristotle's theory of the sun as the efficient cause of such interchanges.

In Aristotle's physiological studies we read about an exhalation (or evaporation) whose function it is to carry the nourishment from "the place which receives" and digests it upward into the veins and to the heart.[54] The similarities between the physical and the physiological hypotheses make it all but certain that one of them inspired the other, but given the long concern of physicists with the cosmic exhalation, it is more likely that the physiologists borrowed the idea from them than vice versa.[55]

The formation, especially in the early morning hours, of a mist rising from the water was a familiar sight to the Greeks. It was a phenomenon of so distinctly physical a nature that even Hesiod could describe it in "naturalistic" terms without bringing in the Olympian gods as causative agents or translating the entire process into genealogical relationships between mythical personalities known or unknown. In a passage of the *Works and Days* the "ever-flowing rivers" are specified as the "source" of this mist, and the mist itself is said to expand throughout the entire space between earth and "starry heaven." [56]

[54] See esp. *De somno* 3.456b2ff. (where Aristotle refers to a fuller treatment of this subject in his περὶ τροφῆς), 18ff., 457a12ff., 458a1ff.; see, further, *De somniis* 3.462b6ff. and *De iuv.* 26.480a10 *et al.*

[55] The parallelism of the two processes was to acquire a new significance in the system of Posidonius (cf. K. Reinhardt, *R.E.*, *s.v.* "Posidonius," 709).

[56] *Op.* 548–553; cf. Otto Gilbert, *Die meteorolog. Theorien des griech. Altertums* (Leipzig, 1907), 440ff. The "Thracian Boreas" (v. 553) appears to co-operate

Where later thinkers would speak of mist or exhalation as turning into either rain or wind, Hesiod, with a somewhat less developed causal sense—or with a language less articulated for such description—refers to the mist itself as "raining" or "blowing." The same phenomenon encouraged some very bold and far-reaching speculations in the earliest physical systems. For Anaximander the action of the hot power in the Cosmos upon its opposite, the cold, materializes in the form of an exhalation. Thanks to it the central area which in the beginning had been "moist" becomes progressively drier; land arises where sea has been; and it stands to reason that the process as it continues will change the entire surface of the earth into land, a development which may lead to the final disintegration of this Cosmos.[57] Also, if it really was Anaximander's belief—and not rather Heraclitus'[58]—that the fiery heavenly bodies need moisture for their sustenance, the exhalation must have had a determining influence upon their movements. Finally winds and rain are (as in Hesiod) products of the exhalation.[59] Regarding Anaximenes' doctrines our evidence is less "copious." It is tempting to surmise that if he dealt with changes into, as well as out of, air he had recourse to some forms and functions of the exhalation, but the only definite statement that mentions exhalation refers to the origin of the stars.[60] These consisted, for him, of fire which was itself a rarefied product of moisture and had risen from the earth. For Aristotle's scheme the distinction between exhalation from the earth and from

---

with the exhalation—a religious or semireligious motif. My attention has been drawn to Genesis 2.6 which would be an interesting "parallel" if we could be sure that "mist" in the Standard Version is a correct rendering. As Isaac Rabinowitz informs me, this is far from certain. The Septuagint has πηγαί.

[57] See for this and what follows *Vorsokr.*, 12B27. Among recent interpreters O. Gigon (*Der Ursprung d. griech. Philosophie* [Basel, 1945], 94, 112) is inclined to see a connection between the continuous drying up and the final end of this Cosmos.

[58] Cf. Lee's note on *Meteor.* II,1.353b7 and especially Cherniss, *Presocr.*, 135 and n.544. Aristotle himself may in the dialogue *On Philosophy* have taken the view that the heavenly bodies derive sustenance from the exhalations. Cf. Jaeger, *Aristotle*, 150, who holds that the doctrines of Cleanthes reported in Cic. *De nat. deor.* 2.43 go back to this dialogue. Plato *Legg.* V,747d, to which Jaeger refers, strongly supports his opinion. Ross has, however, excluded this section of Cicero from his text of frg. 21. Cf. in this connection Karl Reinhardt, *Kosmos und Sympathie* (München, 1926), 61ff., 109.

[59] See *Vorsokr.*, A11.7.

[60] *Ibid.*, 13A7.5. Gigon, *op.cit.*, 113ff., rightly wonders how this statement may be squared with other accounts of his views regarding the origin (esp. A6) and nature of the heavenly bodies. It must be admitted that uncertainties remain.

water is basic, but we should overtax the reliability of our reports if we tried to find both types anticipated in the earliest systems.

We should also beware of advocating too close a connection between Heraclitus' two exhalations, the bright and the dark, and Aristotle's superficially similar pair. For one thing, our information about the dark exhalation in Heraclitus has limited authority—so limited, in fact, that it has recently been altogether called into question.[61] Such radical criticism may overshoot the mark. But if we credit Diogenes Laertius' account, we must accept the distinctive qualities of the two exhalations. That which accounts for the fiery aspect and the light of the heavenly bodies must indeed be bright, and consequently the other dark. Secondarily they may well be dry and moist, but it still makes a good deal of difference that in Aristotle these two qualities furnish the basic distinction. Nor do the functions tally better than the qualities. Heraclitus, always provided that our authority does not mislead us, thought of the bright variety as creating day, the season of summer, and also, it would appear, the winds; of the dark as producing night, winter, and rain. It goes without saying that Aristotle would take a very different view regarding the origin of day and night or of the two principal seasons.[62] In the matter of wind and rain the two systems agree,[63] a fact which is of some importance, since in Hesiod they were developments of one and the same exhalation. Heraclitus may, indeed, have been the first to assign them to different, if parallel, origins. If this is the case, Aristotle is to this extent in his debt. (As a matter of fact, Aristotle does not say that nobody before him has assumed two exhalations, but only that some have not;[64] this may be regarded as "true to form.") On the other hand, Aristotle had the best of reasons for not allowing exhalation, whether bright and dark or dry and moist,

[61] *Vorsokr.*, 22A1.9-11 (Diog. Laert.). See the discussion of G. S. Kirk, *Heraclitus: The Cosmic Fragments* (Cambridge, 1954), 270ff.

[62] One would think that Heraclitus too knew that the movements of the sun accounted for these alternations; in principle much is to be said for efforts, like those made by Burnet (*E. G. Ph.*, 155f.) and Reinhardt (*Parmenides* [Bonn, 1916], 181ff.), to establish a connection between these movements and the exhalations. If the bright exhalation arises from the sea, the dark from the land (Kirk unnecessarily infers the opposite from Diogenes' account), and if the latter increases the ὑγρόν (Diogenes in *Vorsokr.*, 21A1.9), it stands to reason that in either case there is a transition into the next higher element. Incidentally it is probably wrong to say that the sun in Heraclitus "causes" an exhalation.

[63] For Aristotle's views on the origin of the precipitations and the winds see *Meteor.* I,9ff. and II,4f. respectively.

[64] I,4.341b7ff.

any effect in the region above the moon. His rigid separation of the heavenly and the sublunary regions limits the use which he can make of the Heraclitean or, more generally speaking, Presocratic principle—if one gives due weight to this important difference, one may feel less inclined to dismiss the reports about Heraclitus' two exhalations as a retrojection of Aristotle's views.[65]

One other Presocratic thinker, Xenophanes, ought to find a place in this sketch, but it will be convenient to postpone this part of our discussion.[66] With regard to the later Presocratics, little is attested about their interest in exhalation, and this little is not very revealing or relevant. We shall shortly find reasons to think that some of these men believe in the "cycle" of cosmic processes or exchanges.[67] The "upward" component of this cycle corresponds to the exhalation, but correspondence as such signifies little as long as we do not know in what language and with the help of what concepts Anaxagoras and others described the "upward" movement. In Epicurean physics exhalations from sea, rivers, and also land figure in the explanation of cloud formations and precipitations yet, as one might expect, not to the exclusion of other causes.[68] Thus it would not be safe to argue back

[65] Kirk, *op.cit.*, 273, who takes this view, concludes too confidently from Aristotle's text that he is entirely original in his hypothesis of two exhalations. I,13.349a12 allows no inference for originality in this matter. Kirk misinterprets this passage, connecting it too readily with B4,359b27ff.; in truth Aristotle's scathing remarks refer to the theories to be taken up in the immediately following sentences or paragraphs. "Darkness patently comes when the Sun sinks below the horizon" (Kirk, *op.cit.*, 272) is a "solution" which begs the question. Did the sun for Heraclitus "sink" or was it quenched and overcome by the other exhalation? Diogenes' report is much too circumstantial and includes too many un-Aristotelian features to be dismissed as a Peripatetic misinterpretation.

[66] Capelle (*R.E.* Suppl. 6.332) gives no good reasons for believing that Xenophanes went farther than his predecessors in stressing the functions of the sun as ἀρκτικὴ αἰτία. The final sentence of Aetius 3.3.4 (*Vorsokr.*, 21A46) seems to encourage this inference, but the statement as a whole tells against it.

[67] We are relatively well informed about Diogenes of Apollonia; see *Vorsokr.*, 64A17f. For the cycle see below, p. 429. That exhalation figured in Anaxagoras' account may be inferred from *Vorsokr.*, 59A42.4f., and Arist. *Meteor.* I,13.349b3–15 (cf. Lee, *ad loc.*, and Cherniss, *Presocr.*, 129 n.523). Gilbert, *op.cit.*, 458 n.2, rightly refuses to make much of Aetius 2.6.3 where exhalation of air from water is attributed to Empedocles. Whether this statement, as Gilbert suggests, refers to Empedocles' cosmogony is another question.

[68] See esp. Lucr. 6.476ff., 497ff., passages which for our purpose offer somewhat more than Epic. *Epist.* 2.106–9. Lucretius' cosmogony includes at 5.457ff., where the ἔκθλιψις of the *aether* atoms from the central region is described, a comparison of this process with the exhalation of mist from lakes and rivers in the early

from them to the early atomists. The utmost that our material may suggest for Democritus [69] is that he knew as much about the results of exhalation as Hesiod and Xenophanes. This would hardly be a surprise. On the whole the atomists make the ingredients of formations on high come together "from many places."

What, then, is new about Aristotle's material cause of meteorological phenomena? Certainly neither the exhalation as such nor the circumstances which bring it about can be considered as his own discovery. New, as far as we can tell, are the specific qualities dry and moist and, to say it once more, the unlimited and monarchical power now granted to the exhalations. All that comes to pass in the upper and lower atmosphere is their work.

Our historical sketch also suggests that by Aristotle's time subjects like the clouds or the precipitations readily permitted, or even called for, the application of his hypothesis. In the case of others much more ingenuity, not to call it violence, was required. Strong antecedent convictions had to be at work if celestial phenomena, such as the Milky Way or the comets, were to be traced to one of the exhalations. Aristotle himself is witness that some of his precursors had explained them along stellar lines.[70] Nor could he himself afford to ignore the heavenly bodies altogether. He holds that comets and the Milky Way

---

morning hours. Lucretius clearly exploits the poetic potentialities of this comparison; but may it not nevertheless go back to Epicurus? One might even wonder whether it did not originate with the earlier atomists, but seeing how much the details of Epicurus' cosmogony differed from Democritus' (Bailey, *Lucretius: De Rerum Natura* [Oxford, 1947], 3.1386), it would not be wise to pursue this possibility. For Stoic views of *anathymiasis* see *St. V. F.*, 1.501, 504; 2.421, 650, 659f., 1145 (cf. Jaeger's comment, *Aristotle*, 150 n.3).

[69] It is hardly possible to generalize on the basis of *Vorsokr.*, 68A99. According to Arist. *Meteor.* II,3.356b4ff. (= *Vorsokr.*, 68A100), Democritus still believes in the gradual diminution of the sea; yet there is no evidence that he attributed this development to evaporation, and if it was a cause for the disintegration of our world, it can hardly have been the only conceivable cause (in fact, he could imagine a Cosmos with no ὑγρόν at all; see A40.3). Did Anaxagoras and the atomists treat exhalation as an *apokrisis*? To do so would have been in accord with their over-all explanation of changes in the physical world.

[70] See chs. I,6 and I,8. More information will be found in Gilbert, *op.cit.*, 642, and Capelle, *R.E.* Suppl. 6.346ff. (*s.v.* "Meteorologie"). In the Hellenistic period those who *apud Chaldaeos studuisse se dicunt* were again divided as to the nature of the comets; some adhered to the stellar, others to the meteorological, theory (Seneca *Quaest. nat.* 7.4ff.). Cf. Gundel, *R.E.*, *s.v.* "Komet," 1164ff. For Posidonius' doctrine and its relation to that of Aristotle see A. Rehm, *S. B. Bayer. Akad.* (1921), 1.3ff., 36ff.

owe their existence to the movements of a planet or a fixed star which set portions of the dry exhalation on fire.[71] On the other hand, occurrences like thunder or earthquakes which some of the Presocratics had associated with the wind [72] could with relative ease be transferred to the new universal cause. At all events, Aristotle divides the control of the entire atmosphere between two exhalations, a decision the more noteworthy as before him rain and wind had sometimes been treated as identical in origin.[73] The duality of the ruling principle was obviously the maximum in the way of concession that Aristotle was willing to make.

AUXILIARY HYPOTHESES

Nevertheless certain additional hypotheses were needed; but as the processes which they introduce co-operate with the exhalation, the consistency and uniformity of Aristotle's procedure remain unimpaired.

Aristotle had every right to assume that, given suitable conditions, parts of the upper atmosphere could burst into fire and produce shooting stars, comets, and the Milky Way. For the dry exhalation which constitutes this atmosphere is, if no longer actually, still potentially fire [74] and can be ignited by the heavenly movements which are the *pièce de résistance* of the entire system and the principal cause of all *genesis*.[75] But how can rain and other precipitations which are cold and take a downward course be caused by the moist exhalation whose nature it is to move upward and which, being heated by the sun, should be warm rather than cold? Special mechanical processes are needed to bring the material down again. Some concentration of "the cold" must take place within the warm exhalation if the "cycle" is to function. The simplest assumption is perhaps that as the heat moves up-

---

[71] I,7.344a36ff.; 8.345b32ff.

[72] Anaxagoras seems to have emphasized (*Vorsokr.*, 59A89) that identical or similar action of the wind was the cause of both phenomena, yet it is hardly necessary to suppose that this precedent influenced or encouraged Aristotle (see esp. II,9.370a26ff.). Strohm (*Philologus* 92 [1937], 254 and *passim*) makes it probable that Theophrastus returned to the wind as an independent cause of meteorological phenomena, loosening or abandoning its connection with the exhalation (see *ibid.*, 413f., on thunder).

[73] See Aristotle's own statement to this effect in II,4.360a19ff. The specific reference may be to Metrodorus of Chios (*Vorsokr.*, 70A19), though if one allows for some inaccuracies in Aristotle's report greater thinkers may here be under fire.

[74] See above, p. 397.   [75] See, e.g., I,4.341b23ff., 342a29; 7.344a11ff.; 8.346a6ff.

ward and disperses (!)—some of it oddly enough even being quenched
—cold substance is left behind which turns again into water. In the
paragraph which gives the over-all explanation of rain and similar
phenomena Aristotle appears to be satisfied with this hypothesis.[76] Elsewhere he goes a step farther, suggesting that a concentration of hot
material causes a corresponding gathering of the cold stuff below, or,
as it were, on the inside of, the hot. For this process he uses the technical or semitechnical term *antiperistasis* which indicates that he is thinking of the hot as forming a kind of semicircle around the cold.[77] When
cold and hot are thus neatly cut off from one another, there seems to
be no further transformation of the weaker into the stronger; rather,
"the cold," being left to itself, must follow its own natural tendencies
and return to the colder regions—in the center of the Cosmos—from
which the exhalation arose. (A similar *antiperistasis* of hot and cold
and a "return" of the cold accompany the physiological evaporation
to which reference has been made earlier in this chapter.[78] On one
occasion in the *De somno* Aristotle actually points out the parallel
between the meteorological and the physiological "return." [79])

Concentrations of "the cold" by way of *antiperistasis* may take an
extreme form, and Aristotle in fact resorts to this supposition when
accounting for the formation of hail and in particular for the somewhat disturbing occurrence of hailstorms in summer.[80] The extreme
concentration and condensation of the cold is the process known as
freezing. However, something similar if less extreme also takes place

[76] I,9.346b24ff. Similar developments are assumed to account for the occurrence
of thunder (II,9.369a13-30). Theophrastus knows other causes for the formation of
rain besides ψύξις and seems to have applied the principle of *antiperistatis* less
broadly than Aristotle; see H. J. Drossaart Lulofs' discussion of a Syriac manuscript which enriches our knowledge of Theophrastus' meteorology, in *Autour d'*
Aristote . . . offert à Monseigneur A. Mansion (Louvain, 1955), 441ff.

[77] I,12.348b3ff.; see also 348b16ff., 349b8, and II,4.360b31-361a4. On the first of
these passages Lee in his translation has a helpful note in which he sets this meaning of *antiperistatis* apart from others to be found in Aristotle. It is evidently difficult to arrive at a fully satisfactory rendering for the term. Webster's phrasing in
the Oxford translation (vol. 3 [1931]) at 348b3, "warm and cold react upon one
another by recoil," is perhaps the best that can be done.

[78] See above, p. 407.

[79] *De somno* 3.457b31-348a10. The ἄθροον ἀντιστρέφειν καὶ καταφέρεσθαι of the
evaporation which Aristotle first assumes (456b20ff.) is a somewhat different idea;
at 457b31ff., where he seems to give the problem renewed consideration (see
b26ff.), the meteorological theory may have proved useful. For the concept of
antiperistasis see also 457a33-b6.

[80] See I,12, esp. 348b3ff., 16ff.

when the moisture which evaporates under the action of the sun comes, before it has risen very high, under a contrary and cooling influence.[81] This is apt to happen during the night or in the colder season. If such evaporation freezes before it again becomes water, the result is hoarfrost.

Although Aristotle's language may suggest it at times, we should probably not think that "the cold" and "the hot," when each has found its own area of concentration, adopt once more their old Presocratic role as independent substances or "powers." We have found such a return to Presocratic ways of thought in the treatise *On Coming to Be* and are aware that in the biological studies Aristotle, presumably under the influence of medical authorities, freely and extensively resorts to the "powers." [82] But in the *Meteorologica* the hot and the cold do not assert themselves in active fashion. They are passive, being subject to processes like freezing.[83] What Aristotle here, when speaking of "the hot" and "the cold," actually has in mind is the warmer and the colder portions of the exhalation, i.e., the part of it which has remained in the original warm condition and the other which has, as it were, fallen behind and lost its heat.[84] Nevertheless a Presocratic pattern suggests itself as parallel and precedent. In the early cosmologies our world comes into existence when the fundamental opposites break apart and establish themselves in different regions. Among these pairs of opposites the hot and the cold were certainly one of the most important.[85] Compared with their former contributions, the role now assigned to the opposites is rather insignificant. The leading parts in the cosmic drama being reserved for actors of higher standing, the older concepts must, if admitted at all, content themselves with markedly reduced functions.

The reason why Aristotle introduced the concept of *antiperistasis* is

[81] I,10.347a13ff. [82] See above, Ch. 17.

[83] See the evidence cited in Notes 76 and 77. Not much should, I think, be made of passages like I,12.348b16ff. where the cold is said to perform an *antiperistasis* after which "it produces water and freezes" (scil., the water). After he has isolated the cold in a place by itself, it is convenient for Aristotle to use it as grammatical subject and make it to this extent active.

[84] Cf. I,9.346b27–31, where, incidentally, Aristotle appears to use ἡ θερμότης and τὸ θερμόν as equivalents.

[85] For the opposites in Presocratic thought see above, p. 81. Here it may suffice to refer to Fränkel's book (*Dichtg. u. Philos.*, 341ff. and *passim;* see also his "Index," 657f.) which gives special attention to this motif in early Greek philosophy.

not far to seek. He needs the cold as an operating force in regions and under circumstances which would much rather suggest a prevalence and operation of the hot. He had to find a process which would free the opposite quality and allow it to act, and *antiperistasis* is the rational or speculative solution of this problem. Certain empirical observations, or what could pass as such, are called upon to support the theory; further observation, experience, or information is applied to the refutation of alternative doctrines,[86] but the answer itself could only be discovered by the sheer force of thought.

It deserves to be emphasized that the "cause" which Aristotle here introduces is a process. Obviously processes, movements, developments, and other changes are more germane to the subject matter of meteorology than are substances, and by identifying causes of this type Aristotle restored to meteorology something of its peculiar character. In Plato's treatment this specific character had all but disappeared. Even the briefest comparison of the theory of precipitations in the *Timaeus* and the *Meteorologica* will bring the difference into focus. The *Timaeus* explains precipitations in a chapter which deals with water and its various kinds and phases.[87] Water, if it is to be actually fluid, must have an admixture of fire; as soon as the fire particles withdraw, it changes into a frozen state. Having thus defined the cause of freezing, Plato feels that he has the clue to the nature of hail and snow, ice and hoarfrost, and also to the differences between them (dew he merely mentions in passing, and he ignores rain, whose identity with water he probably regarded as obvious).[88] All these phenomena are water, and all presuppose the partial or complete absence of fire. Actually hail and ice, and on the other side snow and hoarfrost, are substantially identical, the only difference in each case being whether they form on the surface of the earth or above it.[89] Plato completely disregards all specific conditions, causes, and circumstances. The Cosmos of the *Timaeus* has no seasons. Even the distinction between different places of formation is in this section kept to a minimum. As for processes, the only one referred to is the withdrawal of fire. Treated

[86] See esp. I,12.348bff., also (in the polemic) 348a21ff. and, of course, 347b37ff.
[87] *Tim.* 58d4–60b5; see in particular 59d4–e5, a remarkably brief passage which yet, with the exception of the still briefer and tantalizingly unspecific passages 58b4–c2 and 80b8–c8, is all that Plato says on these subjects.
[88] The nature of the freezing process has been explained also in a slightly earlier passage, 58d8–59a8, where ice, however, is not mentioned.
[89] 59e1–4.

as they are by Plato, hail, ice, snow, and hoarfrost are not meteorological phenomena but substances; what really interests him is their relation to the basic physical substances, his four elements. Nevertheless these meteorological items come off better in the *Timaeus* than others on which the Presocratics had expended much ingenuity. In this work, which is justly admired for its richness of detail, the winds and clouds are never mentioned. Regarding the rainbow, all that the doxographers could find in Plato was that Iris is the daughter of Thaumas (would Plato not have been amused to see the mild joke of the *Theaetetus* solemnly booked among his "physical opinions"? [90]). On earthquakes, too, these industrious people found a statement in him, yet there was nothing to be culled from the *Timaeus*.[91] And when they compiled doctrines on thunder and lightning, for which the Presocratics from Anaximander down, Aristotle, Strato, and the Stoics furnished them with material, Plato had perforce to be omitted from their list.[92]

Where Plato analyzes hail, snow, etc., he does not think in meteorological terms. It is possible that the "substantial" relations of phenomena —the identity of some, similarity of others—had never been brought out as effectively as in the *Timaeus,* for the simple reason that the Presocratics approached the phenomena primarily as events and processes and wondered what specific forces or developments produced them.[93]

When Plato emphasizes identity or approximate identity, he seems to suggest that popular differentiations (as reflected in the names "hail," "hoarfrost," etc.) are a matter of usage and not in accord with the nature of things.[94] Aristotle, writing probably with this section of

[90] Aetius 3.5 Diels; cf. Plato *Theaet.* 155d.

[91] Aetius 3.15 (derived from *Phaedo* 111dff.?).

[92] Aetius 3.3. Meteorological subjects are clearly on the periphery of Plato's physical interests. However, *Tim.* 79e10–80c8 shows that he saw a possibility of incorporating them. This section, which is very compressed and in some places difficult to the point of obscurity, adumbrates the method for a scientific treatment of these matters.

[93] See, e.g., the accounts dealing with Anaxagoras' explanation of hail, *Vorsokr.*, 59A85 (cf. also Antiphon, *ibid.*, 87B29). Needless to say, the Presocratics, like any moderately intelligent person at their time, knew that hail and snow are water (see, e.g., Anaximenes A7.7). Nevertheless Plato's discussion is peculiar in that it disregards causes and circumstances (weather conditions and the like). What he presents approximates a *diaeresis* of the genus water into various "forms," παγέν, ἡμιπαγές, ἐπὶ γῆς, ὑπὲρ γῆς being the *differentiae.*

[94] The reference to "names" and the use of λέγεται are, however, very persistent in these sections of the *Timaeus*. Plato does not necessarily intend to criticize

the *Timaeus* in mind, pays similar attention to the names, yet makes it clear that in his opinion the different names correspond to real differences.[95] This does not mean that he is less concerned with the common basis of the phenomena. On the contrary, he too treats them jointly (as this fits his scheme, Plato's precedent need not have influenced him); yet for him the underlying identity or similarity is primarily one of process.[96] He describes what happens to the exhalation when it reaches higher cosmic strata and in what manner the *antiperistasis* comes to pass. In other words, it is the how and why that matter. Why does the exhalation sometimes not rise to great height? Why does it sometimes, when turning back to the earth, freeze and sometimes not? Why, if snow is due to the same developments as hoarfrost, and rain to the same as dew, are there yet obvious differences between them? [97] That hail is identical with ice, and hoarfrost with snow, Aristotle states as explicitly as Plato; yet his interest in identity (and in difference within identity) merely strengthens his desire to account for the *genesis* of phenomena so closely related.[98] Plato's clear-cut but oversimplified distinctions between "on the earth" and "above the earth" and between "half frozen" and "frozen" bypass some difficult problems. After all, rain too comes from "above the earth," yet is only cool, not half or entirely frozen.[99] Meteorology has in all these instances to discover causes or connections of causes. It must even be able to account for the different sizes and shapes of hailstones.[100] All these tasks bring Aristotle into closer contact with the explanations put forward by the

---

popular usage; one might even suspect that he wishes to justify the variety of names. Still, the use of such different and entirely unrelated words for kindred objects would hardly suggest that these words are *physei*.

[95] *Meteor.* I,9.347a8ff.; see esp. 13, 16. The beginning of a new chapter at 347a12 in our editions is decidedly awkward, as it makes a break in a coherent explanation of ὀνόματα as well as phenomena. Cf. *Gnomon*, 29 (1957), 132.

[96] 346b24-32 (cf. 347a8-11) introduces us to the basic idea which governs the explanation of all precipitations.

[97] See 347a13ff., 20ff., b13ff.

[98] For identity and yet difference see esp. 347b12-24. When beginning to investigate more closely the *genesis* of hail, Aristotle states that "hail is ice" (347b36); next he proceeds to consider the where, when, and how of its freezing. Incidentally, although Aristotle does not discuss ice per se—presumably because its origin has nothing to do with *atmis*—he would hardly wish to deny that water also freezes on the earth. As recent translators have read such a denial into 347a12f., it may be well to bear in mind that Aristotle in ch. I,10 deals with τὸ ἀναγόμενον ὕδωρ (347a15) and what happens to it in the region below the clouds.

[99] For rain see 347b18ff.   [100] I,12.348a31ff., b24f.

Presocratics. Even when his own theory differs from theirs materially,[101] it is nearer to theirs in type and purpose than either is to Plato's account. The specific concerns of the meteorologist must not be sacrificed to those of a mathematically minded physicist. If we knew how far the Presocratics had gone in bringing all precipitations together, we should be able to assess Plato's and Aristotle's contributions more adequately. However, it is evident that by putting all emphasis on substance Plato left the beaten path and that Aristotle, although primarily concerned with the analysis of processes, preserves what was valid in Plato's approach. Incidentally Aristotle would probably have been embarrassed if he had had to explain freezing and melting by the absence or presence of fire. His open-minded attitude to "the hot" and "the cold" cleared the way and made his task much easier.

It has been mentioned [102] that, in the case of halo and rainbow, exhalation creates only the prior conditions of the phenomenon but not the phenomenon as such. The presence of color or of a color pattern is due to causes of an entirely different nature which fall outside the province of meteorology. When our sight arrives at a region where moisture is gathered, it is reflected to the sun.[103] Rather at variance with the doctrine of vision which he adopts in the *De anima* Aristotle here thinks of sight as a kind of visual ray and as operating from eye to object. The moist region may be pictured as a series of small mirrors placed continuous with one another.[104] When these mirrors are in the right position to the sun, they reflect the sight to it. Accepting this as the principle of his explanation, Aristotle endeavors to account for the color and the shape of both phenomena. Color is treated in his *De sensu;* and the doctrines there propounded include the color scale and the statement that bright color in a dark medium becomes

---

[101] See esp. the polemic against Anaxagoras, I,12.348a15ff., b12ff.

[102] See above, p. 401.

[103] III,2.372a18ff.; 3.372b16ff.; 4.373b14ff. In later Greek thought it was customary to distinguish between phenomena καθ' ὑπόστασιν and κατ' ἔμφασιν (e.g., *De mundo* 4.395a28; cf. Gilbert, *op.cit.*, 587ff.). Note in this connection *Meteor.* I,8.345b24f.

[104] III,2.372a33ff.; 4.373b25ff. It is indeed the case that Presocratic thinkers used *anaklasis* as a principle of explanation (see, e.g., Empedocles' theory of the sun, *Vorsokr.*, 31A56 or, better, B44, and Anaxagoras' of the Milky Way and rainbow, *ibid.*, 59A42.10; A86). But their conception of it must have seemed primitive to Aristotle because they thought of it as taking place between, say, the sun and clouds, ignoring the factor of our vision, i.e., the visual ray which goes from eye to object. Thus their theory lacked a geometrical basis. Cf. Note 111.

red.[105] Both items are useful to Aristotle in the present context; yet besides references clearly pointing to that work [106] there is another to a treatise—or in any case to investigations—about optics. It is optics which teaches that our sight is reflected in specific media and that in some mirrors not the shape but only the colors of the mirrored object are to be seen.[107] In Book II of the *Meteorologica* Aristotle, while reporting Cleidemus' explanation of lightning and rejecting the comparison with the flashing of water at night time, makes more allowance than is his wont for the state of knowledge at the time when the doctrine was propounded. "These men," he says, "were not yet acquainted with the doctrines of reflection." [108] In a passage of the *De sensu* a mistake of Democritus is traced to the same cause.[109] Neither passage suggests that Aristotle is claiming credit for advances made by himself. Although definite evidence is lacking, one may not go amiss in surmising that some of the mathematicians associated with the Academy included optics and the theory of mirrors in their research. The discussion of mirror images in the *Timaeus*, while not particularly close to Aristotle's view, gives further ground for thinking that these matters were studied.[110] Throughout Euclid's optical theorems our vision is conceived as a ray whose direction is from our eye to the object; we have seen that Aristotle, contrary to the theories of the *De anima*,[111] takes the same view when explaining the shape of halo and rainbow. This makes it probable that he conforms to prevailing doctrines of optics and reflection. Yet if there were such doctrines, one may begin

---

[105] See esp. *De sensu* 3.440a10; 4.442a12ff. It remains, however, difficult to find complete correspondence between Aristotle's references to the theory of sensations (2.372b10; 4.374b15f.) and the actual content of the *De sensu*.

[106] See Note 105.

[107] III,2.372a30–34 (the reference may, as a matter of fact, cover more than these five lines).

[108] II,9.370a12ff., 16ff.   [109] 2.437b5–10.

[110] *Tim.* 46aff. (cf. Cornford, *Cosmology*, 154ff.).

[111] The divergence from *De anima* (II,5, 7) is noted by Alexander (*ad* 372a29). In an earlier chapter of our work (I,6.342b36ff.) Aristotle credits Hippocrates of Chius (and his pupil Aeschylus) with a doctrine regarding the tail of the comet which assumes *anaklasis* of our vision from the moisture around the comet to the sun. Slightly later a similar explanation of the Milky Way is mentioned (I,8.345b9ff.). It too may go back to Hippocrates (*Vorsokr.*, 42A6), and he would, as far as our knowledge goes, be the first to assume a reflection of the visual ray, i.e., to hold essentially the same view of reflection as Aristotle. The doxographic tradition associates *anaklasis* with the "Pythagoreans and mathematicians" (Aetius 3.1.2; 4.14.3), and Alexander (*loc.cit.*, 141.4 Hayduck) says in effect that Aristotle in the sections under discussion agrees with the mathematical point of view.

to wonder about the painstaking geometrical demonstrations of these chapters. Are the proofs for the circular shape of the halo and for the semicircular or less than semicircular of the rainbow [112] the fruits of Aristotle's own solitary and independent study? It would not be easy to find another instance of such persistent and careful resort to mathematical methods in his work. To be sure, we ought not to underrate Aristotle's mathematical competence. Yet if optics and reflection were investigated at the time, if Aristotle had studied geometry in the Academy—hardly a bold assumption—and if, as T. L. Heath holds, Aristotle's procedure agrees with a theorem attested for Apollonius of Perge [113] and shows knowledge of this theorem, the question is perhaps no longer whether Aristotle worked out these proofs but rather how much or how little final polish he gave them.

ETERNITY AND CYCLICAL REGULARITY

The Presocratic theory of exhalations carried with it a legacy which Aristotle would not welcome. For although the large powers which exhalation originally enjoyed may have gradually worn off, the dangerous results which it had once produced were not forgotten. It could be more than an explanation of specific and recurrent phenomena. As conceived by Anaximander, the evaporation of moisture causes a progressive drying up of the earth's surface. This changes the balance of the principal powers in the Cosmos and thereby the condition of the Cosmos as a whole. Nothing else—at least nothing that figures in our reports—has so decisive an influence on the physical history and the ultimate fate of this world, and it is possible that the same or a similar fate was mapped out for the other worlds of Anaximander's system. For all we know, evaporation is the process which has power over life and death, both for the Cosmos itself and for the organic beings within it.[114] When Aristotle adopted exhalation as the hypothesis of his *Meteorologica*, he was fully aware of its large and fearful capacities. He had to choose between an exhalation which produces

[112] III,3.372a34ff.; 5.

[113] *Mathematics in Aristotle* (Oxford, 1949), 181ff. Cf. Apollon. 2,180.13ff. Heiberg (a report of Eutocius in his Commentary on the *Conics*). I am not equipped to form a judgment of my own on this question.

[114] Obviously the more highly developed species, such as man—even if the initial stages of their development parallel that of fish (12A30)—need dry land for their existence; on the other hand, when the entire sea dries up, fish will no longer be able to exist.

permanent and progressive changes in the cosmic order and one which leaves its structure and the mutual relations of its parts intact. But it is in the highest degree unlikely that he seriously pondered these alternatives. The eternity of the Cosmos was no longer an open question, and the fundamental relationships which guaranteed its order and character could not be exposed to any but temporary disturbances.

One "specific" problem which brings these alternatives into focus is the nature of the sea.[115] Does the sea have a history? Or has it always covered and will it always cover the same proportion of the earth's surface? The large issues here involved give this problem a peculiar status. More depends on its right solution than on that of numerous other "meteorological" questions theoretically on a par with it.

Aristotle can allow himself to put the matter simply. While "all" his predecessors have assumed that the sea has its *genesis* as much as the Cosmos as a whole, now on the contrary "it is clear that if the whole is eternal the same view must be taken of the sea." [116] There is no need for him here to summarize his arguments for the eternal duration of the Cosmos. The idea that the changes in the distribution of land and sea should have a bearing on cosmic *genesis* and history is branded as "ridiculous" and as due to "limited vision," "for the mass and size of the earth are of course as nothing compared to that of the whole Cosmos." [117] These issues are closed and should not be reopened. Changes there are in the Cosmos (or, more specifically, in its central part); but change is one thing, coming into being and perishing are another. Moreover, even the changes cannot be haphazard or devoid of rhythm. They must be governed by some law of balance and regularity so as not to present a jarring note in the order (*taxis*) which characterizes the world as a whole.

Although dogmatic on fundamentals, Aristotle has no intention of taking the specific problem lightly. On the contrary, he faces it not once but repeatedly, from a clear realization that it has many ramifications and that its treatment can hardly be confined to the discussion of the sea as such. All boils down to the alternative: is the sea—or, rather,

[115] The actual inquiry "about the sea and its nature" begins in II,1, yet, as will be seen, the discussions of previous chapters have a bearing on it.

[116] II,3.356b6ff.; cf. also I,14.352b17ff.

[117] I,14.352a17ff., 25ff. The radical opposition between Aristotle's approach to these questions and the Presocratic is well brought out by Pierre Duhem, *Le système du monde*, 1 (Paris, 1913), 167f.

the amount of water on the earth—constant, or does it diminish (that it increases is a possibility which Aristotle does not deem necessary to discuss [118]). Inasmuch as Aristotle begins his meteorological inquiry with the phenomena bordering on the *aethereal* region and then works his way downward, it takes some time before he arrives at the level of the sea. Yet long before this the great question has thrown its shadows across his path. When coming to the cosmic stratum "on high" where the precipitations are held to originate, Aristotle at once makes it a point to trace them to their real source. What comes down to the earth in the form of rain, snow, hail has also risen from the earth by way of the moist exhalation. The moisture returns; things happen in a "cycle." And this cycle of meteorological events "imitates" the other and more perfect cycle which causes all coming into existence and passing away, to wit, the annual movements of the sun. In fact, the larger cycle creates the smaller. For the sun when close to the earth draws up the moisture and when withdrawing gives it off again.[119] The importance of these statements lies in the implication that moist evaporation does not in the long run diminish the amount of water on the earth. Although Aristotle could not strictly "prove" that the amounts of moisture drawn up and returned are equal, he assumes it, and this assumption stands him in good stead when the sequence of subjects leads him to deal with the sea itself. At that point he has to meet the doctrines of men like Anaximander, who believe that the evaporation causes a gradual drying up of the entire body of water.[120] Having settled beforehand that the evaporated material does not remain on high, Aristotle finds it easy to dispose of these views.

The rivers are another topic which Aristotle takes up prior to the sea and handles in a manner calculated to advance the solution of the major problem.[121] Two questions call for close examination. One con-

---

[118] See, however, Xenophanes in *Vorsokr.*, 21A33.6. After Aristotle, even thinkers who hold that our Cosmos will disintegrate admit *mare non reddere maius naturam* (and obviously not *minus* either) and inquire about the reasons why the amount of its water remains constant. In Lucretius (6.608–638) evaporation by action of the sun is only one of several reasons and the absorption of water by the clouds (with subsequent rain) another and unrelated one. Cf. the comments of C. Bailey and L. Robin in their editions (Oxford, 1947, and Paris, 1928, respectively). Reference to later doctrines will also be found in H. J. Lulofs' "Aristoteles over de Zee" (*Publications of the Geolog. Inst. Univ. of Utrecht* [1947], 39ff.). This very careful study includes an analysis of *Meteor.* I,13–II,3 which should be compared throughout.

[119] I,9.346b24ff., esp. 36ff.   [120] See esp. II,2.355a26ff., but also 354b24ff.
[121] I,13, 14.

cerns the subterranean gathering of the waters before they issue forth
in the form of rivers. The other relates to changes of the river beds
and the temporary nature of rivers in general. Disregarding the first
question, we immediately turn to the second.

Contrary to his usual practice, Aristotle this time does not use "the
opinions of the precursors" as his point of departure but at once comes
forward with the thesis that "not the same parts of the earth are always
moist and dry." [122] To support it he develops his reasons why land and
sea must alternate in some places. These reasons will presently be analyzed. Anticipating some of our results, we may here say that Aristotle
brings two opinions together and uses each of them to balance the
other. There is the long-established fact that rivers silt up their estu-
aries; this has led to the conclusion that the land masses are on the
increase. Yet there is also the Academic theory of periodic deluges.[123]
These recurrent catastrophes undo the patient work of the rivers and
for a time tip the balance between land and sea in the opposite direction. Thus the far-reaching conclusions drawn from the activity of the
rivers are seen to be hasty. The unfortunate earlier physicists went
astray because they knew nothing about the floods that redress the
situation. When Aristotle finally comes face to face with their arguments, he can feel satisfied that their force and threat are gone.[124] Once
more the *genesis* of the Cosmos as a whole and of its parts is not at all
in the picture. All that can be granted, and in fact readily, since it is
Aristotle's own antecedent conviction, is change; yet the change does
not work all the time in one direction. Moreover, it is again regular and
periodic change.[125] The only difference is that in this instance the
periods are considerably larger than in the case of the other "cycle."

Thus it works out that when Aristotle finally comes to discuss the
sea [126] the principal question has already been settled. It is evident by
now that the sea has not come into being and is not on the way to its
final disappearance. If it has a history, this history can no longer invite
bold evolutionary speculations. To be exact, Aristotle has not actually
proved that the sea has no origin or beginning but has given us reasons

[122] I,14.351a19ff.

[123] *Ibid.*, 352a28ff. For a closer consideration of these thoughts see below, pp.
431–436.

[124] II,3.356b31ff. [125] 352a29ff., 356b31–357a2; cf. 355a27ff.

[126] II,1–3. Aristotle's line of reasoning does not at first reading emerge with
great clarity because the side issues (to which we shall presently turn) tend to
interrupt the discussion of the principal topic.

for holding that the amount of its water remains forever constant. This creates a presumption against the evolutionary approach. Some problems more or less closely related to the main issue are, however, left for this chapter. It must still be shown why the evaporation from the sea cannot "feed" the sun; for if this theory were correct, it might exclude a return of the moisture. It is curious to think that Aristotle himself may have played with this idea in his earlier years when he was preoccupied with astral theology and its demands counted for more with him than the meteorological cycle. Now, in any case, he refutes this notion by exposing the error of the underlying assumption that fire is "nourished" by the moist.[127]

Another side issue is the salty quality of the sea water. This had figured in the arguments of the evolutionary school, Anaxagoras and others being of the opinion that the sun in drying up the sea absorbs the sweet and light parts of its water.[128] Rejecting the genetic aspects of this hypothesis, Aristotle offers explanations more consonant with his own "static" world view. These explanations seem to have their basis partly in original observations, conclusions, and even experiments;[129] but Aristotle owes to earlier thinkers the idea that the saltiness is the result of an "admixture" and that in the last analysis it goes back to earthy material (even the notion that this material has passed through a process of combustion is, as he admits, not entirely new[130]). Besides

[127] II,2.354b34–355a32. In spite of Lee's notes, *ad loc.* and on 353b7, and in spite of the reference to Heraclitus (355a13f.), I am not sure that throughout this section he is the only target of Aristotle's criticism. "Heraclitus's followers" (Lee) are not among the physicists whom Aristotle takes into account. For the possibility that Aristotle himself endorsed such views in the dialogue *On Philosophy* see above, Note 58.

[128] See Anaxagoras in *Vorsokr.*, 59A90, and also Diogenes, *ibid.*, 64A17 (for more see Aetius 3.16 in *Doxogr. Gr.* 381f.; cf. again Lulofs' "Aristoteles over de Zee," 28). Aristotle has indicated that doctrines suggesting a *genesis* of the sea are linked to explanations of its salty quality (see II,1.353b12ff. and 2.354b1ff.); the actual discussion of this problem begins, however, only in 3.357a5ff. Like F. C. E. Thurot (*Rev. archéol.*, 21 [1870], 252f.) and Lee (note on p. 147 of his translation) I should regard a11–15 as answering the first alternative (εἰ γάρ . . . a7) and a15ff. as answering the second (εἶτ' . . . a9), though it must be admitted that it is difficult to find one's way through the various conditional clauses. εἰ δὲ . . . (a13) which asks for a "cause" can hardly take up the second alternative because this stated a cause and, moreover, the same one which Aristotle begins to discuss in a15.

[129] II,3.358a3–359b22; for experiments see esp. 358b16ff. (in 18 I should accept the reading πεπειραμένοι λέγομεν in preference to πεπ. λέγωμεν), b35ff.

[130] For admixture see 358a4ff.; cf. the views of Xenophanes (*Vorsokr.*, 21A3, 4), Anaxagoras (*ibid.*, 59A90), and Metrodorus (*ibid.*, 70A9) and see Aristotle's own

such theories of the evolutionary school there is the archaic belief of the "theologians," i.e., of Hesiod,[131] that the sea has sources or "springs" (πηγαί). This belief does not necessarily imply a *genesis* of the sea in the evolutionary sense of the word, but it conflicts with Aristotle's own view that the water which has come down in the precipitations collects gradually and then issues forth in the form of rivers.[132] For this reason Aristotle feels that he has to oppose it strenuously.

To sum up, there is balance between exhalation and precipitation, as well as balance between the developments which increase the amount of land and those which create a preponderance of water. In both instances there is a time pattern, and there are regularity and periodicity which are manifestations of the cosmic order (*taxis*). Aristotle himself speaks of a "cycle." [133] To be sure, the two manifestations of "order" which the *Meteorologica* proclaims are not in all respects alike. In one of them the cumulative result of a long period of slow labor is undone by an elemental catastrophe of presumably short duration. In the other two seasons of the year operate against one another, each canceling the other's work.[134] Yet both times Aristotle underlines the element of "order," and there can be no doubt that he attaches great importance to it. Having found order in the world system as a whole and again a majestic display of order in the heavenly regions, he would be anxious to discover as much of it in the central region of his Cosmos as the facts and conditions here prevailing allowed—and the doctrine of periodic deluges, based as it is on mythical traditions, actually goes beyond the

---

summary of such views in 357a8ff.; for his reference to, and criticism of, the combustion theory see 358a14ff.

[131] Webster and Lee (in their notes to 353b1) rightly refer their readers to Hesiod's *Theogony*. However, *Theog.* 282 and 785ff. cannot be the lines which Aristotle has in mind; for he would hardly confuse the Ὠκεανός (whose sources are here mentioned) with θάλαττη. J. L. Ideler's note (*Arist. Meteor. Libri IV* [Leipzig, 1834–1836], 1.496) is more accurate, though not more helpful. The pertinent passages are 736ff. or 807ff. and, for the "roots" of land and sea, 727ff. Moreover, as Aristotle goes on to say that these "theologians" thought of the earth as the most important part of the Universe, supposing that the whole rest of this had formed "around it and for its sake," he is clearly again alluding to the *Theogony* and specifically to vv. 126ff., where an idea of the kind is expressed. Thus it is futile to look for "theologians" other than Hesiod as the target of the polemic. Cherniss, *Presocr.*, 131 n.588, identifies the reference to Hesiod in 353b1f. correctly, but his attempt to include Thales in Aristotle's criticism involves a misunderstanding of b4f., where οὗτος ὁ τόπος is not the sea but the whole central part of the Cosmos.

[132] See II,1, esp. 353b17ff.; Aristotle has established his own view in I,13.
[133] I,9.346b24ff., esp. 36ff.   [134] See esp. I,14.352a29–32.

observable "facts." The preceding treatise teaches that the "cyclical" transformation of the elements into one another "imitates" the cyclical movements on high; it also speaks of the approach and retreat of the sun in the course of a year as the cause of coming to be and perishing, treating this "cycle" and "period" as the "measure" or unit of life and working out a connection between the "life cycles" and the heavenly cycles. Our work establishes a similar "imitation" of the cycles on high by bringing the moist exhalation and the precipitations together in a cyclical pattern.[135] And floods, too, return "in a cycle." For Aristotle to say that events on earth form a cycle means that they realize the closest approximation to the perfection of the heavenly regions of which earthly things are capable. In a historical perspective it is significant that one of the cycles is inherent in the pattern of the seasons and that in describing the other Aristotle compares the floods to a "Great Winter." [136] For ever since the first primitive stirrings of thought the regular sequence of day and night, summer and winter must have led the minds of men to the realization of cyclical order.[137]

[135] *De gen.* II,10.337a3, cf. 336a29–b15; *Meteor.* I,9.346b36ff.; II,3.357a2. The *Meteorologica* does not actually show a "cyclical" transformation of all the elements. When expressing his belief in such a cycle (*De gen.* II,10.337a4), Aristotle fails to include earth in the transformations (a curious omission, somehow reminiscent of the situation in the *Timaeus*); yet even for the remaining three elements the "cyclical" relation is not worked out in meteorological detail. Joachim (139f., 266) tries hard, but unsuccessfully, to find the complete cycle realized. Its necessity is established in *De gen.* II,11 through an analysis of the principles of causality, and in II,4 (331a20–b4) it is shown to be not only possible but "easiest."

[136] See *Meteor.* I,9.346b36ff. and I,14.352a30ff. Cf. Charles Mugler, *Deux thèmes de la cosmologie grècque* (Paris, 1953), 117. For a corresponding idea of a "Great Summer" see *ibid.*, 127. Of special importance in this connection is Censor. *De die nat.* 18.11. Here we find the Great Year definitely associated with Aristotle's name, but his authority for the Great Winter and Great Summer (= conflagration) remains open to doubt, since Censorinus, where he mentions these, may no longer report Aristotle's views. In view of this uncertainty Valentin Rose (frg. 25) and Ross (*Protrept.*, frg. 19) admit only the statement regarding the Great Year into their collections of Aristotle's fragments, whereas Walzer (frg. 25) accepts the entire passage of Censorinus, adding a reference to the Great Winter in the *Meteorologica*. Cf. also Ideler, *op.cit.*, 1.484.

[137] Cf. *De gen.* II,11.338b1ff. For the "cycle" of the seasons and its importance in primitive and early thought I content myself with referring to Sir James Frazer's "Introduction" to *Adonis* (*The Golden Bough*, vol. 5); Jane E. Harrison, *Themis* (Cambridge, 1912); F. M. Cornford, *From Religion to Philosophy* (London, 1912), 165ff., *Essays and Studies Presented to W. Ridgeway* (Cambridge, 1913), 153ff., 163, and *C.A.H.*, 4: 530ff. (see also his *Principium Sapientiae* [Cambridge, 1952], 225 and *passim*).

One may wonder whether Aristotle derived greater satisfaction from tracing many phenomena so resourcefully to the operation of the two exhalations or from distilling these elements of order in the welter of facts. Important as it must have seemed to work up this remaining field of physical events, it was the cyclical pattern which gave the enterprise its philosophical dignity and meaning. In one of his biological treatises Aristotle adumbrates a further causal connection between meteorological events and the heavenly *periodoi*. Motion and rest of the winds are caused by the periods of sun and moon, and the winds in turn are responsible for motion and rest of the waters. From these positions Aristotle even tries to find his way to the "life cycle" of organic beings.[138] Yet, although this pattern must have been attractive to his mind, Aristotle does little to substantiate it. When engaged on the *Meteorologica*, Aristotle may still have been unaware of this pattern— or he may have despaired of bringing the observations at his disposal into harmony with it. Undeveloped as it is, the idea is significant because the origin of the wind would parallel that of the precipitations and because some more events on earth would be controlled by the heavenly *periodoi*.

Neither of the two cycles came to Aristotle as a suddenly illuminating discovery while he was surveying and investigating the meteorological phenomena. In both instances Aristotle adapts to his scheme ideas with which he must have been familiar since the early days of his philosophical studies. One of them, the evaporation-precipitation cycle, was an idea of long and probably firm standing; the other had its roots in the environment of his twenties and thirties.

While Aristotle rejects the "evolutionary" version of exhalation, he accepts the cyclical without a word of gratitude for its authors.[139] As we know, the sequence water on earth, mist rising from it (clouds), rain is described by Hesiod.[140] In the case of some Presocratic thinkers it is difficult to ascertain what became of the moisture after it had been

[138] *De gen. anim.* IV,10.777b17–778a10.
[139] I,4.341b7f. hardly has the character of an acknowledgment. I,13.349b3ff. is an incidental admission that the "cycle" theory of water first drawn upward and later returning to earth was known to others; here, as often, Aristotle stresses the points in which he differs from his precursors. From II,2.355a29ff. it may be inferred that earlier physicists allowed for some of the evaporated water to come back to the earth, while the rest "remained" air. In this way the cyclical theory could be upheld alongside of the gradual drying up and final disappearance of the sea.
[140] Cf. for this and what follows pp. 407–411 above.

drawn up. Still, Anaximander appears to have taught that some vapor returns as rain, and for Xenophanes the evidence is authentic and conclusive; "the large sea is the begetter of clouds, winds, and rivers." [141] The moisture which the sun has taken from the sea is transformed into clouds, and clouds in turn produce wind and rain. Sooner or later the philosophers would know as much as the Boeotian peasant. In some respects they even know more; Xenophanes' sequence would not be the same as Hesiod's, but rather sea, exhalation, clouds, rain, rivers, sea. This is a better cycle which includes all phases of moisture [142] (Hesiod in his particular context had no reason for taking the sea into consideration, nor was it his intention to offer a complete statement of physical transformations).

However, not all the moisture that has risen comes back; a part of it has become wind, and that the wind returns is neither stated nor need it be surmised. But is Aristotle's own position more satisfactory? Even in his scheme the cycle holds good only for the moist exhalation. It does not seem to have worried him that the dry which produces wind is not brought back to the region of its origin and that he here leaves a gap in his doctrine of the never-varying condition of our world.[143]

Aristotle may, however, be more specific than Xenophanes about the quantity of the moisture involved. For he asserts, albeit without proof, that the entire amount of the moist exhalation returns in the form of rain and other precipitations.[144]

Xenophanes still holds that land will pass into sea and sea into land; [145] yet it is not recorded that for the latter change he counted on evaporation. However this may be, we may confidently assume that he, like Anaximander before him, knew something of the "cycle." The exhalation which alters the balance between sea and land, moist and dry was not the only kind that Aristotle found in the Presocratic tradition.

[141] *Vorsokr.*, 12A11.7; 21B30. Cf. 21A46 (here and in 21A1.19 the sun is mentioned as *aitia*). Are we to believe the doxographer (A46) who asserts that only the "sweet" part of the water drawn up forms clouds, etc.? If so, what becomes of the salty portion? Does it not return, and is the cycle in this regard, as in others, incomplete? According to Anaxagoras (A90) and Diogenes (A17) only the sweet part of the sea water is drawn up. Xenophanes in A46 reads differently, but as it is not supported by B30, I prefer to suspend judgment.

[142] Already in Anaximander the sea would be the principal source of the exhalation. In serious physical theory it is decidedly preferable to Hesiod's rivers.

[143] The Greeks speak of the setting wind as "falling" (πίπτων, first so used Hom. *Od.* 19.202), so that the idea of its "return" to the earth should not present great difficulties. But could it simply be regarded as "understood"?

[144] See for this point esp. II,2.355a26–33.

[145] *Vorsokr.*, 21A33.6. Cf. K. Deichgräber, *Rh. Mus.*, 87 (1938), 16f.

It is not likely that the later Presocratics should have ignored the cycle of evaporation and precipitation. There are indications that it figured in Anaxagoras' system,[146] and if our material does not attest it for others, the reason may be that it was taken for granted and could be incorporated without creating new problems. And as the cycle was neither the discovery nor the monopoly of the physicists, we need not be surprised to find it also in Herodotus and in the "Hippocratic" treatise *On Airs, Waters, and Places*, to say nothing of the playful allusions in Aristophanes' *Clouds*.[147]

The crucial question is whether anyone before Aristotle had taught a complete balance or exact correspondence between "the way up" and "the way down." Inevitably Heraclitus' name is the first that comes to mind, and although this dictum has recently been expelled from his cosmology, I still incline to link it to the idea which we are tracing.[148] For Heraclitus, fire turns into water, water into earth, and from earth the changes work their way back. As the next change on this way back is from earth to water, not to fire, we do not, strictly speaking, have here a "cycle" [149]—or have a cycle only between water and earth and between fire and water. For a comparison with Aristotle's meteorology this cycle may suffice, and the statement that when earth changes into sea it is "measured into the same ratio" (λόγος) which it had before changing into earth should take us a good deal farther.[150] It seems prob-

---

[146] Metrodorus of Chius (*Vorsokr.*, 70.A16) suggests the cycle inasmuch as the exhalation produces the clouds (and these, we may take it, rain).

[147] Herodotus states as his "personal opinion" that the sun does not let go the entire amount of water that it has drawn from the rivers (2.25.3). "Hipp." *De aer.* 8 emphasizes that the sun takes to itself the lightest and sweetest parts of the water; cf. Arist. II,2.354b29ff., 355a33ff., and Note 141. For references to the cycle and to the unchanging amount of water in the sea see also Aristoph. *Nub.* 1278ff., 1290–1294. The two passages are complementary; the reason why the sea does not increase although the rivers flow into it (vv. 1292ff.) is stated in vv. 1278ff. Some of its water is drawn up by the sun. This water comes back as rain (and, we may supply, the rain swells the rivers). This may be the "meteorological" (v. 1284) doctrine of Diogenes of Apollonia.

[148] *Vorsokr.*, 22B60. See Kirk, *op.cit.*, 105ff. The use of the crucial words ἄνω κάτω in Plato *Tim.* 58b8, where exchanges of place and mutual transformations of the elements are described, may be an argument in favor of a similar context or meaning in Heraclitus (cf. 22A1.9) to whom Plato here appears to allude; cf. Cornford, *Cosmology*, 246 n.1.

[149] *Vorsokr.*, 22B31. Cf. Kirk, *op.cit.*, 114.

[150] *Vorsokr.*, 22B31; see Vlastos' recent comments on this point, *A. J. Ph.*, 76 (1955), 359ff. Is *logos* in B31 the ratio between earth and the sea into which it changes or between the amount of water involved in this change and the entire sea?

able that λόγος in combination with the concept of "measuring" denotes not only the ratio but also the actual amounts. Heraclitus may not have known about periodic floods—any more than, *pace* Stoic and other interpreters, about periodic conflagrations; yet he clearly approximates or anticipates Aristotle's conviction that in the eternal Cosmos there can be no permanent or progressive encroachment of land on sea or of sea on land.[151] Does the same combination of *logos* and measuring hold also elsewhere in his world? We may wish to think so and may feel confident that the two exhalations played their part in keeping the exchanges of the upper regions balanced but must confess ourselves ignorant on important points of detail.[152] Evidently the bright exhalation changes into fire (I should think by way of the unhappily controversial *prester*),[153] and fire itself turns into water. The dark exhalation, on the other hand, produces rain, and to that extent we are sure of its return. If in addition the one causes day and summer, the other night and winter, we may again surmise that, having acted their parts, they come back to sea and land. Here are many details that must be left to conjecture.[154] But it is reassuring to think that the *logos* cannot be confined to changes between sea and land but must govern all cosmic processes, and we may argue that if Heraclitus' Cosmos is to continue unchanged and without a disturbance in the relationship of its parts [155] balance and equality must prevail between all "opposite" changes. But how much of this Heraclitus actually said and how much he merely hinted, how he developed his concept of balance and to what extent he implemented it by meteorological detail are questions,[156] and questions they must remain. We cannot be positive that the correspondence between exhalations and the processes of "the way down" was more fully worked out

---

[151] Cf. Kirk, *op.cit.*, 355: "Heraclitus' doctrine of μέτρα, in particular in frg. 31, shows that Heraclitus anticipated, and was perhaps responsible for, Aristotle's theory of cosmological stability." Kirk rightly believes (333) that, despite the "schematic form" of frg. 31 and its rigid avoidance of substantiating details, concrete and specific observations should be assumed to underlie the statement.

[152] See above, p. 409.

[153] *Vorsokr.*, 22B31, A1.9; for the *prester* (B31) cf. O. Gigon, *Untersuchgg. zu Heraklit* (diss., Basel, 1935), 68.

[154] See above, pp. 409–410. For the winds we only have the brief statement regarding their origin in Diog. Laert. (*Vorsokr.*, 22A1.10).

[155] B30f. is probably the strongest and decisive evidence; next comes B90 (yet see also A1.8f.); and it deserves to be stressed that *metra* which regulate the changes between sea and earth also govern the kindling and extinguishing of the cosmic fire.

[156] For possibilities see Kirk, *op. cit.*, 333ff.

in his book than it is in the *Meteorologica,* where the dry exhalation finds no "way down." Even if we had more pertinent fragments or testimonies for Heraclitus, we might still find it difficult to project his thoughts about atmospheric phenomena upon the conceptual plane on which Aristotle is moving.

Yet if it is possible that Aristotle here falls short of previous achievements, he makes up for it by his second instance of cosmic balance. Here he does not fall behind Heraclitus' pioneering intuition and by all odds offers more in the way of concrete implementation.

The floods and the scheme of which they form a part had no place in the Presocratic tradition. In fact, one may ask whether the scheme was meant to counteract and replace the Presocratic theories about progressive changes and a final destruction of the Cosmos. Whenever Plato speaks of these floods, their ravages are either gradually undone or counterbalanced by catastrophic events of an opposite type and effect. Aristotle had probably come under the spell of this doctrine when it had been first promulgated; he certainly believed in the idea of cyclical return long before he outlined, in his *Meteorologica,* its cosmological presuppositions. Our treatise shows clearly the connection between the catastrophes and the belief in an eternal Cosmos; yet inasmuch as it uses the doctrine to account for changes within the Cosmos, it is more "scientific" than the Platonic dialogues which embody the same theory.

Already in Plato emphasis is put on the regularity with which the catastrophes occur. There is some indication that this element of order and regularity is related to the heavenly movements. However, Plato refrains from developing this idea; all he actually says is that these catastrophes reflect a displacement or "derangement of the bodies in heaven which circle around the earth." [157] The notion that heavenly movements could affect things on earth would strike the men in the Academy as not nearly so absurd as the reverse doctrine which Aristotle scornfully rejects (to wit, that changes between land and sea should have a bearing on the history of the entire Cosmos).[158] But there is no cogent reason why, e.g., the completion of the Great Year should cause a "derangement," and if Plato himself was content with a rather vague hint, others too may have hesitated to be specific about the connection of events in heaven and on the earth.

The desire to find some pattern and rhythm in the history of the earth goes far to account for the origin and the vogue of the new theory.

[157] *Tim.* 22d1; cf. 23a7.   [158] *Meteor.* I,14.352a26ff. (cf. a17ff.).

Still, it was not the only motive here at work. A contrast was felt between the brevity of human history and the long or eternal life of the Cosmos.[159] In the measure in which the belief that the Cosmos and all its parts were indestructible gained ground it became necessary to distrust the time-honored views about radical and progressive changes in the distribution between land and sea. The hypothesis of periodic floods could neutralize the impressive evidence that had been adduced for a continuing increase of dry land,[160] and it could at the same time help to explain the painful limitations of man's memory with regard to his past.

In its original form, however, the Academic doctrine knew more than one kind of catastrophe. Not only floods but great conflagrations too were held to occur at regular intervals. The destruction wrought by fire counterbalanced the effects of the deluge. While the one belief found support in the myth about Deucalion, the other assumed a kernel of truth in the story of Phaethon's chariot ride.[161] Besides floods and conflagrations, the *Timaeus*, which gives us the fullest evidence, mentions "countless other causes" as responsible for the periodic disappearance of human civilization after a time of hopeful progress. Among these other causes earthquakes seem to have been particularly favored.[162] In fact, the earthquake motif may link the theory of catastrophes to an idea entertained in a slightly earlier dialogue; for the radical disturbance which, in the myth of the *Statesman*, plays havoc with the laws of the Cosmos takes the form of an earthquake.[163]

In the end, however, floods may have provided the most convincing explanation for the short span of recorded human history. The three late dialogues of Plato which embody the doctrine of catastrophes use it primarily for this purpose.[164] Here the advantages of the flood theory

[159] The short span embraced by human records is mentioned in *Tim.* 22bff., where this fact is brought into direct causal connection with the floods; see also *ibid.*, 23af. *Legg.* III,677aff. develops in a more general fashion the idea that all continuity of civilization is broken through such floods.

[160] It must be pointed out, however, that as far as our knowledge goes an integration of the older (Presocratic) and newer (Academic) theory is for the first time worked out in the *Meteorologica*.

[161] *Tim.* 22a–e.

[162] *Tim.* 22c3; yet see the entire section c1–23b3. Cf. also *Tim.* 25c7 and *Crit.* 108e8, 112aff., in all of which passages earthquakes too are mentioned. *Legg.* III,677a4ff. gives a somewhat different impression; here Plato speaks of "floods, epidemics, and many other causes."

[163] *Polit.* 272dff. (note the *seismos* motif in 273a3).

[164] This is the theory which provoked Epicurus' retort (preserved in Lucr. 5.338ff.): if you believe that everything has existed here before but that the

come to light when Plato himself points out that civilization makes greater strides in the river valleys than in the lonely mountains. Therefore, when inundations occur and the settlers in the valleys suffer, much greater damage is done than when the illiterate mountain dwellers become the victims of a conflagration.[165]

In the *Meteorologica* Aristotle has a different axe to grind. It is a measure of the difference that not floods account for the lack of records and historical recollections but causes of another kind must explain why the floods themselves, and with them the changes of the earth, are no longer remembered.[166] Aristotle would not be at a loss for such causes. He mentions wars, epidemics, famine, and large-scale migrations. In addition, though Egypt, very appropriately, figures in Aristotle's as well as in Plato's argument, Aristotle's references to this country and its history serve a new purpose. In the *Timaeus* it is said that Egypt has been spared both widespread conflagrations and the deluges produced by protracted rainstorms (the inundations of the Nile are regarded as normal); therefore it must have the most continuous history and records extending far beyond those possessed by any other civilization.[167] In the *Meteorologica* Egypt is, on the contrary, the prime example of a country of which a large part is "young" and in which the gradual retreat of the sea and the corresponding increase of dry land can still easily be realized. "The whole land of the Egyptians, whom we take to be the most ancient of men, has evidently gradually come into existence and been produced by the river." [168] This approach takes due account of Herodotus' reports [169] about that country and in particular about the

---

continuity has been broken (and earlier civilizations destroyed) through conflagration, earthquakes, and large floods, it is no more than logical to assume that *si tristior incubuisset causa* (i.e., if such elementary forces act with greater vehemence) the whole Cosmos will be reduced to ruins. In this way Epicurus tries to restore the older view and pattern, availing himself of the Academic hypotheses which had been developed in opposition to them. E. Bignone's pioneering treatment of these matters (*L'Aristotele perduto e la formazione filos. di Epicuro* [Florence, 1935–1936], 2.335ff., 446ff., and esp. 475ff.) is well known. See also my study, *A. J. Ph.*, 72 (1951), 1ff.

[165] *Tim.* 22d6ff., 23a7ff.; *Legg.* III,677b1ff.   [166] *Meteor.* I,14.351b8ff.

[167] *Tim.* 22bff., esp. d5f.; *Meteor.* I,14.351b28ff.

[168] *Meteor.* I,14.352b20ff. (Oxford translation).

[169] Herod. 2.4.3ff. While Herodotus says that Thebes was of old called Egypt (2.15.3), Aristotle rather oddly reverses this statement by asserting that the old name of Egypt was Thebes (351b34f.). He refers in this connection to the fact that Homer mentions Thebes (352a1, correctly translated by Webster, whereas Lee mistakenly refers the words ἐκείνου τοῦ τόπου to Egypt). As Homer men-

origin of Lower Egypt and the so-called Delta.[170] (The commentator Olympiodorus even suggests that by calling Egypt "the work of the Nile" Aristotle wished to go Herodotus' "gift of the river" one better,[171] an observation whose lack of brilliance might be condoned if it had a chance of being true.) In short, Plato's interest in these geological changes is that of a humanist and cultural anthropologist, Aristotle's that of a scientist and naturalist.

The large floods are in our treatise no longer, as in Plato and perhaps in Aristotle's own *Protrepticus* and *On Philosophy*,[172] balanced by conflagrations or other alternative catastrophes. As the theory now stands, there is after every flood a long period of gradual drying up, in the course of which large areas of water turn again into land. The agents of this process are the rivers. Aristotle dwells on their activity, pointing

---

tions Αἴγυπτος repeatedly, Herodotus' inference would seem to be the sounder of the two. He too may have Homer in mind when speaking of τὸ πάλαι; cf. *Il.* 9.381 and *Od.* 4.126f. At least it is difficult to think of any other justification for his statement, although from 11.4 one might gather that he reckons with somewhat longer periods for the formation of land than Aristotle, who concludes that at Homer's time Memphis either did not exist or was insignificant. In ch. 10 Herodotus gives other examples of regions that are the result of alluvial deposit. The land-producing activity of the Achelous had figured in the myth of Alcmaeon (mentioned by Thucydides in 2.102.3f. with pertinent remarks about πρόσχωσις in past and future). Again Aristotle goes farther than Herodotus when asserting—in the same chapter, though in a slightly changed context—that the Achelous has often changed its course (352b1). For the debt of the *Meteorologica* to Herodotus see Ideler, *op.cit.*, 1.479ff.

[170] Herodotus, to be sure, is not the first to propagate the geological hypothesis about the origin of Lower Egypt. His large debt to Hecataeus seems to be generally recognized; see *F.G.H.* 1.301 with Jacoby's comments and W. A. Heidel, *Hecataeus and the Egyptian Priests in Herodotus, Book II* (Mem. Am. Acad. 18.2), 61ff. There is, however, no evidence for Aristotle's familiarity with Hecataeus either here or elsewhere. In Aristotle's account one misses a reference to the shells found on mountains far inland and similar items which Herodotus adduces (2.12.1) in support of his view. Olympiodorus, in his commentary on the *Meteorologica* (116.14 Stüve), adds proofs of this kind to those mentioned by Aristotle. As is well known, the pioneer in the use of such evidence is Xenophanes, who besides shells also mentioned his discovery of fossils in the quarries of Syracuse, in Malta, and on the island of Paros (?), all with a view to proving that the sea had once covered much or all of the earth's surface. Yet fossils too are ignored by Aristotle.

[171] Olympiodorus 112.30.

[172] The only relevant testimony for the latter (Synes. *Enc. calv.* I,234 Krabinger = frg. 13 Rose, 8 Walzer) speaks merely of μέγισται φθοραί; and it would surely be rash to base far-reaching conclusions on the word φθοραί. For the *Protrepticus* see above, Note 136.

to Lower Egypt and other regions as evidence, even before he sees fit
to introduce the floods.[173] The rivers and the precipitations which produce them are legitimate topics of a meteorological study. Having dealt
with them, Aristotle quite properly puts forward his conviction that
not the same places of the earth have always been moist or dry. Obviously conflagrations would not have been germane to this sequence of
subjects.

We need not doubt that the silting activity of the rivers was a matter
of common knowledge. Even Herodotus cannot have been the first [174]
to explain the Egyptian Delta along such lines, and similar observations
had been made elsewhere. We need not suppose that some of the evidence adduced in our chapter goes back to Aristotle's personal observation or that he himself had to draw the conclusions. As we have seen, he
denies the "evolutionists" the right to treat the evidence as proofs for a
limited lifetime of our world. Availing himself of the data which they
had stressed but misinterpreted,[175] he treats the silting as the second act
in the drama of earth's history for which the Academic doctrine of
great floods supplies the first. Both doctrines have been removed from

---

[173] The discussion of the rivers begins in I,13. I,14 deals from the beginning
with their contributions to changes in the relations of land and sea. The first
reference to the great floods occurs rather late in the chapter, at 352a28ff. Having
brought out the importance of these periodic occurrences, Aristotle once more
discusses Egypt as an example of a "recent" country (352b20ff.). The proofs
which he brings this time are not identical with those of the first discussion
(351b18ff.); they make use of information not to be found in Herodotus (2.4–
16, 158), and the conclusion drawn in 352b31, although brilliant, is more sweeping
than that of Herodotus (2.10–12). The discussion of Egypt and its geological
evidence in two different places may not be in harmony with the best rules of
rational composition, but we probably have to acquiesce in it and should not use
it to distinguish several strata. As Aristotle cannot offer any positive proof for
the floods, he may feel that he should once more stress the evidence for the
gradual and recent growth of some land areas. This creates a presumption in
favor of the deluge theory.

[174] See Note 170.

[175] Herodotus did not relate the silting activities of the Nile to the κόσμου γένεσις
(cf. *Meteor.* I,14.352a26), and as Aristotle tells us that this was done, we are
driven to conclude that some Presocratic physicists used the observations about
the Nile and others of a similar type to argue for a constant increase of land
since the origin of the Cosmos. It may well be the case that some of the later
Presocratics preferred this hypothesis to the doctrine of progressive evaporation,
but as the physical result in both cases is the same, we need not regard the two
theories as mutually exclusive. The "cosmogonical" interpretation of the fluvial
operations is by Lee (note on 352a20) tentatively assigned to Democritus, which
may be correct.

their original setting and resemble fragments that have been fitted together as parts of a new whole. The persistent efforts of the rivers are no longer permitted to reach their logical end, and the floods are not counteracted by a catastrophic event with opposite effects. Yet there is no impression of patchwork; the synthesis as such is perfect. As now combined, the two theories substantiate Aristotle's conception of cosmic regularity and rhythm. *Taxis* and symmetrical periods which once governed the history of successive Cosmoi now determine the large internal changes that alternate in this one and only Cosmos.

A reader of the *Meteorologica* may form the impression that the rivers by themselves would suffice to maintain the balance between land and sea. Whenever they oust the sea from a portion of its former possession, the sea recoups itself by breaking in on some part of the land, and as soon as the rivers begin to dry up, the sea can return to its former property, presumably giving up what in the meantime it has taken over.[176] Moreover, Aristotle has a geological theory to support his conviction that the river beds have not always been in the same places. The parts of the earth's interior undergo at different times a change from youth to old age and also, it would appear, in the reverse direction.[177] Biological doctrines allowed a correlation of life and death, and thus probably a fortiori of youth and old age, with moist and dry.[178] As efficient cause for these changing age phases of the earth Aristotle again uses the sun and its course (even though he merely throws out this suggestion and leaves the matter at that).[179] Bearing all this in mind, one may wonder whether the subsequent introduction of the flood the-

---

[176] This is clearly the idea of I,14.351a19–b8, even though doubt remains as to the text and the precise meaning of the important last sentence. The explanations offered by Webster and Lee (in the notes to their translations) give the impression of proceeding on the best lines.

[177] I,14.351a27ff.

[178] *De gen. anim.* II,1.733a11: ζωτικὸν γὰρ τὸ ὑγρόν, πορρωτάτω δὲ τοῦ ἐμψύχου τὸ ξηρόν is probably the clearest and strongest affirmation of this conviction. The tendency to associate life and the causes or agents of life with "the moist" is very old (cf. R. B. Onians, *The Origins of European Thought* [Cambridge, 1951], 118f., 202f., and *passim*).

[179] I,14.351a32ff. One may understand that regions most exposed to the sun reach their γῆρας first and thus are in need of a new βιώσκεσθαι. Yet how should the sun now give them more ψύξις (351a31)? Should the flood already here be in Aristotle's mind? It would be odd to suppose that the sun and its περιφορά (a32) cause the deluges. The Great Year, which is completed when all planets have simultaneously performed their revolutions, may have been regarded as the occasion for such catastrophes (see Lee's note on p. 115 of his translation), but it is not natural to understand περιφορά as referring to the Great Year.

ory [180] is not gratuitous. It is somewhat out of tune with the mature stage of Aristotle's scientific thinking when, to use Jaeger's words, he had "emancipated himself from the presuppositions of the mythical interpretation of nature." [181] If we understand it as a tribute paid to his past, we may look upon its severance from the complementary theory of conflagrations as a kind of "naturalization." But did the naturalization produce fully satisfactory results? Or is Aristotle, through the earth-biological speculations at the beginning of this chapter, groping for another and more "scientific" basis—a basis which would have made it possible to dispense with the floods? We cannot do more than ask these questions. The "reviving" or rejuvenescing so essential for the biological theory may after all involve a tacit assumption of the floods.[182] If we are surprised that Aristotle, to work out his cycle, uses a "belief" rather than the results of scientific reasoning, we should remember that of the other cycle too one phase—the complete return of the moist exhalation—is far from "proved." "We see clearly that the water drawn up returns again" [183] is the best that Aristotle there can say. The antecedent belief in *taxis* must have been strong indeed.

"Earth dissolves as sea and is measured by the same *logos* which was there before earth came to be." [184] Once more Aristotle has, even if by a new road, arrived at one of Heraclitus' great discoveries. The relation between exhalation and precipitation is fundamentally the same as that between alluvial and diluvial processes. Here and there is restoration of the loss, preservation of the original balance between the major parts of the Cosmos. The moisture that has taken "the way up" soon finds "the way down," and the sea that has yielded to land—another "way down" for Heraclitus—receives its compensation "in the justice of time" when large areas of land become flooded. What a pity that for the dry exhalation and the winds Aristotle did not work out a similar scheme. Here some links are missing in the cyclical transformation of the elements, that irresistibly attractive idea which the *De generatione* proclaimed on the strength of metaphysical necessities and which the present work goes far to implement concretely and by specific meteorological doctrines. Still, for all his intense concern with the cosmic order, Aristotle could treat meteorological topics without relating them

---

[180] *Ibid.,* 352a28ff.   [181] Jaeger, *Aristotle,* 293.

[182] See Note 176 for the problems posed by 351a19–b8.   [183] II,2.355a26f.

[184] *Vorsokr.,* 22B31. I think that with or without the addition of the word γῆ the sentence has the meaning here assumed. See also Notes 150 and 151 above.

to this supreme issue. He establishes the rule of *taxis* where suitable doctrines are ready at hand or where he sees his way to synthesizing different traditions into a new proof.

None of his precursors had made profounder contributions to the subject of immanent order than Heraclitus. Aristotle's incorporation of Heraclitean discoveries into his own system has a certain historical logic. We do not know whether he did full measure of justice to these discoveries or whether Heraclitus' scheme of "reparations" was complete in the phases where Aristotle's appears to us incomplete. But we must not forge that the parts of the Cosmos with which Aristotle is concerned in this treatise could exhibit order only in a limited degree. They could not for him have the same decisive importance as for Heraclitus. Perfect order is to be found elsewhere—in regions where Heraclitus may have looked for it too but where only the recent progress of astronomical knowledge and Plato's philosophical adaptation of it had laid the ground for a systematic study and full appreciation of this order. This order can never be disturbed; there is no threat of even a temporary predominance on the part of one element over another. The cyclical movements in the medium of the first body do not signify an alteration between injustice and reparation, whereas the sublunary cycles could easily be thus understood if these ethical concepts of the Presocratics were still valid in Aristotle's physical system.[185] But physics is now restricted to its own concepts. Where formerly justice ruled and governed cosmic events by its necessity, necessity now owes its credentials to the belief in cosmic eternity and to the logical analysis of the causality pattern.[186] And the concept of order, although still capable of inspiring admiration and linking the terrestrial to the divine, is not allowed to display its political and ethical connotations. It could form a bridge to these realms of human values [187]—almost as good a bridge, perhaps, as the Heraclitean and the Stoic *logos*—but it is not treated in this spirit.

To say it once more, the flawless perfection of the heavenly spheres cannot be matched in the "place around the center." When Aristotle

---

[185] Cf. Jaeger, *Paideia*, 1.217ff., 236ff., 245ff., and *Theology*, 34ff., 115ff., and *passim;* Vlastos, *Cl. Ph.*, 42 (1947), 156ff.

[186] *De gen.* II,11; note how the ἀνάγκη of the γενέσθαι is established (in analogy to that of εἶναι), 337b10f.; from it follows the cyclical *genesis*, 338a2ff.

[187] For the importance of *taxis* in the political sphere see, e.g., *Pol.* III,6.1278b8ff.; IV,1.1289a15ff., 3.1309b33ff. For a comparison of *physis* and *polis* under this point of view see *De anim. motu* 10.703a29–b2. Cf., further, *Metaph.* Λ10.1075a11ff.

turned to the strata below the first body, his expectations of finding *taxis* were correspondingly modest. He would no longer pursue aims as high as when he set out to establish the laws which govern the Cosmos as a whole or to provide a philosophical basis for the new system of the astronomers. Still it remains true: τὰ ὄντα οὐ βούλεται πολιτεύεσθαι κακῶς.[188]

[188] *Metaph.* Λ 10.1076a3.

Part Six

CONCLUSION

22

Summaries and Perspectives

THE results of our chapters cannot easily be synthesized. Aristotle himself does not investigate each topic of his physical system with his mind focused on a final synthesis of all major conclusions. Between the different phases of his work there prevails an attitude of mutual, though by no means uncritical, respect. The findings of one inquiry are often accepted in another; but if they interfere with the legitimate interests of the latter subject, they are modified or disregarded. Not rarely problems examined in one treatise do not arise again elsewhere; in such cases the answers remain valid but—on the whole—ineffective. The definition of place as given in *Physics* IV does not prove useful anywhere else. Of the conclusions regarding the first and the last instant of change, none reappears in other contexts. The new concepts of organic *genesis* and organic mixture, although of importance for the *Metaphysics* and for the biological treatises, are irrelevant for the inquiries of the books *On the Heaven* and of the *Meteorologica*. There are centrifugal as well as centripetal tendencies in Aristotle's physical studies. Not every decision or discovery contributes to the over-all pattern of cosmic *taxis*.

In view of this situation it would be pointless to recapitulate here the principal results of our chapters one by one. A synthesis must concentrate on the results which converge, must try to integrate them and to show what each contributes to a larger "whole." It may rescue some broader aspects and the main lines of historical development from obliteration under a mass of detail and reformulate questions about Aristotle's relation to his predecessors on the level of our final positions, ignoring the steps and way stations by which they were reached.

The legacies of previous thinkers and Aristotle's new contributions have been fused in a fashion which would thoroughly satisfy his own requirements for a true mixture. The individual ingredients are still "potentially" present but cannot "actually" be separated from one another. There should be no doubt that the Platonic component prevails; for not only does Aristotle share some basic convictions with Plato (e.g., with regard to the nature of the Cosmos) but also he owes to him many of his methodical devices and logical distinctions, and there is every probability that he developed his capacity for fashioning new conceptual instruments while he was a member of the Academy and partook in its debates.

The closeness of Aristotle's contact with the Presocratic tradition varies from treatise to treatise. The *Physics* is on the whole remote from the concerns of the cosmologists. It keeps almost throughout on a high plane of generality, and even where it discusses processes, the fact that these processes would have to materialize in the Cosmos is of no particular importance. True, the definition of place is scrutinized for its applicability to the Cosmos, and that of time is in the end related to a cosmic unit of movement and measurement, but these instances and others which come to mind—including some in polemical sections— are hardly typical. More important than occasional contacts with Presocratic opinions is the continuation of a trend which had emerged in their systems. The later Presocratics were not only cosmologists but also physicists in a sense approximating Aristotle's *Physics*. They had to define their attitude to certain fundamental questions, and their discussion of subjects like the reality of *genesis* and infinite divisibility foreshadows Aristotle's intense struggle with the same and similar topics. If we trace these discussions to their origin, we are led to the conclusion that the original begetter of physics is none other than the man whose philosophy was one great negation of its legitimacy. In restating and reformulating Parmenides' position, in arguing for or against Parmenides and Zeno, later thinkers dealt with issues which transcended cosmology but whose clarification was a prior condition for any new cosmology. Actually we know of no 'arguments' against Parmenides in the later Presocratic systems; for us the first philosopher who challenged his authority is Plato.

Plato's vindication of not-being is much more elaborate and logically more circumspect than his declaration in favor of movement, a concept which, as a matter of fact, the later Presocratics had needed and employed without, it seems, justifying themselves against Parmenides' veto. Still, for the future of physics and in particular for Aristotle's conception of it Plato's philosophical interest in movement was of even greater import than his rehabilitation of not-being. Rehabilitated or not, not-being still throws its shadow over Aristotle's analysis of *genesis*, although it is becoming increasingly innocuous. But the core concept of Aristotle's *Physics* is movement. Movement needs no defense; Aristotle can proceed to its study without first proving its reality against Parmenides. One-half of his large treatise is given over to the investigation of movement. In the other half even nature itself is defined with reference to movement. So is time, and it is under the heading of movement, not of *genesis* or time, that Aristotle incorporates as much of Zeno's legacy as he considers valid.

Plato needs movement where the Presocratics too had needed it, in the account of the Cosmos; the *Timaeus* explains the movements in the celestial as well as (albeit more briefly) in the sublunary area of the world and establishes some connection between both. But Plato also "analyzed" movement; he applied the method of *diaeresis* to it, specified its Forms and their mutual relations, distinguished spontaneous movement from movement coming from outside, and raised the question as to the relation of mover and moved. We have seen how large a benefit the *Physics* derives from these and other Platonic analyses and differentiations.

Although all major topics of the *Physics* would be legitimate in the eyes of Plato, hardly one would be legitimate for Parmenides. Not Parmenides but Plato's reaction against Parmenides had prepared and encouraged Aristotle's discussion of *genesis* and movement. Still, not only the concept of not-being but also the denial of a maximal Infinite, the interest in the "continuous," and perhaps even the motif of the "unmoved" point back to their origin in Parmenides. But the denial of a maximal Infinite is now coupled with an affirmation of its minimal counterpart, the continuous is almost synonymous with the infinitely divisible, and the unmoved entity has become the mover of a complex, though well-organized plurality of things not one of which is unmoved. It has been fully borne out that there is need to posit being as well as not-being, rest as well as movement, "the one" as well as the many, but not as independent of each other. If the mover is one—we may here forget that in the end Aristotle in addition to the one knew fifty-five other movers—the physical world of many or innumerable entities which he heads and keeps going is also one, not only numerically but intrinsically; it is one by *taxis*. And the countless movements that come to pass in this world, whether movements of heavenly spheres, of elements, or of exhalations and precipitations, do not prevent the whole of the world from remaining "in the same state"—ἐν τῷ αὐτῷ, a Parmenidean conception; on the contrary, they keep it in this condition.

The *De generatione* is another treatise which one would hesitate to call cosmological. Here, however, the situation is somewhat different. For many of the subjects and problems antecedents can be found in the cosmogonies of the sixth and fifth centuries B.C. The elements, the powers, the mutual relations between them had been persistent topics of Presocratic speculation; so had the problem of transformation and the idea of mixture. But Aristotle does not make very clear that the entities and processes which he investigates can materialize only in the Cosmos —just as in the *Physics* he does not emphasize that there is no *physis* outside the Cosmos. The reason is again that he has to deal with fundamental and "general" (καθόλου) questions regarding the nature of *genesis* and other changes. In the larger part of this work his preoccupation is not with the occurrence of *genesis* in the cosmic transformations but with the relation between *genesis* and qualitative alteration, *genesis* and growth, *genesis* and aggregation. These clarifications could be achieved by conceptual means, and it was best to remain on a purely conceptual level. Not-being, prime matter, acting and suffering, contact, wholesale change, and organic mixture are each and all of them notions which could be treated without reference to the cosmological network. When the hot and the cold, the dry and the moist fight and overcome each other, Aristotle does not point out that these powers encounter each other on the battlefield of the Cosmos. It may, in fact, not be very relevant.

Plato too deals with the metaphysical aspects of *genesis* and gives a "mathematical" account of transformation and intermutation before he projects these events upon the cosmic scene. When he proceeds to the subject of mixture and the composition of secondary substances, the cosmological background again fades from sight. These chemical topics could be severed from cosmology. In the evolutionary cosmologies of Empedocles and Anaxagoras the separation was far from complete; we can see why it was natural for them to correlate cosmic origins and the origin of at least some substances or mixed entities. But it is perfectly possible that Democritus kept the discussion of compound substances outside the framework of his cosmogony. If he did so, he would (like Epicurus and Lucretius) explain how the prevalence of certain types of atoms or the mixture of such and such atoms determined the nature of the compounds. It stands to reason that such compounds may form at any time, not only at a juncture when a Cosmos comes into existence. Aristotle, whose Cosmos is ἀγέννητος, had even less reason for integrating the *genesis* of substances into his cosmological scheme.

The comparison with the atomists shows again that their topics, although analogous, are yet considerably more specific than Aristotle's. In the *De generatione* Aristotle had to expose too many errors and misconceptions, to analyze and define too many basic concepts; it would have been incongruous to include a description of even the more important tissues and to specify the fashion in which the elements contribute to the formation of each of them. The "abstract" quality of the disquisition seems to affect even the conclusions; we have seen how the qualities hot and cold and their congeners have for the time being lost their individual powers—which, needless to say, are restored to them in the biological treatises—and must instead be satisfied with the power of acting and suffering.

When at the end of this work Aristotle remembers that *genesis*, besides matter and "sense-perceived differences," also needs an efficient cause, he again refutes erroneous doctrines as to the nature and function of this cause; but when this polemic has cleared the ground, he at once mentions the very specific cause of all *genesis* which operates in his own Cosmos. Rather suddenly we find ourselves carried back into the cosmic—more precisely, into the celestial—system of movements. The first cause of all *genesis* must be identified in cosmological terms, just as the prime mover, to whom this cause points back, is primarily characterized by his cosmic functions, even though Book VIII of the *Physics* keeps the cosmological references at a minimum.

The Presocratics had made it their task to find eternal principles. They needed the eternal to explain the temporary. Would this still be true of Aristotle's *Physics*? If we base our answer on the first half of this treatise, the actual "physical inquiries," it would be negative. The quality of eternity is in any case no longer connected with elements or other entities which outlast the Cosmos (as usually in the Presocratic scheme), but the Cosmos itself is now eternal, and this doctrine is proclaimed not in the *Physics* but in *De caelo*. In *Physics* I–IV Aristotle's search aims at propositions which are universally and, if we like to put it thus, eternally true rather than at eternal entities. To be sure, *genesis* and *physis* must be eternal, but when Aristotle examines them (in *Physics* I and II), this is not the aspect which claims his attention. Form, privation, and the substratum, as treated in *Physics* I, would vary in every instance of *genesis;* they are identical only "by analogy" (*Metaph.* Λ4). Again, Aristotle would not agree with Plato's tenet that time has come into being simultaneously with the Cosmos; for him there has always been time. But Book IV of the *Physics* does not even raise the question whether it has come into being or whether it has always been and will continue to be forever. As for the possible existence of eternal Forms, this is the subject of another science. The *Physics* shows no desire to interfere with the *Metaphysics* or to influence its scrutinies. The prospects of finding eternally subsisting Forms may not be very good, and if the Platonic Forms must really be abandoned, the subject matter of physics would gain correspondingly in significance. But the *Physics* does not anticipate any results of the supposedly more important sister science; except for a few parenthetical remarks it keeps strictly to its own business. So at least it looks; but this may be only one facet of the situation.

If the *Physics* does not interfere with metaphysics, it also does not allow metaphysics to meddle in physical concerns. We have noticed that in sharp contrast to the *Timaeus* Aristotle never admits any inferiority of physical studies. The science of true being must not set limits or give directions; still less can it provide eternal and perfect prototypes to which physical objects and phenomena would relate as do shadows to the true realities. Aristotle's theories of *physis* and *genesis* need a concept of Form, but what satisfies this need is not the transcendent but Aristotle's own immanent Form. For the rest, place can be understood without reference to beings that are not in place, and time need not be set off from eternity or *genesis* contrasted with realities which have never come into being (each of these three concepts, place, time, and *genesis*, had been used by Plato to distinguish objects of lower standing from the truly and ultimately real). The Infinite as Aristotle understands it in Book III is not primarily the indefinite or indeterminate which needs the Form to attain reality; but when it does appear in this character, the Form which raises it into being is not the Platonic. In his discussion of *physis* Aristotle ignores other essential Platonic conceptions. For him *physis* itself is the initiator of movement and thereby takes over a characteristic function of the

Platonic soul. Also thanks to its own teleological orientation *physis* has all—or almost all—that mind could give it and can dispense with a mind coming *ab extra*. The last statements would, it must be admitted, need qualifications in the light of *Physics* VIII and even more of *Metaphysics* Λ, but in *Physics* II the conclusions of these books regarding the prime mover are never within the horizon. It may be more to the point that the world soul would not necessarily be among the subjects of a "first philosophy"; theoretically the Platonic Forms could still be retained even if the soul were discarded. Granted, then, that the increased powers of *physis* and possibly also some other new departures of the *Physics* do not directly violate the interests of Plato's Forms, it still is a question whether these Forms could exist side by side with a physical world which has become so self-sufficient. Departmentalization as Aristotle here practices it goes far to undermine Platonic metaphysics, which cannot be, and by Plato certainly was not, kept in a department by itself.

For the second half of the *Physics*, the exhaustive study of movement, different conclusions seem indicated. Here we have no right to expect references to the Forms. The realm of movement had been set up and given philosophical sanction with the understanding that it should complement that of rest; even in Plato it does not depend on, or reflect, the Forms. It is true that the Forms and species which figure in Plato's and Aristotle's classifications of the movements presuppose the Academic practice of *diaeresis*, but this classification itself is—in Aristotle at any rate—a mere matter of logic and method which has no ontological significance. The new developments which have ontological implications of the greatest consequence are to be found in another phase of Aristotle's inquiry. From his analysis of movement and the origins of movement there emerges in the end a first mover who must be forever at rest, not like the corresponding Platonic world soul forever in self-caused motion. When the Platonic kingdom of Forms had been destroyed, being could find its highest realization, and the hierarchy of beings its apex in this unchanging and nonmaterial pure Form.

What would strike a Platonist as unorthodox (or as paradox) is that this perfect being should be defined with reference to movement and that it should have its place—primarily—in the scheme of movements. Plato certainly did not expect his incorporation of movement to have consequences of this kind. Still it was Plato who decided that, in contrast to his own foremost concern with things at rest, movement was the common denominator of the physical systems; and it was again Plato who insisted that the origin of movement be approached by way of a methodical *regressus* from moved to mover and from this to the prior mover until the first mover comes into view (Empedocles and Anaxagoras knew nothing of this procedure). And Plato had also indicated the point in the cosmic scheme where the first moving principle can effectively exert its influence and keep the entire complex mechanism of physical changes functioning. In all these matters Aristotle follows his master's lead. Neither the praise which he gives to Anaxagoras nor the fact that his own God is, like that of Anaxagoras, definable as mind should obscure the much larger debt which Aristotle owes to Plato's methodical precedent.

Once again, then, a Greek physicist has found a principle at once ultimate and divine through speculation about the ways of nature. In this tradition of physical philosophy Plato's divine world soul may claim a place too; but in Plato's scheme soul could not at the same time be the ultimate reality. Aristotle's God occupies the place which seems normal and natural for the deity. He heads the hierarchy of Forms and is thus the principle of all realities in the Platonic sense—but he also is the first principle of all nature in the sense of the physicists.

Aristotle was not from the outset committed to the Anaxagorean idea that the divine must be outside the physical pattern of the world. He had early in life been won for the Academic belief in the divinity of the heavenly bodies, and though he does not use this belief like a well-established scientific theorem from which further propositions may be deduced, he is ready to reaffirm it where the context of his reasoning offers an opportunity. But it may not even suffice to regard planets and fixed stars as divine. The entire cosmic zone in which they move had acquired a new august and venerable quality; it was difficult to think of it as filled by the same kind of stuff and as subject to the same kind of laws that the physicists found on and near the earth, in the "place around the center." Greeks and barbarians were after all prompted by the right feeling when they associated the celestial spaces with the deity. Already in the dialogue *On Philosophy* Aristotle provided these spaces with an element of their own. It had to be a body different in nature from the four elements of the sublunary area; it had to be superior to them in essential respects; indeed Aristotle in this dialogue made it a point that even its specific motion could not, like that of the other four, be a physical characteristic, something inherent in the material nature of this body. To be divine motion it had to be voluntary motion.

When Aristotle worked out Book I of the treatise *On the Heaven*, his convictions in the matter had changed. He had decided to extend the concept of natural movement—the physical motif—to the new element and to put it fundamentally under the same laws which rule the other simple bodies. The superior, divine rank of the new element was sufficiently safeguarded by the eternity of its forever identical movement and by many other qualities long associated with the deity. In Aristotle's own system none of these qualities—"indestructible," "not suffering," etc.—could be shared by the other elements. But each of these other elements had been eternal in one or the other Presocratic system, and all four had enjoyed divine status in that of Empedocles where they had also been regarded as "unchanging." Even the eternity of the Cosmos had once before Aristotle been conceived as bound up with that of an element (though not of an unchanging element), Heraclitus' fire. Thus what principally sets Aristotle's "first body" apart from all earlier conceptions is that it is the element of the celestial regions, that the eternity which it ensures is in the first place the eternity of the heaven, and that it confers or confirms the superior worth which Plato's dichotomy had postulated for this region. In one word, it symbolizes the perfection ($\tau \acute{\epsilon} \lambda \epsilon \iota o \nu$) of this region. On the "material" side too it is finer and nobler than the other elements.

But however superior it may be to these elements, the *aether* still is a physical body and in a sense even a material body (although strictly speaking it has no matter since it always is actual, never potential). If Aristotle ever meant his *aether* theory to be not only the final word of his cosmology but also his answer to the questions as to the nature and action of the deity, one is bound to wonder whether he felt no obligation to the tradition which emphasized the immaterial quality of the divine. This is the tradition to which his doctrine of the unmoved mover does justice. The same doctrine defines the relation of God to the physical world without making him a part of this world. And as the *aether* in the theology of *Metaphysics* Λ, and evidently also of *Physics* VIII, is subordinated to the prime mover, so has the Presocratic tradition which identified the deity with a physical principle become subordinate to the other which considered body unworthy of the divine and declared God to be "all mind."

On the whole it is easier to find debts to the Presocratics in Aristotle's cosmology than in his generalized physics. Leaving aside other topics large and small, we may here concentrate on two motifs which had been of cardinal importance throughout the history of physical thought and which retain their importance in Aristotle. One of them relates to the architecture of the Cosmos, the other to its survival. Ever since Anaximander the entire cosmos-forming substance had been divided into one large part which settles and consolidates itself in the center of our world and another whose tendency is toward the peripheral areas. In thus splitting up, the cosmic masses were originally supposed to obey their own natural impulse. In later accounts this impulse does not seem to suffice—or is no longer felt to be present. Now the cosmic distribution requires a specific explanation and indeed —in Empedocles and Anaxagoras—a specific agent of movement (the power of this initiating agent extends even to the phenomena which Plato explains through the structure of his world soul and which Aristotle relates to the "first body"). Aristotle revives the impulse theory. Thanks to his new concept of nature he can endow the elements with tendencies and movements which guarantee their distribution into the right cosmic strata. Moreover, these tendencies are so integral to the nature of the elements that these can never have been in places other than their present. This means that the Cosmos must be eternal. The distribution of the elements has no longer any connection with the obsolete topic of cosmic origins.

However, what takes the fire to the circumference of our world is no longer its "hot" power but its lightness. In the books *On the Heaven* Aristotle abstracts from all other qualities of his elements, concentrating exclusively on those which may be most easily associated with locomotion. When he subsequently in the *Meteorologica* deals in a more concrete fashion with movements up and down in the Cosmos, the natural impulses of the elements are presumably still active, but the movements in question, exhalation and precipitation, are due to the influence of the sun. Thus there is an outside mover, and when we read of the approaching and receding of the sun, we may recall the pattern of *Physics* VIII ("everything that moves is moved by something") and by a few intermediate stages find our way from the annual movement of the sun to the rotation of the first heaven and to its source, the prime mover.

Exhalation is the other major topic which shows Aristotle deeply indebted to the Presocratic tradition. From a methodological point of view his theory of the exhalations is even closer to its antecedents than is the dualism of cosmic directions. This time there is less reinterpretation, less remolding; no new conceptual basis need be provided. The hypothesis of exhalation fits Aristotle's own cosmological scheme, and though we should not minimize the innovations in matters of detail, it may yet be said that not only the hypothesis itself but also Aristotle's methodical attitude to his task recalls earlier stages of physical speculation. To trace a goodly number of seemingly disparate phenomena to the same underlying principle had been the endeavor of physical science from its beginnings. It is true that some of the physicists had not been content with using exhalation to account for recurrent phenomena; as long as the Cosmos had a history, exhalation could play a part in shaping this history. In Aristotle's eternal Cosmos exhalation must be balanced by precipitation. This important idea of cosmic balance Aristotle owes to Heraclitus' great intuition; if it had not been for him, Aristotle could not have used exhalation as the principle of his meteorology without apprehending large and progressive changes in at least the sublunary part of his Cosmos. As things are, exhalation and precipitation, so far from disturbing the delicate proportions of the sublunary world, impart to it some measure of the celestial order, some reflection or imitation of the eternal heavenly *periodoi.*

Plato had no intention of channeling some portion of the abundant heavenly *taxis* into the processes and events on earth. What little there is of meteorology in the *Timaeus* is not fashioned toward this end; the approaching and receding of the sun have no influence on the sublunary part of the world; and this part of the world is not provided with regular changes between summer and winter, hot and cold, moist and dry. The section of the *Timaeus* which (by implication) credits the world soul with the initiation of all cosmic changes gives us of these changes a picture of turmoil rather than of mutual balance. Although the Demiurge has wrested some measure of order from necessity, there is no connection between this limited order of the central region and the perfect order of the heavenly movements.

We can understand that this existence side by side of two patterns of order would not recommend itself to Aristotle. It was desirable that the Cosmos should be as unified as possible. Plato was on the right way when he traced the changes between the elements of the sublunary world to the same first mover as the planetary revolutions, but the details of his construction would strike Aristotle as misconceived. What the lower area should derive from its links with the higher was not simply movement, change, and transformation. The regularity of the heavenly cycles should communicate itself to things on earth. As Aristotle's own concept of natural movements enabled him to take the first important step toward unifying the system of the Cosmos, so Heraclitus' identification of "the way up" and "the way down" made possible the second and final step. The seasons which are absent in the pattern of the *Timaeus* are now again evidence for the *taxis* of the world. But the new doctrine of the *Meteorologica*, although conceived in opposition to Plato's and probably running counter to his intention, is yet a Platonist's doctrine. For when Aristotle describes the cycles of the Lower Cosmos as "imitations" of the heavenly rotations, he links the perfect model and the imperfect copy by the same relationship as had prevailed between the Platonic Forms and their counterparts in the visible world.

Not even the departmentalization of the subjects, which has left fissures and inconsistencies in Aristotle's system, has blurred the coherence and continuity of this new cosmic order. As Aristotle says in the concluding chapter of *Metaphysics* Λ, the "good" (τὸ εὖ, τὸ ἀγαθόν, τὸ ἄριστον) is not confined to the prime mover of the world but is present everywhere in the *taxis*, just as in an army the "good" does not reside solely in the commander but is spread throughout its organization. "Everything is composed with reference to a common principle. But as in a household the freeborn members of the family are subject to more and stricter regulations than the slaves," so, we may supply, is the principle of order and regularity more fully realized in the divine phases of the Cosmos than in "the place around the center." For in the central regions irregularities abound, and matter has here succeeded to the role of Plato's necessity.

INDEXES

Passages

[This Index includes passages discussed or used as the basis for inference.]

Authors

Abderites, 6-7, 10, 15, 48 and n.106, 98, 135-136, 140 n.91 and 92, 201, 220, 246, 278, 323, 329, 364; *see also* Democritus *and* Leucippus

Alcmaeon, 17

Anaxagoras, 6-7, 9, 13, 16, 32, 48 n.106, 77-78, 97, 119, 167, 223, 246, 255, 277, 301, 317, 364, 384; Aristotle's praise of, 243, 450; on exhalation, 410 and n.67, 424, 429; on infinite divisibility, 7-8, 201, 203-204, 220; on mixture, 6, 369 n.5, 371-372, 375; on powers, 343, 348; Plato and, 16, 272; *see also* Presocratics

Anaximander, 4, 6, 10, 17, 98, 109, 118-119, 156 n.51, 164-165, 167, 290, 328, 342; on exhalation, 408, 420, 422, 428; on movement and separation in the Infinite, 97, 286, 452

Anaximenes, 12, 97, 140 n.91, 167 n.30, 247, 400, 405, 408

Aristarchus of Samus, 318

Aristophanes, 429

Aristotle: Academic background of his thought, 69-70, 83-84, 116-117, 178, 182-184, 185, 189, 198, 212, 221, 225-227, 308-309, 419, 431, 444; and biological research, 111-112, 114-115, 285, 346-348, 360-361, 403; departmentalism, 87, 99, 128, 259-262, 264, 274, 365, 443, 449; integration of his physical system, 406; methods of proceeding, 184-186, 365-366; Platonic conceptions preserved in his *Physics*, 87, 146-147, 162, 181-183, 228, 235-236; theology in its relations to physics, 222-249, 450-451

Works:

De caelo: earlier and later stages, 293-303; references to *Physics*, 301 n.47; relation to *On Philosophy*, 287 n.1, 292, 301, 450

De gen. et corr.: relation to *De caelo* III and IV, 257 n.12, 296-298, 321

Meteorologica IV (spurious), 9-10, 111-112, 402-404

Physics: Book VIII compared with Book VII, 222 n.1, 228 n.19, 231 n.32, 248 n.87; origin of, 71-73; relation to *Metaphysics*, 448-449

Avempace, 138 n.83

Cleidemus, 419

Democritus, 13, 15, 32, 114 n.85, 120, 137, 141-142, 202, 204, 340 and n.15, 343, 345, 411, 419, 446-447; *see also* Abderites *and* Presocratics

Diogenes of Apollonia, 6, 7, 16, 116 n.94, 290 n.13, 410 n.67, 428 n.141, 429 n.147

Empedocles, 6, 8-9, 11, 14-17, 32-33, 77-78, 97, 119, 156 n.51, 246, 255, 329, 345, 353 n.4, 364, 451; elements of in later Greek thought, 48 n.106, 285, 321; on kinship of living beings, 8-9; on mixture, 55, 368, 372 and n.16,

Topics